S0-BAX-748

HYMNAL
of the
CHURCH OF GOD

Serve the Lord with gladness:
Come before his presence with singing.

WARNER PRESS
Anderson, Indiana

PRINTED IN THE UNITED STATES OF AMERICA

Preface

We have been a singing people. Our songs have served both to draw us into greater communion with God and to provide a witness to others of what Christ has done.

Throughout the history of the Church of God reformation movement new songbooks and hymnals have been developed as the need became apparent. Such books as *Truth in Song, Select Hymns, Melodies of Zion,* and *Hymns and Spiritual Songs* have proclaimed the truth of God in a wonderful manner. With the passing of nearly twenty-five years since the publication of *Hymns and Spiritual Songs,* and with the coming of a "new age" with its peculiar needs and opportunities, many of our pastors and music leaders have felt the need of a new general hymnal. Thus, the *Hymnal of the Church of God* is presented with a prayer that it may be, for *this* day, an instrument of God.

The task of developing policies for the content of the book, along with the general overseeing of the compilation, was done by the General Hymnal Committee. Members of this committee were: Robert A. Nicholson, chairman, Paul Breitweiser, Max Gaulke, Vernon Guttenfelder, Cleopatra Jackson, Cynthia Kane, Naomi Kempin, Dale Oldham, K. Y. Plank, Marvin Proctor, Fred Shackleton, Walter Shriner, Herbert Thompson.

A subcommittee on Worship Aids, consisting of W. Albert Donaldson, chairman, V. J. Gritzmacher, Gertrude Little, and Eugene Newberry, gave valuable assistance in the preparation of these materials.

Robert A. Nicholson was appointed music editor of the book; he, working with Harold L. Phillips, editor in chief of the Gospel Trumpet Company publications (now Warner Press), and Lottie M. Franklin, book editor, co-ordinated planning and managed the details of production.

The desire of these committees was to formulate a volume which would, in a comprehensive way, meet the music and worship needs of the congregations of the Church of God. With this in mind, fifty leaders representing twenty-four states—ministers, evangelists, song leaders, and instrumentalists—were asked to rate nearly one thousand songs which, out of many thousands of songs surveyed, were being particularly considered for inclusion in this volume. These ratings proved an invaluable guide in the selection of music material.

PREFACE

Through the thousands of hours gladly given to the cause of church music and worship by these leaders, the *Hymnal of the Church of God* is presented as a comprehensive volume designed for every service of the church. A wide variety of hymns and gospel songs provides adequate sections on Praise and Adoration, Devotion and Supplication, Testimony and Exhortation. In keeping with the increased interest in special days and seasons, the sections for Thanksgiving, Christmas, the New Year, Easter, the Christian home and family, and those for special services of communion, baptism, and dedications, have been strengthened.

In order to allow for a more flexible use of the book by ministers and music leaders, the indexes have been greatly expanded. Metrical and alphabetical tune name indexes are included. The topical index is most comprehensive. It is to be observed, for example, that all songs usable in the invitation service are listed under one heading, "Invitation and Acceptance." Of special note are two separate indexes: The first lists songs from the hymnal which are particularly suitable for presentation by a choir; the second, for use with children. These special indexes enhance the value of the hymnal to the leader.

The section on Worship Aids is more than five times the size of any such section in any previous Church of God hymnal. Eighty-four unison and responsive readings are included. These are listed topically in an index and provide the congregation with a rich collection of Scripture for group use. It is hoped that, through the availability of these worship aids, God's Word may receive a more prominent place in the church services of his people.

The Warner Press desires to acknowledge the considerable contribution made by the more than fifty persons who directly participated in the formulation of this volume. It also wishes to thank the many authors, composers, and publishers who have allowed the use of copyright materials. Permissions are indicated on pages where the hymns appear; any failure to apply for or acknowledge permission was unintentional.

The *Hymnal of the Church of God* is dedicated to the work of God with the prayer that as it is used in churches and homes it may, in a vital manner, present "the unsearchable riches of Christ."

Contents

HYMNS

Worship

Adoration and Praise 1-8
Opening of Worship 9-13
Closing of Worship 14-17
Morning Hymns 18-19
Evening Hymns 20-23

God the Father

Majesty and Power 24-28
Providence and Care 29-36

Jesus Christ the Lord

Christ's Advent and Nativity 37-53
Christ's Life and Ministry 54-60
Christ's Suffering and Death 61-67
Christ's Resurrection 68-71
The Ever-Living Christ 72-75
Christ's Second Coming 76-78
Praise to Christ 79-93

The Holy Spirit

The Holy Spirit 94-97
Sanctification 98-104

The Holy Scriptures 105-112

The Invitations of Christ and the Holy Spirit

Provisions and Promises 113-123
Warnings and Invitations 124-144
Repentance and Acceptance 145-156
The Spirit-Filled Life 157-178

The Christian Life

The Call to Service 179-189
Decision and Loyalty 190-221
Christian Conquest 222-244
Examination and Example 245-254

HYMNS

Experience and Rejoicing 255-314
Faith, Trust, Assurance 315-332
Guidance and Keeping 333-352
Security and Peace 353-367
Devotion, Aspiration 368-399
Prayer, Watchfulness 400-409

The Living Church

The Church 410-419
Restoration and Return 420-430
The Ordinances 431-436

The Church at Work in the World

Brotherhood and Peace 437-441
World Missions 442-449
Healing 450-453

Christian Home and Family 454-465

The Future Life 466-489

Special Seasons and Services

The New Year 490-492
Thanksgiving 493-497
Patriotism 498-500
Doxologies and Responses 501-507

Worship Aids PAGES

Index 448
Responsive Readings 449
Unison Readings 484

Indexes

Alphabetical Tune Name 490
Metrical 491
Songs Suitable for Choir 492
Songs Suitable for Children 493
Topical 494
Title and First Line 503

Hymnal of the Church of God

ADORATION AND PRAISE

Come, Thou Almighty King 1

ITALIAN HYMN. 6.6.4.6.6.6.4.

Anonymous — Felice de Giardini, 1716-1796

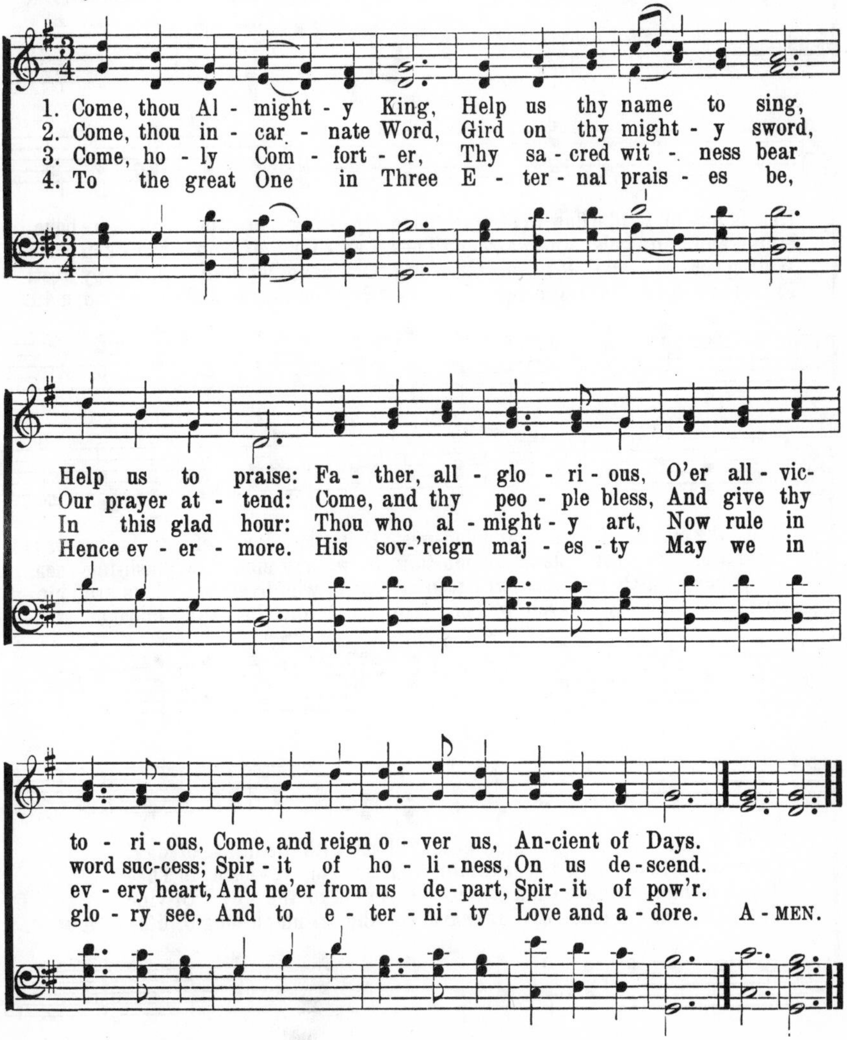

1. Come, thou Al - might - y King, Help us thy name to sing,
2. Come, thou in - car - nate Word, Gird on thy might - y sword,
3. Come, ho - ly Com - fort - er, Thy sa - cred wit - ness bear
4. To the great One in Three E - ter - nal prais - es be,

Help us to praise: Fa - ther, all - glo - ri - ous, O'er all - vic-
Our prayer at - tend: Come, and thy peo - ple bless, And give thy
In this glad hour: Thou who al - might - y art, Now rule in
Hence ev - er - more. His sov'reign maj - es - ty May we in

to - ri - ous, Come, and reign o - ver us, An-cient of Days.
word suc-cess; Spir - it of ho - li - ness, On us de - scend.
ev - ery heart, And ne'er from us de - part, Spir - it of pow'r.
glo - ry see, And to e - ter - ni - ty Love and a - dore. A - MEN.

2 Joyful, Joyful, We Adore Thee

HYMN TO JOY. 8.7.8.7.D.

Henry van Dyke, 1852-1933 Arr. from Ludwig van Beethoven, 1770-1827

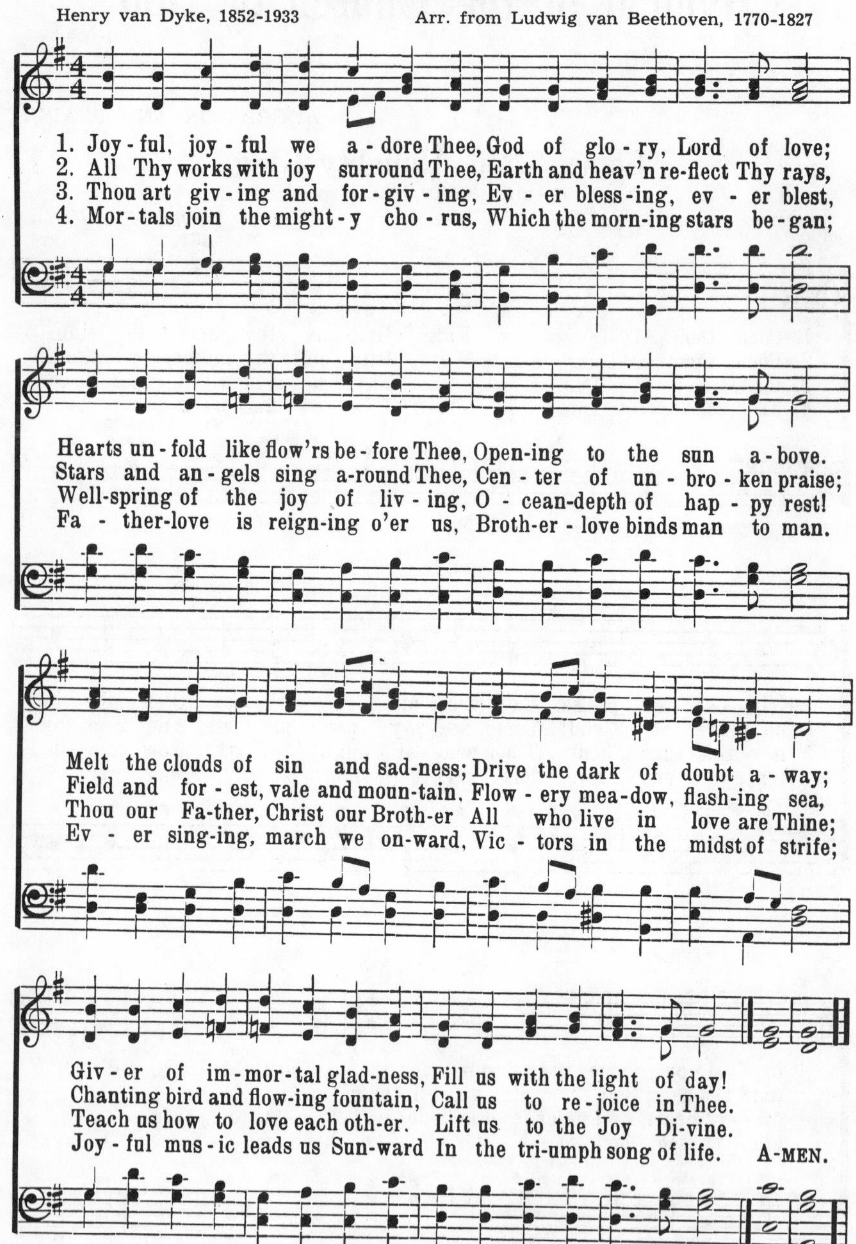
1. Joy - ful, joy - ful we a - dore Thee, God of glo - ry, Lord of love;
2. All Thy works with joy surround Thee, Earth and heav'n re-flect Thy rays,
3. Thou art giv - ing and for - giv - ing, Ev - er bless - ing, ev - er blest,
4. Mor - tals join the might - y cho - rus, Which the morn-ing stars be - gan;
Hearts un - fold like flow'rs be - fore Thee, Open-ing to the sun a - bove.
Stars and an - gels sing a-round Thee, Cen - ter of un - bro - ken praise;
Well-spring of the joy of liv - ing, O - cean-depth of hap - py rest!
Fa - ther-love is reign-ing o'er us, Broth-er - love binds man to man.
Melt the clouds of sin and sad-ness; Drive the dark of doubt a - way;
Field and for - est, vale and moun-tain, Flow - ery mea-dow, flash-ing sea,
Thou our Fa-ther, Christ our Broth-er All who live in love are Thine;
Ev - er sing-ing, march we on-ward, Vic - tors in the midst of strife;
Giv - er of im - mor - tal glad-ness, Fill us with the light of day!
Chanting bird and flow-ing fountain, Call us to re - joice in Thee.
Teach us how to love each oth-er. Lift us to the Joy Di-vine.
Joy - ful mus - ic leads us Sun-ward In the tri-umph song of life.
A-MEN.

Holy, Holy, Holy

3

NICAEA. 11.12.12.10.

Reginald Heber, 1783-1826

John B. Dykes, 1823-1876

1. Ho - ly, ho - ly, ho - ly! Lord God Al - might - y!
2. Ho - ly, ho - ly, ho - ly! all the saints a - dore thee,
3. Ho - ly, ho - ly, ho - ly! tho' the dark-ness hide thee,
4. Ho - ly, ho - ly, ho - ly! Lord God Al - might - y!
Ear - ly in the morn - ing our song shall rise to thee;
Cast - ing down their gold - en crowns a - round the glass - y sea;
Tho' the eye of sin - ful man thy glo - ry may not see,
All thy works shall praise thy name, in earth, and sky, and sea;
Ho - ly, ho - ly, ho - ly, mer - ci - ful and might - y!
Cher - u - bim and ser-a - phim fall - ing down be - fore thee,
On - ly thou art ho - ly, there is none be - side thee,
Ho - ly, ho - ly, ho - ly, mer - ci - ful and might - y!
God in Three Per - sons, bless - ed Trin - i - ty!
Which wert, and art, and ev - er - more shalt be.
Per - fect in pow'r, in love and pu - ri - ty.
God in Three Per - sons, bless - ed Trin - i - ty! A - MEN.

4 O Worship the Lord

WORSHIP THE LORD. Irregular

Robert Lowry, 1826-1899 | Robert Lowry, 1826-1899

1. O wor-ship the Lord in the beau-ty of ho-li-ness, in the
2. O wor-ship the Lord in the beau-ty of ho-li-ness, in the
3. O wor-ship the Lord in the beau-ty of ho-li-ness, in the
beau-ty of ho-li-ness, in the beau-ty of ho-li-ness! Glo-ry to the
beau-ty of ho-li-ness, in the beau-ty of ho-li-ness! Glo-ry be to
beau-ty of ho-li-ness, in the beau-ty of ho-li-ness! Glo-ry to the
Fa-ther, a-bound-ing in mer-cy! Be joy-ful, all ye peo-ple, and
Je-sus, our gra-cious Re-deem-er! We praise him, for he loved us, and
Spir-it, the ho-ly Re-veal-er! We praise him, with the Fa-ther and
CHORUS
mag-ni-fy Je-ho-vah.
bro't a great sal-va-tion. O glo-ry, hal-le-lu-jah! hal-le-lu-jah! hal-le-
with the Son, our Sav-ior.
lu-jah! O come be-fore his pres-ence and glo-ri-fy his name! A-MEN.

We Praise Thee, O God, Our Redeemer 5

KREMSER. 12.11.12.11.

Julia Bulkley Cady, b. 1882

Netherland folk song, 1625
Arr. by Edward Kremser, 1838-1914

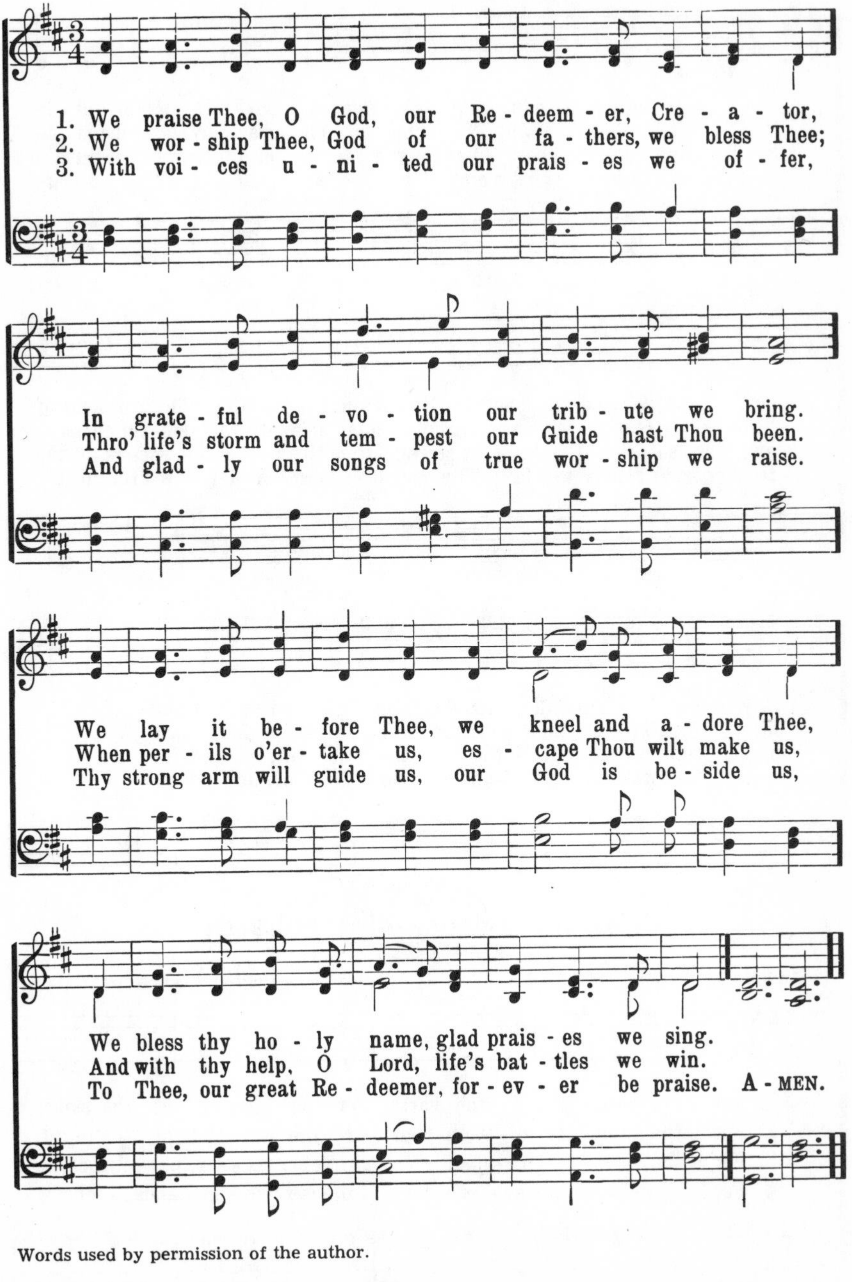
1. We praise Thee, O God, our Re - deem - er, Cre - a - tor,
2. We wor - ship Thee, God of our fa - thers, we bless Thee;
3. With voi - ces u - ni - ted our prais - es we of - fer,
In grate - ful de - vo - tion our trib - ute we bring.
Thro' life's storm and tem - pest our Guide hast Thou been.
And glad - ly our songs of true wor - ship we raise.
We lay it be - fore Thee, we kneel and a - dore Thee,
When per - ils o'er - take us, es - cape Thou wilt make us,
Thy strong arm will guide us, our God is be - side us,
We bless thy ho - ly name, glad prais - es we sing.
And with thy help, O Lord, life's bat - tles we win.
To Thee, our great Re - deemer, for - ev - er be praise. A - MEN.

Words used by permission of the author.

6 O Worship the King

LYONS. 10.10.11.11.

Psalm 104
Robert Grant, 1786-1838

Arr. from J. Michael Haydn, 1737-1806

1. O wor - ship the King all - glo - rious a - bove, O grate - ful - ly
2. O tell of his might, O sing of his grace, Whose robe is the
3. Thy boun - ti - ful care what tongue can re - cite? It breathes in the
4. Frail chil-dren of dust, and fee - ble as frail, In thee do we

sing his pow'r and his love; Our Shield and De - fend-er, the An-cient of
light, whose can-o - py space. His char-iots of wrath the deep thunder-clouds
air, it shines in the light; It streams from the hills, it de-scends to the
trust, nor find thee to fail; Thy mer-cies how ten-der, how firm to the

Days, Pa - vil - ioned in splen-dor, and gird - ed with praise.
form, And dark is his path on the wings of the storm.
plain, And sweet-ly dis - tils in the dew and the rain
end, Our Mak - er, De - fend - er, Re - deem-er, and Friend! A - MEN.

7 For the Beauty of the Earth

DIX. 7.7.7.7.7.7.

Folliott S. Pierpoint, 1835-1917

Adapted from Conrad Kocher, 1786-1872

1. For the beau - ty of the earth, For the glo - ry of the skies,
2. For the won - der of each hour, Of the day and of the night,
3. For the joy of hu - man love, Broth-er, sis - ter, par - ent, child,
4. For Thy church that ev - er - more Lift - eth ho - ly hands a - bove,

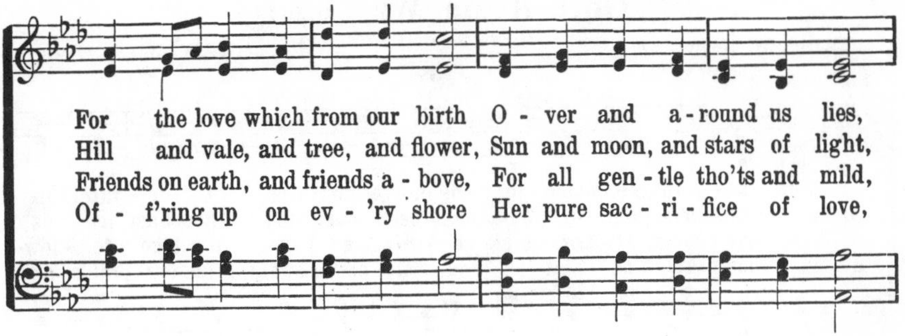

For the love which from our birth O - ver and a - round us lies,
Hill and vale, and tree, and flower, Sun and moon, and stars of light,
Friends on earth, and friends a - bove, For all gen - tle tho'ts and mild,
Of - f'ring up on ev - 'ry shore Her pure sac - ri - fice of love,

REFRAIN

Lord of all, to Thee we raise This our hymn of grate - ful praise.

In Holy Reverence, Lord 8

REVERENA. 8.6.8.8.6.

D. Otis Teasley, 1876-1942 D. Otis Teasley, 1876-1942

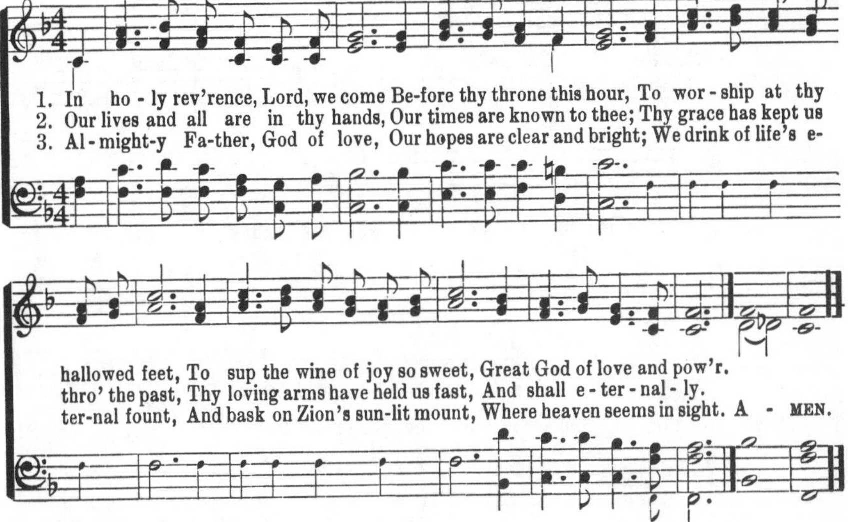
1. In ho - ly rev'rence, Lord, we come Be-fore thy throne this hour, To wor - ship at thy
2. Our lives and all are in thy hands, Our times are known to thee; Thy grace has kept us
3. Al - might-y Fa-ther, God of love, Our hopes are clear and bright; We drink of life's e-
hallowed feet, To sup the wine of joy so sweet, Great God of love and pow'r.
thro' the past, Thy loving arms have held us fast, And shall e - ter - nal - ly.
ter-nal fount, And bask on Zion's sun-lit mount, Where heaven seems in sight. A - MEN.

9 Once Again We Come

Charles W. Naylor, 1904 Charles W. Naylor, 1904

1. Once a - gain we come to the house of God, To u - nite in songs of praise; To ex - tol with joy our Re - deem - er's name, And to tell his works and ways.
2. In the days gone by thou hast been our stay, Thou hast led us safe - ly on To the bless - ed light of the pres - ent day, Where the dark - ness now is gone.
3. May our hearts, O Lord, e'er u - nit - ed be In true fel - low - ship and love; May thy will be done by us here on earth, As by an - gel hosts a - bove.
4. May our prayers as - cend as an in - cense sweet, And our praise ac - cept - ed be, As in grat - i - tude all our hearts o'er - flow In a trib - ute un - to thee.

CHORUS

To thy house, O Lord, with re - joic - ing we come, For we know that we are thine; We will wor - ship thee in the Bi - ble way, As the eve - ning light doth shine. A - MEN.

O Day of Peace and Gladness 10

MENDEBRAS. 7.6.7.6.D.

Christopher Wordsworth, 1807-1885 Arr. by Lowell Mason, 1792-1872

1. O day of peace and glad - ness, O day of joy and light,
2. On thee at the cre - a - tion The light first had its birth;
3. To - day on wea - ry na - tions The heav'n-ly man-na falls;
4. New grac - es ev - er gain - ing From this our day of rest,

O balm of care and sad - ness, Most beau - ti - ful, most bright:
On thee, for our sal - va - tion, Christ rose from depths of earth;
To ho - ly con - vo - ca - tions The sil - ver trump-et calls,
We reach the rest re - main - ing To spir - its of the blest;

On thee the high and low - ly, Who bow be - fore the throne,
On thee, our Lord, vic - to - rious, The Spir - it sent from heav'n;
Where gos - pel light is glow - ing With pure and ra - diant beams,
To Ho - ly Ghost be prais - es, To Fa - ther and to Son;

Sing "Ho - ly, ho - ly, ho - ly," To the great Three in One.
And thus on thee, most glo-rious, A tri - ple light was giv'n.
And liv - ing wa - ter flow - ing With soul - re - fresh-ing streams.
The church her voice up - rais - es To thee, blest Three in One. A-MEN.

11 Come, O Thou God of Grace

ITALIAN HYMN. 6.6.4.6.6.6.4.

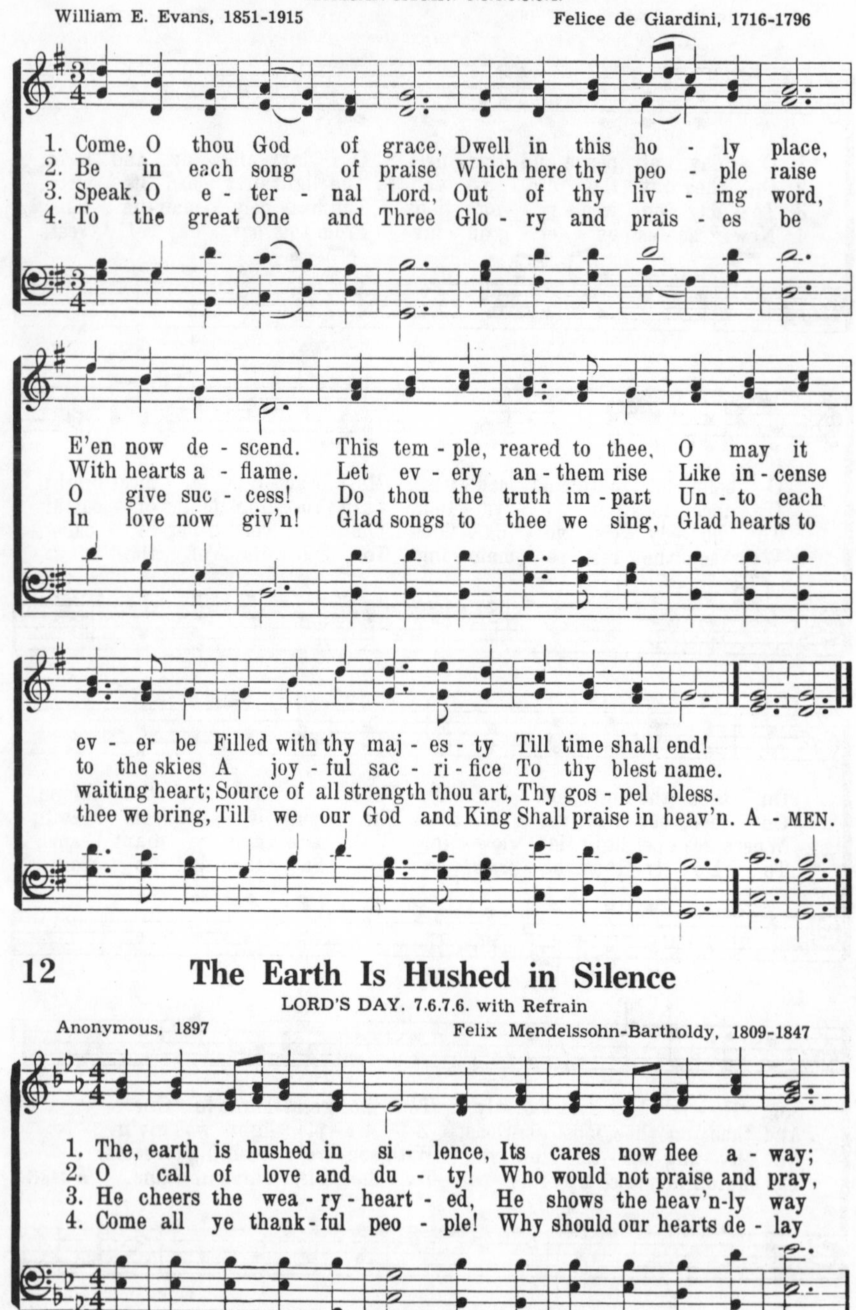
William E. Evans, 1851-1915
Felice de Giardini, 1716-1796
1. Come, O thou God of grace, Dwell in this ho - ly place,
2. Be in each song of praise Which here thy peo - ple raise
3. Speak, O e - ter - nal Lord, Out of thy liv - ing word,
4. To the great One and Three Glo - ry and prais - es be
E'en now de - scend. This tem - ple, reared to thee, O may it
With hearts a - flame. Let ev - ery an - them rise Like in - cense
O give suc - cess! Do thou the truth im - part Un - to each
In love now giv'n! Glad songs to thee we sing, Glad hearts to
ev - er be Filled with thy maj - es - ty Till time shall end!
to the skies A joy - ful sac - ri - fice To thy blest name.
waiting heart; Source of all strength thou art, Thy gos - pel bless.
thee we bring, Till we our God and King Shall praise in heav'n. A - MEN.
12 The Earth Is Hushed in Silence
LORD'S DAY. 7.6.7.6. with Refrain
Anonymous, 1897
Felix Mendelssohn-Bartholdy, 1809-1847
1. The, earth is hushed in si - lence, Its cares now flee a - way;
2. O call of love and du - ty! Who would not praise and pray,
3. He cheers the wea - ry - heart - ed, He shows the heav'n-ly way
4. Come all ye thank - ful peo - ple! Why should our hearts de - lay

Let all things bow in rev - 'rence On this the Lord's own day.
And thank the Lord of heav - en On this his cho - sen day?
To those who kneel be - fore him On this his ho - ly day.
To greet the Lord of heav - en On this his ho - ly day?

REFRAIN

O praise and pray on this, the Lord's own day! A - MEN.

Come, Thou Fount

13

NETTLETON. 8.7.8.7.D.

Robert Robinson, 1735-1790

John Wyeth, 1770-1858

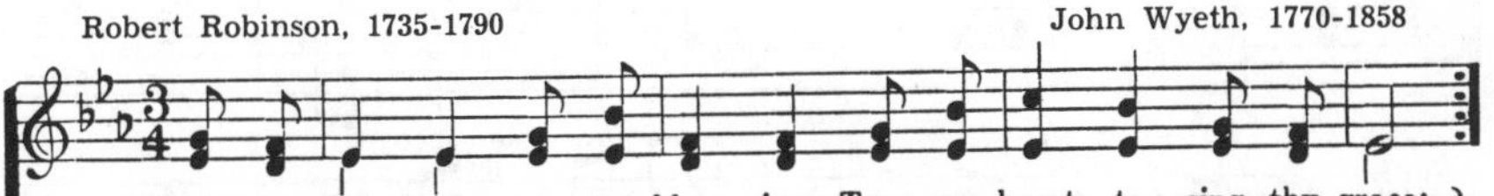

1. Come, thou Fount of ev - ery bless - ing, Tune my heart to sing thy grace;
Streams of mer - cy, nev - er ceas - ing, Call for songs of loud - est praise.
Teach me some me - lo - dious son - net, Sung by flam - ing tongues a - bove;
Praise the mount! I'm fixed up - on it, Mount of thy re - deem - ing love!

2. Here I raise my Eb - en - e - zer; Hith - er by thy help I'm come;
And I hope, by thy good pleas - ure, Safe - ly to ar - rive at home.
Je - sus sought me when a stran - ger, Wan - d'ring from the fold of God;
He, to res - cue me from dan - ger, In - ter - posed his pre - cious blood.

3. O to grace how great a debt - or Dai - ly I'm con - strained to be!
Let thy good - ness, like a fet - ter, Bind my wan - d'ring heart to thee:
Prone to wan - der, Lord, I feel it, Prone to leave the God I love;
Here's my heart, O take and seal it, Seal it for thy courts a - bove. A - MEN.

14 Lord, Dismiss Us with Thy Blessing

SICILIAN MARINERS' HYMN. 8.7.8.7.8.7.

John Fawcett, 1740-1817, alt.

Arr. from a Sicilian melody

1. Lord, dis - miss us with thy bless-ing, Fill our hearts with joy and peace;
2. Thanks we give, and ad - o - ra - tion, For thy gos - pel's joy - ful sound;
3. So that when thy love shall call us, Sav - ior, from the world a - way,

Let us each, thy love pos - sess - ing, Tri-umph in re - deem - ing grace:
May the fruits of thy sal - va - tion In our hearts and lives a - bound:
Let no fear of death ap - pal us, Glad thy sum - mons to o - bey:

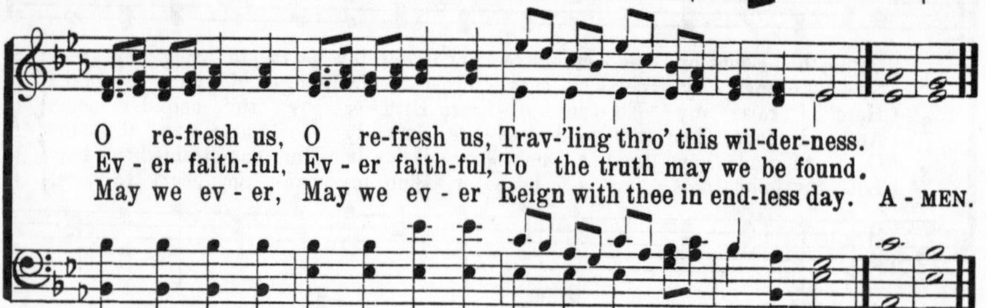

O re-fresh us, O re-fresh us, Trav-'ling thro' this wil-der-ness.
Ev - er faith-ful, Ev - er faith-ful, To the truth may we be found.
May we ev - er, May we ev - er Reign with thee in end-less day. A - MEN.

15 Once More, Before We Part

LABAN. S.M.

Joseph Hart, 1712-1768

Lowell Mason, 1792-1872

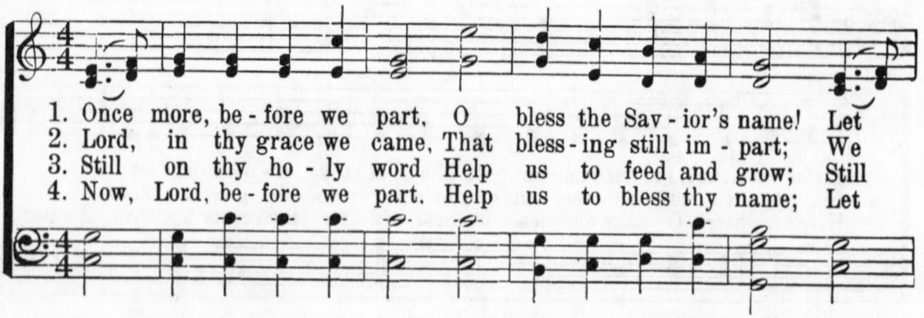

1. Once more, be - fore we part, O bless the Sav - ior's name! Let
2. Lord, in thy grace we came, That bless - ing still im - part; We
3. Still on thy ho - ly word Help us to feed and grow; Still
4. Now, Lord, be - fore we part, Help us to bless thy name; Let

ev - ery tongue and ev - ery heart A - dore and praise the same.
met in Je - sus' sa - cred name, In Je - sus' name we part.
to go on to know the Lord, And prac - tice what we know.
ev - ery tongue and ev - ery heart A - dore and praise the same. A - MEN.

Savior, Again to Thy Dear Name 16

ELLERS. 10.10.10.10.

John Ellerton, 1826-1893 — Edward J. Hopkins, 1818-1901

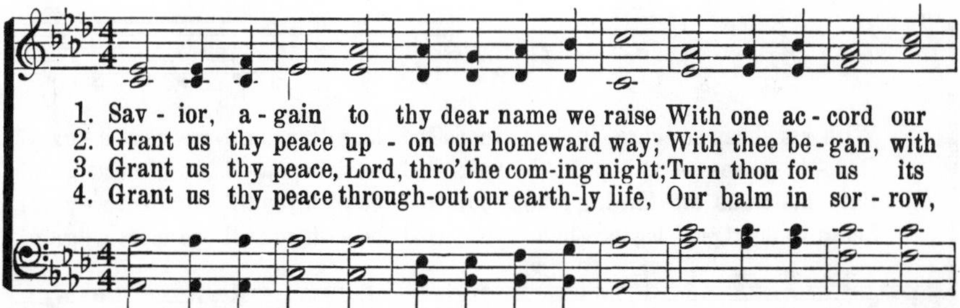

1. Sav - ior, a - gain to thy dear name we raise With one ac - cord our
2. Grant us thy peace up - on our homeward way; With thee be - gan, with
3. Grant us thy peace, Lord, thro' the com - ing night; Turn thou for us its
4. Grant us thy peace through - out our earth - ly life, Our balm in sor - row,

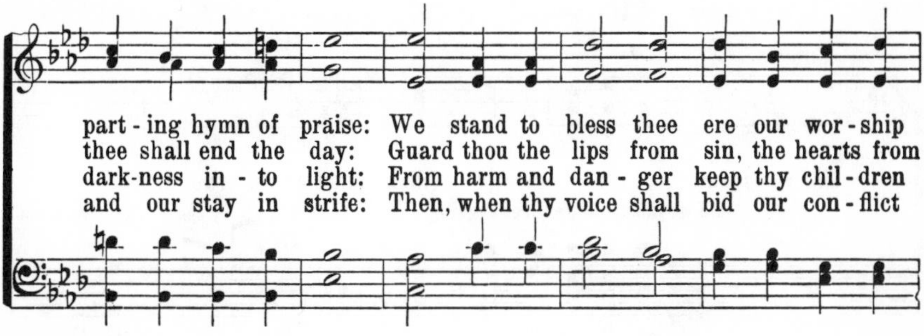

part - ing hymn of praise: We stand to bless thee ere our wor - ship
thee shall end the day: Guard thou the lips from sin, the hearts from
dark - ness in - to light: From harm and dan - ger keep thy chil - dren
and our stay in strife: Then, when thy voice shall bid our con - flict

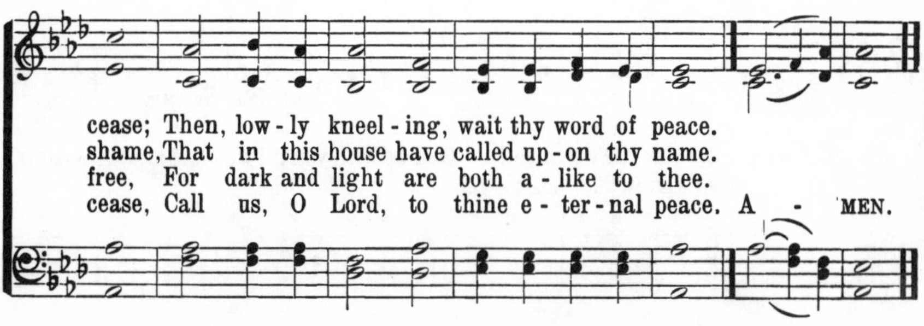

cease; Then, low - ly kneel - ing, wait thy word of peace.
shame, That in this house have called up - on thy name.
free, For dark and light are both a - like to thee.
cease, Call us, O Lord, to thine e - ter - nal peace. A - MEN.

17 God Be with You

Jeremiah E. Rankin, 1828-1904 — William G. Tomer, 1833-1896

1. God be with you till we meet a-gain! By his counsels guide, up-hold you,
2. God be with you till we meet a-gain! 'Neath his wings securely hide you,
3. God be with you till we meet a-gain! When life's perils thick confound you,
4. God be with you till we meet a-gain! Keep love's banner floating o'er you,
With his sheep se-cure-ly fold you; God be with you till we meet a-gain!
Dai-ly man-na still pro-vide you; God be with you till we meet a-gain!
Put his arms un-fail-ing round you; God be with you till we meet a-gain!
Smite death's threat'ning wave before you; God be with you till we meet a-gain!
CHORUS
Till we meet, . . till we meet, Till we meet at Je-sus' feet!
Till we meet, till we meet a-gain, Till we meet!
Till we meet, . . till we meet! God be with you till we meet again! A-MEN.
Till we meet, till we meet a-gain!

A Hymn of Morning Praise 18

Daniel S. Warner, 1842-1895 — Clarence E. Hunter, 1869-1945

1. O God, in-spire our morn-ing hymn Of love and grat - i - tude;
2. Thy mir - a - cle of love so sweet Pre-served us all se - cure;
3. 'Tis blest to rise, O Lord, and join With na-ture's min strel-sy,
4. Sweet morn-ing is the time to pray: How love - ly and how meet
5. The glo - rious sun has driv - en far The mys - tic shades of night;

O bless the sac - ri - fice we bring, Thou source of ev - ery good.
While help-less in un - con-scious sleep, Thy pres-ence kept us pure.
To hymn thy praise at ear - ly morn, And of - fer thanks to thee.
To send our ear - ly thoughts a - way, Up to the mer - cy - seat!
So in our souls the Morn - ing Star Hath shed his won-drous light.

CHORUS

Touched by thy hand of love, we wake, And rise from sweet re - pose;

Thy praise shall first the si-lence break, Thy peace with-in us flows. A - MEN.

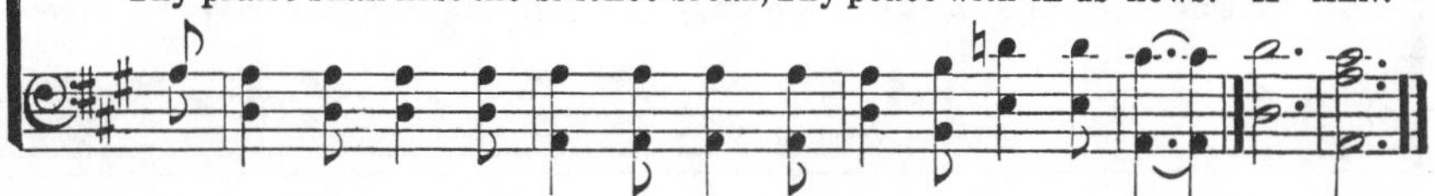

19 When Morning Gilds the Skies

LAUDES DOMINI. 6.6.6.6.6.6.

From the German, c. 1800
Tr. by Edward Caswall, 1814-1878

Joseph Barnby, 1838-1896

1. When morn - ing gilds the skies, My heart a - wak - ing cries,
2. The night be - comes as day, When from the heart we say,
3. In heav'n's e - ter - nal bliss The love - liest strain is this,
4. Be this, while life is mine, My song of love di - vine,

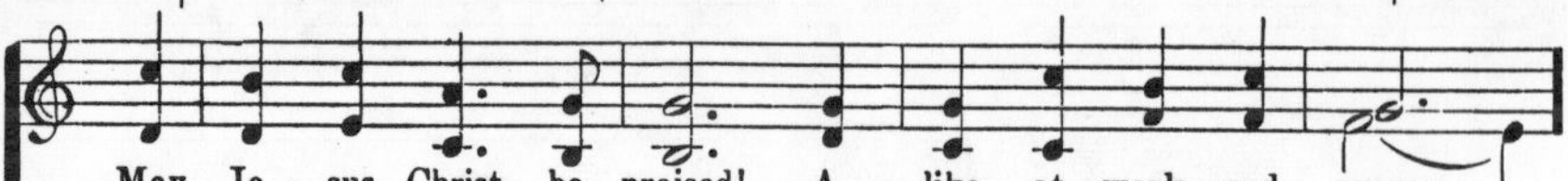

May Je - sus Christ be praised! A - like at work and prayer, . .
May Je - sus Christ be praised! The pow'rs of dark - ness fear, . . .
May Je - sus Christ be praised! Let earth, and sea, and sky, . . .
May Je - sus Christ be praised! Be this th' e - ter - nal song . . .

To Je - sus I re - pair; May Je - sus Christ be praised!
When this sweet chant they hear, May Je - sus Christ be praised!
From depth to height re - ply, May Je - sus Christ be praised!
Thro' all the a - ges long, May Je - sus Christ be praised! A-MEN.

20 Sun of My Soul

HURSLEY. L.M.

John Keble, 1792-1866

Adapted from *Katholisches Gesangbuch,*
Vienna, c. 1774

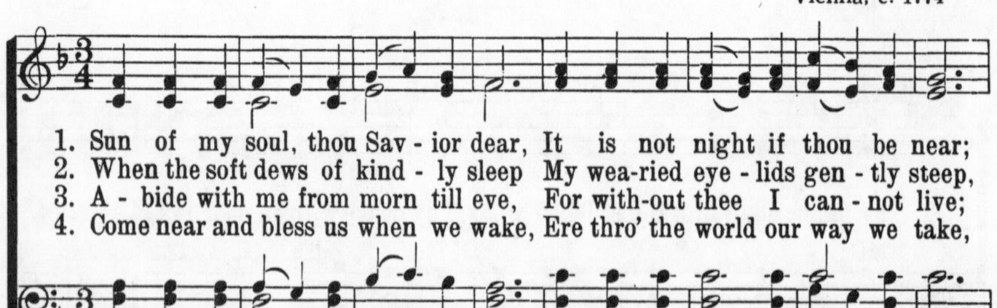
1. Sun of my soul, thou Sav - ior dear, It is not night if thou be near;
2. When the soft dews of kind - ly sleep My wea-ried eye - lids gen - tly steep,
3. A - bide with me from morn till eve, For with-out thee I can - not live;
4. Come near and bless us when we wake, Ere thro' the world our way we take,

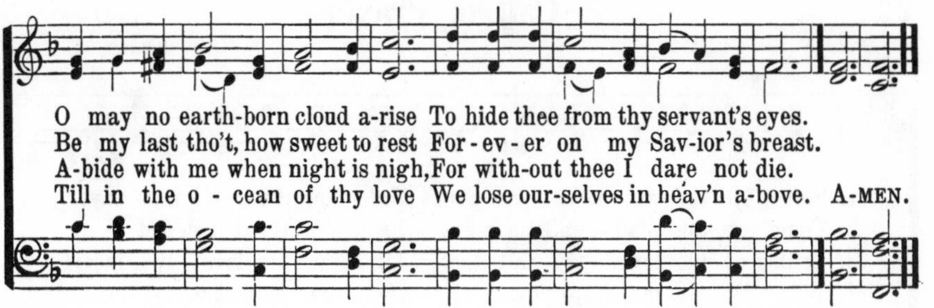
O may no earth-born cloud a-rise To hide thee from thy servant's eyes.
Be my last tho't, how sweet to rest For-ev-er on my Sav-ior's breast.
A-bide with me when night is nigh, For with-out thee I dare not die.
Till in the o-cean of thy love We lose our-selves in heav'n a-bove. A-MEN.

Now the Day Is Over 21

MERRIAL. 6.5.6.5.

Sabine Baring-Gould, 1834-1924

Joseph Barnby, 1838-1896

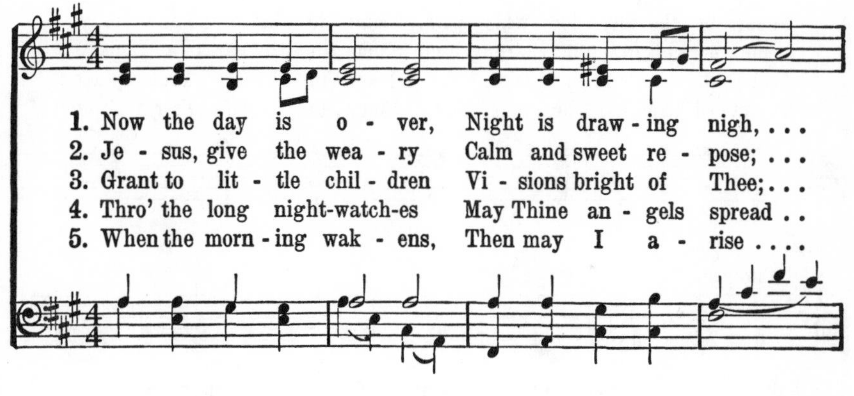
1. Now the day is o-ver, Night is draw-ing nigh, . . .
2. Je-sus, give the wea-ry Calm and sweet re-pose; . . .
3. Grant to lit-tle chil-dren Vi-sions bright of Thee; . . .
4. Thro' the long night-watch-es May Thine an-gels spread . .
5. When the morn-ing wak-ens, Then may I a-rise . . . .

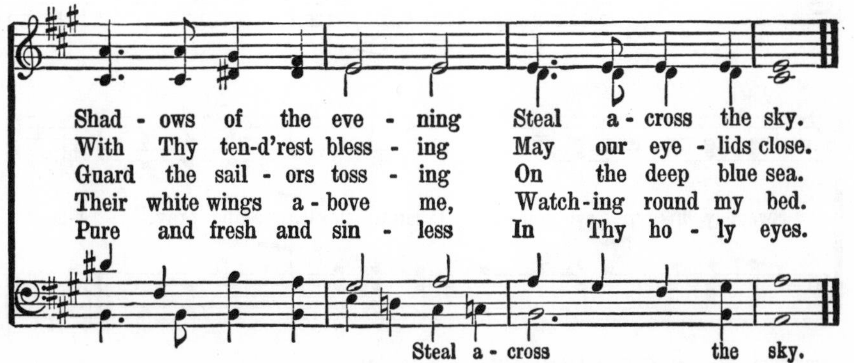
Shad-ows of the eve-ning Steal a-cross the sky.
With Thy ten-d'rest bless-ing May our eye-lids close.
Guard the sail-ors toss-ing On the deep blue sea.
Their white wings a-bove me, Watch-ing round my bed.
Pure and fresh and sin-less In Thy ho-ly eyes.
Steal a-cross the sky.

22 A Call to Prayer

Clara M. Brooks, 1914 D. Otis Teasley, 1914

1. Soft - ly the eve - ning ves - pers Hal - low the clos - ing day;
2. Come, ere the shad - ows length-en, Bring him thy bur-dened heart;
3. Smiles of his love a - wait thee, Light-ing his love - ly face;
4. Bold - ly we may ap - proach him, Mer - cy and grace to own;
Sweet - ly the Sav - ior whis - pers, "Come to the throne and pray."
Come where his grace may strength-en, Come from thy cares a - part.
Just to be - hold his beau - ty, Dwell in the se - cret place.
Tempt - ed like us, he bids us Come to the Fa - ther's throne.
CHORUS
Soft - ly I hear him call - ing, Call - ing at close of day;
Sweet-ly his tones are fall - ing, "Come to the throne and pray." A-MEN.

Day Is Dying in the West 23

CHAUTAUQUA. 7.7.7.7.4. with Refrain

Mary A. Lathbury, 1841-1913 William F. Sherwin, 1826-1888

1. Day is dy-ing in the west, Heav'n is touching earth with rest; Wait and
2. Lord of life, beneath the dome Of the u-ni-verse, thy home, Gath-er
3. While the deep'ning shadows fall, Heart of Love, en-fold-ing all, Thro' the
4. When for-ev-er from our sight Pass the stars, the day, the night, Lord of

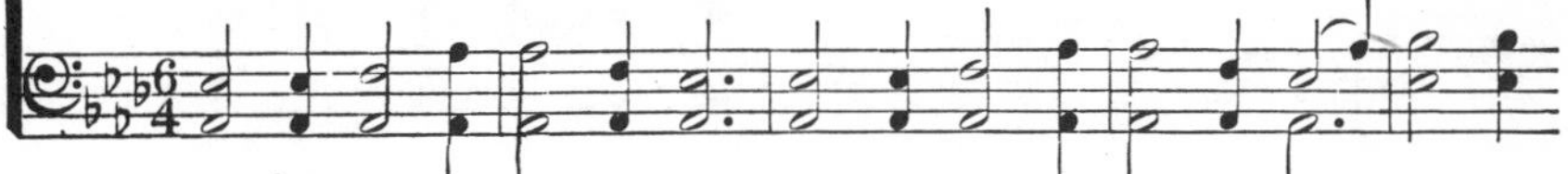

wor-ship while the night Sets her ev'ning lamps a-light Thro all the sky.
us who seek thy face To the fold of thy embrace, For thou art nigh.
glo-ry and the grace Of the stars that veil thy face, Our hearts as-cend.
an-gels, on our eyes Let e-ter-nal morning rise, And shad-ows end.

REFRAIN *p* *f*

Ho-ly, ho-ly, ho-ly Lord God of Hosts! Heav'n and earth are full of thee,

ff

Heav'n and earth are prais-ing thee, O Lord most high! A-MEN.

24 O God, the Rock of Ages

GREENLAND. 7.6.7.6.D.

Edward H. Bickersteth, 1825-1906 Arr. from J. Michael Haydn, 1737-1806

1. O God, the Rock of A - ges, Who ev - er - more hast been,
2. Our years are like the shad - ows On sun - ny hills that lie,
3. O Thou who canst not slum - ber, Whose light grows nev - er pale,
4. Lord, crown our faith's en - deav - or With beau - ty and with grace,
What time the tem - pest ra - ges, Our dwell - ing place se - rene:
Or grass - es in the mead - ows That blos - som but to die;
Teach us a - right to num - ber Our years be - fore they fail.
Till, clothed in light for - ev - er, We see thee face to face:
Be - fore thy first cre - a - tions, O Lord, the same as now,
A sleep, a dream, a sto - ry By stran - gers quick - ly told,
On us thy mer - cy light - en, On us thy good - ness rest,
A joy no lan - guage meas - ures, A foun - tain brim - ming o'er,
To end - less gen - er - a - tions The Ev - er - last - ing Thou!
An un - re - main - ing glo - ry Of things that soon are old.
And let thy Spir - it bright - en The hearts thy - self hast blessed.
An end - less flow of pleas - ures, An o - cean with - out shore. A - MEN.

A Mighty Fortress Is Our God

25

EIN' FESTE BURG. 8.7.8.7.6.6.6.6.7.

Martin Luther, 1483-1546
Tr. by Frederick H. Hedge, 1805-1890

Martin Luther, 1483-1546

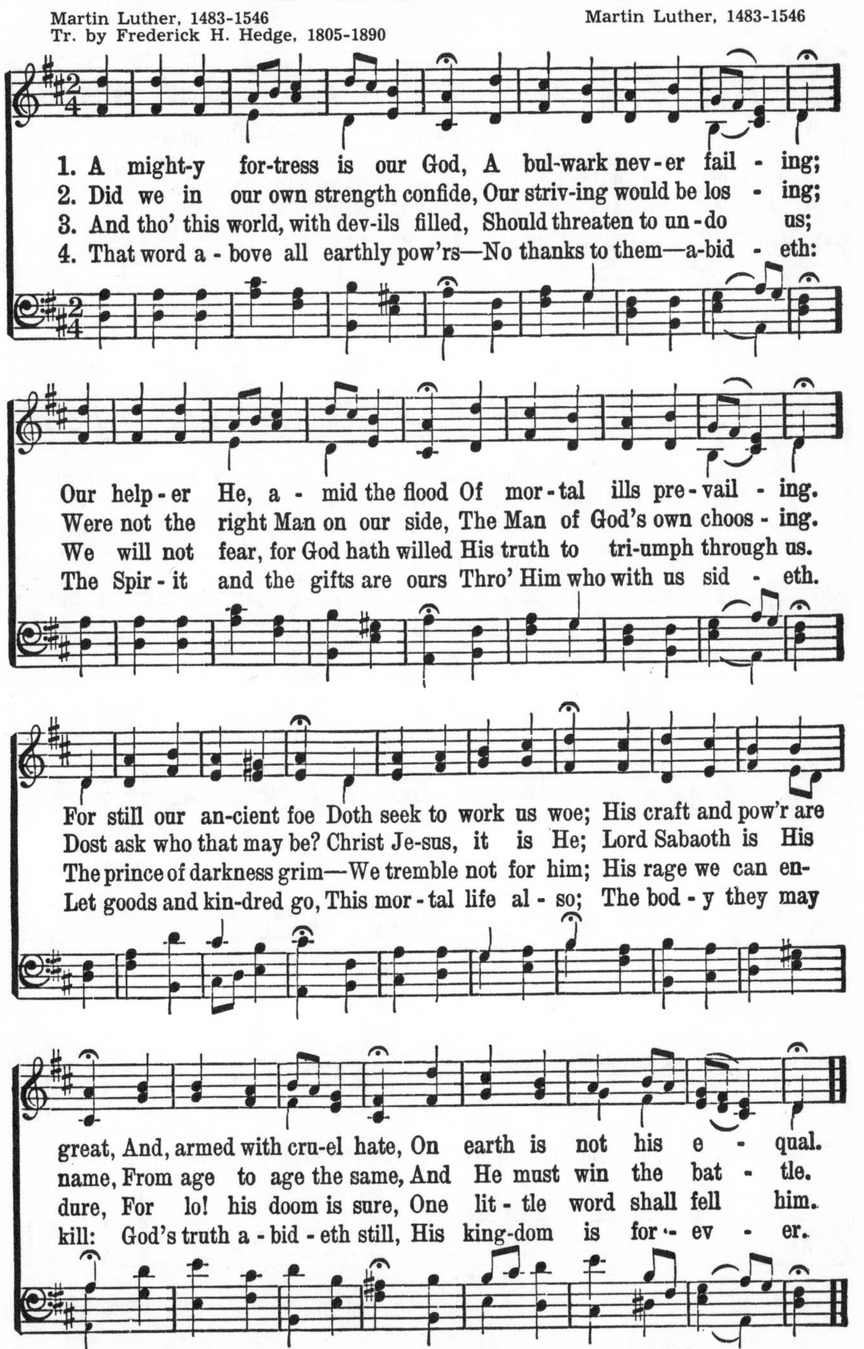
1. A mighty fortress is our God, A bul-wark nev-er fail - ing;
2. Did we in our own strength confide, Our striv-ing would be los - ing;
3. And tho' this world, with dev-ils filled, Should threaten to un-do us;
4. That word a - bove all earthly pow'rs—No thanks to them—a-bid - eth:
Our help-er He, a - mid the flood Of mor-tal ills pre-vail - ing.
Were not the right Man on our side, The Man of God's own choos - ing.
We will not fear, for God hath willed His truth to tri-umph through us.
The Spir - it and the gifts are ours Thro' Him who with us sid - eth.
For still our an-cient foe Doth seek to work us woe; His craft and pow'r are
Dost ask who that may be? Christ Je-sus, it is He; Lord Sabaoth is His
The prince of darkness grim—We tremble not for him; His rage we can en-
Let goods and kin-dred go, This mor - tal life al - so; The bod - y they may
great, And, armed with cru-el hate, On earth is not his e - qual.
name, From age to age the same, And He must win the bat - tle.
dure, For lo! his doom is sure, One lit - tle word shall fell him.
kill: God's truth a - bid - eth still, His king-dom is for - ev - er.

26 What a Mighty God We Serve!

Clara M. Brooks, 1907 — Barney E. Warren, 1907

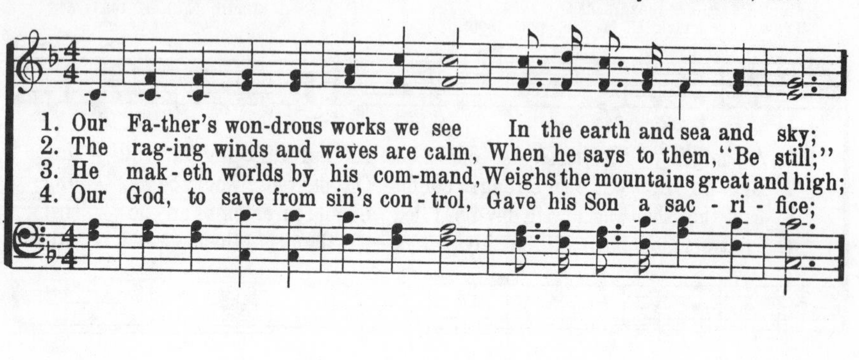

1. Our Fa-ther's won-drous works we see In the earth and sea and sky;
2. The rag-ing winds and waves are calm, When he says to them, "Be still;"
3. He mak-eth worlds by his com-mand, Weighs the mountains great and high;
4. Our God, to save from sin's con-trol, Gave his Son a sac - ri - fice;

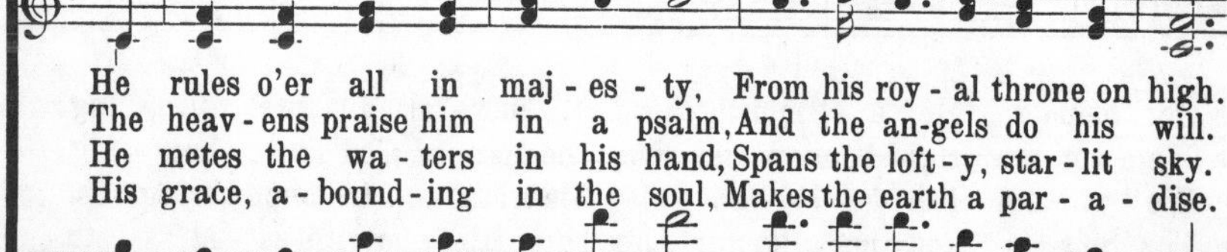

He rules o'er all in maj - es - ty, From his roy - al throne on high.
The heav-ens praise him in a psalm, And the an-gels do his will.
He metes the wa - ters in his hand, Spans the loft - y, star - lit sky.
His grace, a - bound - ing in the soul, Makes the earth a par - a - dise.

CHORUS

What a might-y God we serve! we serve! What a might-y God we serve! . . . we serve!

Reign-ing now a-bove on his throne of love, What a mighty God we serve! A-MEN.

Holy, Holy, Holy Is the Lord 27

Fanny J. Crosby, 1820-1915 William B. Bradbury, 1816-1868

1. Ho - ly, ho - ly, ho - ly is the Lord! Sing, O ye peo - ple,
2. Praise him, praise him! shout a - loud for joy! Watch-man of Zi - on,
3. King e - ter - nal, bless - ed be his name! So may his chil - dren

glad - ly a - dore him: Let the moun-tains trem - ble at his word;
her - ald the sto - ry: Sin and death his king-dom shall de - stroy;
glad - ly a - dore him, When in heav'n we join the hap - py strain,

Let the hills be joy - ful be - fore him. Might-y in wis-dom, bound-less in
All the earth shall sing of his glo - ry. Praise him, ye an - gels, ye who be-
When we cast our bright crowns before him. There in his like-ness joy - ful a-

mer - cy, Great is Je - ho - vah, king o - ver all.
hold him Robed in his splen-dor, match-less, di - vine.
wak - ing, There we shall see him, there we shall sing:

CHORUS

Ho - ly, ho - ly, ho - ly is the Lord! Let the hills be joy - ful be - fore him. A - MEN.

28 Hallelujah, Praise Jehovah

Psalm 148 — William J. Kirkpatrick, 1838-1921

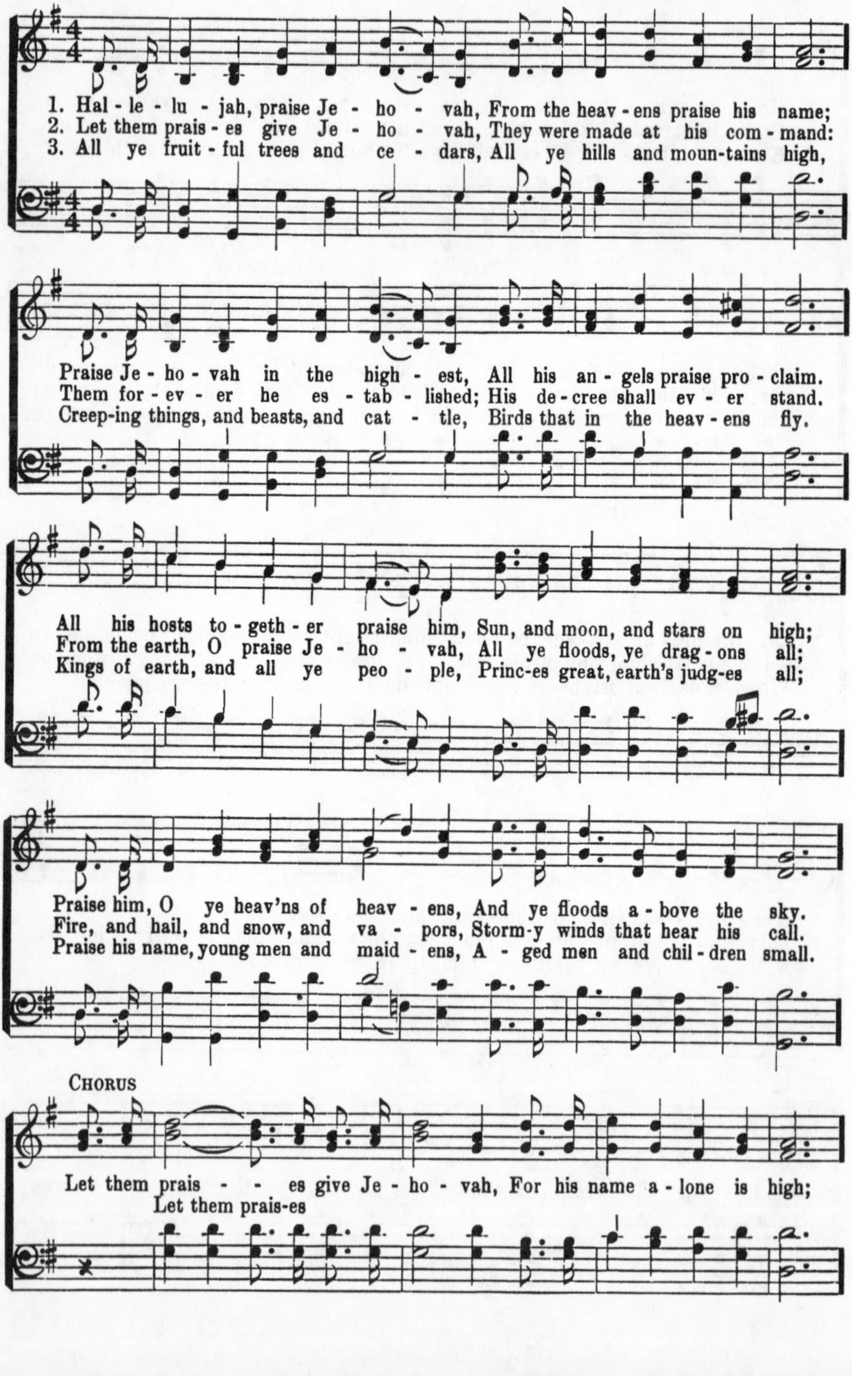

1. Hal - le - lu - jah, praise Je - ho - vah, From the heav - ens praise his name;
2. Let them prais - es give Je - ho - vah, They were made at his com - mand:
3. All ye fruit - ful trees and ce - dars, All ye hills and moun-tains high,

Praise Je - ho - vah in the high - est, All his an - gels praise pro - claim.
Them for - ev - er he es - tab - lished; His de - cree shall ev - er stand.
Creep-ing things, and beasts, and cat - tle, Birds that in the heav - ens fly.

All his hosts to - geth - er praise him, Sun, and moon, and stars on high;
From the earth, O praise Je - ho - vah, All ye floods, ye drag - ons all;
Kings of earth, and all ye peo - ple, Princ-es great, earth's judg-es all;

Praise him, O ye heav'ns of heav - ens, And ye floods a - bove the sky.
Fire, and hail, and snow, and va - pors, Storm-y winds that hear his call.
Praise his name, young men and maid - ens, A - ged men and chil - dren small.

CHORUS

Let them prais - - es give Je - ho - vah, For his name a - lone is high;
Let them prais-es

And his glo - - ry is ex-alt-ed, And his glo - - ry is ex-alt-ed,
And his glo-ry
And his glo-ry
pp
p
ff
And his glo - - ry is ex-alt-ed Far a-bove the earth and sky. A-MEN.
And his glo-ry

The King of Love My Shepherd Is 29

DOMINUS REGIT ME. 8.7.8.7.

Henry W. Baker, 1821-1877 — John B. Dykes, 1823-1867

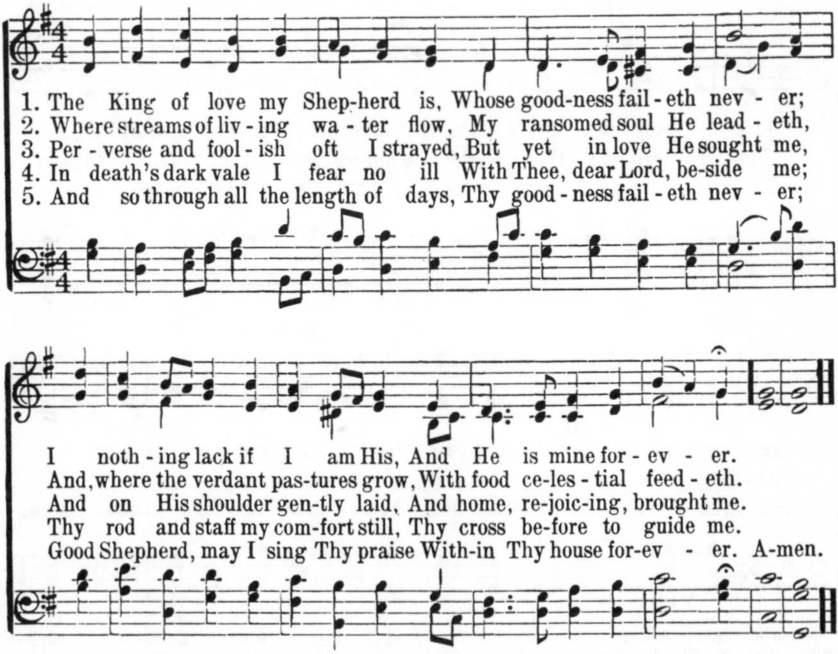

1. The King of love my Shep-herd is, Whose good-ness fail-eth nev - er;
I noth-ing lack if I am His, And He is mine for-ev - er.

2. Where streams of liv-ing wa-ter flow, My ransomed soul He lead-eth,
And, where the verdant pas-tures grow, With food ce-les-tial feed-eth.

3. Per-verse and fool-ish oft I strayed, But yet in love He sought me,
And on His shoulder gen-tly laid, And home, re-joic-ing, brought me.

4. In death's dark vale I fear no ill With Thee, dear Lord, be-side me;
Thy rod and staff my com-fort still, Thy cross be-fore to guide me.

5. And so through all the length of days, Thy good-ness fail-eth nev - er;
Good Shepherd, may I sing Thy praise With-in Thy house for-ev - er. A-men.

30 This Is My Father's World

TERRA BEATA. S.M.D.

Maltbie D. Babcock, 1858-1901 — Franklin L. Sheppard, 1852-1930

1. This is my Fa - ther's world, And to my lis - t'ning ears, All
2. This is my Fa - ther's world, The birds their car - ols raise, The
3. This is my Fa - ther's world, O let me ne'er for - get That

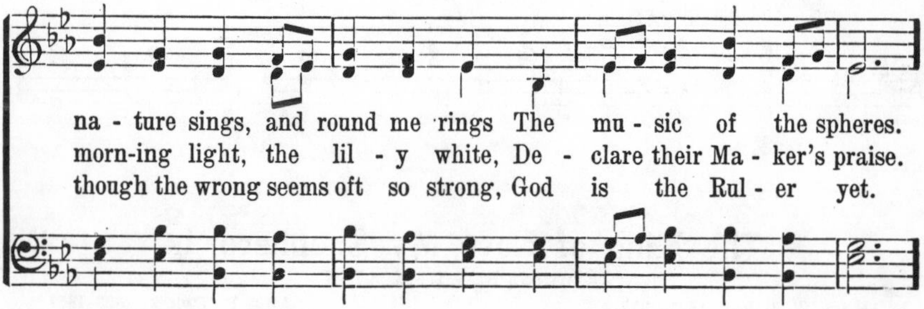

na - ture sings, and round me rings The mu - sic of the spheres.
morn-ing light, the lil - y white, De - clare their Ma - ker's praise.
though the wrong seems oft so strong, God is the Rul - er yet.

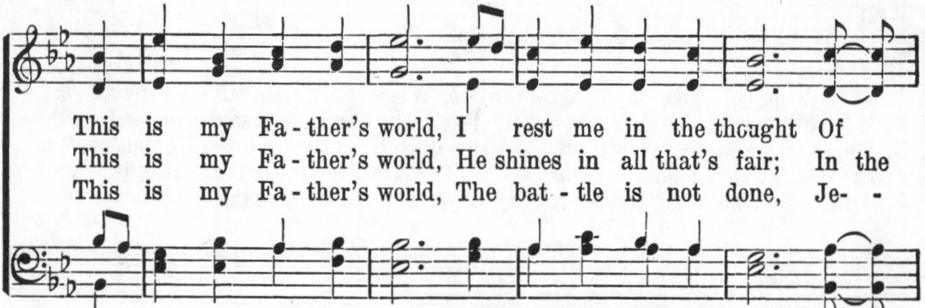

This is my Fa - ther's world, I rest me in the thought Of
This is my Fa - ther's world, He shines in all that's fair; In the
This is my Fa - ther's world, The bat - tle is not done, Je- -

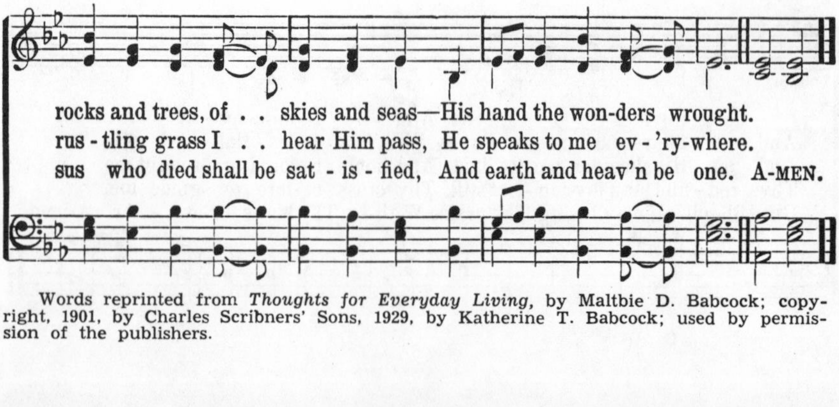

rocks and trees, of . . skies and seas—His hand the won-ders wrought.
rus - tling grass I . . hear Him pass, He speaks to me ev - 'ry-where.
sus who died shall be sat - is - fied, And earth and heav'n be one. A-MEN.

How Gentle God's Commands 31

DENNIS. S.M.

Philip Doddridge, 1702-1751

Arr. from Hans G. Naegeli, 1773-1836
by Lowell Mason, 1792-1872

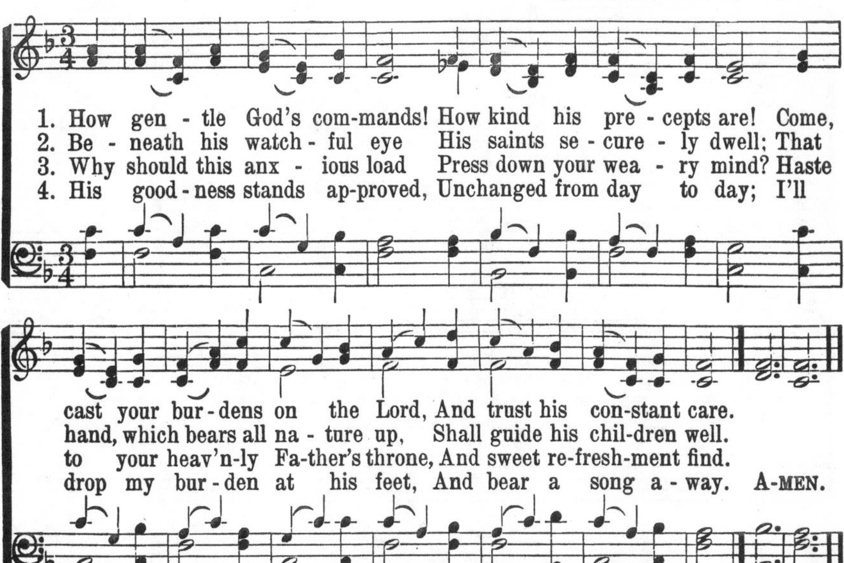
1. How gen - tle God's com-mands! How kind his pre - cepts are! Come,
2. Be - neath his watch - ful eye His saints se - cure - ly dwell; That
3. Why should this anx - ious load Press down your wea - ry mind? Haste
4. His good - ness stands ap-proved, Unchanged from day to day; I'll
cast your bur - dens on the Lord, And trust his con-stant care.
hand, which bears all na - ture up, Shall guide his chil-dren well.
to your heav'n-ly Fa-ther's throne, And sweet re-fresh-ment find.
drop my bur - den at his feet, And bear a song a - way. A-MEN.

There's a Wideness in God's Mercy 32

WELLESLEY. 8.7.8.7.

Frederick W. Faber, 1814-1863

Lizzie S. Tourjee, 1858-1913

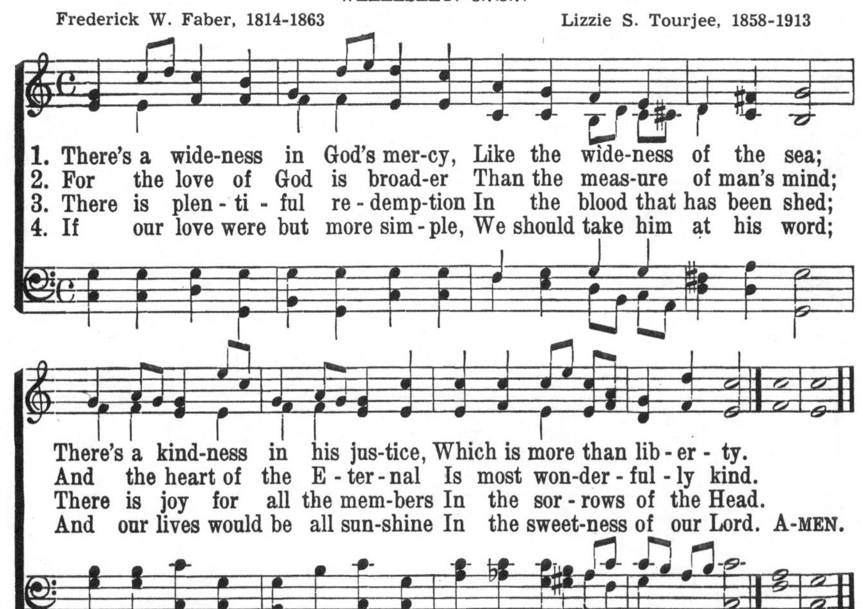
1. There's a wide-ness in God's mer-cy, Like the wide-ness of the sea;
2. For the love of God is broad-er Than the meas-ure of man's mind;
3. There is plen - ti - ful re - demp-tion In the blood that has been shed;
4. If our love were but more sim - ple, We should take him at his word;
There's a kind-ness in his jus-tice, Which is more than lib - er - ty.
And the heart of the E - ter - nal Is most won-der - ful - ly kind.
There is joy for all the mem-bers In the sor - rows of the Head.
And our lives would be all sun-shine In the sweet-ness of our Lord. A-MEN.

33 O Praise the Lord!

Psalm 117
Charles W. Naylor 1874-1950

Barney E. Warren, 1867-1951

1. O praise the Lord, all ye na - tions! Praise him, all ye peo - ple!
2. O praise the Lord, all ye na - tions! Praise him for his good - ness!
3. O praise the Lord, all ye na - tions! He is strong and might - y:
4. O praise the Lord, all ye na - tions! For his love un - fail - ing!
For his mer - ci - ful kind - ness is great toward us, And the
For he sav - eth his peo - ple from all their sins, And pre-
For he keep - eth our steps, that we shall not fall, And de-
He doth ten - der - ly lead in the path of peace, And his
truth of the Lord en - dur - eth for - ev - er: Praise ye the Lord!
serv - eth the souls of all who will trust him: Praise ye the Lord!
liv - ers his saints from all their temp - ta - tions: Praise ye the Lord!
name is a ref - uge from the op-press - or: Praise ye the Lord!
CHORUS
Praise him, praise him! Praise ye the Lord!.......
Praise him, praise him, praise, O praise him! Praise ye the Lord, O praise the Lord!
Praise him, praise him! Praise ye the Lord! A - MEN.
Praise him, praise him, praise, O praise him!

O God, Our Help in Ages Past 34

ST. ANNE. C.M.

Isaac Watts, 1674-1748 — Probably by William Croft, 1678-1727

1. O God, our help in a - ges past, Our hope for years to come,
Our shel-ter from the storm-y blast, And our e - ter - nal home!

2. Be - fore the hills in or - der stood, Or earth re-ceived her frame,
From ev - er - last-ing Thou art God, To end-less years the same.

3. A thous-and a - ges, in Thy sight, Are like an ev - 'ning gone;
Short as the watch that ends the night, Be - fore the ris - ing sun.

4. Time, like an ev - er - roll-ing stream, Bears all its sons a - way;
They fly, for - got - ten, as a dream Dies at the ope-ning day.

5. O God, our help in a - ges past, Our hope for years to come;
Be Thou our guide while life shall last, And our e - ter - nal home! A - men.

None Is like God 35

ST. AGNES. C.M.

John Burton, 1808-1877 — John B. Dykes, 1823-1876

1. None is like God, who reigns a - bove, So great, so pure, so high;
None is like God, whose name is Love, And who is al - ways nigh.

2. In all the earth there is no spot Ex - clud - ed from his care;
We can-not go where God is not, For he is ev - 'ry - where.

3. He is our best and kind - est Friend, And guards us night and day;
To all our wants he will at - tend, And an-swer when we pray.

4. O if we love him as we ought, And on his grace re - ly,
We shall be joy - ful at the thought That God is al - ways nigh. A-MEN.

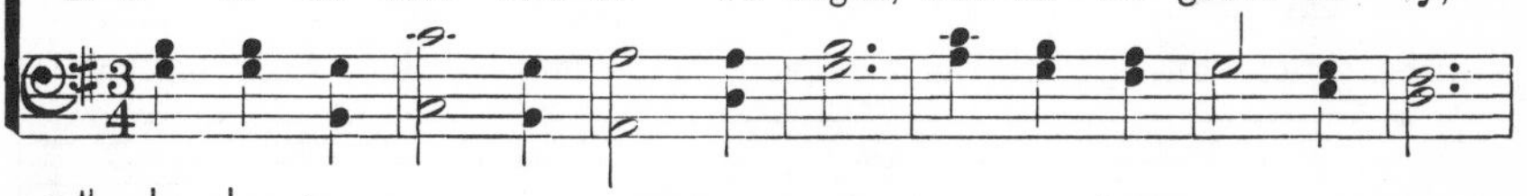

36 God Is Love

D. Otis Teasley, 1905 — D. Otis Teasley, 1905

1. Hark! my soul, se-raph-ic mu-sic From an-gel-ic choirs a-bove,
2. See the depths of his com-pas-sion, Giv-ing heav-en's best to prove,
3. Lo, I feel the Ho-ly Spir-it, Like a peace-ful heav'n-ly dove,
4. Sing, my soul, and all with-in me, Sing till all the clouds re-move;

Breaks to earth the joy-ful ti-dings, That the Lord our God is love.
By a life of pain and sor-row, That the Lord our God is love.
Wit-ness-ing with-in my bos-om That the Lord our God is love.
Sing and praise and shout for-ev-er, For the Lord our God is love.

CHORUS

God . . . . . is love, ... God . . . . is love, ...
God is love, yes, God is love, Hal-le-lu-jah! God is love,

Song of an-gel choirs a-bove; Hal-le-lu-jah! God is love.

Par-a-dise now helps to swell it, Saints on earth, a-far go tell it,

cres.
rall.
Sa-tan's host can nev-er quell it, For the Lord our God is love. A-MEN.

O Come, All Ye Faithful 37

ADESTE FIDELES. Irregular, with Refrain

Latin Hymn, 18th century
Tr. by Frederick Oakeley, 1802-1880

Unknown: probably 18th century

1. O come, all ye faith - ful, joy - ful and tri - um - phant, O
2. Sing, choirs of an - gels, sing in ex - ul - ta - tion, O
3. Yea, Lord, we greet Thee, born this hap - py morn - ing, O

come ye, O come ye to Beth - le - hem; Come and be - hold Him,
sing, all ye bright hosts of heav'n a - bove; Glo - ry to God, all
Je - sus, to Thee be all glo - ry giv'n; Word of the Fa - ther,

born the King of an - gels:
glo - ry in the high - est:
now in flesh ap - pear - ing:

REFRAIN

O come, let us a - dore Him, O
come, let us a - dore Him, O come, let us a - dore Him, Christ, the Lord.

38 Joy to the World

ANTIOCH. C.M.

From Psalm 98
Isaac Watts, 1674-1748

From *The Messiah*, by George F. Handel, 1685-1759
Arr. by Lowell Mason, 1792-1872

1. Joy to the world, the Lord is come! Let earth receive her King; Let ev - 'ry heart prepare him room, And heav'n and nature sing, And heav'n and nature sing, And heav'n, and heav'n and nature sing.
2. Joy to the world, the Savior reigns! Let men their songs employ, While fields and floods, rocks, hills and plains, Repeat the sounding joy, Repeat the sounding joy, Repeat, repeat the sounding joy!
3. No more let sin and sorrow grow Nor thorns infest the ground; He comes to make his blessings flow Far as the curse is found, Far as the curse is found, Far as, far as the curse is found.
4. He rules the world with truth and grace, And makes the nations prove The glories of his righteousness, And wonders of his love, And wonders of his love, And wonders, wonders of his love. A-MEN.

(Lower voices: And heav'n, and heav'n and nature sing, And heav'n and nature sing,)

It Came upon the Midnight Clear 39

CAROL. C.M.D.

Edmund H. Sears, 1810-1876 — Richard S. Willis, 1819-1900

1. It came up - on the mid-night clear, That glo - rious song of old,
2. Still thro' the clo - ven skies they come, With peace-ful wings un - furled,
3. O ye, be - neath life's crushing load, Whose forms are bend - ing low,

From an - gels bend - ing near the earth To touch their harps of gold;
And still their heav'n-ly mu - sic floats O'er all the wea - ry world;
Who toil a - long the climb-ing way With pain-ful steps and slow,

"Peace on the earth, good-will to men, From heav'n's all-gra-cious King:"
A - bove its sad and low - ly plains They bend on heav'n-ly wing,
Look now! for glad and gold - en hours Come swift - ly on the wing;

The world in sol-emn still-ness lay To hear the an - gels sing.
And ev - er o'er its Ba-bel sounds The bless-ed an - gels sing.
O rest be - side the wea - ry road, And hear the an - gels sing. A - MEN.

40 O Little Town of Bethlehem

ST. LOUIS. 8.6.8.6.7.6.8.6.

Phillips Brooks, 1835-1893 Lewis H. Redner, 1831-1908

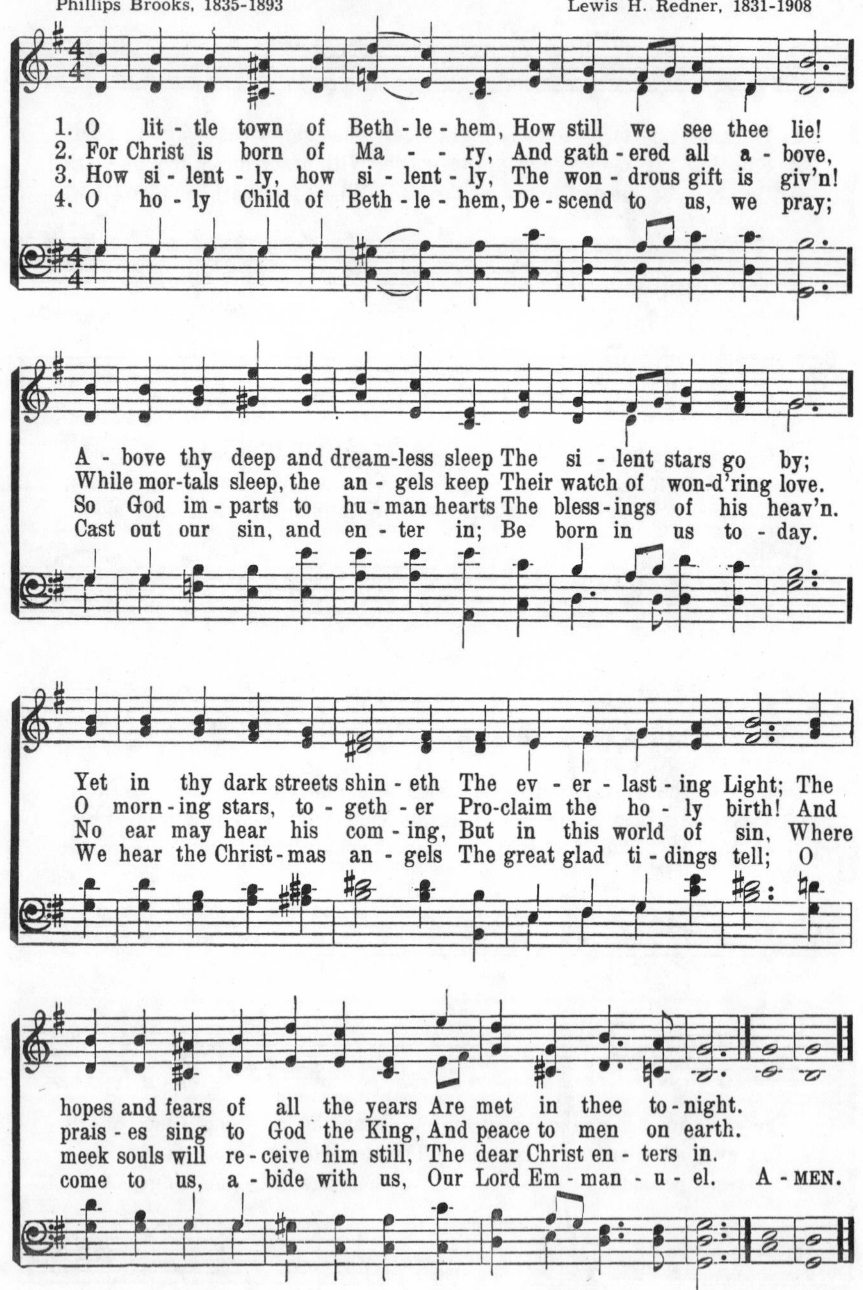
1. O lit - tle town of Beth - le - hem, How still we see thee lie!
2. For Christ is born of Ma - - ry, And gath - ered all a - bove,
3. How si - lent - ly, how si - lent - ly, The won - drous gift is giv'n!
4. O ho - ly Child of Beth - le - hem, De - scend to us, we pray;
A - bove thy deep and dream-less sleep The si - lent stars go by;
While mor-tals sleep, the an - gels keep Their watch of won-d'ring love.
So God im - parts to hu - man hearts The bless - ings of his heav'n.
Cast out our sin, and en - ter in; Be born in us to - day.
Yet in thy dark streets shin - eth The ev - er - last - ing Light; The
O morn - ing stars, to - geth - er Pro-claim the ho - ly birth! And
No ear may hear his com - ing, But in this world of sin, Where
We hear the Christ - mas an - gels The great glad ti - dings tell; O
hopes and fears of all the years Are met in thee to - night.
prais - es sing to God the King, And peace to men on earth.
meek souls will re - ceive him still, The dear Christ en - ters in.
come to us, a - bide with us, Our Lord Em - man - u - el. A - MEN.

Hark, the Herald Angels Sing 41

MENDELSSOHN. 7.7.7.7.D. with Refrain

Charles Wesley, 1707-1788
Alt. by George Whitefield

Arr. from Felix Mendelssohn, 1809-1847
by William H. Cummings, 1831-1915

1. Hark! the her - ald an - gels sing, 'Glo - ry to the new - born King;
2. Christ, by high - est heav'n a - dored, Christ, the ev - er - last - ing Lord!
3. Hail, the heav'n-born Prince of Peace! Hail, the Sun of Right-eous - ness!
Peace on earth, and mer - cy mild, God and sin - ners rec - on - ciled!'
Come, De - sire of Na - tions, come, Fix in us thy hum - ble home.
Light and life to all he brings, Ris'n with heal - ing in his wings;
Joy - ful, all ye na - tions, rise, Join the tri - umph of the skies;
Veiled in flesh the God - head see; Hail th' In - car - nate De - i - ty,
Mild he lays his glo - ry by, Born that man no more may die,
With th' an - gel - ic host pro - claim, 'Christ is born in Beth - le - hem!'
Pleased as man with men to dwell; Je - sus, our Em - man - u - el!
Born to raise the sons of earth, Born to give them sec - ond birth:
Hark! the her - ald an - gels sing, 'Glo - ry to the new-born King!' A - MEN.

42 The First Noel

THE FIRST NOEL. Irregular with Refrain

Old English carol

Traditional melody, from W. Sandys' *Christmas Carols*, 1833

1. The first No - el the an - gel did say Was to cer - tain poor shepherds in fields as they lay; In fields where they lay keep ing their sheep, On a cold win - ter's night that was so deep.
2. They look - ed up and saw a star Shin - ing in the east, be - yond them far, And to the earth it gave great light, And so it con - tin - ued both day and night.
3. And by the light of that same star, Three wise - men came from coun - try far; To seek for a king was their in - tent, And to fol - low the star wher - ev - er it went.
4. This star drew nigh to the north - west, O'er Beth - le - hem it took its rest, And there it did both stop and stay, Right o - ver the place where Je - sus lay.
5. Then en - tered in those wise - men three, Full rev - er - ent - ly up - on the knee, And of - fered there, in His pres - ence, Their gold, and myrrh, and frank - in - cense.

Refrain

No - el, No - el, No - el, No - el, Born is the King of Is - ra - el.

There's a Song in the Air 43

(First Tune)

Josiah G. Holland, 1819-1881 Andrew L. Byers, 1870-1952

1. There's a song in the air! There's a star in the sky!
2. There's a tu - mult of joy O'er the won - der - ful birth,
3. In the light of that star Lie the a - ges im - pearled;
4. We re - joice in the light, And we ech - o the song
There's a moth-er's deep prayer, And a ba - by's low cry!
For the Vir - gin's sweet boy Is the Lord of the earth.
And that song from a - far Has swept o - ver the world.
That comes down through the night From the heav - en - ly throng.
And the star rains its fire while the beau - ti - ful sing,
Ay! the star rains its fire while the beau - ti - ful sing,
Ev - 'ry hearth is a - flame, and the beau - ti - ful sing,
Ay! we shout to the love - ly e - van - gel they bring,
For the man - ger of Beth - le - hem cra - dles a King!
For the man - ger of Beth - le - hem cra - dles a King!
In the homes of the na - tions, that Je - sus is King!
And we greet in his cra - dle our Sav - ior and King! A - MEN.

44 There's a Song in the Air

CHRISTMAS SONG. 6.6.6.6.12.12.
(Second Tune)

Josiah G. Holland, 1819-1881 — Karl P. Harrington, b. 1861

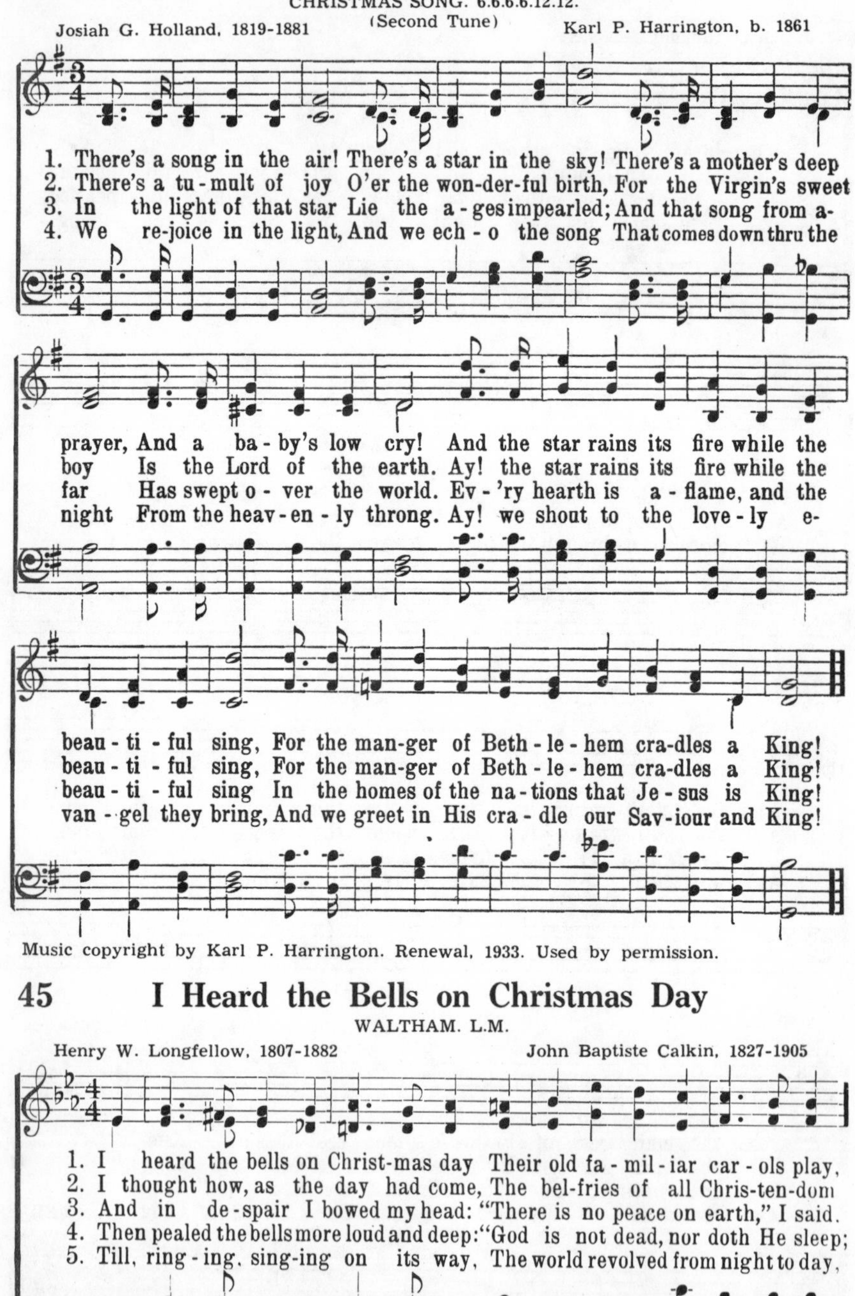
1. There's a song in the air! There's a star in the sky! There's a mother's deep prayer, And a ba - by's low cry! And the star rains its fire while the beau - ti - ful sing, For the man-ger of Beth - le - hem cra-dles a King!
2. There's a tu - mult of joy O'er the won-der-ful birth, For the Virgin's sweet boy Is the Lord of the earth. Ay! the star rains its fire while the beau - ti - ful sing, For the man-ger of Beth - le - hem cra-dles a King!
3. In the light of that star Lie the a - ges impearled; And that song from a-far Has swept o - ver the world. Ev - 'ry hearth is a - flame, and the beau - ti - ful sing In the homes of the na - tions that Je - sus is King!
4. We re-joice in the light, And we ech - o the song That comes down thru the night From the heav - en - ly throng. Ay! we shout to the love - ly e-van - gel they bring, And we greet in His cra - dle our Sav-iour and King!
1. I heard the bells on Christ-mas day Their old fa - mil - iar car - ols play,
2. I thought how, as the day had come, The bel-fries of all Chris-ten-dom
3. And in de - spair I bowed my head: "There is no peace on earth," I said.
4. Then pealed the bells more loud and deep: "God is not dead, nor doth He sleep;
5. Till, ring - ing, sing-ing on its way, The world revolved from night to day,

45 I Heard the Bells on Christmas Day

WALTHAM. L.M.

Henry W. Longfellow, 1807-1882 — John Baptiste Calkin, 1827-1905

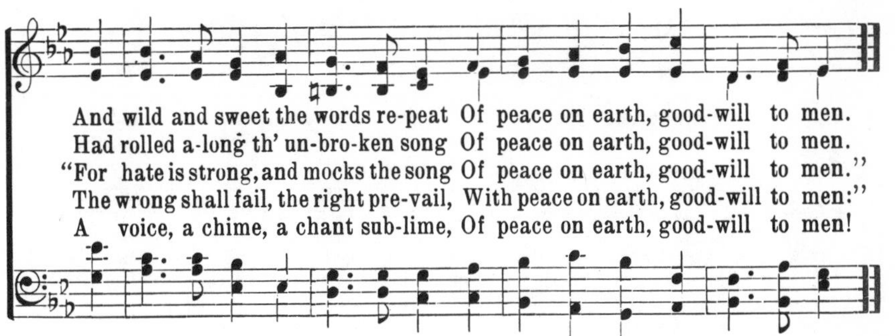
And wild and sweet the words re-peat Of peace on earth, good-will to men.
Had rolled a-long th' un-bro-ken song Of peace on earth, good-will to men.
"For hate is strong, and mocks the song Of peace on earth, good-will to men."
The wrong shall fail, the right pre-vail, With peace on earth, good-will to men:"
A voice, a chime, a chant sub-lime, Of peace on earth, good-will to men!

Silent Night, Holy Night 46

STILLE NACHT. Irregular

Joseph Mohr, 1792-1848
Tr. compiled from various sources

Franz Gruber, 1787-1863

1. Si - lent night! Ho - ly night! All is calm, all is bright
2. Si - lent night! Ho - ly night! Shep-herds quake at the sight!
3. Si - lent night! Ho - ly night! Son of God, love's pure light

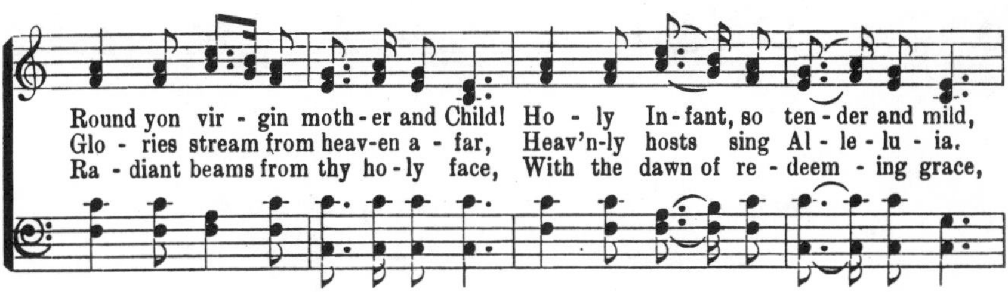

Round yon vir - gin moth - er and Child! Ho - ly In - fant, so ten - der and mild,
Glo - ries stream from heav-en a - far, Heav'n-ly hosts sing Al - le - lu - ia.
Ra - diant beams from thy ho - ly face, With the dawn of re - deem - ing grace,

rit.

Sleep in heav - en - ly peace, Sleep in heav - en - ly peace.
Christ, the Sav - ior, is born! Christ, the Sav - ior, is born!
Je - sus, Lord, at thy birth, Je - sus, Lord, at thy birth. A - MEN.

47 As with Gladness Men of Old

DIX. 7.7.7.7.7.7.

William C. Dix, 1837-1898

Abridged from a chorale by Conrad Kocher, 1786-1872

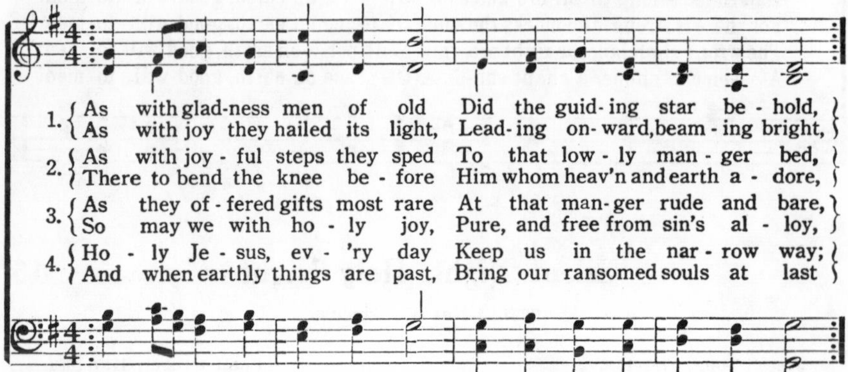

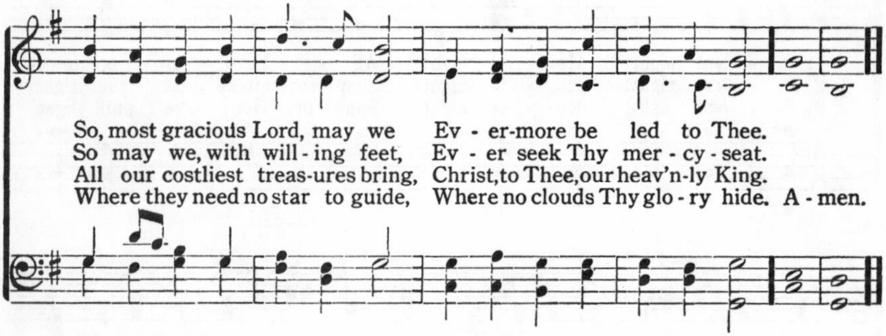

1. As with glad-ness men of old Did the guid-ing star be-hold,
As with joy they hailed its light, Lead-ing on-ward, beam-ing bright,
So, most gracious Lord, may we Ev-er-more be led to Thee.

2. As with joy-ful steps they sped To that low-ly man-ger bed,
There to bend the knee be-fore Him whom heav'n and earth a-dore,
So may we, with will-ing feet, Ev-er seek Thy mer-cy-seat.

3. As they of-fered gifts most rare At that man-ger rude and bare,
So may we with ho-ly joy, Pure, and free from sin's al-loy,
All our costliest treas-ures bring, Christ, to Thee, our heav'n-ly King.

4. Ho-ly Je-sus, ev-'ry day Keep us in the nar-row way;
And when earthly things are past, Bring our ransomed souls at last
Where they need no star to guide, Where no clouds Thy glo-ry hide. A-men.

48 Angels, from the Realms of Glory

REGENT SQUARE. 8.7.8.7.8.7.

James Montgomery, 1771-1854

Henry Smart, 1813-1879

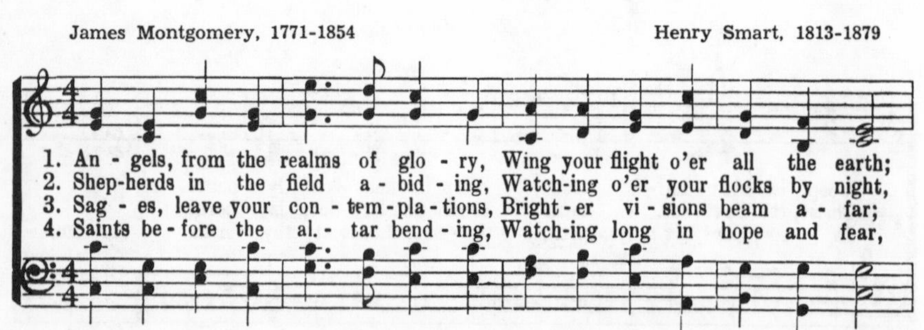
1. An-gels, from the realms of glo-ry, Wing your flight o'er all the earth;
2. Shep-herds in the field a-bid-ing, Watch-ing o'er your flocks by night,
3. Sag-es, leave your con-tem-pla-tions, Bright-er vi-sions beam a-far;
4. Saints be-fore the al-tar bend-ing, Watch-ing long in hope and fear,

Ye who sang cre - a - tion's sto - ry, Now pro - claim Mes - si - ah's birth:
God with man is now re - sid - ing, Yon - der shines the in - fant light:
Seek the great De - sire of na - tions, Ye have seen his na - tal star:
Sud - den - ly the Lord, de - scend - ing, In his tem - ple shall ap - pear:
Come and wor - ship, Come and wor - ship, Wor - ship Christ, the new - born King! A - MEN.

Away in a Manger

49

MUELLER. 11.11.11.11.

Attributed to Martin Luther, 1483-1546

Carl Mueller

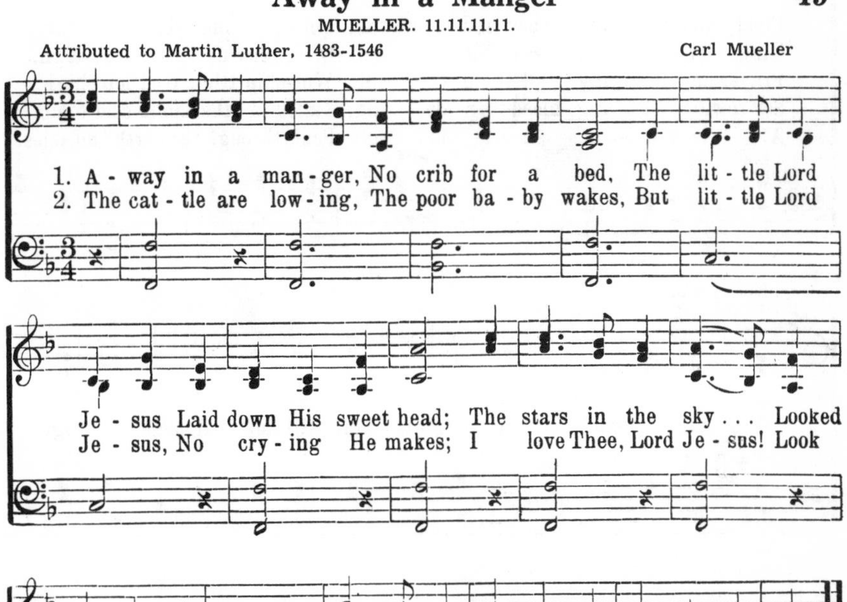
1. A - way in a man - ger, No crib for a bed, The lit - tle Lord Je - sus Laid down His sweet head; The stars in the sky . . . Looked
2. The cat - tle are low - ing, The poor ba - by wakes, But lit - tle Lord Je - sus, No cry - ing He makes; I love Thee, Lord Je - sus! Look

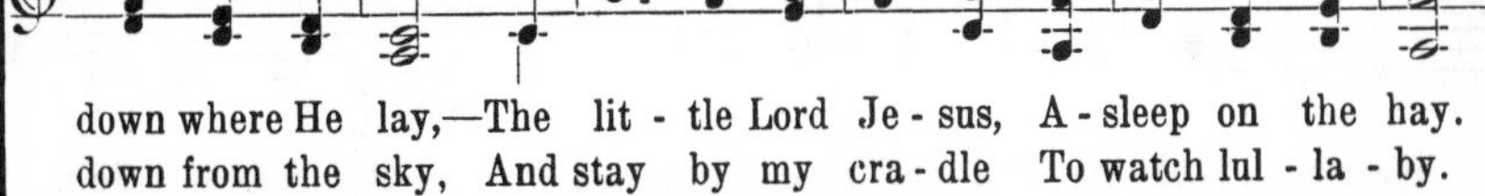

down where He lay,—The lit - tle Lord Je - sus, A - sleep on the hay.
down from the sky, And stay by my cra - dle To watch lul - la - by.

50 We Three Kings of Orient Are

KINGS OF ORIENT. 8.8.8.6. with Refrain

John H. Hopkins, 1820-1891 — John H. Hopkins, 1820-1891

1. We three kings of O - ri - ent are, Bear - ing gifts we trav-erse a - far
2. Born a King on Beth-le-hem's plain, Gold I bring to crown Him a-gain,
3. Frank-in-cense to of - fer have I, In - cense owns a De - i - ty nigh;
4. Myrrh is mine; its bit - ter per-fume Breathes a life of gath-er-ing gloom;
5. Glo - rious now be - hold Him a - rise, King and God and Sac - ri - fice;
Field and foun - tain, moor and moun-tain, Fol - low - ing yon - der star.
King for - ev - er, ceas - ing nev - er O - ver us all to reign.
Prayer and prais - ing, all men rais - ing, Wor-ship Him, God on high.
Sor-rowing, sigh - ing, bleed-ing, dy - ing, Sealed in the stone-cold tomb.
Al - le - lu - ia, Al - le - lu - ia! Peals through the earth and skies.
REFRAIN
O star of won - der, star of night, Star with loy - al beau - ty bright,
West-ward lead - ing, still pro - ceed - ing, Guide us to thy per - fect light.

All My Heart This Night Rejoices 51

EBELING. (BONN) 8.3.3.6.D.

Paul Gerhardt, 1607-1676
Tr. by Catherine Winkworth, 1829-1878

Johann G. Ebeling, 1620-1676

1. All my heart this night re - joic - es, As I hear,
2. Hark! a voice from yon - der man - ger, Soft and sweet,
3. Come, then, let us has - ten yon - der; Here let all,
Far and near, Sweet - est an - gel voic - es;
Doth en - treat, "Flee from woe and dan - ger;
Great and small, Kneel in awe and won - der,
"Christ is born," the choirs are sing - ing, Till the air,
Breth - ren, come; from all that grieves you You are freed;
Love Him who with love is yearn - ing; Hail the Star
Ev - 'ry - where, Now with joy is ring - ing.
All you need I will sure - ly give you."
That from far Bright with hope is burn - ing.
A - MEN.

52 While Shepherds Watched Their Flocks

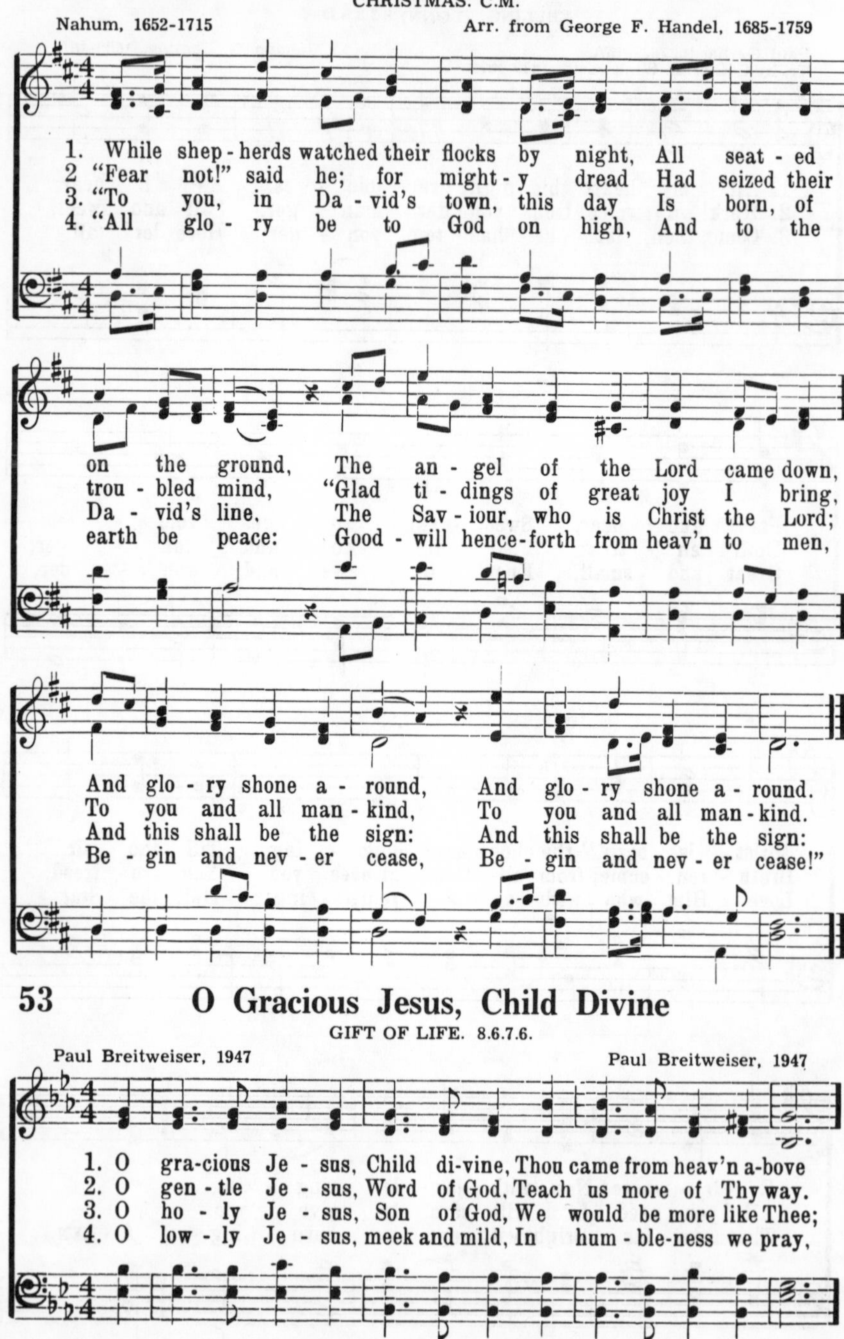
CHRISTMAS. C.M.
Nahum, 1652-1715
Arr. from George F. Handel, 1685-1759
1. While shep - herds watched their flocks by night, All seat - ed on the ground, The an - gel of the Lord came down, And glo - ry shone a - round, And glo - ry shone a - round.
2 "Fear not!" said he; for might - y dread Had seized their trou - bled mind, "Glad ti - dings of great joy I bring, To you and all man - kind, To you and all man - kind.
3. "To you, in Da - vid's town, this day Is born, of Da - vid's line, The Sav - iour, who is Christ the Lord; And this shall be the sign: And this shall be the sign:
4. "All glo - ry be to God on high, And to the earth be peace: Good - will hence-forth from heav'n to men, Be - gin and nev - er cease, Be - gin and nev - er cease!"
53 O Gracious Jesus, Child Divine
GIFT OF LIFE. 8.6.7.6.
Paul Breitweiser, 1947
Paul Breitweiser, 1947
1. O gra-cious Je - sus, Child di-vine, Thou came from heav'n a-bove
2. O gen - tle Je - sus, Word of God, Teach us more of Thy way.
3. O ho - ly Je - sus, Son of God, We would be more like Thee;
4. O low - ly Je - sus, meek and mild, In hum - ble-ness we pray,

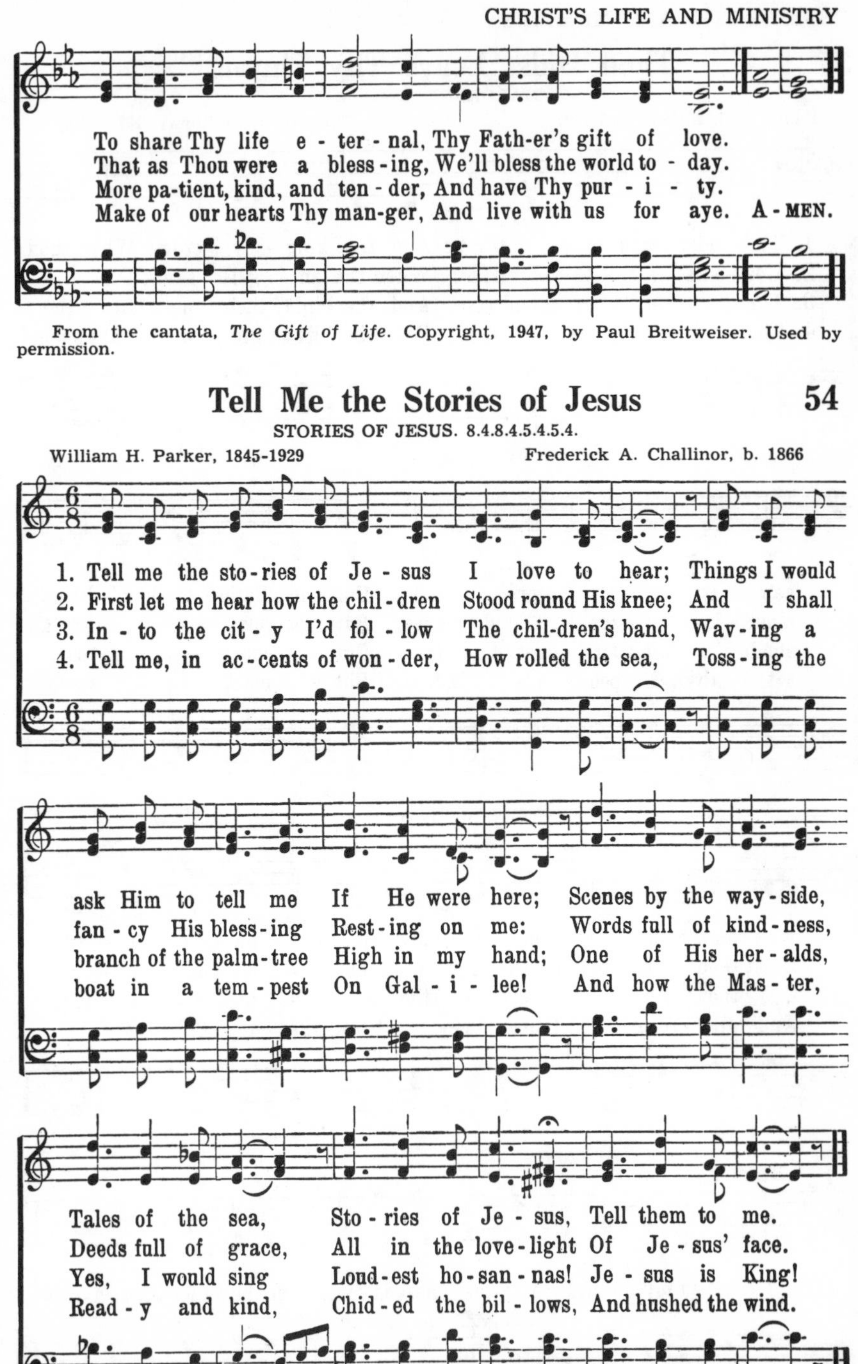
To share Thy life e - ter - nal, Thy Fath-er's gift of love.
That as Thou were a bless - ing, We'll bless the world to - day.
More pa-tient, kind, and ten - der, And have Thy pur - i - ty.
Make of our hearts Thy man-ger, And live with us for aye. A - MEN.
From the cantata, The Gift of Life. Copyright, 1947, by Paul Breitweiser. Used by permission.
Tell Me the Stories of Jesus
54
STORIES OF JESUS. 8.4.8.4.5.4.5.4.
William H. Parker, 1845-1929
Frederick A. Challinor, b. 1866
1. Tell me the sto - ries of Je - sus I love to hear; Things I would ask Him to tell me If He were here; Scenes by the way - side, Tales of the sea, Sto - ries of Je - sus, Tell them to me.
2. First let me hear how the chil - dren Stood round His knee; And I shall fan - cy His bless - ing Rest - ing on me: Words full of kind - ness, Deeds full of grace, All in the love - light Of Je - sus' face.
3. In - to the cit - y I'd fol - low The chil - dren's band, Wav - ing a branch of the palm - tree High in my hand; One of His her - alds, Yes, I would sing Loud - est ho - san - nas! Je - sus is King!
4. Tell me, in ac - cents of won - der, How rolled the sea, Toss - ing the boat in a tem - pest On Gal - i - lee! And how the Mas - ter, Read - y and kind, Chid - ed the bil - lows, And hushed the wind.

55 Thou Didst Leave Thy Throne

MARGARET. Irregular

Emily E. S. Elliott, 1836-1897

Timothy R. Matthews, 1826-1910

1. Thou didst leave thy throne And thy king - ly crown When thou cam - est to earth for me; But in Beth - le - hem's home Was there found no room For thy ho - ly na - tiv - i - ty:
2. Heav-en's arch - es rang When the an - gels sang, Pro- claim - ing thy roy - al de - gree; But of low - ly birth Didst thou come to earth, And in great - est hu - mil - i - ty:
3. The fox - es found rest, And the birds their nest In the shade of the for - est tree; But thy couch was the sod, O thou Son of God, In the des - erts of Gal - i - lee:
4. Thou cam - est, O Lord, With the liv - ing word That should set thy peo - ple free; But with mock - ing scorn, And with crown of thorn, They bore thee to Cal - va - ry:
REFRAIN
O come to my heart, Lord Je-sus, There is room in my heart for thee. A-MEN.

We Would See Jesus; Lo! His Star 56

CUSHMAN. 11.10.11.10

J. Edgar Park, b. 1879 — Herbert B. Turner, 1852-1927

1. We would see Je - sus; lo! His star is shin - ing
A - bove the sta - ble while the an - gels sing;
There in a man - ger on the hay re - clin - ing;
Haste, let us lay our gifts be - fore the King.

2. We would see Je - sus, Ma - ry's Son most ho - ly,
Light of the vil - lage life from day to day;
Shin - ing re - vealed through ev - ery task most low - ly,
The Christ of God, the Life, the Truth, the Way.

3. We would see Je - sus, on the moun - tain teach - ing,
With all the lis - tening peo - ple gath - ered round;
While birds and flowers and sky a - bove are preach - ing,
The bless - ed - ness which sim - ple trust has found.

4. We would see Je - sus, in His work of heal - ing,
At ev - en - tide be - fore the sun was set;
Di - vine and hu - man, in His deep re - veal - ing,
Of God and man in lov - ing ser - vice met.

5. We would see Je - sus, in the ear - ly morn - ing
Still as of old He call - eth, "Fol - low me";
Let us a - rise, all mean - er ser - vice scorn - ing:
Lord, we are Thine, we give our - selves to Thee.

A-MEN.

57 Tell Me the Story of Jesus

TELL ME THE STORY. 8.7.8.7.D. with Refrain

Fanny J. Crosby, 1820-1915 John R. Sweney, 1837-1899

1. Tell me the sto - ry of Je - sus, Write on my heart ev - ery word;
2. Fast-ing a - lone in the des - ert, Tell of the days that are past,
3. Tell of the cross where they nailed Him, Writh-ing in an-guish and pain;

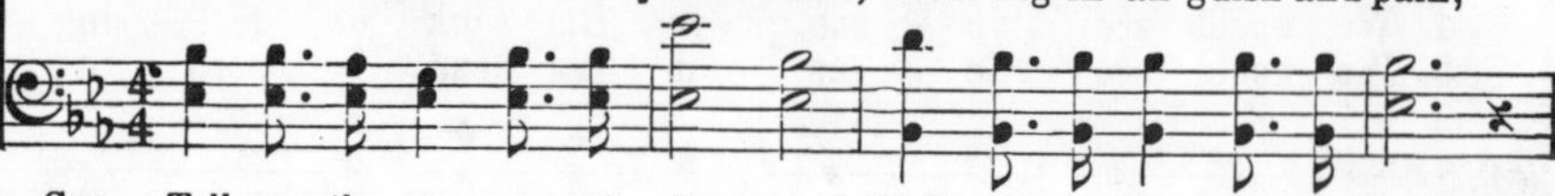

CHO.—*Tell me the sto - ry of Je - sus, Write on my heart ev - ery word;*

FINE

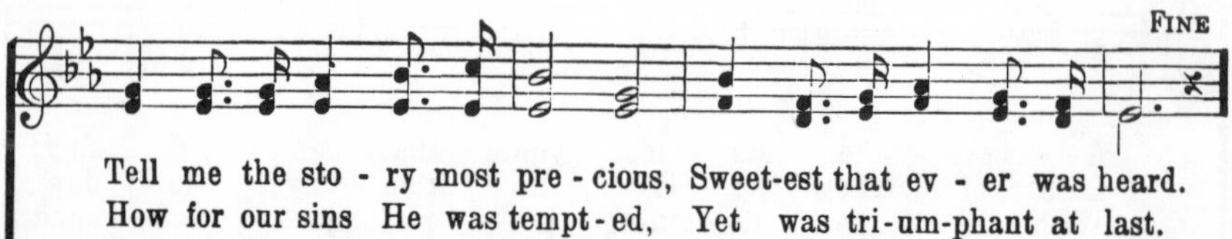

Tell me the sto - ry most pre - cious, Sweet-est that ev - er was heard.
How for our sins He was tempt - ed, Yet was tri - um-phant at last.
Tell of the grave where they laid Him, Tell how He liv - eth a - gain.

Tell me the sto - ry most pre - cious, Sweet - est that ev - er was heard.

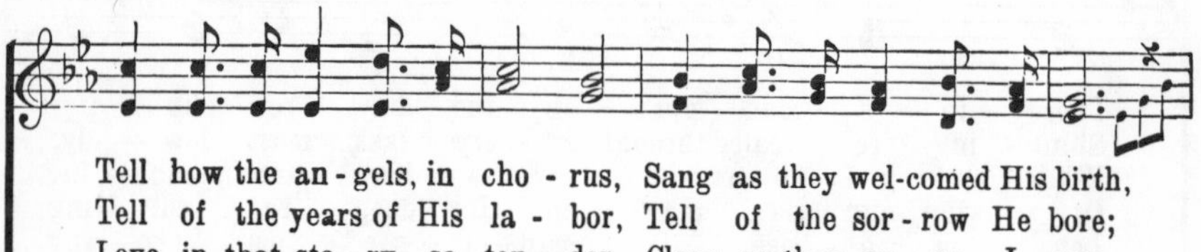

Tell how the an - gels, in cho - rus, Sang as they wel-comed His birth,
Tell of the years of His la - bor, Tell of the sor - row He bore;
Love in that sto - ry so ten - der, Clear - er than ev - er I see:

D. C. for Chorus

"Glo - ry to God in the high - est! Peace and good ti - dings to earth."
He was de-spised and af - flict - ed, Home-less, re - ject - ed and poor.
Stay, let me weep while you whis - per, Love paid the ran-som for me.

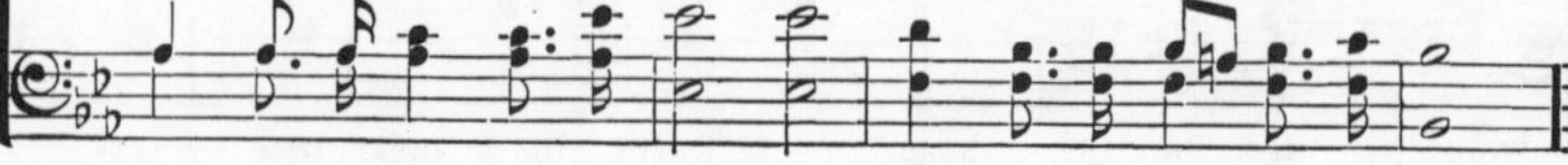

O Master Workman of the Race 58

MATERNA. C.M.D.

Jay T. Stocking, 1879-1936 Samuel A. Ward, 1847-1903

1. O Mas - ter-work - man of the race, Thou Man of Gal - i - lee,
2. O Car - pen - ter of Naz - a-reth, Build - er of life di - vine,
3. O Thou who didst the vi - sion send And gives to each his task,

Who with the eyes of ear - ly youth E - ter - nal things did see,
Who shap - est man to God's own law, Thy - self the fair de - sign,
And with the task suf - fi-cient strength, Show us Thy will, we ask;

We thank Thee for Thy boy-hood faith That shone Thy whole life through;
Build us a tow'r of Christ-like height, That we the land may view,
Give us a con-science bold and good, Give us a pur - pose true,

"Did ye not know it is my work My Fa-ther's work to do?"
And see like Thee our no - blest work Our Fa-ther's work to do.
That it may be our high - est joy Our Fa-ther's work to do. A - MEN.

59 I Think When I Read That Sweet Story

SWEET STORY. Irregular

Jemima Luke, 1813-1906

Greek melody
Arr. by William B. Bradbury, 1816-1868

1. I think when I read that sweet sto - ry of old, When
2. I wish that His hands had been placed on my head, That His
3. Yet still to His foot - stool in prayer I may go, And

Je - sus was here a - mong men, How He called lit - tle chil - dren as
arm had been thrown a - round me, And that I might have seen His kind
ask for a share in His love; And if I now ear - nest - ly

lambs to His fold, I should like to have been with them then.
look when He said, "Let the lit - tle ones come un - to Me."
seek Him be - low, I shall see Him and hear Him a - bove.

60 Jesus Was a Loving Teacher

BROCKLESBURY. 8.7.8.7.

Wilhelmina Stephens, 1945

Charlotte A. Barnard, 1830-1869

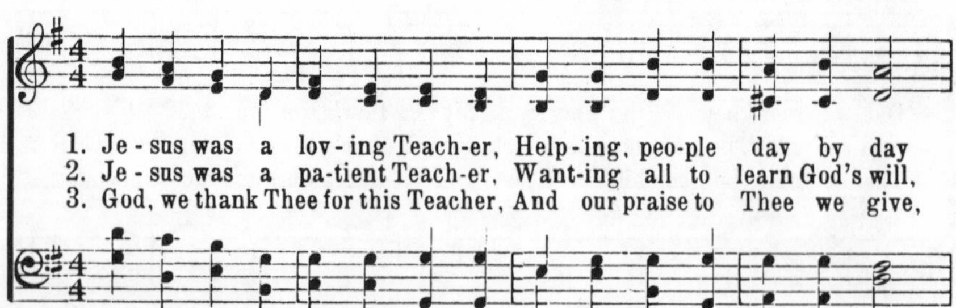
1. Je - sus was a lov - ing Teach - er, Help - ing, peo - ple day by day
2. Je - sus was a pa - tient Teach - er, Want - ing all to learn God's will,
3. God, we thank Thee for this Teacher, And our praise to Thee we give,

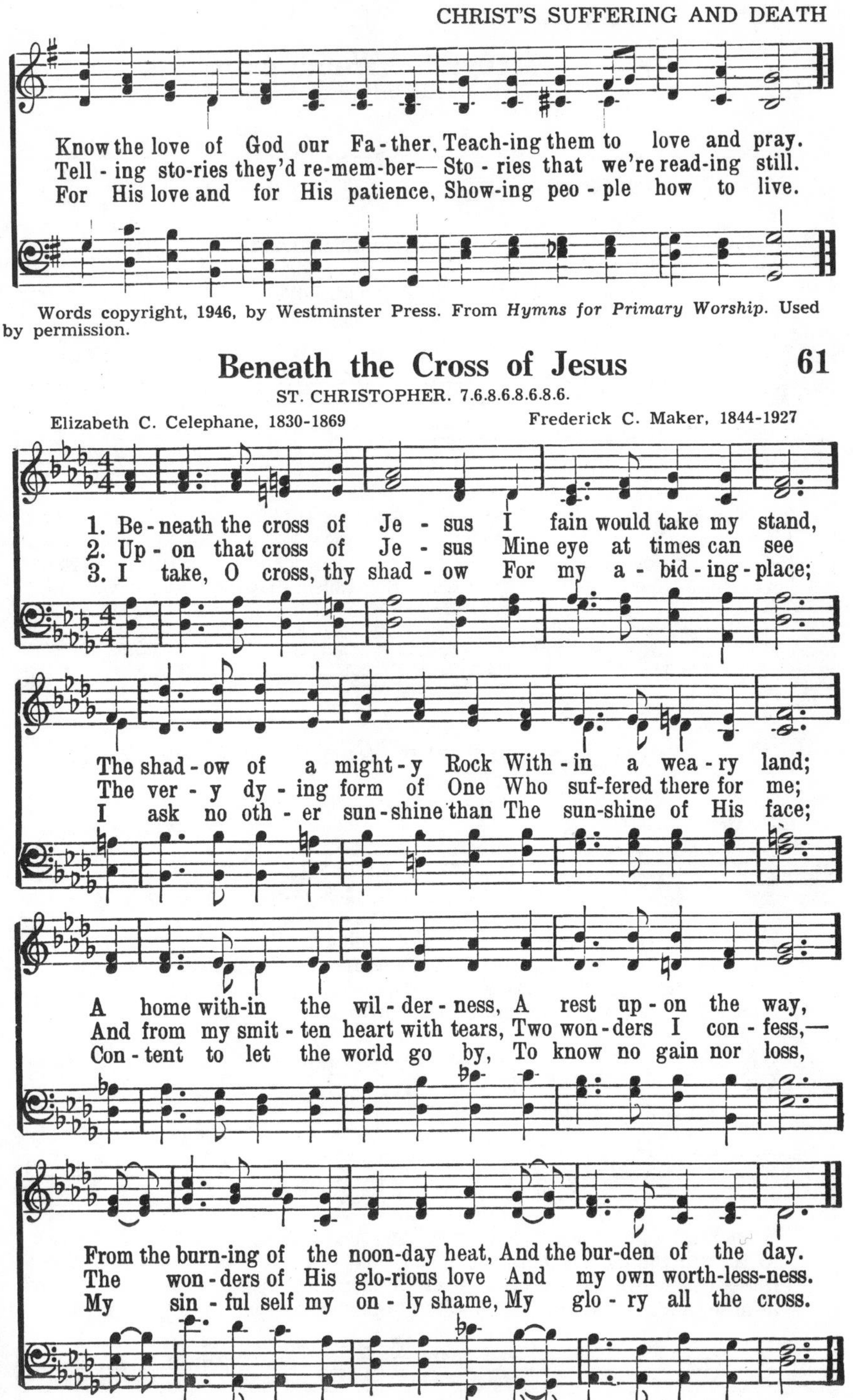
Know the love of God our Fa-ther, Teach-ing them to love and pray.
Tell-ing sto-ries they'd re-mem-ber— Sto-ries that we're read-ing still.
For His love and for His patience, Show-ing peo-ple how to live.
Words copyright, 1946, by Westminster Press. From Hymns for Primary Worship. Used by permission.
Beneath the Cross of Jesus
61
ST. CHRISTOPHER. 7.6.8.6.8.6.8.6.
Elizabeth C. Celephane, 1830-1869
Frederick C. Maker, 1844-1927
1. Be-neath the cross of Je-sus I fain would take my stand,
2. Up-on that cross of Je-sus Mine eye at times can see
3. I take, O cross, thy shad-ow For my a-bid-ing-place;
The shad-ow of a might-y Rock With-in a wea-ry land;
The ver-y dy-ing form of One Who suf-fered there for me;
I ask no oth-er sun-shine than The sun-shine of His face;
A home with-in the wil-der-ness, A rest up-on the way,
And from my smit-ten heart with tears, Two won-ders I con-fess,—
Con-tent to let the world go by, To know no gain nor loss,
From the burn-ing of the noon-day heat, And the bur-den of the day.
The won-ders of His glo-rious love And my own worth-less-ness.
My sin-ful self my on-ly shame, My glo-ry all the cross.

62 When I Survey the Wondrous Cross

HAMBURG. L.M.
(First Tune)

Isaac Watts, 1674-1748

Arr. by Lowell Mason, 1792-1872

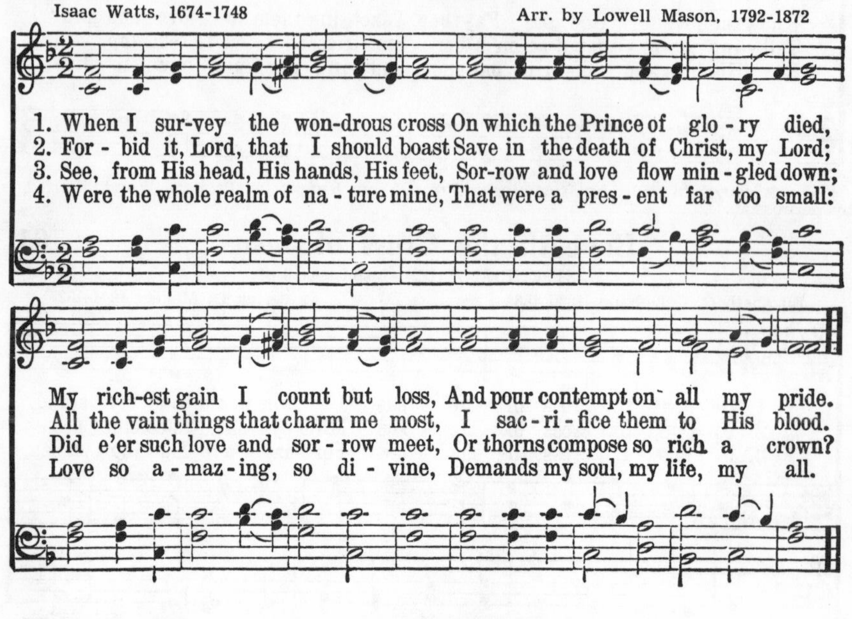
1. When I sur-vey the won-drous cross On which the Prince of glo - ry died,
2. For - bid it, Lord, that I should boast Save in the death of Christ, my Lord;
3. See, from His head, His hands, His feet, Sor-row and love flow min - gled down;
4. Were the whole realm of na - ture mine, That were a pres - ent far too small:
My rich-est gain I count but loss, And pour contempt on all my pride.
All the vain things that charm me most, I sac - ri - fice them to His blood.
Did e'er such love and sor - row meet, Or thorns compose so rich a crown?
Love so a - maz - ing, so di - vine, Demands my soul, my life, my all.

63 When I Survey the Wondrous Cross

EUCHARIST. L.M.
(Second Tune)

Isaac Watts, 1674-1748

Isaac B. Woodbury, 1819-1858

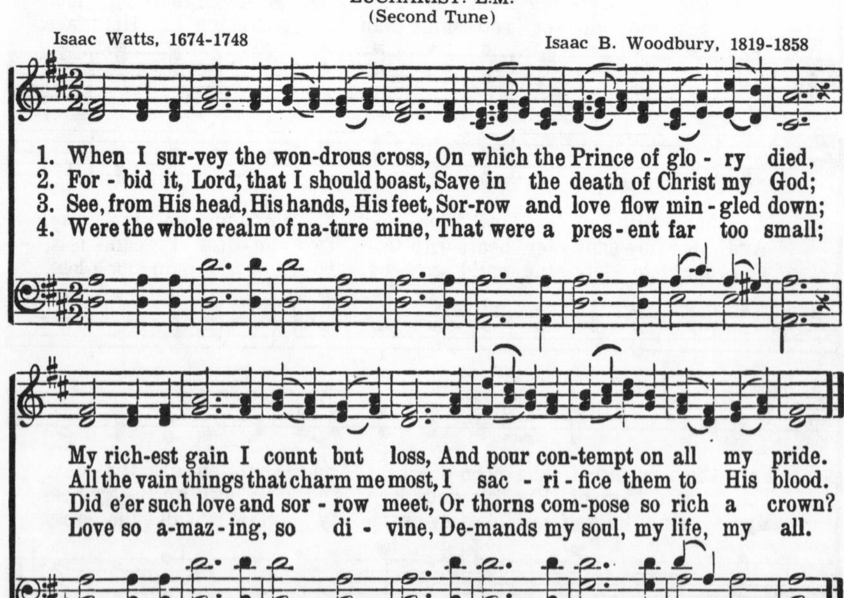
1. When I sur-vey the won-drous cross, On which the Prince of glo - ry died,
2. For - bid it, Lord, that I should boast, Save in the death of Christ my God;
3. See, from His head, His hands, His feet, Sor-row and love flow min - gled down;
4. Were the whole realm of na-ture mine, That were a pres - ent far too small;
My rich-est gain I count but loss, And pour con-tempt on all my pride.
All the vain things that charm me most, I sac - ri - fice them to His blood.
Did e'er such love and sor - row meet, Or thorns com-pose so rich a crown?
Love so a-maz - ing, so di - vine, De-mands my soul, my life, my all.

'Tis Midnight, and on Olive's Brow 64

OLIVE'S BROW. L.M.

William B. Tappan, 1794-1849 William B. Bradbury, 1816-1868

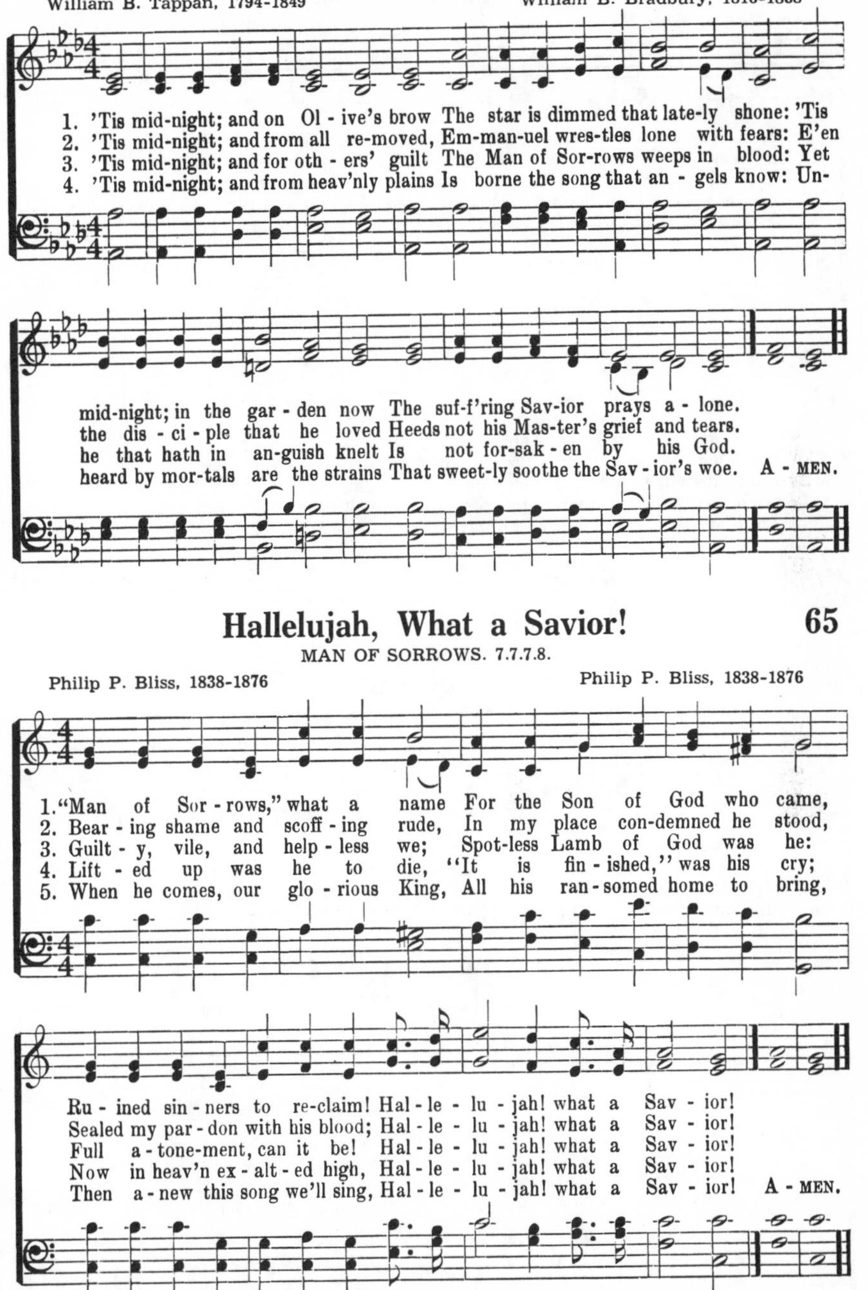
1. 'Tis mid-night; and on Ol - ive's brow The star is dimmed that late-ly shone: 'Tis
2. 'Tis mid-night; and from all re-moved, Em-man-uel wres-tles lone with fears: E'en
3. 'Tis mid-night; and for oth - ers' guilt The Man of Sor-rows weeps in blood: Yet
4. 'Tis mid-night; and from heav'nly plains Is borne the song that an - gels know: Un-
mid-night; in the gar - den now The suf-f'ring Sav-ior prays a - lone.
the dis - ci - ple that he loved Heeds not his Mas-ter's grief and tears.
he that hath in an-guish knelt Is not for-sak - en by his God.
heard by mor-tals are the strains That sweet-ly soothe the Sav - ior's woe. A - MEN.
Hallelujah, What a Savior! 65
MAN OF SORROWS. 7.7.7.8.
Philip P. Bliss, 1838-1876 Philip P. Bliss, 1838-1876
1. "Man of Sor - rows," what a name For the Son of God who came,
2. Bear - ing shame and scoff - ing rude, In my place con-demned he stood,
3. Guilt - y, vile, and help - less we; Spot-less Lamb of God was he:
4. Lift - ed up was he to die, "It is fin - ished," was his cry;
5. When he comes, our glo - rious King, All his ran - somed home to bring,
Ru - ined sin - ners to re-claim! Hal - le - lu - jah! what a Sav - ior!
Sealed my par - don with his blood; Hal - le - lu - jah! what a Sav - ior!
Full a - tone-ment, can it be! Hal - le - lu - jah! what a Sav - ior!
Now in heav'n ex - alt - ed high, Hal - le - lu - jah! what a Sav - ior!
Then a - new this song we'll sing, Hal - le - lu - jah! what a Sav - ior! A - MEN.

66 Alas! and Did My Savior Bleed

MARTYRDOM (AVON). C.M.

Isaac Watts, 1674-1748 — Hugh Wilson, 1764-1824

1. A - las! and did my Sav - ior bleed, And did my Sov-'reign die? Would he de - vote that sa - cred head For such a worm as I?
2. Was it for crimes that I had done, He groaned up - on the tree? A- maz - ing pit - y! grace un-known! And love be - yond de - gree!
3. Well might the sun in dark - ness hide, And shut his glo - ries in, When Christ, the might - y Mak - er, died For man the crea-ture's sin.
4. Thus might I hide my blush - ing face While his dear cross ap - pears; Dis- solve my heart in thank - ful - ness, And melt my eyes to tears.
5. But drops of grief can ne'er re - pay The debt of love I owe: Here, Lord, I give my - self a - way—'Tis all that I can do. A - MEN.

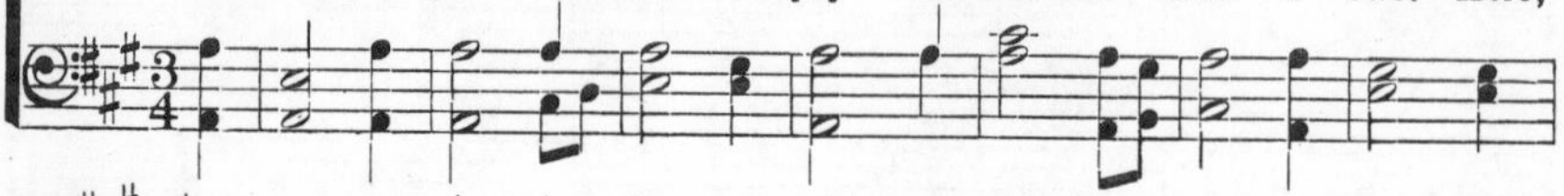

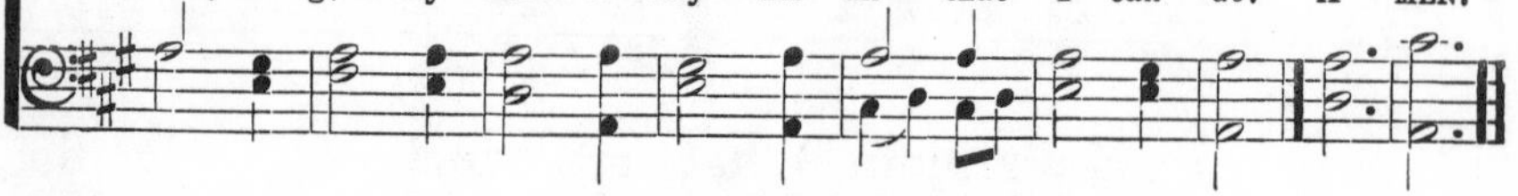

67 In the Cross of Christ I Glory

RATHBUN. 8.7.8.7.

John Bowring, 1792-1872 — Ithamar Conkey, 1815-1867

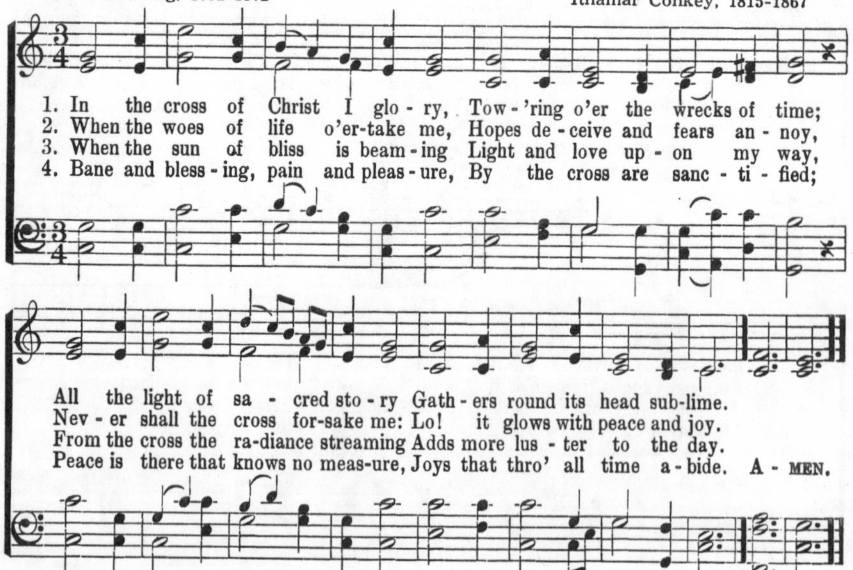
1. In the cross of Christ I glo - ry, Tow - 'ring o'er the wrecks of time;
2. When the woes of life o'er-take me, Hopes de - ceive and fears an - noy,
3. When the sun of bliss is beam - ing Light and love up - on my way,
4. Bane and bless - ing, pain and pleas - ure, By the cross are sanc - ti - fied;
All the light of sa - cred sto - ry Gath - ers round its head sub-lime.
Nev - er shall the cross for-sake me: Lo! it glows with peace and joy.
From the cross the ra-diance streaming Adds more lus - ter to the day.
Peace is there that knows no meas-ure, Joys that thro' all time a - bide. A - MEN.

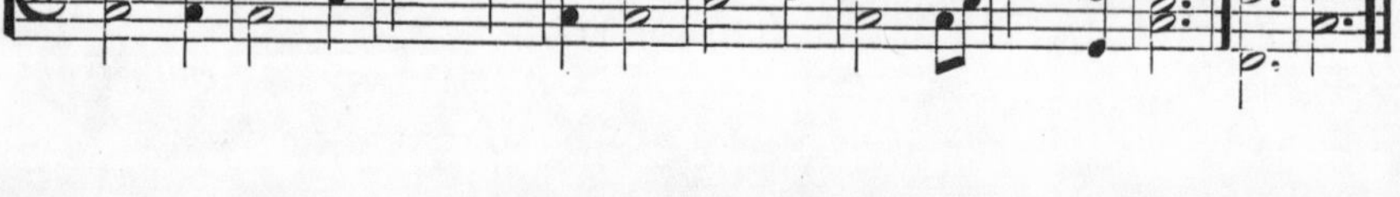

Christ the Lord Is Risen Today 68

EASTER HYMN. 7.7.7.7. with Alleluias

Charles Wesley, 1707-1788, and others — From *Lyra Davidica,* 1708

1. Christ the Lord is ris'n to - day, Al - le - lu - ia!
2. Lives a - gain our glo - rious King: Al - le - lu - ia!
3. Love's re - deem - ing work is done, Al - le - lu - ia!
4. Soar we now, where Christ has led, Al - le - lu - ia!

Sons of men and an - gels say: Al - le - lu - ia!
Where, O death, is now thy sting? Al - le - lu - ia!
Fought the fight, the bat - tle won; Al - le - lu - ia!
Fol - l'wing our ex - alt - ed Head; Al - le - lu - ia!

Raise your joys and tri - umphs high, Al - le - lu - ia!
Dy - ing once, He all doth save: Al - le - lu - ia!
Death in vain for - bids Him rise; Al - le - lu - ia!
Made like Him, like Him we rise; Al - le - lu - ia!

Sing, ye heav'ns, and earth re - ply, Al - le - lu - ia!
Where thy vic - to - ry, O grave? Al - le - lu - ia!
Christ has o - pened Par - a - dise. Al - le - lu - ia!
Ours the cross, the grave, the skies. Al - le - lu - ia!

69 Christ Arose

Robert Lowry, 1826-1899 Robert Lowry, 1826-1899

1. Low in the grave he lay—Je - sus my Sav - ior! Wait-ing the com-ing day—
2. Vain-ly they watch his bed—Je - sus my Sav - ior! Vain-ly they seal the dead—
3. Death can-not keep his prey—Je - sus my Sav - ior! He tore the bars a - way—

Je - sus my Lord!

CHORUS *Faster*

Up from the grave he a - rose, he a - rose, With a might-y tri-umph o'er his foes; he a - rose; He a - rose a vic - tor from the dark do - main, And he lives for - ev - er with his saints to reign. He a - rose! He a - rose! he a - rose! he a - rose! Hal - le - lu-jah! Christ a - rose! *rall.* A - MEN.

He Arose 70

Barney E. Warren, 1897, 1911 Barney E. Warren, 1897, 1911

1. "He is ris - en," said the an - gel on that morn - ing When the sad dis - ci - ples
2. He is ris - en, sure - ly death is now a - bol - ished: Grave, where is thy vic - t'ry?
3. He is ris - en, hence, the fear of that grim mon - ster Is for - ev - er ban - ished
4. He is ris - en: let the na - tions hear the ti - dings, That the Christ who once was

sought their Lord in vain; Je - sus burst the might - y bars of death a - sun - der;
death, where is thy sting? Je - sus flash - es light in - to the dark - ened val - ley;
in - to dark - est night; And the grave and death are robbed of all their ter - ror;
dead now lives a - gain, That he tri - umphed o - ver sin and death for - ev - er,

From the grave he rose tri - um - phant - ly to reign.
Swell the might - y cho - rus, men and an - gels sing.
Life and im - mor - tal - i - ty he brought to light.
And he now gives life e - ter - nal un - to men.

CHORUS

He a - rose, my Sav - ior, He a - rose, my Sav - ior, He a - rose, my Sav - ior, Tri - um - phant from the grave. A - MEN.

He a - rose, my Sav - ior rose, He a - rose, my Sav - ior rose, He a - rose, he a - rose, my Sav - ior rose,

71 Rejoice and Be Glad

Horatius Bonar, 1808-1889 — John J. Husband, 1760-1825

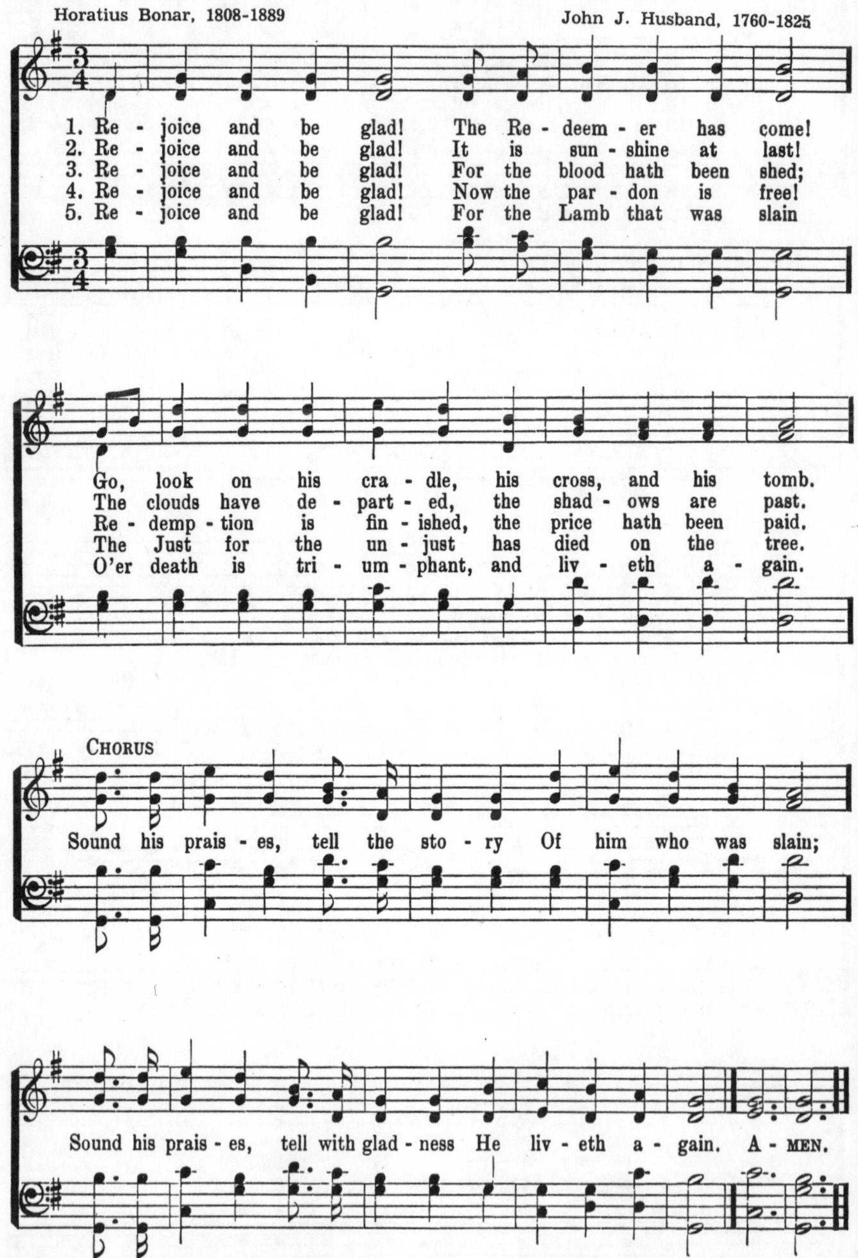
1. Re - joice and be glad! The Re - deem - er has come! Go, look on his cra - dle, his cross, and his tomb.
2. Re - joice and be glad! It is sun - shine at last! The clouds have de - part - ed, the shad - ows are past.
3. Re - joice and be glad! For the blood hath been shed; Re - demp - tion is fin - ished, the price hath been paid.
4. Re - joice and be glad! Now the par - don is free! The Just for the un - just has died on the tree.
5. Re - joice and be glad! For the Lamb that was slain O'er death is tri - um - phant, and liv - eth a - gain.
CHORUS
Sound his prais - es, tell the sto - ry Of him who was slain;
Sound his prais - es, tell with glad - ness He liv - eth a - gain. A - MEN.

We May Not Climb the Heavenly Steeps 72

SERENITY. C.M.

John G. Whittier, 1807-1892 — William V. Wallace, 1814-1865

1. We may not climb the heav'n-ly steeps To bring the Lord Christ down;
2. But warm, sweet, ten-der, e - ven yet A pres - ent help is he;
3. The heal - ing of his seam-less dress Is by our beds of pain;
4. Thro' him the first fond prayers are said Our lips of child-hood frame;

In vain we search the lowest deeps, For him no depths can drown.
And faith has still its Ol - i - vet, And love its Gal - i - lee.
We touch him in life's throng and press, And we are whole a - gain.
The last low whis-pers of our dead Are burdened with his name. A - MEN.

I Know That My Redeemer Lives 73

BRADFORD. C.M.

Charles Wesley, 1707-1788 — George F. Handel, 1685-1759

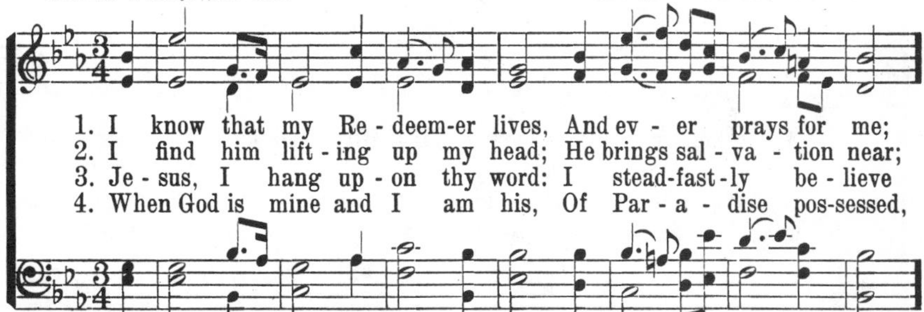

1. I know that my Re - deem-er lives, And ev - er prays for me;
2. I find him lift - ing up my head; He brings sal - va - tion near;
3. Je - sus, I hang up - on thy word: I stead-fast - ly be - lieve
4. When God is mine and I am his, Of Par - a - dise pos-sessed,

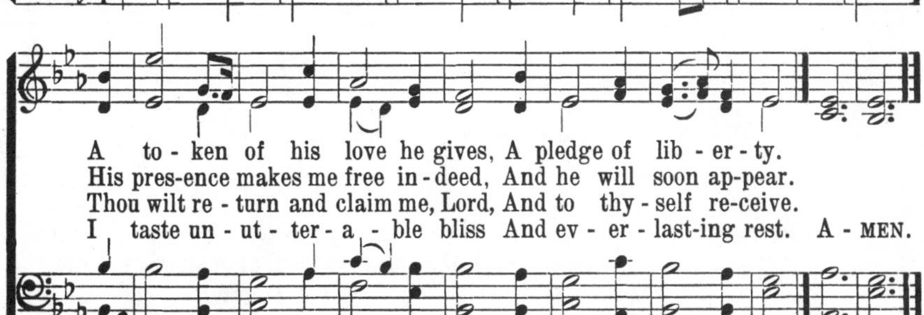

A to - ken of his love he gives, A pledge of lib - er - ty.
His pres-ence makes me free in - deed, And he will soon ap-pear.
Thou wilt re - turn and claim me, Lord, And to thy - self re-ceive.
I taste un - ut - ter - a - ble bliss And ev - er - last-ing rest. A - MEN.

74 Crown Him with Many Crowns

DIADEMATA. S.M.D.

Matthew Bridges, 1800-1894 and
Godfrey Thring, 1823-1903

George J. Elvey, 1816-1893

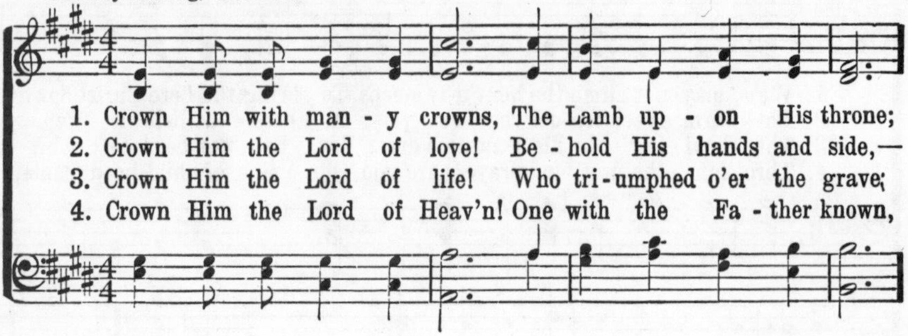

1. Crown Him with man - y crowns, The Lamb up - on His throne;
2. Crown Him the Lord of love! Be - hold His hands and side,—
3. Crown Him the Lord of life! Who tri - umphed o'er the grave;
4. Crown Him the Lord of Heav'n! One with the Fa - ther known,

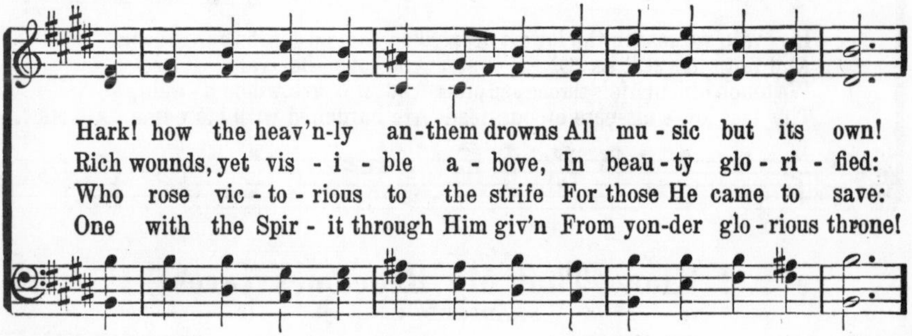

Hark! how the heav'n-ly an-them drowns All mu - sic but its own!
Rich wounds, yet vis - i - ble a - bove, In beau - ty glo - ri - fied:
Who rose vic - to - rious to the strife For those He came to save:
One with the Spir - it through Him giv'n From yon-der glo - rious throne!

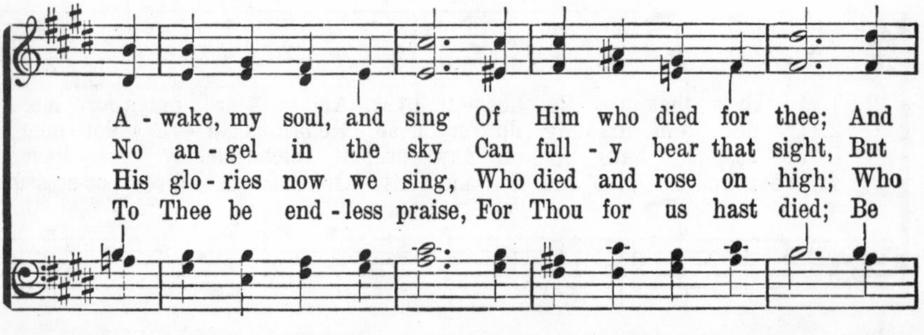

A - wake, my soul, and sing Of Him who died for thee; And
No an - gel in the sky Can full - y bear that sight, But
His glo - ries now we sing, Who died and rose on high; Who
To Thee be end - less praise, For Thou for us hast died; Be

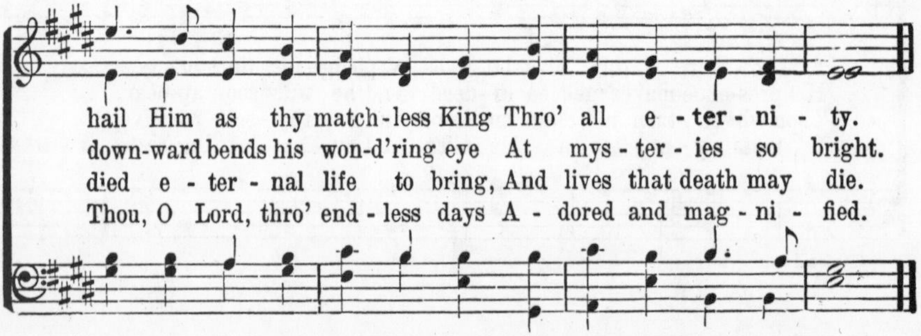

hail Him as thy match - less King Thro' all e - ter - ni - ty.
down-ward bends his won-d'ring eye At mys - ter - ies so bright.
died e - ter - nal life to bring, And lives that death may die.
Thou, O Lord, thro' end - less days A - dored and mag - ni - fied.

Worthy Is the Lamb

Charles W. Naylor, 1923 — Andrew L. Byers, 1923

1. On his throne of glo-ry sits our Lord to-day, Won-drous-ly ex-alt-ed he doth reign; Hear the throng-ing an-gels joy-ful as they say, Wor-thy is the Lamb that was slain!
2. Once on earth he suf-fered, for us bled and died, Paid the debt of sin we could not pay; Glo-ry to our Sav-ior, who was cru-ci-fied! By his blood he saves us to-day.
3. Make the world re-sound till all shall hear his fame, Till the mul-ti-tudes of earth shall know He is the Re-deem-er, and through his dear name Riv-ers of sal-va-tion do flow.
4. All shall bow to him and ev-ery tongue con-fess That he is the Lord of all for aye; That he is the King who rules in right-eous-ness, Glad-ly now his will we o-bey.

CHORUS

Wor-thy is the Lamb for-ev-er-more! for-ev-er-more!
Wor-thy is the Lamb whom we a-dore! whom we a-dore!
Sound his praise to-day! Let all cre-a-tion say, Wor-thy, wor-thy, wor-thy is the Lamb! A-MEN.

76 Rejoice, All Ye Believers

LANCASHIRE. 7.6.7.6.D.

Laurentius Laurenti, 1660-1722
Tr. by Mrs. Sarah B. Findlater, 1823-1907

Henry Smart, 1813-1879

1. Re - joice, all ye be - liev - ers, And let your lights ap - pear;
2. The watch-ers on the moun - tain Pro - claim the Bride-groom near;
3. Ye saints, who here in pa - tience Your cross and suf-f'rings bore,
4. Our Hope and Ex - pec - ta - tion, O Je - sus, now ap - pear;
The eve - ning is ad - vanc - ing, And dark - er night is near.
Go meet him as he com - eth, With hal - le - lu - jahs clear.
Shall live and reign for - ev - er, Where sor - row is no more:
A - rise, thou Sun so longed for, O'er this be - night - ed sphere.
The Bride-groom is a - ris - ing, And soon he draw - eth nigh;
The mar - riage-feast is wait - ing, The gates wide - o - pen stand;
A - round the throne of glo - ry The Lamb ye shall be - hold,
With hearts and hands up - lift - ed, We plead, O Lord, to see
Up, pray, and watch, and wres - tle: At mid-night comes the cry.
Up, up, ye heirs of glo - ry! The Bride-groom is at hand!
In tri - umph cast be - fore him Your di - a - dems of gold.
The day of earth's re - demp - tion, That brings us un - to thee.
A - MEN.

We Know Not the Hour 77

Franklin E. Belden, b. 1886 — Franklin E. Belden, b. 1886

1. We know not the hour of the Master's appearing, Yet signs all foretell that the moment is nearing When he shall return—'tis a promise most cheering—But we know not the hour.
2. There's light for the wise who are seeking salvation, There's truth in the Book of divine revelation, Each prophecy points to the great consummation—But we know not the hour.
3. We'll watch and we'll pray, with our lamps trimmed and burning, We'll work and we'll wait till the Master's returning, We'll sing and rejoice, every omen discerning—But we know not the hour.

FINE

D. S.—*come in the clouds of his Father's bright glory—But we know not the hour.*

CHORUS

He will come, . . . (He will come,) let us watch and be ready; He will come, . . . (He will come,) hallelujah! hallelujah! He will

D. S.

Amen.

78 Gleams of the Golden Morning
S. J. Graham
S. J. Graham
1. The gold - en morn - ing is fast ap-proach-ing; Je - sus soon will come
2. The gos - pel sum-mons will soon be car - ried To the na-tions round;
3. At - tend - ed by all the shin-ing an - gels, Down the flam-ing sky
4. The loved of earth who have long been part - ed, Meet in that glad day;
To take his faith - ful and hap - py chil - dren To their prom-ised home.
The Bridegroom then will cease to tar - ry, And the trump - et sound.
The Judge will come, and will take his peo - ple Where they will not die.
The tears of those who are bro - ken-heart - ed Shall be wiped a - way.
CHORUS
O we see the gleams of the gold - en morning Piercing thro' this night of gloom:
O we see the gleams of the gold-en morn-ing That will burst the tomb. A-MEN.
79 Fairest Lord Jesus
CRUSADER'S HYMN. 5.6.8.5.5.8.
From the German, 17th century
From Schlesischen Volkslieder, 1842
Arr. by Richard S. Willis, 1819-1900
1. Fair - est Lord Je - sus! Rul - er of all na - ture!
2. Fair are the mead - ows, Fair - er still the wood - lands,
3. Fair is the sun - shine, Fair - er still the moon - light,

O Thou of God and man the Son! Thee will I cher - ish,
Robed in the bloom - ing garb of spring; Je - sus is fair - er,
And all the twin - kling star - ry host; Je - sus shines bright - er,
Thee will I hon - or, Thou, my soul's glo - ry, joy, and crown!
Je - sus is pur - er, Who makes the woe - ful heart to sing!
Je - sus shines pur - er, Than all the an - gels heav'n can boast! A - MEN.

Jesus Shall Reign Where'er the Sun 80

DUKE STREET. L.M.

From Psalm 72
Isaac Watts, 1674-1748

John Hatton, d. 1793

1. Je - sus shall reign wher-e'er the sun Does his suc-ces-sive jour-neys run;
2. From north to south the princ-es meet To pay their hom-age at His feet;
3. To Him shall end-less prayer be made, And end-less prais-es crown His head;
4. Peo-ple and realms of ev - 'ry tongue Dwell on His love with sweet-est song,

His kingdom spread from shore to shore, Till moons shall wax and wane no more.
While western em-pires own their Lord, And sav-age tribes at-tend His word.
His name like sweet per-fume shall rise With ev-'ry morn-ing sac - ri - fice.
And in-fant voic-es shall pro-claim Their earthly bless-ings on His name.

81 Praise Him! Praise Him!

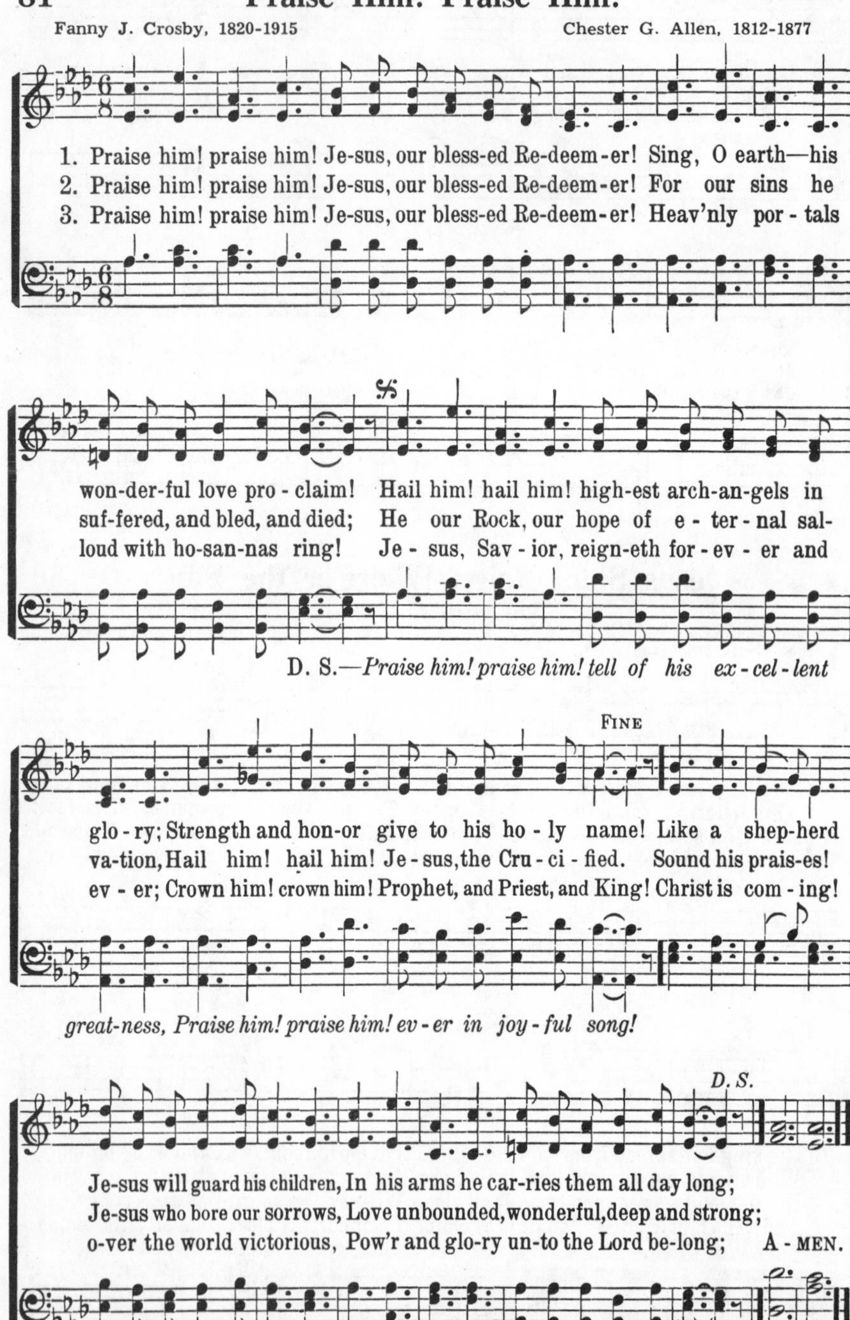
Fanny J. Crosby, 1820-1915
Chester G. Allen, 1812-1877
1. Praise him! praise him! Je-sus, our bless-ed Re-deem-er! Sing, O earth—his
2. Praise him! praise him! Je-sus, our bless-ed Re-deem-er! For our sins he
3. Praise him! praise him! Je-sus, our bless-ed Re-deem-er! Heav'nly por-tals
won-der-ful love pro-claim! Hail him! hail him! high-est arch-an-gels in
suf-fered, and bled, and died; He our Rock, our hope of e-ter-nal sal-
loud with ho-san-nas ring! Je-sus, Sav-ior, reign-eth for-ev-er and
D. S.—Praise him! praise him! tell of his ex-cel-lent
FINE
glo-ry; Strength and hon-or give to his ho-ly name! Like a shep-herd
va-tion, Hail him! hail him! Je-sus, the Cru-ci-fied. Sound his prais-es!
ev-er; Crown him! crown him! Prophet, and Priest, and King! Christ is com-ing!
great-ness, Praise him! praise him! ev-er in joy-ful song!
D. S.
Je-sus will guard his children, In his arms he car-ries them all day long;
Je-sus who bore our sorrows, Love unbounded, wonderful, deep and strong;
o-ver the world victorious, Pow'r and glo-ry un-to the Lord be-long;
A-MEN.

There Is No Name So Sweet on Earth 82

George W. Bethune, c. 1858 William B. Bradbury 1816-1868

1. There is no name so sweet on earth, No name so sweet in heav - en,
2. And when he hung up - on the tree, They wrote this name a - bove him,
3. So now, up - on his Fa-ther's throne, Al-might - y to re - lease us
4. O Je - sus, by that match-less name Thy grace shall fail us nev - er:

The name be - fore his won-drous birth To Christ the Sav - ior giv - en.
That all might see the rea - son we For - ev - er - more must love him.
From sin and pains, he glad - ly reigns, The Prince and Sav - ior Je - sus.
To - day as yes - ter - day the same, Thou art the same for - ev - er.

Refrain

We love to sing a - round our King, And hail him bless - ed Je - sus;

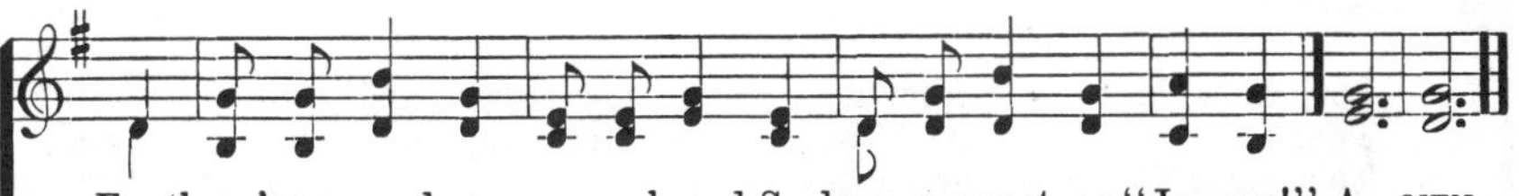

For there's no word ear ev - er heard So dear, so sweet, as "Je - sus!" A - men.

83 I Ought to Love My Savior

Daniel S. Warner, 1883 | Joseph C. Fisher, 1883

Not too slow
1. I ought to love my Sav - ior; He loved me long a - go,
2. I ought to love my Sav - ior; He bore my sin and shame;
3. I ought to love my Sav - ior; He par - doned all my sin,
4. O Christ, I can but love thee: What heart could e'er with - hold
Looked on my soul with fa - vor, When deep in guilt and woe:
From glo - ry to the man - ger On wings of love he came:
Then sanc - ti - fied my na - ture, And keeps me pure with - in:
A love that cost so dear - ly The of - f'ring of thy soul?
And though my sin had grieved him, His Fa - ther's law had crossed,
He trod this earth in sor - row, En - dured the pains of hell,
He fills me with his glo - ry, And bears my soul a - bove;
O King of love im - mor - tal, Reign in my heart a - lone,
Love drew him down from heav - en To seek and save the lost;
That I should not be ban - ished, But in his glo - ry dwell;
This world, O won - drous sto - ry! 'Tis love, re - deem - ing love;
And flood this earth - en tem - ple With glo - ry from thy throne;

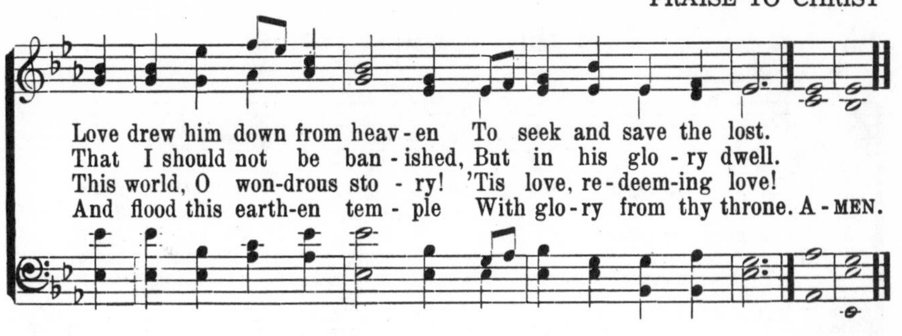
Love drew him down from heav - en To seek and save the lost.
That I should not be ban - ished, But in his glo - ry dwell.
This world, O won-drous sto - ry! 'Tis love, re - deem-ing love!
And flood this earth-en tem - ple With glo - ry from thy throne. A - MEN.

O Could I Speak the Matchless Worth 84

ARIEL. 8.8.6.D.

Samuel Medley, 1738-1799 — Wolfgang A. Mozart, 1756-1791; Arr. by Lowell Mason, 1792-1872

1. O could I speak the matchless worth, O could I sound the glo-ries forth
2. I'd sing the pre-cious blood he spilt, My ran-som from the dreadful guilt
3. I'd sing the char - ac-ters he bears, And all the forms of love he wears,
4. Well, the de - light - ful day will come When my dear Lord will bring me home

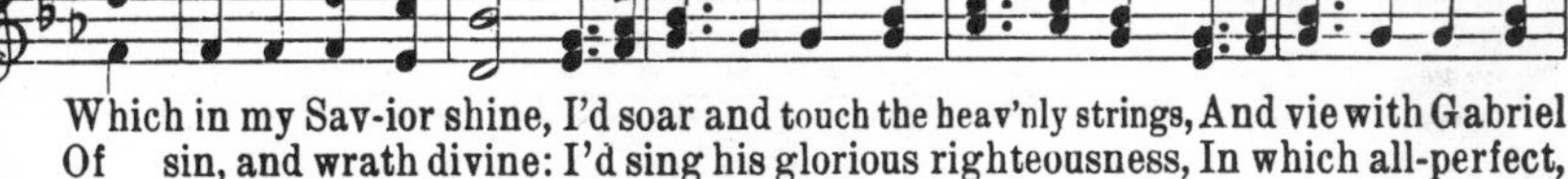

Which in my Sav-ior shine, I'd soar and touch the heav'nly strings, And vie with Gabriel
Of sin, and wrath divine: I'd sing his glorious righteousness, In which all-perfect,
Ex - alt-ed on his throne: In loft-iest songs of sweetest praise, I would to ev - er-
And I shall see his face: Then with my Savior, Brother, Friend, A blest e-ter - ni-

while he sings In notes al-most di-vine, In notes al-most di - vine.
heav'nly dress My soul shall ev-er shine, My soul shall ev - er shine.
last - ing days Make all his glories known, Make all his glo - ries known.
ty I'll spend. Tri-um-phant in his grace, Tri-um-phant in his grace. A-MEN.

85 'Tis the Sweetest Name

O. A. Miller, 1918 O. A. Miller, 1918

1. 'Tis the sweet-est name that the an - gels know, 'Tis the sweet-est name
2. 'Tis the sweet-est name that all heav - en sings, And the dear-est name;
3. O that sweet-est name gives from sin re - lease, In the vale of sighs
4. 'Tis the sweet-est name e'er employed in song, And it thrills my heart
1. 'Tis the sweet-est name that the an-gels know, 'Tis the sweetest name
here on earth be - low, 'Tis the sweet-est name, and I love it so;
to it man-kind clings: O that sweet-est name full sal - va-tion brings;
bids my sor-row cease; 'Tis the sweet-est name, for it brings us peace;
as it makes me strong; O that sweet-est name o - ver-comes all wrong;
here on earth be - low, 'Tis the sweet-est name, and I love it so;
CHORUS
Tell it out to all the world that name is Je - sus. Je - sus,
Tell it out.................. ..... that name is Je - sus.
Je - sus, earth and heaven's sweetest name, Je-sus, Je - sus,
Je - sus, bless-ed Je - sus, Je-sus, precious Je-sus,
Here and there it means the same; It will ev - er keep my soul, While the

end-less a-ges roll; Je-sus, earth and heaven's sweet-est name. A-MEN.
sweet-est name.

All Hail the Power of Jesus' Name! 86

CORONATION. C.M.
(First Tune)

Edward Perronet, 1726-1792
Alt. by John Rippon, 1751-1836

Oliver Holden, 1765-1844

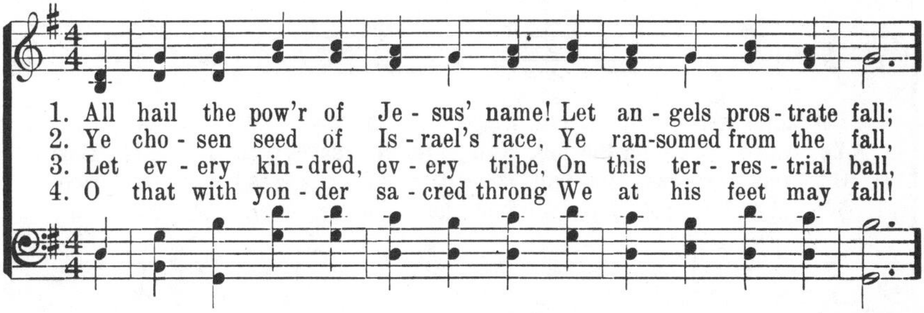

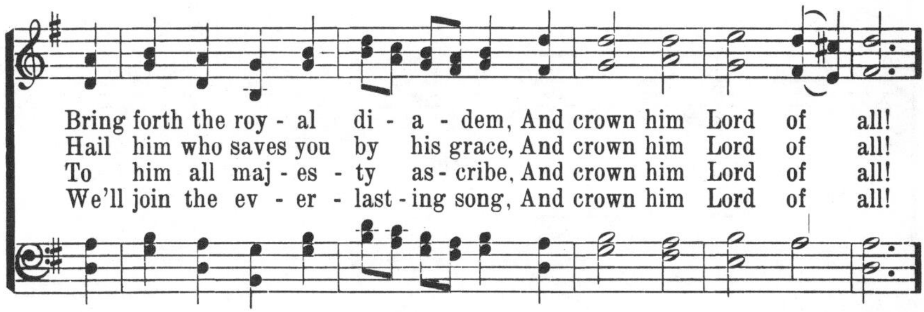

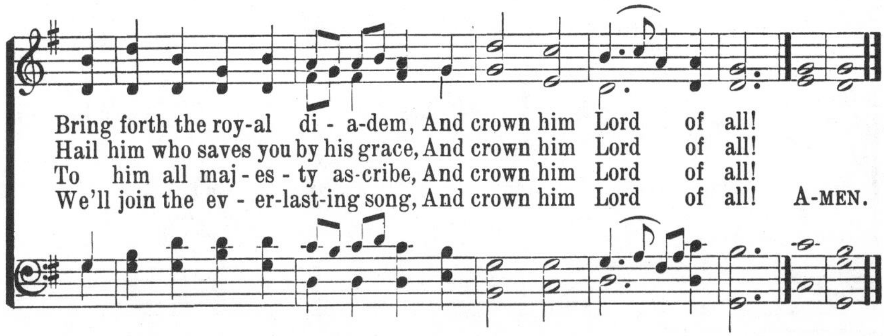

1. All hail the pow'r of Je-sus' name! Let an-gels pros-trate fall;
Bring forth the roy-al di-a-dem, And crown him Lord of all!
Bring forth the roy-al di-a-dem, And crown him Lord of all!

2. Ye cho-sen seed of Is-rael's race, Ye ran-somed from the fall,
Hail him who saves you by his grace, And crown him Lord of all!
Hail him who saves you by his grace, And crown him Lord of all!

3. Let ev-ery kin-dred, ev-ery tribe, On this ter-res-trial ball,
To him all maj-es-ty as-cribe, And crown him Lord of all!
To him all maj-es-ty as-cribe, And crown him Lord of all!

4. O that with yon-der sa-cred throng We at his feet may fall!
We'll join the ev-er-last-ing song, And crown him Lord of all!
We'll join the ev-er-last-ing song, And crown him Lord of all! A-MEN.

87 All Hail the Power of Jesus' Name!

DIADEM. C.M.
(Second Tune)

Edward Perronet, 1726-1792
Alt. by John Rippon, 1751-1836

James Ellor, 1819-1899

1. All hail the power of Je - sus' name! Let an-gels pros-trate fall,
2. Ye cho - sen seed of Is - rael's race, Ye ran-somed from the fall,
3. Let ev - ery kin - dred, ev - ery tribe, On this ter-res-trial ball,
4. O that with yon - der sa - cred throng We at His feet may fall,
Let an - gels pros-trate fall; Bring forth the roy - al di - a - dem,
Ye ran-somed from the fall, Hail Him who saves you by His grace,
On this ter - res - trial ball, To Him all maj - es - ty as - cribe,
We at His feet may fall! We'll join the ev - er - last - ing song,
And crown.. Him, Crown Him,
And crown Him, crown Him, crown Him, crown Him, And crown Him Lord of
And crown.. Him, Crown Him,
And crown Him, crown Him, crown Him, Crown..............................
crown Him, crown Him;
all, crown Him; And crown Him Lord of all!
crown............ Him;
.... Him; And crown Him Lord of all!

O Sing of His Mighty Love 88

Frank Bottome, 1869 — William B. Bradbury, 1816-1868

1. O bliss of the pu - ri - fied, bliss of the free! I plunge in the
2. O bliss of the pu - ri - fied, Je - sus is mine! No lon - ger in
3. O bliss of the pu - ri - fied, bliss of the pure! No wound hath the
4. O Je - sus the cru - ci - fied! thee will I sing, My bless - ed Re-
crim - son tide o - pened for me; O'er sin and un-clean-ness ex-
dread con - dem - na - tion I pine; In con - scious sal - va - tion I
soul that his blood can - not cure; No sor - row-bowed head but may
deem - er, my God and my King; My soul, filled with rap - ture, shall
ult - ing I stand, And point to the print of the nails in His hand.
sing of his grace, Who lift - eth up - on me the light of his face.
sweet - ly find rest, No tears but be wiped a - way on Je - sus' breast.
shout o'er the grave, And tri - umph in death in the "Might-y to Save."
CHORUS
O sing of His might - y love, Sing of His might - y love,
rall.
Sing of His might - y love, Might - y to save.

89 Blessed Be the Name

W. H. Clark — Arr. by William J. Kirkpatrick, 1838-1921

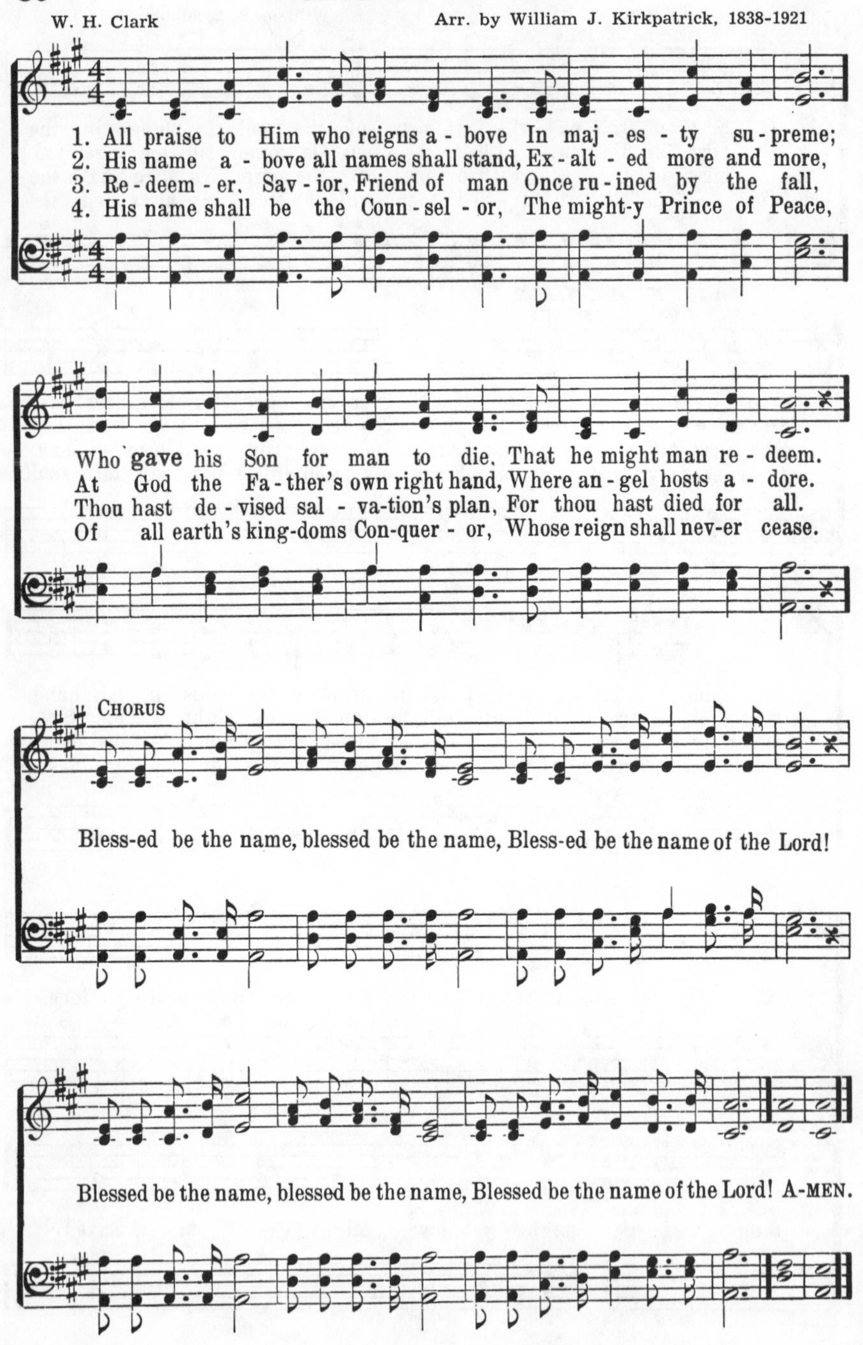
1. All praise to Him who reigns a - bove In maj - es - ty su - preme;
2. His name a - bove all names shall stand, Ex - alt - ed more and more,
3. Re - deem - er, Sav - ior, Friend of man Once ru - ined by the fall,
4. His name shall be the Coun - sel - or, The might-y Prince of Peace,
Who gave his Son for man to die, That he might man re - deem.
At God the Fa - ther's own right hand, Where an - gel hosts a - dore.
Thou hast de - vised sal - va-tion's plan, For thou hast died for all.
Of all earth's king-doms Con-quer - or, Whose reign shall nev-er cease.
CHORUS
Bless-ed be the name, blessed be the name, Bless-ed be the name of the Lord!
Blessed be the name, blessed be the name, Blessed be the name of the Lord! A-MEN.

All Glory, Laud, and Honor

90

ST. THEODULPH. 7.6.7.6.D.

Theodulph of Orleans, d. 821
Tr. by John M. Neale, 1818-1866

Melchoir Teschner, 16th or 17th century

1. All glo - ry, laud, and hon - or, To Thee, Re - deem - er, King,
2. The com - pa - ny of an - gels Are prais - ing Thee on high,
3. To Thee, be - fore Thy pas - sion They sang their hymns of praise;
To whom the lips of chil - dren Made sweet ho - san - as ring.
And mor - tal men and all things Cre - a - ted make re - ply.
To Thee, now high ex - alt - ed, Our mel - o - dy we raise;
Thou art the King of Is - ra - el, Thou Da - vid's roy - al Son,
The peo - ple of the He - brews With palms be - fore Thee went;
Thou didst ac - cept their prais - es; Ac - cept the praise we bring,
Who in the Lord's name com - est, The King and Bless - ed One.
Our praise and prayer and anthems Be - fore Thee we pre - sent.
Who in all good de - light - est, Thou good and gracious King.
A - MEN.

91 We'll Crown Him Lord of All

D. Otis Teasley, 1902 D. Otis Teasley, 1902

1. We'll shout and sing our Re-deem-er's praise, Con-tend-ing for the truth and right;
2. Tho' the hosts of sin should a - bout us camp, We'll shout and sing the vic-tor's song;
3. To Christ all pow - er on earth is giv'n, See now his might-y scep - ter's sway;
4. Soon Christ shall come with the trumpet sound, To raise the dead from land and sea;
5. Then in that heav-en and earth a - new, Where love's e-ter-nal bless-ings fall,
We'll crown him King in ev - ery heart, And con-quer in Je - ho-vah's might.
For Christ, our Sav - ior, with-in us dwells, To save and keep us from the wrong.
While oth - ers dream of an age to come, He's reign-ing in our hearts to - day.
Then we shall meet him in the air And reign with him e - ter - nal - ly.
We'll sing his praise while the a - ges roll, And crown the Sav-ior Lord of all.
CHORUS
Crown him, we'll crown him, Crown the bless - ed
Crown him Lord of all, crown him Lord of all,
Sav - ior Lord of all;...... We'll crown him, yes,
Crown him Lord of all,
crown him, Crown the bless-ed Sav-ior Lord of all. A - MEN.
crown him Lord of all, Lord of all.

O for a Thousand Tongues 92

AZMON. C.M.

Charles Wesley, 1707-1788

Carl G. Glaser, 1784-1829
Arr. by Lowell Mason, 1792-1872

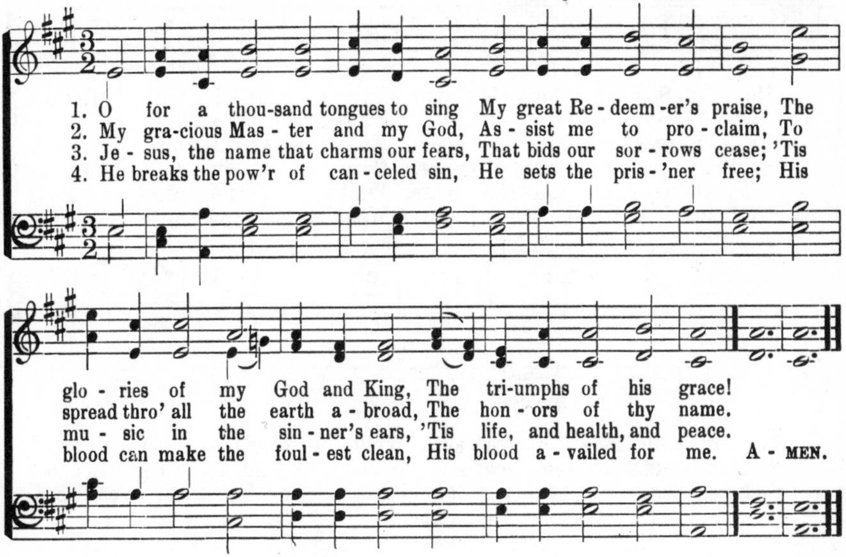

1. O for a thou-sand tongues to sing My great Re-deem-er's praise, The
2. My gra-cious Mas-ter and my God, As-sist me to pro-claim, To
3. Je-sus, the name that charms our fears, That bids our sor-rows cease; 'Tis
4. He breaks the pow'r of can-celed sin, He sets the pris-'ner free; His

glo-ries of my God and King, The tri-umphs of his grace!
spread thro' all the earth a-broad, The hon-ors of thy name.
mu-sic in the sin-ner's ears, 'Tis life, and health, and peace.
blood can make the foul-est clean, His blood a-vailed for me. A-MEN.

Jesus, the Very Thought of Thee 93

ST. AGNES. C.M.

Bernard of Clairvaux, 1091-1153
Tr. by Edward Caswall, 1814-1878

John B. Dykes, 1823-1876

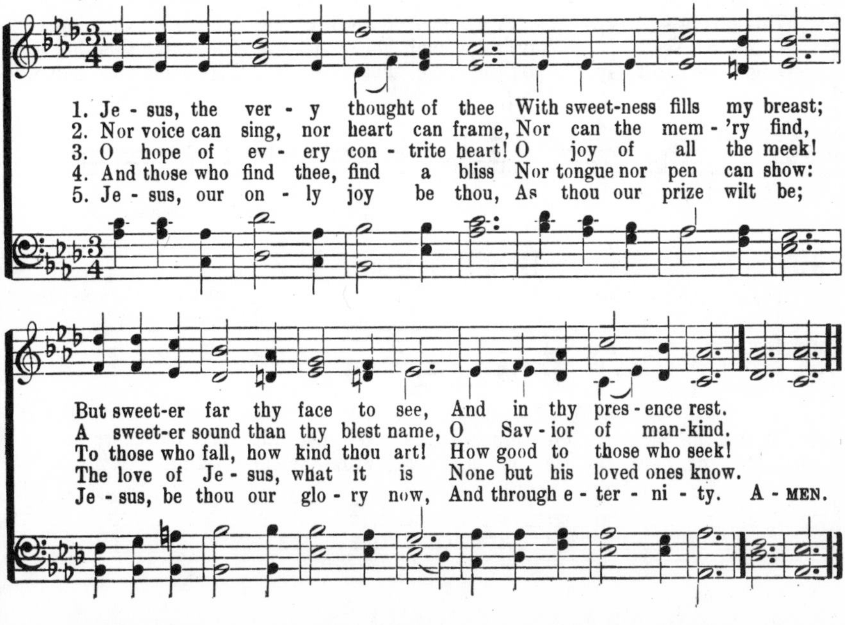

1. Je-sus, the ver-y thought of thee With sweet-ness fills my breast;
2. Nor voice can sing, nor heart can frame, Nor can the mem-'ry find,
3. O hope of ev-ery con-trite heart! O joy of all the meek!
4. And those who find thee, find a bliss Nor tongue nor pen can show:
5. Je-sus, our on-ly joy be thou, As thou our prize wilt be;

But sweet-er far thy face to see, And in thy pres-ence rest.
A sweet-er sound than thy blest name, O Sav-ior of man-kind.
To those who fall, how kind thou art! How good to those who seek!
The love of Je-sus, what it is None but his loved ones know.
Je-sus, be thou our glo-ry now, And through e-ter-ni-ty. A-MEN.

94 Holy Spirit, Faithful Guide

FAITHFUL GUIDE. 7.7.7.7.D.
Marcus M. Wells, 1815-1895
Marcus M. Wells, 1815-1895
1. Ho - ly Spir - it, faith - ful Guide, Ev - er near the Chris-tian's side;
Gen - tly lead us by the hand, Pil - grims in a des - ert land;
2. Ev - er pres - ent, tru - est Friend, Ev - er near Thine aid to lend,
Leave us not to doubt and fear, Grop-ing on in dark - ness drear;
3. When our days of toil shall cease, Wait-ing still for sweet re - lease,
Noth - ing left but heav'n and prayer, Wond'ring if our names were there;
Wea - ry souls for - e'er re - joice, While they hear that sweet - est voice,
When the storms are rag - ing sore, Hearts grow faint, and hopes give o'er,
Wad - ing deep the dis - mal flood, Plead - ing naught but Je - sus' blood,
Whis-p'ring soft - ly, "Wand'rer, come! Fol - low Me, I'll guide thee home."
Whis - per soft - ly, "Wand'rer, come! Fol - low Me, I'll guide thee home."
Whis - per soft - ly, "Wand'rer, come! Fol - low Me, I'll guide thee home."
95 Breathe upon Us
R. Kelso Carter, 1891
R. Kelso Carter, 1891
1. Breathe up - on us, Lord from heav-en, Fill us with the Ho - ly Ghost;
2. While the Spir - it hov - ers o'er us, O - pen all our hearts, we pray;
3. Lift us, Lord, O lift us high - er, From the car - nal mind set free;

FINE
Prom - ise of the Fa - ther giv - en, Send us now a Pen - te - cost.
To thine im - age, Lord, re - store us, Wit - ness in our souls to - day.
Fill us with re - fin - ing fire, Give us per - fect lib - er - ty.
D.S.–Breathe up-on us, breathe up-on us, Lord, bap - tize us now with fire.
CHORUS
rit. D. S.
Breathe up-on us, breathe up-on us, With thy love our hearts in-spire; A - MEN.

Holy Spirit, Truth Divine 96

MERCY. 7.7.7.7.

Samuel Longfellow, 1819-1892 Arr. from Louis M. Gottschalk, 1829-1869

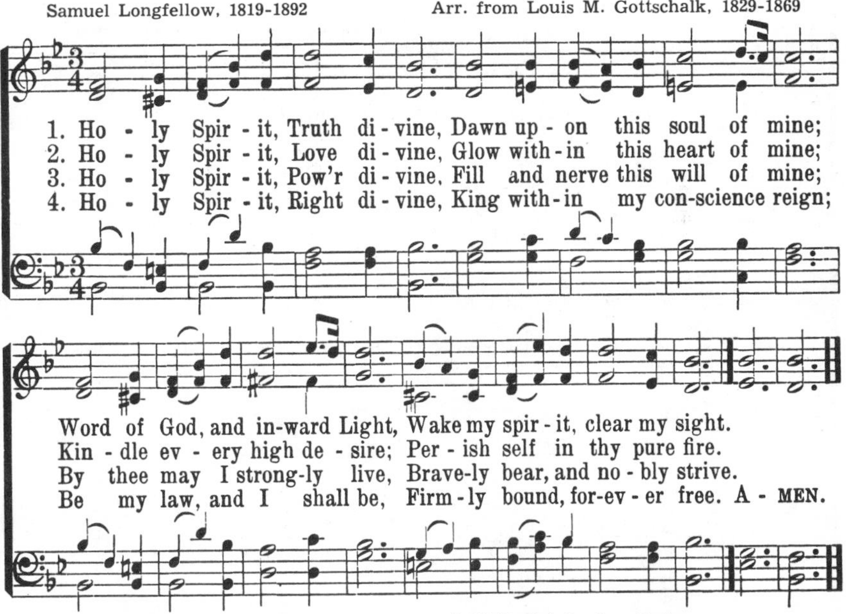
1. Ho - ly Spir - it, Truth di - vine, Dawn up - on this soul of mine;
2. Ho - ly Spir - it, Love di - vine, Glow with - in this heart of mine;
3. Ho - ly Spir - it, Pow'r di - vine, Fill and nerve this will of mine;
4. Ho - ly Spir - it, Right di - vine, King with - in my con - science reign;
Word of God, and in - ward Light, Wake my spir - it, clear my sight.
Kin - dle ev - ery high de - sire; Per - ish self in thy pure fire.
By thee may I strong - ly live, Brave - ly bear, and no - bly strive.
Be my law, and I shall be, Firm - ly bound, for - ev - er free. A - MEN.

5 Holy Spirit, Peace divine,
Still this restless heart of mine;
Speak to calm this tossing sea,
Stayed in thy tranquillity.

6 Holy Spirit, Joy divine,
Gladden thou this heart of mine;
In the desert ways I sing,
"Spring, O Well, forever spring!"

97 Spirit Holy

Charles W. Naylor, 1918 — Andrew L. Byers, 1918

1. Spir - it ho - ly in me dwell-ing. Ev - er work as thou shalt choose;
2. O how sweet is thy a - bid - ing! O how ten - der is the love
3. Thou hast cleansed me for thy tem - ple, Garnished with thy grac-es rare;
4. In me now re - veal thy glo - ry, Let thy might be ev - er shown;
All my ran-somed pow'rs and tal-ents For thy pur - pose thou shalt use.
Thou dost shed a - broad with-in me From the Fa - ther-heart a - bove!
All my soul thou art en-rich - ing By thy full - ness dwell-ing there.
Keep me from the world's de-file - ment, Sa - cred for thy-self a - lone.
Chorus
Spir - it ho - - ly, Spir - it ho - - ly, All my
Spir - it ho - ly, Spir - it ho - ly,
be - - ing now pos - sess; Lead me, rule me, work with-
All my be - ing now pos - sess; Lead me, rule me,
in me, Through my life. . . . thy will ex - press. A - MEN.
work with-in me, Through my life thy will ex - press.

Love Divine, All Loves Excelling 98

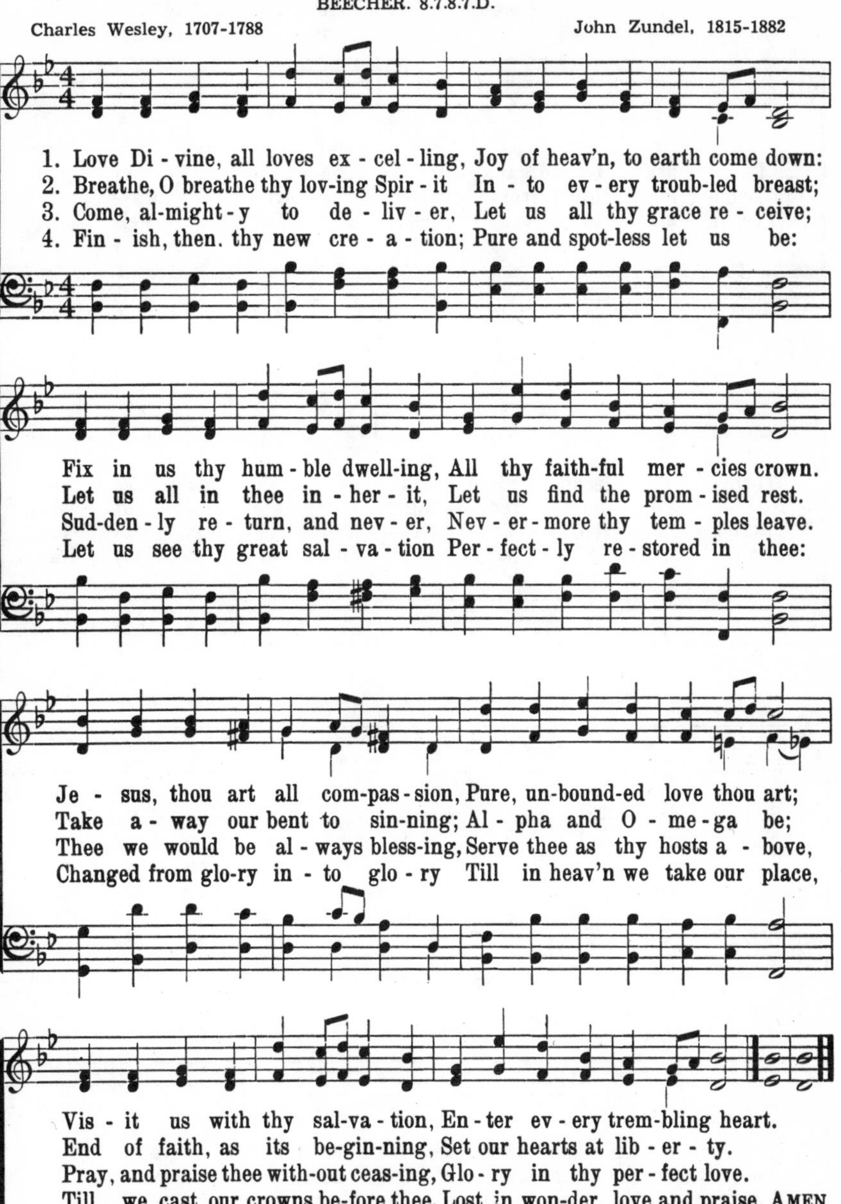
BEECHER. 8.7.8.7.D.
Charles Wesley, 1707-1788
John Zundel, 1815-1882
1. Love Di - vine, all loves ex - cel - ling, Joy of heav'n, to earth come down:
2. Breathe, O breathe thy lov-ing Spir - it In - to ev - ery troub-led breast;
3. Come, al-might - y to de - liv - er, Let us all thy grace re - ceive;
4. Fin - ish, then, thy new cre - a - tion; Pure and spot-less let us be:
Fix in us thy hum - ble dwell-ing, All thy faith-ful mer - cies crown.
Let us all in thee in - her - it, Let us find the prom - ised rest.
Sud-den - ly re - turn, and nev - er, Nev - er - more thy tem - ples leave.
Let us see thy great sal - va - tion Per - fect - ly re - stored in thee:
Je - sus, thou art all com-pas - sion, Pure, un-bound-ed love thou art;
Take a - way our bent to sin-ning; Al - pha and O - me - ga be;
Thee we would be al - ways bless-ing, Serve thee as thy hosts a - bove,
Changed from glo-ry in - to glo - ry Till in heav'n we take our place,
Vis - it us with thy sal-va - tion, En - ter ev - ery trem-bling heart.
End of faith, as its be-gin-ning, Set our hearts at lib - er - ty.
Pray, and praise thee with-out ceas-ing, Glo - ry in thy per - fect love.
Till we cast our crowns be-fore thee, Lost in won-der, love and praise. AMEN.

99 Spirit of God, Descend upon My Heart

MORECAMBE. 10.10.10.10.
George Croly, 1780-1860
Frederick C. Atkinson, 1841-1897
1. Spir - it of God, de - scend up - on my heart;
2. I ask no dream, no proph - et ec - sta - sies,
3. Teach me to feel that Thou art al - ways nigh;
4. Teach me to love Thee as Thine an - gels love,
Wean it from earth; thro' all its puls - es move;
No sud - den rend - ing of the veil of clay,
Teach me the strug - gles of the soul to bear,
One ho - ly pas - sion fill - ing all my frame,
Stoop to my weak - ness, might - y as Thou art,
No an - gel - vis - i - tant, no open - ing skies;
To check the ris - ing doubt, the reb - el sigh;
The bap - tism of the heaven - de - scend - ed Dove,
And make me love Thee as I ought to love.
But take the dim - ness of my soul a - way.
Teach me the pa - tience of un - an - swered prayer.
My heart an al - tar, and Thy love the flame. A-MEN.

The Kingdom of Peace 100

Barney E. Warren, 1897 Barney E. Warren, 1897

Not too fast
1. There's a theme that is sweet to my mem-'ry, There's a joy that I can-not ex-press, There's a treas-ure that glad-dens my be-ing, 'Tis the king-dom of God's right-eous-ness.
2. There's a scene of its grand-ness be-fore me, Of its great-ness there can be no end; It is joy, it is peace, it is glo-ry, In my heart, how these rich-es do blend!
3. I am lost in its splen-dor and beau-ty, To its ne'er-fad-ing heights I would rise, Till I see the King come to re-ceive me, And ex-plore it with him in the skies.
4. What a pleas-ure in life it is bring-ing! What as-sur-ance and hope ev-er bright! O what rap-ture and bliss are a-wait-ing, When our faith shall be lost in the sight!
CHORUS
'Tis a king-dom of peace, it is reign-ing with-in, It shall ev-er in-crease in my soul; We pos-sess it right here when he saves from all sin, And 'twill last while the a-ges shall roll. A-MEN.

101 Come Over into Canaan

Jacob W. Byers, 1906 — Andrew L. Byers, 1906

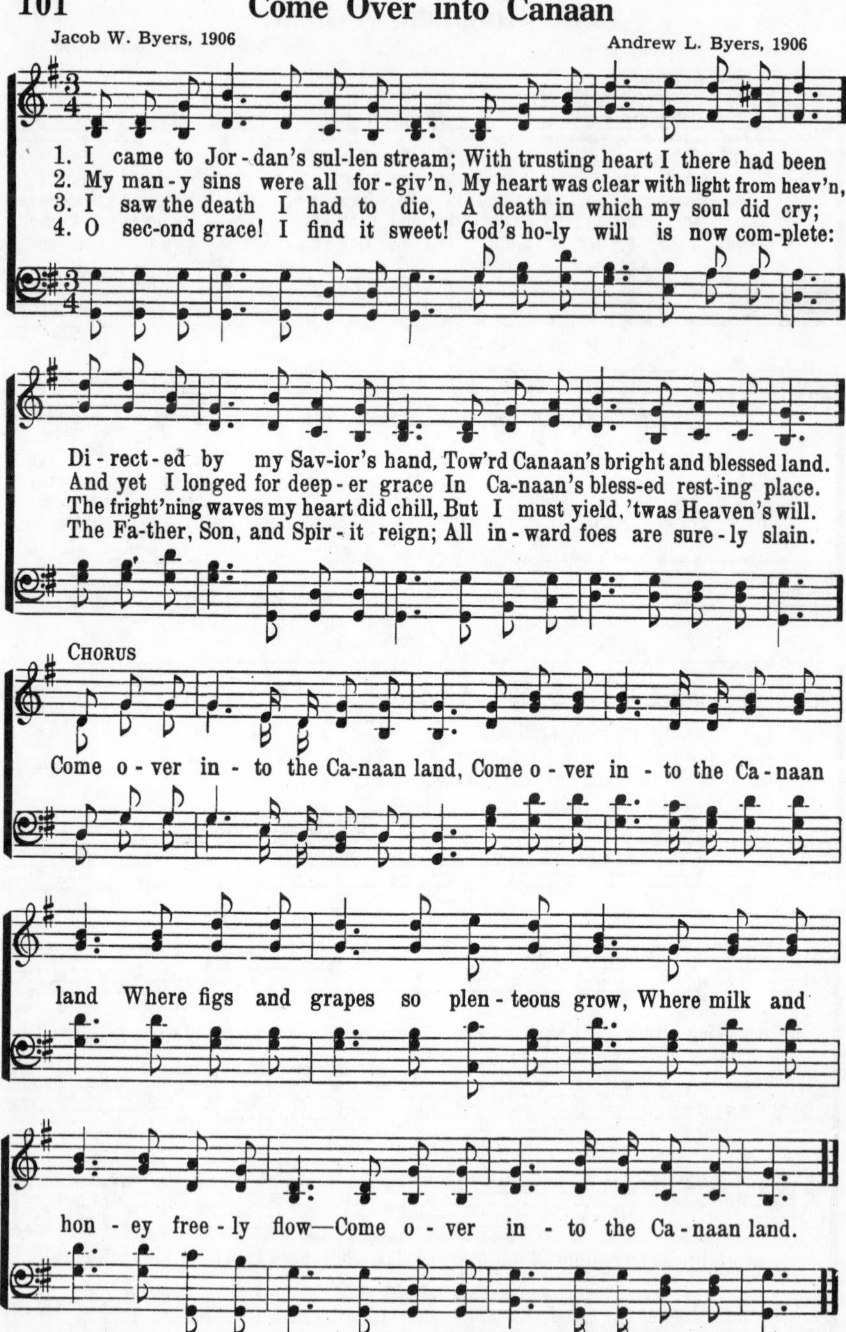
1. I came to Jor - dan's sul-len stream; With trusting heart I there had been
2. My man - y sins were all for - giv'n, My heart was clear with light from heav'n,
3. I saw the death I had to die, A death in which my soul did cry;
4. O sec-ond grace! I find it sweet! God's ho-ly will is now com-plete:
Di - rect - ed by my Sav-ior's hand, Tow'rd Canaan's bright and blessed land.
And yet I longed for deep - er grace In Ca-naan's bless-ed rest-ing place.
The fright'ning waves my heart did chill, But I must yield, 'twas Heaven's will.
The Fa-ther, Son, and Spir - it reign; All in - ward foes are sure - ly slain.
CHORUS
Come o - ver in - to the Ca-naan land, Come o - ver in - to the Ca - naan
land Where figs and grapes so plen - teous grow, Where milk and
hon - ey free - ly flow—Come o - ver in - to the Ca - naan land.

I Am Dwelling on the Mountain 102

William Hunter, 1811-1877 John W. Dadman, 1819-1890

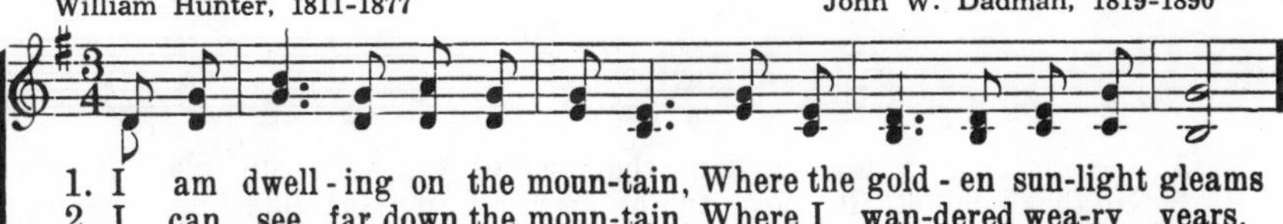

1. I am dwell-ing on the moun-tain, Where the gold-en sun-light gleams
2. I can see far down the moun-tain, Where I wan-dered wea-ry years,
3. I am drink-ing at the foun-tain, Where I ev-er would a-bide;
4. Tell me not of heav-y cross-es, Nor of bur-dens hard to bear,
5. O the cross has won-drous glo-ry! Oft I've proved this to be true;

O'er a land whose won-drous beau-ty Far ex-ceeds my fond-est dreams:
Oft-en hin-dered in my jour-ney By the ghosts of doubts and fears:
For I've tast-ed life's pure riv-er, And my soul is sat-is-fied:
For I've found this great sal-va-tion Makes each bur-den light ap-pear:
When I'm in the way so nar-row, I can see a path-way through:

Where the air is pure, e-the-real, La-den with the breath of flow'rs;
Bro-ken vows and dis-ap-point-ments Thick-ly sprin-kled all the way;
There's no thirst-ing for life's pleas-ures, Nor a-dorn-ing, rich and gay,
And I love to fol-low Je-sus, Glad-ly count-ing all but dross,
And how sweet-ly Je-sus whis-pers, "Take the cross, thou need'st not fear,

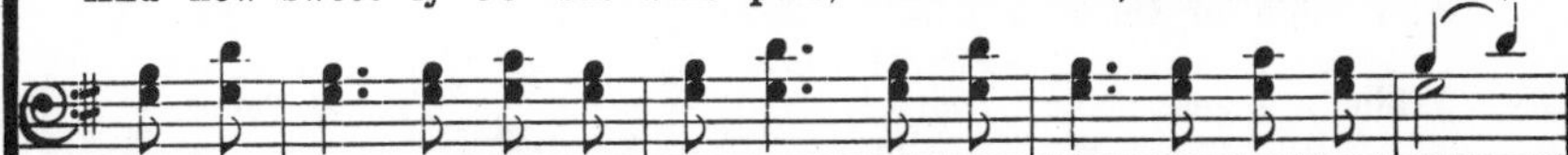

CHORUS *Is not this the land of Beu-lah, Bless-ed, bless-ed land of light,*

D.S. for Chorus

They are bloom-ing by the foun-tain, 'Neath the am-a-ran-thine bow'rs.
But the Spir-it led, un-err-ing, To the land I hold to-day.
For I've found a rich-er treas-ure, One that fad-eth not a-way.
World-ly hon-ors all for-sak-ing For the glo-ry of the cross.
For I've tried the way be-fore thee, And the glo-ry lin-gers near."

Where the flow-ers bloom for-ev-er, And the sun is al-ways bright?

103 The Home of the Soul

Daniel S. Warner, 1842-1895 — Andrew L. Byers, 1870-1952

1. Let us sing a sweet song of the home of the soul, The glo - ri - ous
2. He that dwell-eth in love ev - er dwell-eth in God, Sweet home nev-er
3. We are on - ly at home in the bos - om of God, On earth or in
4. Do not ven-ture the hope that is wait - ing for death To waft you to
5. We will en - ter no door that is o - pened by men Who prom - ise a
place of our rest; It is not far a - way in the heav-ens un - told,
cloud - ed by fears; And this heav-en of love is our na - tive a - bode
heav - en a - bove; Ev - ery one who would en - ter must pass thro' the blood,
com - fort and peace; There's no rest for a soul in this world or a - bove
home for the soul; For in Christ we a - bide in the church that will stand
But deep in the In - fi - nite breast.
Thro' time and e - ter - ni - ty's years. I'm at home, bless - ed
And reign in the king - dom of love.
Not saved in the Fa - ther's em-brace.
While a - ges e - ter - nal - ly roll.
CHORUS
I'm at home,
home, I am safe in the bos - om Di - vine; O the
sweet home, the bos - om Di - vine;

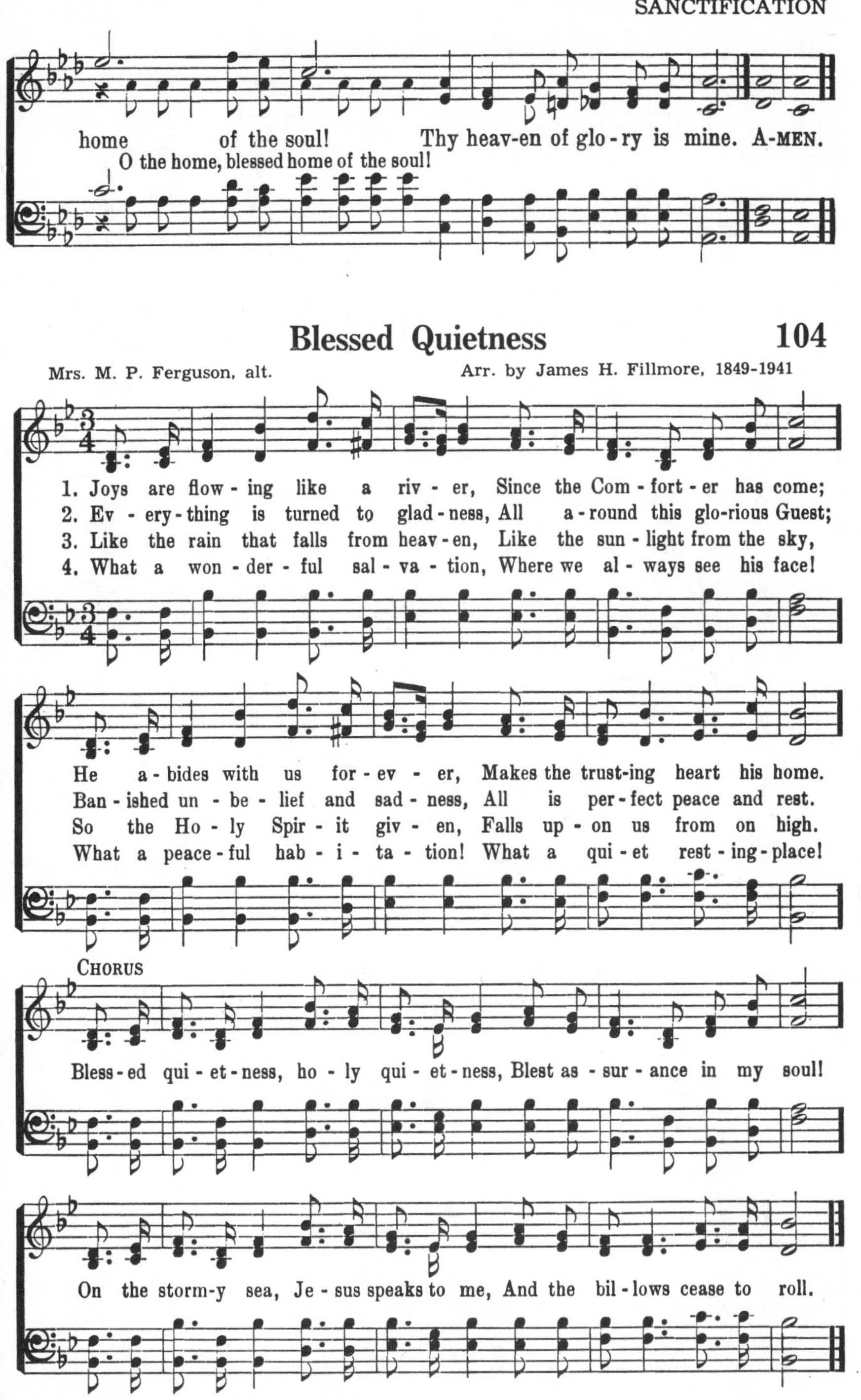
home of the soul! Thy heav-en of glo-ry is mine. A-MEN.
O the home, blessed home of the soul!
Blessed Quietness
104
Mrs. M. P. Ferguson, alt.
Arr. by James H. Fillmore, 1849-1941
1. Joys are flow-ing like a riv-er, Since the Com-fort-er has come;
2. Ev-ery-thing is turned to glad-ness, All a-round this glo-rious Guest;
3. Like the rain that falls from heav-en, Like the sun-light from the sky,
4. What a won-der-ful sal-va-tion, Where we al-ways see his face!
He a-bides with us for-ev-er, Makes the trust-ing heart his home.
Ban-ished un-be-lief and sad-ness, All is per-fect peace and rest.
So the Ho-ly Spir-it giv-en, Falls up-on us from on high.
What a peace-ful hab-i-ta-tion! What a qui-et rest-ing-place!
CHORUS
Bless-ed qui-et-ness, ho-ly qui-et-ness, Blest as-sur-ance in my soul!
On the storm-y sea, Je-sus speaks to me, And the bil-lows cease to roll.

105 Wonderful Words of Life

Philip P. Bliss, 1838-1876 Philip P. Bliss, 1838-1876

1. Sing them o - ver a - gain to me, Won-der-ful words of life,
2. Christ, the bless-ed One, gives to all Won-der-ful words of life,
3. Sweet - ly ech - o the gos - pel call. Won-der-ful words of life,
Let me more of their beau - ty see, Won-der-ful words of life.
Sin - ner, list to the lov - ing call, Won-der-ful words of life.
Of - fer par-don and peace to all, Won-der-ful words of life.
Words of life and beau - ty, Teach me faith and du - ty;
All so free - ly giv - en, Woo - ing us to heav - en,
Je - sus, on - ly Sav - ior, Sanc - ti - fy for - ev - er,
Refrain
Beau - ti - ful words, won - der - ful words, Won-der - ful words of life, . . .
Beau - ti - ful words, won-der-ful words, Won-der-ful words of life. A - men.

Hold Fast to the Word 106

J. M. Henson — Samuel W. Beazley

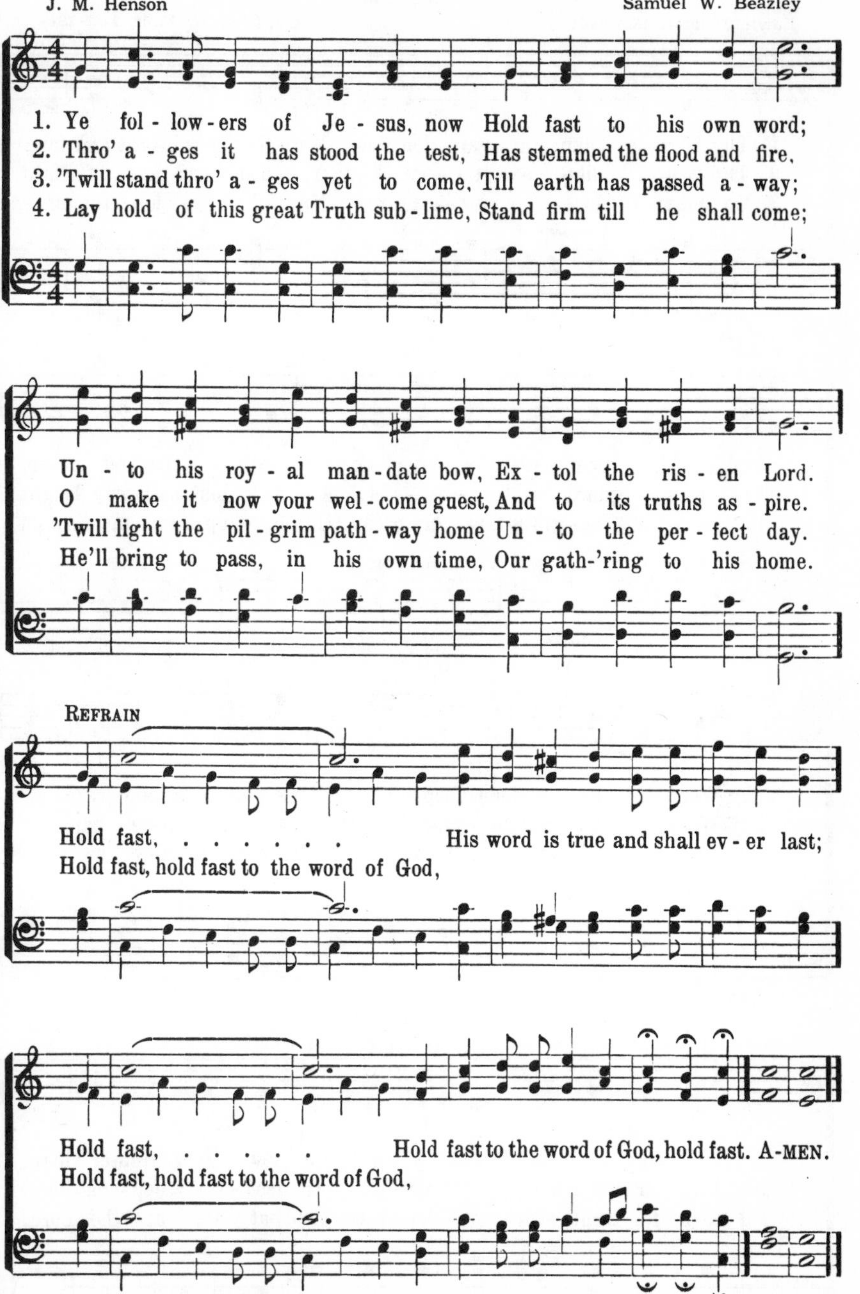
1. Ye fol - low - ers of Je - sus, now Hold fast to his own word;
2. Thro' a - ges it has stood the test, Has stemmed the flood and fire,
3. 'Twill stand thro' a - ges yet to come, Till earth has passed a - way;
4. Lay hold of this great Truth sub - lime, Stand firm till he shall come;
Un - to his roy - al man - date bow, Ex - tol the ris - en Lord.
O make it now your wel - come guest, And to its truths as - pire.
'Twill light the pil - grim path - way home Un - to the per - fect day.
He'll bring to pass, in his own time, Our gath-'ring to his home.
Refrain
Hold fast, ... His word is true and shall ev - er last;
Hold fast, hold fast to the word of God,
Hold fast, ... Hold fast to the word of God, hold fast. A-men.
Hold fast, hold fast to the word of God,

107 Thy Word Is like a Garden, Lord

GABRIEL. C.M.D.

Edwin Hodder, 1837-1904 | Gottfried W. Fink, 1783-1846

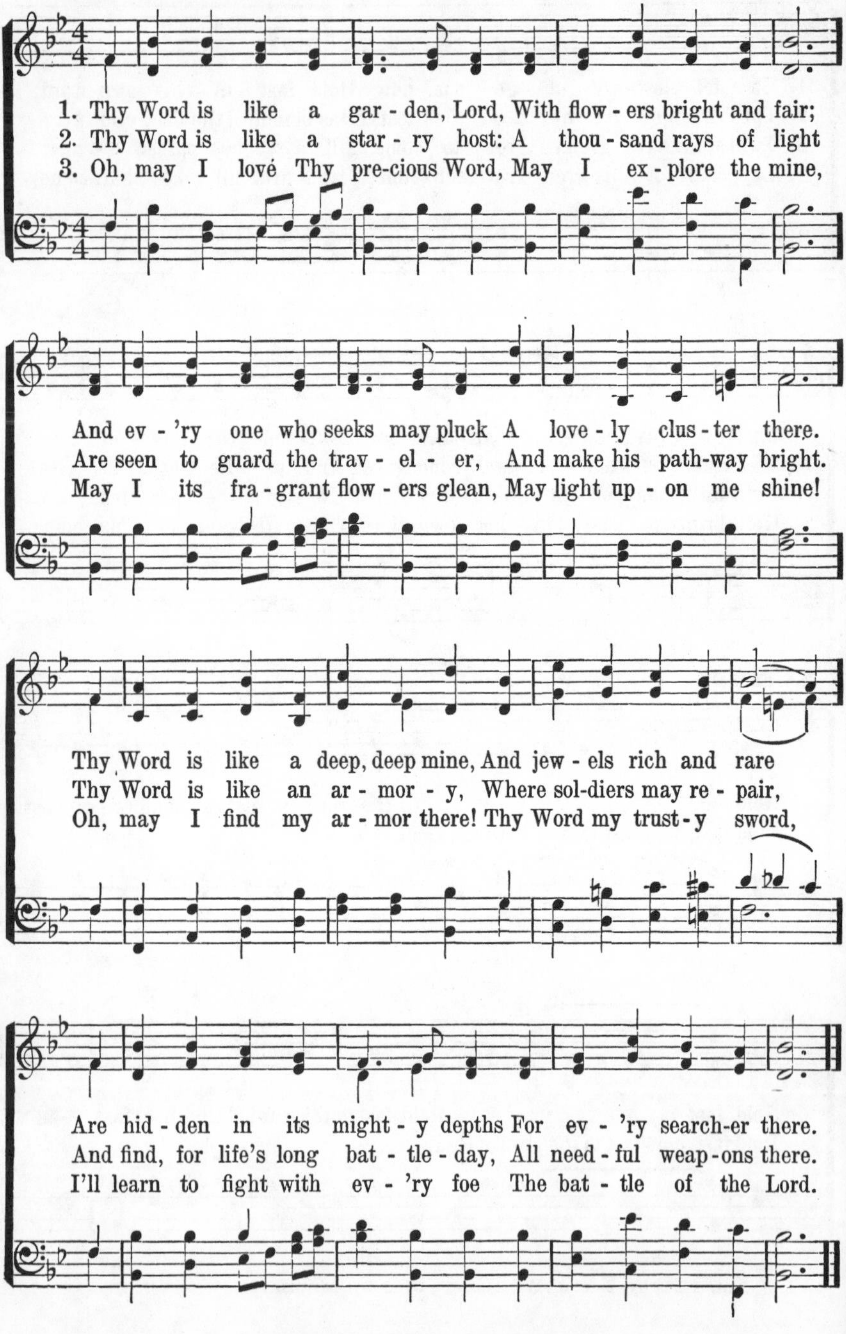

1. Thy Word is like a gar - den, Lord, With flow - ers bright and fair;
2. Thy Word is like a star - ry host: A thou - sand rays of light
3. Oh, may I love Thy pre-cious Word, May I ex - plore the mine,

And ev - 'ry one who seeks may pluck A love - ly clus - ter there.
Are seen to guard the trav - el - er, And make his path-way bright.
May I its fra - grant flow - ers glean, May light up - on me shine!

Thy Word is like a deep, deep mine, And jew - els rich and rare
Thy Word is like an ar - mor - y, Where sol-diers may re - pair,
Oh, may I find my ar - mor there! Thy Word my trust - y sword,

Are hid - den in its might - y depths For ev - 'ry search-er there.
And find, for life's long bat - tle - day, All need - ful weap - ons there.
I'll learn to fight with ev - 'ry foe The bat - tle of the Lord.

Tell Me the Old, Old Story 108

EVANGEL. 7.6.7.6.D. with Refrain

Katherine Hankey, 1834-1911 William Howard Doane, 1832-1915

1. Tell me the Old, Old Sto - ry, Of un-seen things a - bove, Of Je - sus
2. Tell me the sto - ry slow - ly, That I may take it in— That won-der-
3. Tell me the sto - ry soft - ly, With ear-nest tones and grave; Re - mem-ber
4. Tell me the same old sto - ry, When you have cause to fear That this world's
and His glo - ry, Of Je - sus and His love; Tell me the sto - ry
ful re - demp-tion, God's rem - e - dy for sin; Tell me the sto - ry
I'm the sin - ner Whom Je - sus came to save; Tell me the sto - ry
emp-ty glo - ry Is cost - ing me too dear; Yes, and when that world's
sim - ply, As to a lit - tle child, For I am weak and wea - ry,
oft - en, For I for-get so soon, The "ear - ly dew" of morn-ing
al - ways, If you would real-ly be, In an - y time of troub-le,
glo - ry is dawn-ing on my soul, Tell me the Old, Old Sto - ry:
And help - less and de - filed.
Has passed a - way at noon.
A com - fort - er to me.
"Christ Je - sus makes thee whole."
Chorus
Tell me the Old, Old Sto - ry, Tell me the
Old, Old Sto - ry, Tell me the Old, Old Sto - ry Of Je - sus and His love.

109 Praise God for His Word

George O. Webster, b. 1866 — James H. Fillmore, 1849-1941

1. Praise God for his word! from its pag - es di - vine Came the light of his
2. Praise God for his word; for the heav-en - ly light It is send-ing a-
3. Praise God for his word! not a prom-ise shall fail; What-so-e'er may op-
love to this poor heart of mine: I had wan-dered a - far in the
far in - to sin's dark-some night; For the hope which it gives, where be-
pose, still its truth will pre - vail: 'Tis the word of our God and for-
by - ways of sin, When the light of his truth to my heart en-tered in.
fore was de-spair, For the heav-en re-vealed, and the way lead-ing there!
e'er must en-dure; Earth and heav-en may pass, but it stand-eth se - cure.
CHORUS
Praise God for his grace which its pa - ges un - fold! For the sto - ry of
love which will nev - er grow old! For the light on life's path-way which

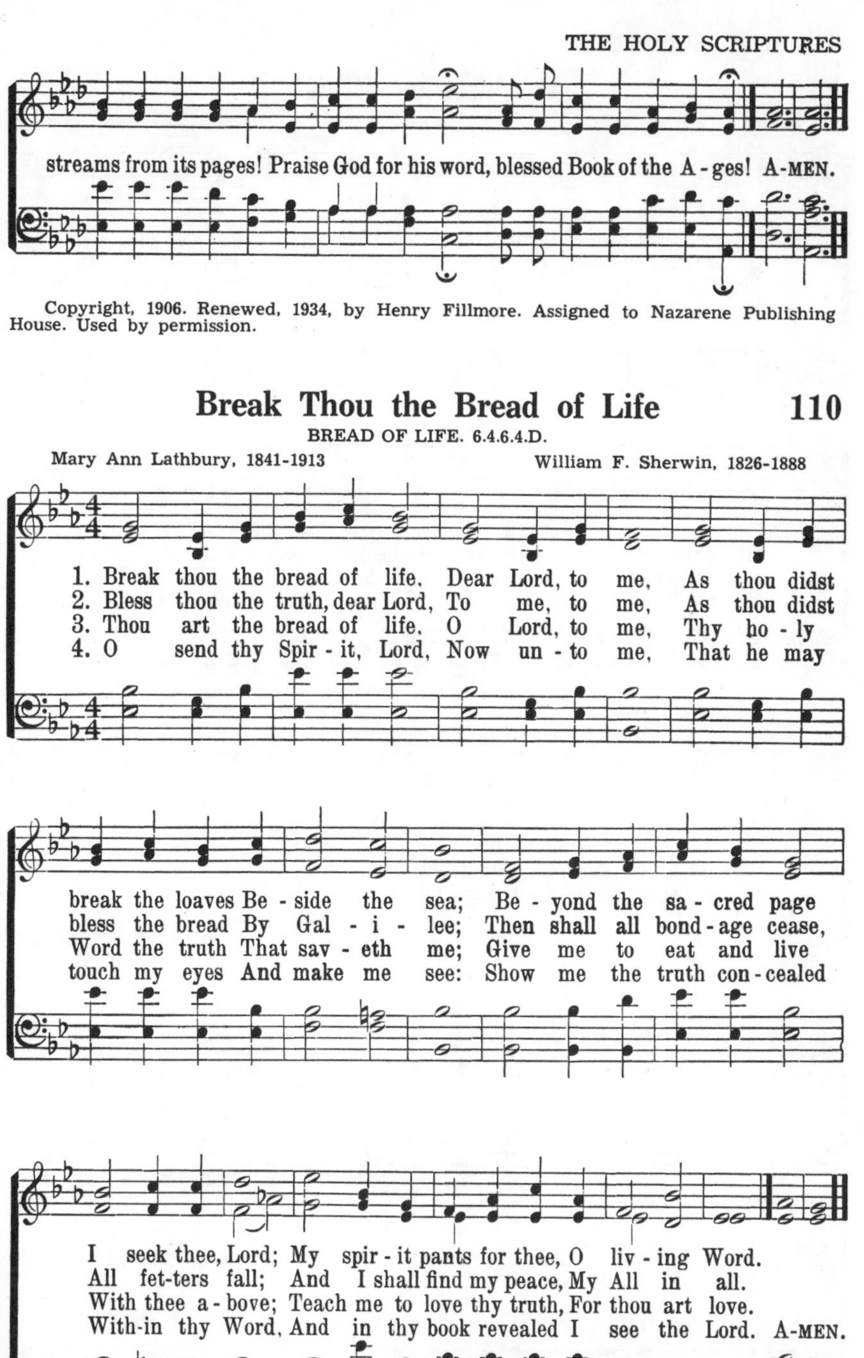
streams from its pages! Praise God for his word, blessed Book of the A - ges! A-MEN.

Break Thou the Bread of Life 110
BREAD OF LIFE. 6.4.6.4.D.
Mary Ann Lathbury, 1841-1913
William F. Sherwin, 1826-1888
1. Break thou the bread of life, Dear Lord, to me, As thou didst break the loaves Be - side the sea; Be - yond the sa - cred page I seek thee, Lord; My spir - it pants for thee, O liv - ing Word.
2. Bless thou the truth, dear Lord, To me, to me, As thou didst bless the bread By Gal - i - lee; Then shall all bond - age cease, All fet-ters fall; And I shall find my peace, My All in all.
3. Thou art the bread of life, O Lord, to me, Thy ho - ly Word the truth That sav - eth me; Give me to eat and live With thee a - bove; Teach me to love thy truth, For thou art love.
4. O send thy Spir - it, Lord, Now un - to me, That he may touch my eyes And make me see: Show me the truth con - cealed With-in thy Word, And in thy book revealed I see the Lord. A-MEN.

111 O Precious Bible!

Daniel S. Warner, 1893 — Barney E. Warren, 1893

1. O pre-cious Bi-ble! burning words from heaven, We'll ev - er cher - ish thee in our heart: Sweet is the coun - sel by thy pag - es giv - en; On life's dark o - cean our on - ly chart.
2. O pre-cious vol-ume! on - ly in thy pag - es We read the du - ty of all our race; On - ly thy sun-beams, shin-ing thro' the a - ges, Re - veal the won-ders of sav - ing grace.
3. This Book of heav-en shall en-dure for - ev - er, And from its wis - dom we'll nev - er turn; Weighed in its bal - ance, all the creeds that sev - er Are on - ly stub-ble, ere long to burn.
4. Dear Book of mer-cy, on thy sure foun-da - tion We build a dwell - ing-place for the soul, Hear - ing and do - ing all thy rev - e - la - tion: It stands un - shak-en, though bil - lows roll.
CHORUS
Bless - ed Bi - ble! bless - ed Bi - ble! Joy - ful ti - dings from our home! Thou art the rock of ev - er-last-ing a - ges; Hope of e - ter-nal bliss at heaven's throne. A - MEN.

The Word of God 112

Clara M. Brooks, 1907 — Barney E. Warren, 1907

1. By the word of God the worlds were made, And are held in place by
2. More to be de - sired than hon - ey sweet, Rich - er are its treas-ures,
3. Thy e - ter - nal law is my de - light, Strength and dai-ly man-na
4. Stream of life from heav - en, crys - tal pure, Shed thy cool - ing fresh-ness

his com-mands; All the grass - es with - er and the flow - ers fade,
far, than gold; Like a bril - liant light it shines to guide my feet,
to my soul; 'Tis my med - i - ta - tion all the day and night,
o - ver me; Let my thirst - ing spir - it, till I thirst no more,

But his truth for - ev - er stands.
Nev - er grows its sto - ry old.
Balm to make the wound-ed whole.
Drink thy sparkling wa - ters free.

CHORUS

O the pre-cious Bi - ble! Coun-sel for the soul; Path the faith - ful saints and mar - tyrs trod: Set - tled in the heav-ens, True while a - ges roll, Change-less as the throne of God. A-MEN.

113 There Is Power in the Blood

L. E. Jones — L. E. Jones

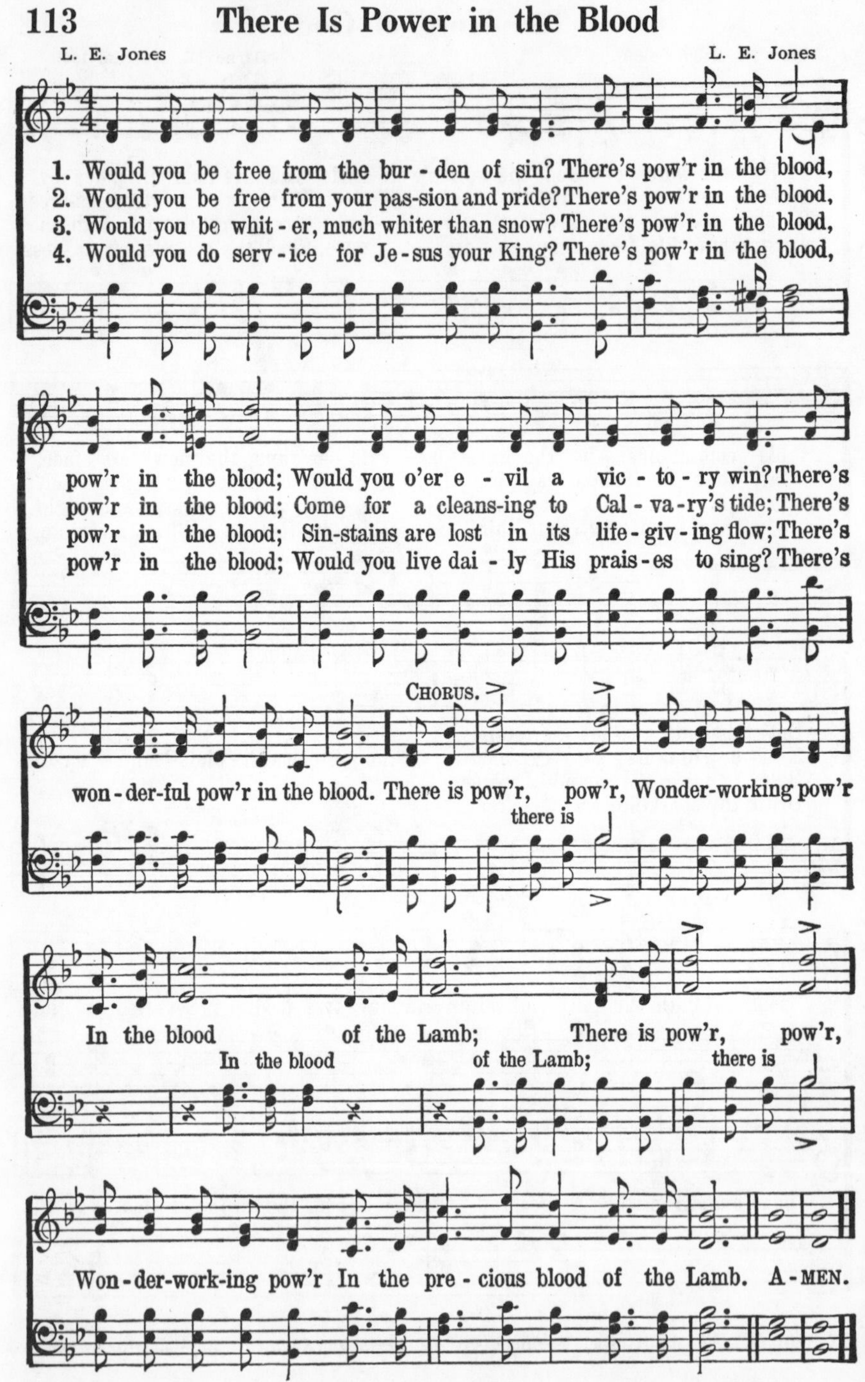
1. Would you be free from the bur - den of sin? There's pow'r in the blood,
2. Would you be free from your pas-sion and pride? There's pow'r in the blood,
3. Would you be whit - er, much whiter than snow? There's pow'r in the blood,
4. Would you do serv - ice for Je - sus your King? There's pow'r in the blood,
pow'r in the blood; Would you o'er e - vil a vic - to - ry win? There's
pow'r in the blood; Come for a cleans-ing to Cal - va-ry's tide; There's
pow'r in the blood; Sin-stains are lost in its life - giv - ing flow; There's
pow'r in the blood; Would you live dai - ly His prais - es to sing? There's
won - der-ful pow'r in the blood.
CHORUS.
There is pow'r, there is pow'r, Wonder-working pow'r
In the blood of the Lamb;
In the blood of the Lamb;
There is pow'r, there is pow'r,
Won - der-work-ing pow'r In the pre - cious blood of the Lamb. A-MEN.

Are You Washed in the Blood? 114

Elisha A. Hoffman, 1839-1929 Elisha A. Hoffman, 1839-1929

1. Have you been to Je - sus for the cleans-ing pow'r? Are you washed in the blood of the Lamb? Are you ful - ly trust-ing in His grace this hour? Are you washed in the blood of the Lamb?
2. Are you walk-ing dai - ly by the Sav - ior's side? Are you washed in the blood of the Lamb? Do you rest each mo-ment in the Cru - ci - fied? Are you washed in the blood of the Lamb?
3. When the Bridegroom cometh will your robes be white? Are you washed in the blood of the Lamb? Will your soul be read - y for the mansions bright, And be washed in the blood of the Lamb?
4. Lay a - side the gar-ments that are stained with sin, Are you washed in the blood of the Lamb? There's a fountain flow-ing for the soul un-clean, O be washed in the blood of the Lamb?

CHORUS

Are you washed (Are you washed) in the blood, (in the blood,) In the soul-cleans-ing blood of the Lamb? (of the Lamb?) Are your gar-ments spot-less? Are they white as snow? Are you washed in the blood of the Lamb?

115 The Great Physician

William Hunter, 1811-1877 — Arr. by John H. Stockton, 1813-1877

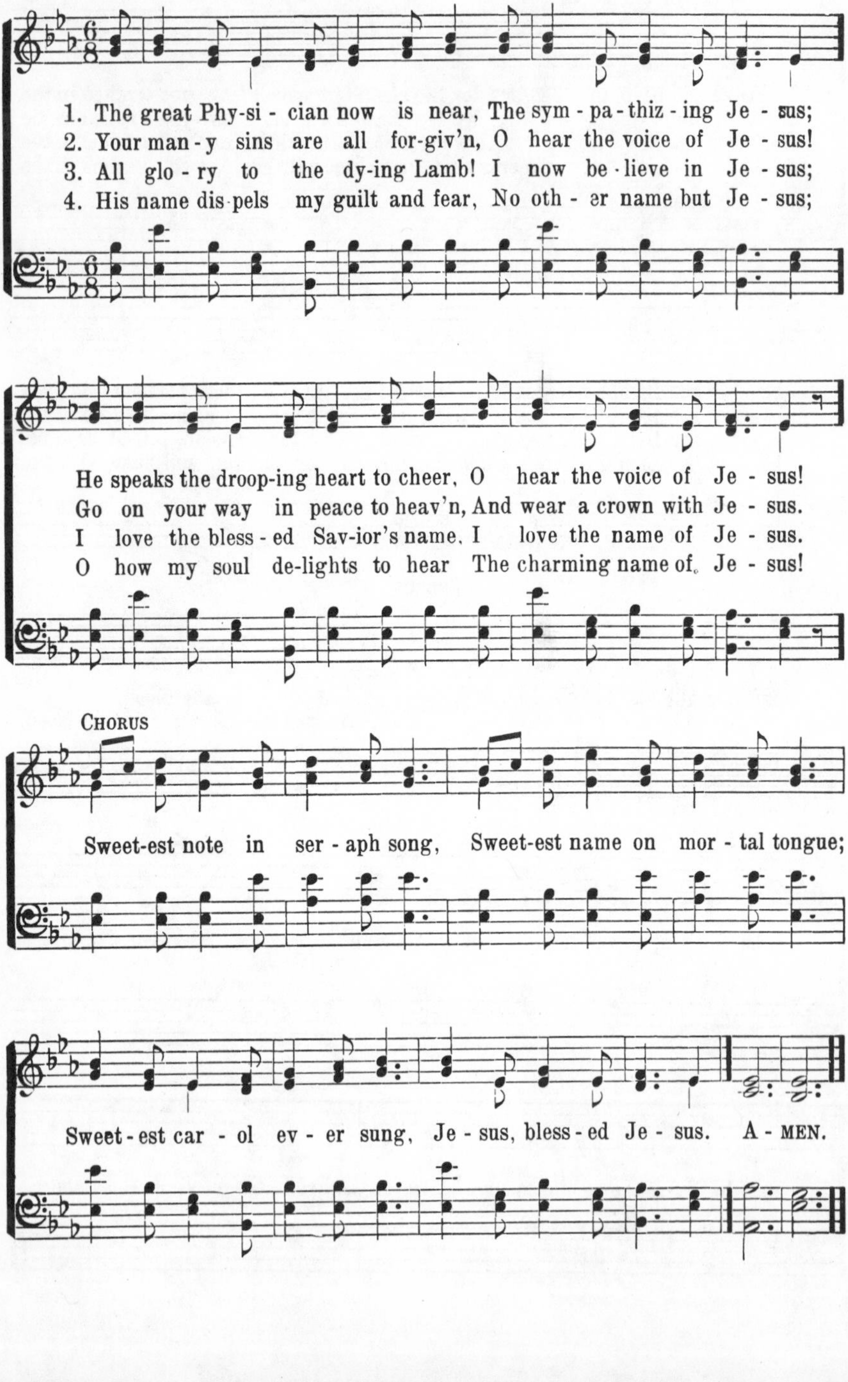

1. The great Phy-si - cian now is near, The sym - pa - thiz - ing Je - sus;
He speaks the droop-ing heart to cheer, O hear the voice of Je - sus!

2. Your man - y sins are all for-giv'n, O hear the voice of Je - sus!
Go on your way in peace to heav'n, And wear a crown with Je - sus.

3. All glo - ry to the dy-ing Lamb! I now be - lieve in Je - sus;
I love the bless - ed Sav-ior's name, I love the name of Je - sus.

4. His name dis-pels my guilt and fear, No oth - er name but Je - sus;
O how my soul de-lights to hear The charming name of Je - sus!

CHORUS

Sweet-est note in ser - aph song, Sweet-est name on mor - tal tongue;
Sweet - est car - ol ev - er sung, Je - sus, bless - ed Je - sus. A - MEN.

There Is a Fountain Filled with Blood 116

CLEANSING FOUNTAIN. C.M.D.

William Cowper, 1731-1800

Early American melody
Arr. by Lowell Mason, 1792-1872

1. There is a foun-tain filled with blood Drawn from Im-man-uel's veins;
And sin-ners, plunged be-neath that flood, Lose all their guilt-y stains.
Lose all their guilt-y stains, Lose all their guilt-y stains;
And sin-ners, plunged be-neath that flood, Lose all their guilt-y stains.

2. The dy-ing thief re-joiced to see That foun-tain in his day;
And there have I, though vile as he, Washed all my sins a-way.
Washed all my sins a-way, Washed all my sins a-way;
And there have I, though vile as he, Washed all my sins a-way.

3. Thou dy-ing Lamb, thy pre-cious blood Shall nev-er lose its pow'r
Till all the ran-somed church of God Are saved, to sin no more.
Are saved, to sin no more, Are saved, to sin no more;
Till all the ran-somed church of God Are saved, to sin no more.

4. E'er since by faith I saw the stream Thy flow-ing wounds sup-ply,
Re-deem-ing love has been my theme, And shall be till I die.
And shall be till I die, And shall be till I die;
Re-deem-ing love has been my theme, And shall be till I die.

5. Then in a no-bler, sweet-er song I'll sing thy pow'r to save,
When this poor lisp-ing, stamm'ring tongue Lies si-lent in the grave.
Lies si-lent in the grave, Lies si-lent in the grave;
When this poor lisp-ing, stamm'ring tongue Lies si-lent in the grave. A-MEN.

117 Power in the Blood of Jesus

Barney E. Warren, 1926 Barney E. Warren, 1926

1. There's pow-er in the blood to save from sin, To bring the peace of God where guilt hath been; A new and hap-py life will then be-gin, There's pow-er in the blood of Je-sus.
2. There's pow-er in the blood to-day, I see, As when he set the pal-sied sin-ner free; And now his sav-ing grace ex-tends to me,
3. No right-eous-ness of ours can e'er a-vail, But through the Lamb of God we shall pre-vail; There's pow-er in his blood, all else will fail,
4. There's pow-er in the blood for our re-lease, There's pow-er in the blood to bring soul-peace; The mer-its of his blood will not de-crease,

CHORUS

There's pow-er in the blood of Je-sus, There's pow-er in the blood of Je-sus To save the soul to-day, Wash ev-ery sin a-way; There's pow-er in the blood of Je-sus.

Nothing but the Blood of Jesus 118

Robert Lowry, 1826-1899 Robert Lowry, 1826-1899

1. What can wash a - way my stain? Noth-ing but the blood of Je - sus.
What can make me whole a - gain? Noth-ing but the blood of Je - sus.

2. For my cleans-ing this I see, Noth-ing but the blood of Je - sus;
For my par - don this my plea, Noth-ing but the blood of Je - sus.

3. Noth - ing can for sin a - tone, Noth-ing but the blood of Je - sus;
Naught of good that I have done, Noth-ing but the blood of Je - sus.

4. This is all my hope and peace, Noth-ing but the blood of Je - sus;
This is all my right-eous - ness, Noth-ing but the blood of Je - sus.

5. Now by this I'll o - ver - come, Noth-ing but the blood of Je - sus;
Now by this I'll reach my home, Noth-ing but the blood of Je - sus.

6. Glo - ry! glo - ry! thus I sing, Noth-ing but the blood of Je - sus;
All my praise for this I bring, Noth-ing but the blood of Je - sus.

CHORUS

O pre - cious is the flow That makes me white as snow!
No oth - er fount I know, Noth-ing but the blood of Je - sus.

119 Sin Can Never Enter There

Charles W. Naylor, 1899 — Barney E. Warren, 1902

1. Heav-en is a ho-ly place Filled with glory and with grace; Sin can nev-er en-ter there: All with-in its gates are pure, From de-file-ment kept se-cure,
2. If you hope to dwell at last, When your life on earth is past, In that home so bright and fair, You must here be cleansed from sin, Have the life of Christ with-in,
3. You may live in sin be-low, Heaven's grace re-fuse to know, But you can-not en-ter there; It will stop you at the door, Bar you out for-ev-er-more,
4. If you cling to sin till death, When you draw your latest breath, You will sink in dark de-spair To the re-gions of the lost, Thus to prove at aw-ful cost,

Sin can nev-er en-ter there.

CHORUS

Sin can nev-er en-ter there,
Sin can nev-er en-ter, nev-er en-ter there,
Sin can nev-er en-ter there;
Sin can nev-er en-ter, nev-er en-ter there;
So if at the judgment bar, Sin-ful spots your soul shall mar, *You* can nev-er en-ter there.

Ye Must Be Born Again 120

Charles W. Naylor, 1907 — Andrew L. Byers, 1907

1. That heav-en-ly Teach-er, in words that are plain, This truth de-clared to men:
If ev-er they would to his king-dom at-tain They must be born a-gain.
2. No mere ref-or-ma-tion your sins can e-rase, You can-not remove their stain;
If ev-er in heav-en your soul has a place Ye must be born a-gain.
3. Good works will not an-swer, no pen-ance will do, Mo-ral-i-ty, too, is vain;
For naught will a-vail but a crea-ture made new, Ye must be born a-gain.
4. In Ad-am we lost all our right-eous es-tate, And would we it re-gain,
To Je-sus must come and re-pent ere too late—Ye must be born a-gain.

CHORUS

Ye must be born a-gain,...... Ye must be born a-gain;......
Ye must be born a-gain, Ye must be born a-gain;
1. His words are true, he speaks to you, Ye must be born a-gain (a-gain).
2. His words are true, he speaks to you, Ye must be born a-gain (a-gain).

121 He Is Able to Deliver

Barney E. Warren, 1900 | Barney E. Warren, 1900

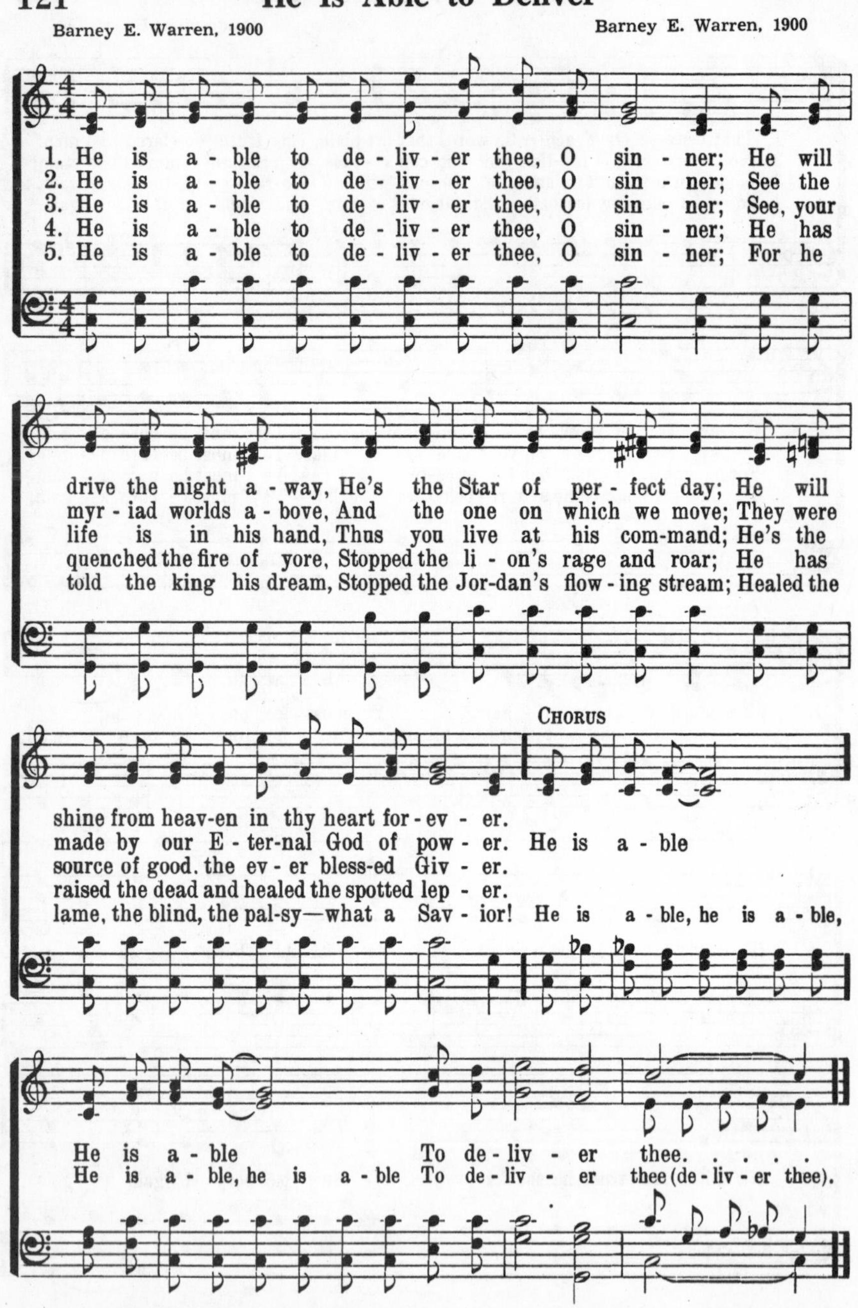
1. He is a - ble to de - liv - er thee, O sin - ner; He will
2. He is a - ble to de - liv - er thee, O sin - ner; See the
3. He is a - ble to de - liv - er thee, O sin - ner; See, your
4. He is a - ble to de - liv - er thee, O sin - ner; He has
5. He is a - ble to de - liv - er thee, O sin - ner; For he
drive the night a - way, He's the Star of per - fect day; He will
myr - iad worlds a - bove, And the one on which we move; They were
life is in his hand, Thus you live at his com-mand; He's the
quenched the fire of yore, Stopped the li - on's rage and roar; He has
told the king his dream, Stopped the Jor-dan's flow - ing stream; Healed the
CHORUS
shine from heav-en in thy heart for - ev - er.
made by our E - ter-nal God of pow - er. He is a - ble
source of good. the ev - er bless-ed Giv - er.
raised the dead and healed the spotted lep - er.
lame, the blind, the pal-sy—what a Sav - ior! He is a - ble, he is a - ble,
He is a - ble To de - liv - er thee. . . . .
He is a - ble, he is a - ble To de - liv - er thee (de - liv - er thee).

Savior, Like a Shepherd Lead Us 122

BRADBURY. 8.7.8.7.D.

From *Hymns for the Young*, 1836
Ascribed to Dorothy A. Thrupp, 1779-1847

William B. Bradbury, 1816-1868

1. Sav - ior, like a shep-herd lead us, Much we need thy ten - der care;
2. We are thine, do thou be - friend us, Be the guard-ian of our way;
3. Thou hast promised to re - ceive us, Poor and sin - ful tho' we be;
4. Ear - ly let us seek thy fa - vor, Ear - ly let us do thy will;

In thy pleas-ant pas-tures feed us, For our use thy folds pre-pare:
Keep thy flock, from sin de - fend us, Seek us when we go a - stray:
Thou hast mer - cy to re - lieve us, Grace to cleanse, and pow'r to free:
Bless - ed Lord and on - ly Sav - ior, With thy love our bos - oms fill:

Bless-ed Je - sus, bless - ed Je - sus, Thou hast bought us, thine we are,
Bless-ed Je - sus, bless - ed Je - sus, Hear thy chil - dren when they pray,
Bless-ed Je - sus, bless - ed Je - sus, Ear - ly let us turn to thee,
Bless-ed Je - sus, bless - ed Je - sus, Thou hast loved us, love us still,

Bless-ed Je - sus, bless-ed Je - sus, Thou hast bought us, thine we are.
Bless-ed Je - sus, bless-ed Je - sus, Hear thy children when they pray.
Bless-ed Je - sus, bless-ed Je - sus, Ear - ly let us turn to thee.
Bless-ed Je - sus, bless-ed Je - sus, Thou hast loved us, love us still. A-MEN.

123 Look and Live

W. A. Ogden, 1841-1897 W. A. Ogden, 1841-1897

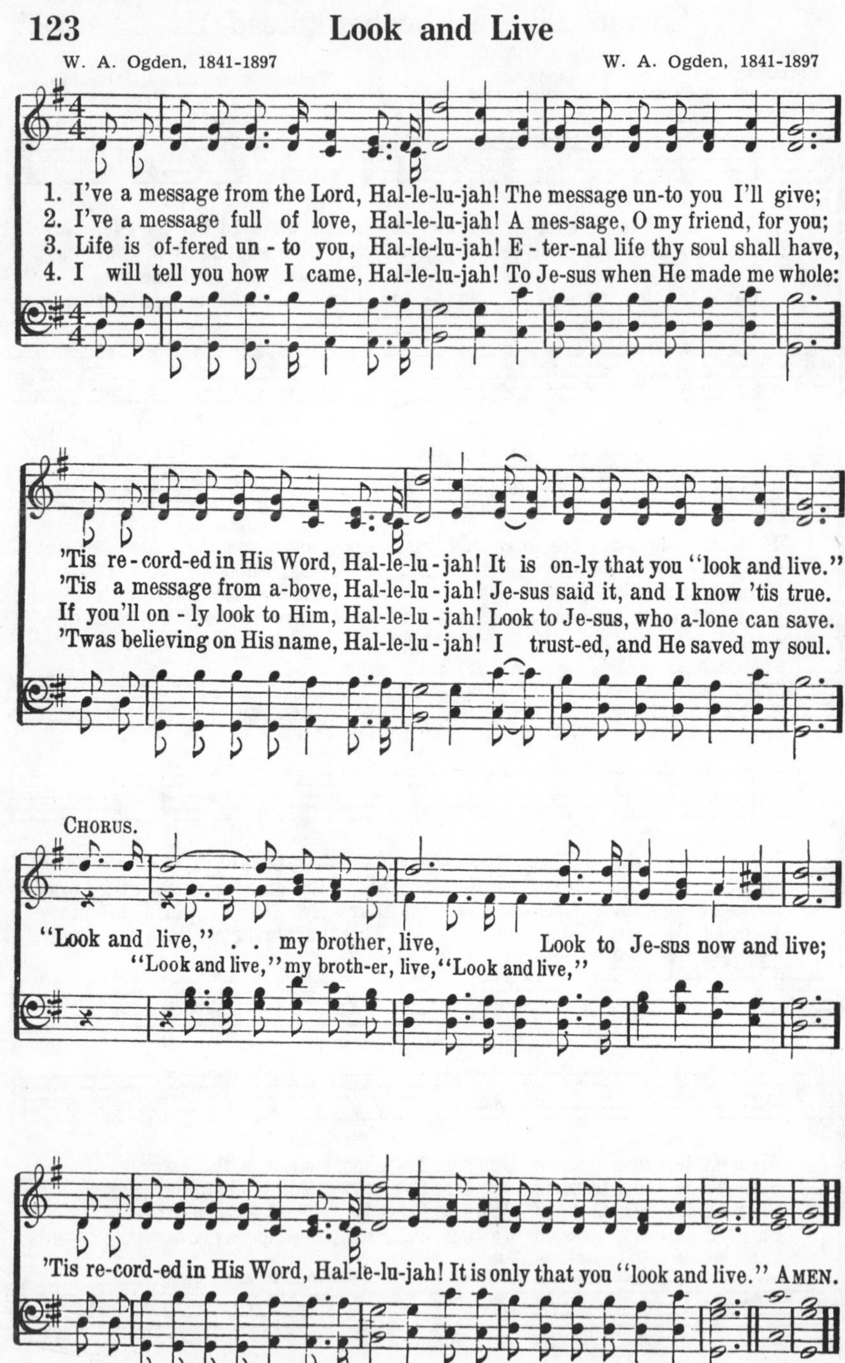
1. I've a message from the Lord, Hal-le-lu-jah! The message un-to you I'll give;
2. I've a message full of love, Hal-le-lu-jah! A mes-sage, O my friend, for you;
3. Life is of-fered un - to you, Hal-le-lu-jah! E - ter-nal life thy soul shall have,
4. I will tell you how I came, Hal-le-lu-jah! To Je-sus when He made me whole:
'Tis re-cord-ed in His Word, Hal-le-lu-jah! It is on-ly that you "look and live."
'Tis a message from a-bove, Hal-le-lu-jah! Je-sus said it, and I know 'tis true.
If you'll on - ly look to Him, Hal-le-lu-jah! Look to Je-sus, who a-lone can save.
'Twas believing on His name, Hal-le-lu-jah! I trust-ed, and He saved my soul.
CHORUS.
"Look and live," . . my brother, live, Look to Je-sus now and live;
"Look and live," my broth-er, live, "Look and live,"
'Tis re-cord-ed in His Word, Hal-le-lu-jah! It is only that you "look and live." AMEN.

I Am Praying for You 124

S. O'Maley Cluff, 1837-1910 — Ira D. Sankey, 1840-1908

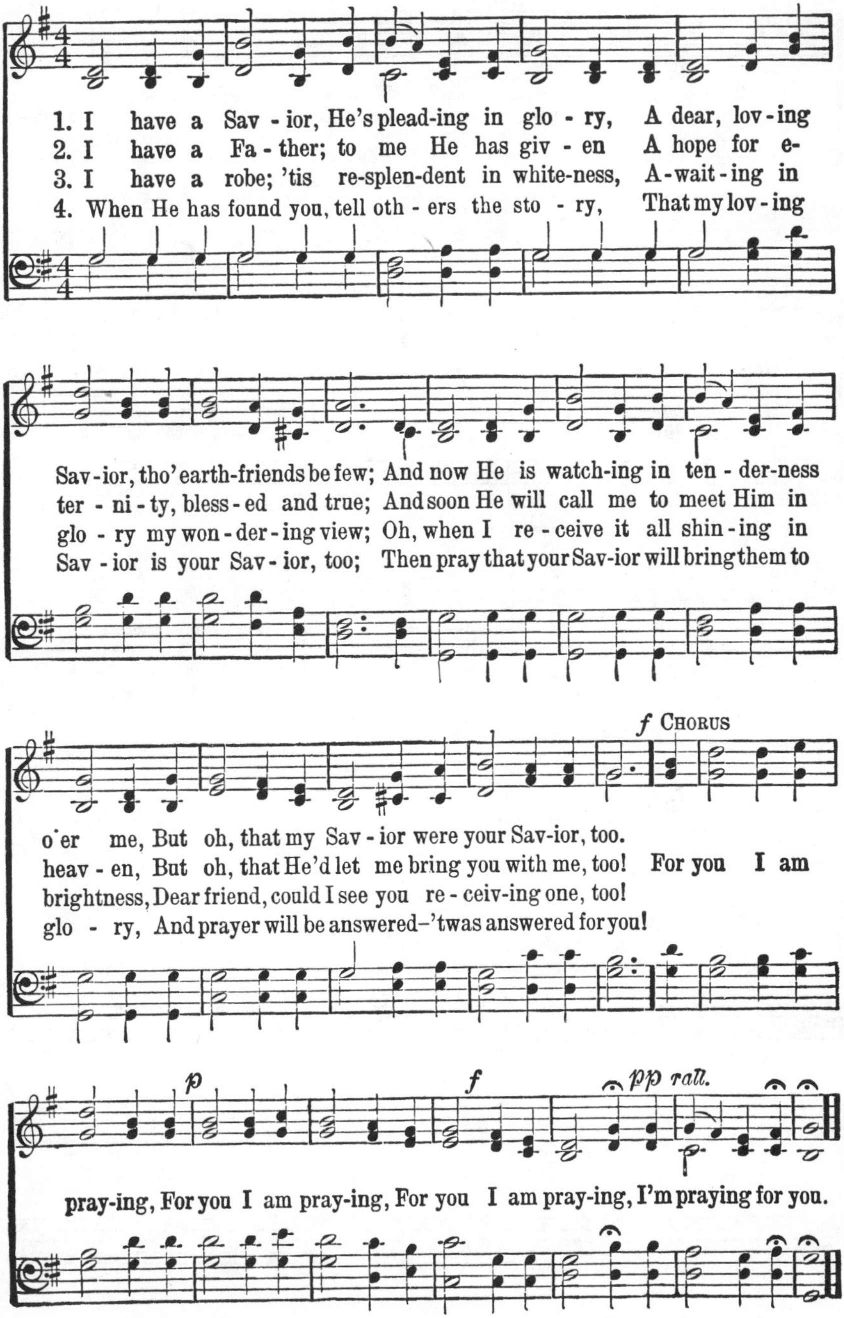

1. I have a Sav - ior, He's plead-ing in glo - ry, A dear, lov - ing
2. I have a Fa - ther; to me He has giv - en A hope for e-
3. I have a robe; 'tis re-splen-dent in white-ness, A-wait - ing in
4. When He has found you, tell oth - ers the sto - ry, That my lov - ing

Sav - ior, tho' earth-friends be few; And now He is watch-ing in ten - der-ness
ter - ni - ty, bless - ed and true; And soon He will call me to meet Him in
glo - ry my won - der - ing view; Oh, when I re - ceive it all shin - ing in
Sav - ior is your Sav - ior, too; Then pray that your Sav-ior will bring them to

o'er me, But oh, that my Sav - ior were your Sav-ior, too.
heav - en, But oh, that He'd let me bring you with me, too! For you I am
brightness, Dear friend, could I see you re - ceiv-ing one, too!
glo - ry, And prayer will be answered—'twas answered for you!

f CHORUS

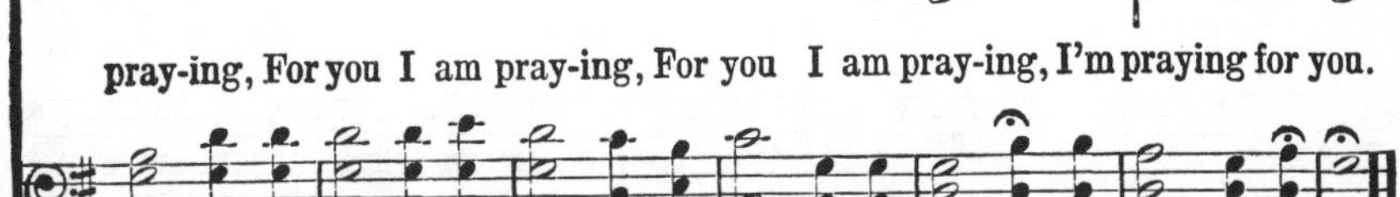
p *f* *pp* *rall.*
pray-ing, For you I am pray-ing, For you I am pray-ing, I'm praying for you.

125 Lost Forever

Barney E. Warren, 1893
Barney E. Warren, 1893
1. Where is thy pros - pect, sin - ner? What are you go - ing to do?
2. Where is thy ref - uge, sin - ner? Look where your path-way will end, Re-
3. What can you plead, poor sin - ner, In the great judg - ment day?
4. Where will you go, poor sin - ner? How will your soul es - cape?
Hope is a bless - ed soul - an - chor, Of - fered so free - ly to you;
pent, or you'll per - ish for - ev - er, Aw - ful de - struc - tion's at hand;
Heav - en now of - fers you fa - vor, O do not cast it a - way;
Think of thy lot, when for - ev - er Cast in the dark burn - ing lake:
If it is fixed in the Sav - ior, On that bright shore you will
Heav - en or hell you are choos - ing, Fix - ing and seal - ing your
Slight - ed, the warn - ings re - peat - ed, Leave you in Sa - tan's con-
If then you're lost and for - got - ten, Writh - ing in flames of de-
land; But if in sin you still lin - ger, Sad your end.
fate, God and his mer - cy re - fus - ing, Lost! too late!
trol; And with all heav - en re - ject - ed, Lost, your soul!
spair, You will re - mem - ber you've cho - sen To be there.
Refrain
rit.
Lost for - ev - er! Lost for - ev - er! O how sad!

Why Carelessly Wait? 126

Barney E. Warren, 1907 Barney E. Warren, 1907

1. O come to the Lord to-day, Come, sin-ner, with-out de - lay; O give him your heart, I pray,. Why care-less-ly wait? Soon you will be called to die, Poor soul, to the Sav-ior fly; You know that the end is nigh, Why care-less-ly wait?

2. Your day of grace will be past, And hope-less you'll be at last, With mercy's door closed and fast, Why care-less-ly wait? When there at the judgment throne, Your sins will be all made known, Then Sa - tan will claim his own, Why care-less-ly wait?

3. O soul, do not i - dly stand, Un-heed-ing the Lord's command; You'll per-ish in sink - ing sand, Why care-less-ly wait? Your pulse will ere long be still. In death will your blood soon chill; O has - ten, o - bey God's will, Why care-less-ly wait?

4. Soon, soon in e - ter - ni - ty, Poor sin-ner, your soul shall be, What then can a-tone for thee? Why care-less-ly wait? You'll stand at the judgment seat, Your rec-ord of sins you'll meet; Come bow-ing at Je - sus' feet, Why care-less-ly wait?

FINE

D. S.—*You know that the end is nigh, Why care-less-ly wait?*

CHORUS

Why care - less - ly wait?.......... Why care - less - ly wait?..........
Why care - less - ly, care - less - ly wait? Why care - less - ly, care - less - ly wait?

D. S.

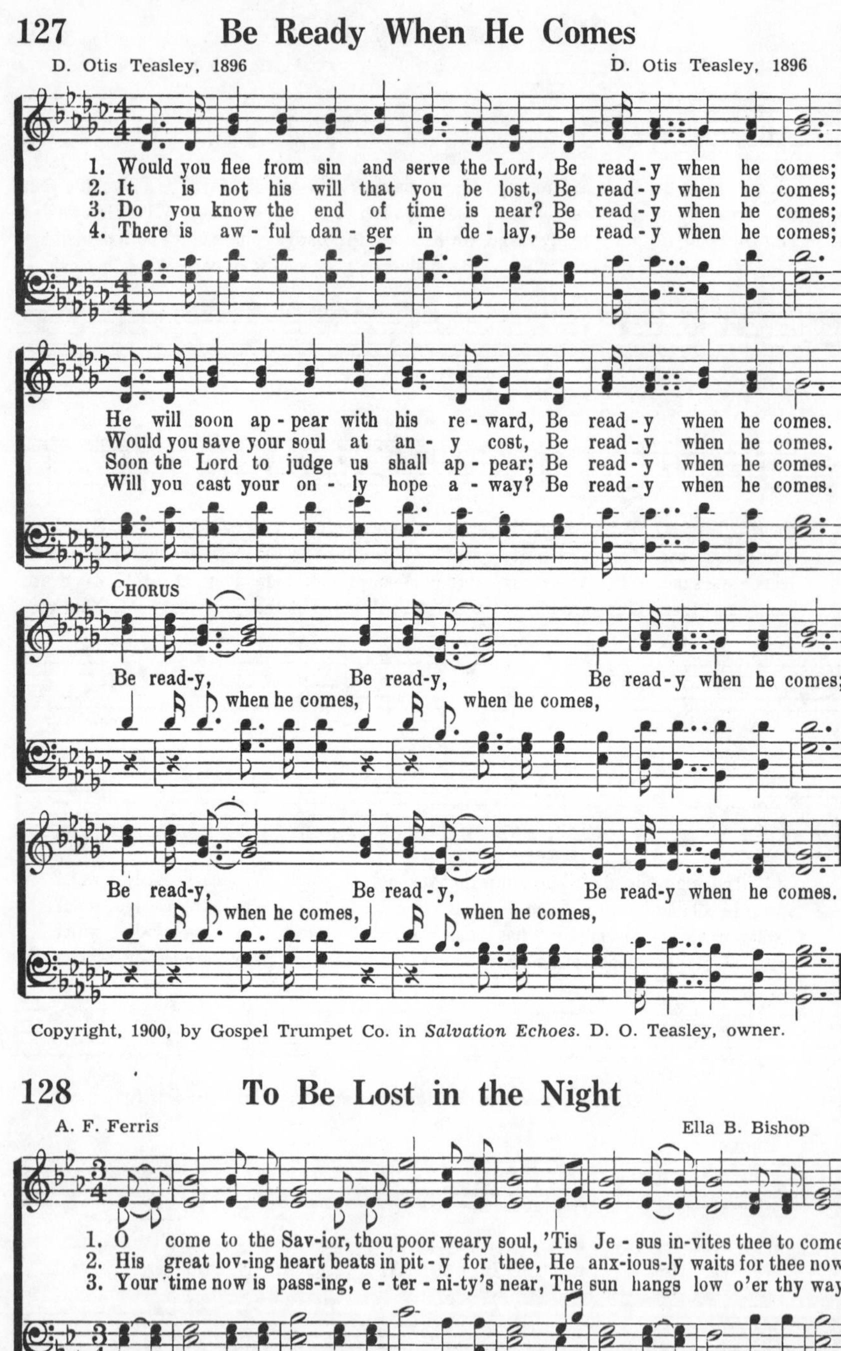
127 Be Ready When He Comes
D. Otis Teasley, 1896
D. Otis Teasley, 1896
1. Would you flee from sin and serve the Lord, Be read-y when he comes;
2. It is not his will that you be lost, Be read-y when he comes;
3. Do you know the end of time is near? Be read-y when he comes;
4. There is aw-ful dan-ger in de-lay, Be read-y when he comes;
He will soon ap-pear with his re-ward, Be read-y when he comes.
Would you save your soul at an-y cost, Be read-y when he comes.
Soon the Lord to judge us shall ap-pear; Be read-y when he comes.
Will you cast your on-ly hope a-way? Be read-y when he comes.
CHORUS
Be read-y, when he comes, Be read-y, when he comes, Be read-y when he comes;
Be read-y, when he comes, Be read-y, when he comes, Be read-y when he comes.
Copyright, 1900, by Gospel Trumpet Co. in Salvation Echoes. D. O. Teasley, owner.
128 To Be Lost in the Night
A. F. Ferris
Ella B. Bishop
1. O come to the Sav-ior, thou poor weary soul, 'Tis Je-sus in-vites thee to come;
2. His great lov-ing heart beats in pit-y for thee, He anx-ious-ly waits for thee now;
3. Your time now is pass-ing, e-ter-ni-ty's near, The sun hangs low o'er thy way;

CHORUS—*To be lost in the night, in e-ter-ni-ty's night, To sink in de-spair and in woe!*

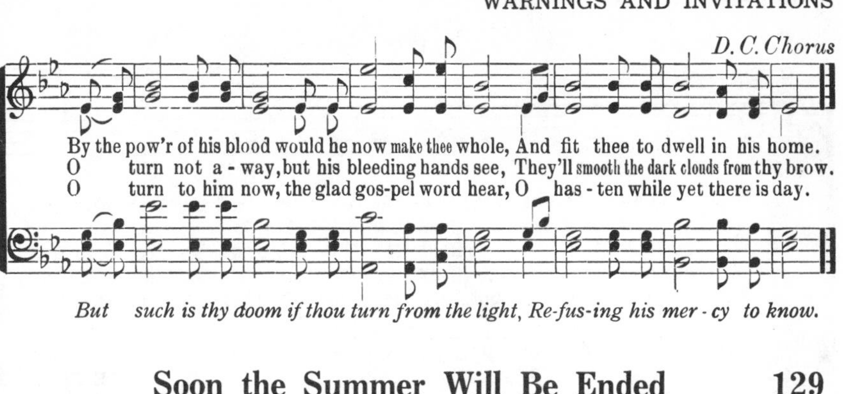
D. C. Chorus
By the pow'r of his blood would he now make thee whole, And fit thee to dwell in his home.
O turn not a - way, but his bleeding hands see, They'll smooth the dark clouds from thy brow.
O turn to him now, the glad gos-pel word hear, O has - ten while yet there is day.
But such is thy doom if thou turn from the light, Re-fus-ing his mer - cy to know.

Soon the Summer Will Be Ended 129

Lorenzo Cook, 1900 Barney E. Warren, 1900

1. Grace is of - fered you, dear sin - ner, In this gos - pel day of time,
2. If you live and die a sin - ner, And re - ject God's of - fered grace,
3. While in life is time ac - cept - ed To pre - pare to meet the Lord,
4. Will this be your lam - en - ta - tion: "Thro' neg-lect I'm lost at last,

Grace to save and keep from e - vil, And to make your life sub - lime.
You will cry for rocks and moun-tains Thus to hide you from his face.
Be as - sured that he is faith - ful To ful - fill his ho - ly word.
For the sum - mer now is end - ed, And the har - vest time is past"?

CHORUS

Soon the sum - mer will be end - ed, And the har - vest will be o'er;
Soon the day of of - fered mer - cy Will be past for - ev - er - more.

130 O Why Not Now?

D. Otis Teasley, 1912 D. Otis Teasley, 1912

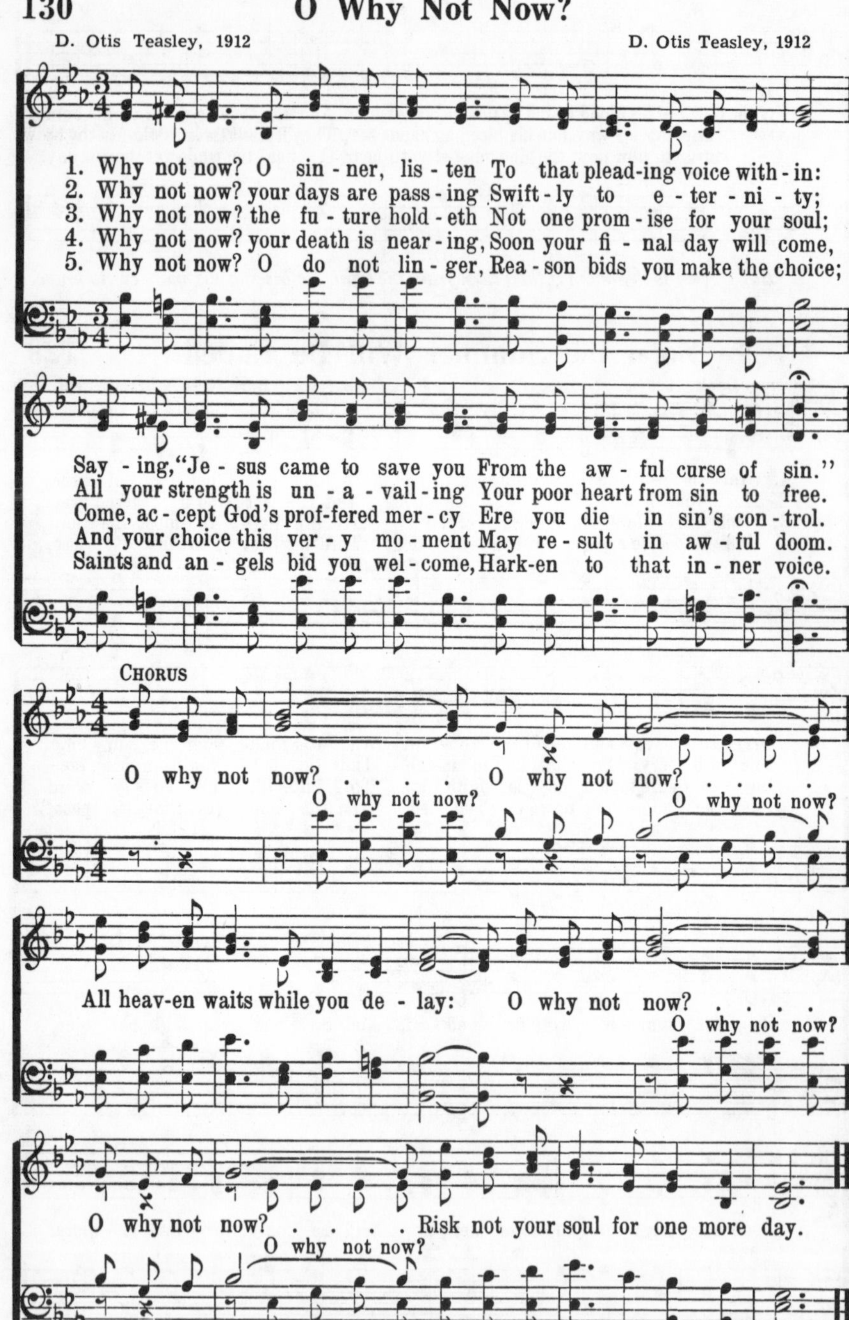
1. Why not now? O sin - ner, lis - ten To that plead-ing voice with - in:
2. Why not now? your days are pass - ing Swift - ly to e - ter - ni - ty;
3. Why not now? the fu - ture hold - eth Not one prom - ise for your soul;
4. Why not now? your death is near - ing, Soon your fi - nal day will come,
5. Why not now? O do not lin - ger, Rea - son bids you make the choice;
Say - ing, "Je - sus came to save you From the aw - ful curse of sin."
All your strength is un - a - vail - ing Your poor heart from sin to free.
Come, ac - cept God's prof-fered mer - cy Ere you die in sin's con - trol.
And your choice this ver - y mo - ment May re - sult in aw - ful doom.
Saints and an - gels bid you wel - come, Hark-en to that in - ner voice.
CHORUS
O why not now? . . . . . O why not now? . . . . .
O why not now? O why not now?
All heav-en waits while you de - lay: O why not now? . . . .
O why not now?
O why not now? . . . . . Risk not your soul for one more day.
O why not now?

O Why Not Tonight? 131

Elizabeth Reed, 1794-1867 J. Calvin Bushey

1. O do not let the word de-part, And close thine eyes a-gainst the light;
2. To - mor-row's sun may nev-er rise To bless thy long de - lud - ed sight;
3. Our Lord in pit - y lin-gers still, And wilt thou thus his love re - quite?
4. Our bless - ed Lord re - fus - es none Who would to him their souls u - nite;
Poor sin - ner, hard - en not your heart, Be saved, O to - night.
This is the time, O then be wise, Be saved, O to - night.
Re - nounce at once thy stub - born will, Be saved, O to - night.
Be - lieve in him, the work is done, Be saved, O to - night.
CHORUS
O why not to-night? O why not to-night?
O why not to-night? why not to-night? Why not to-night? why not to-night?
Wilt thou be saved? Then why not to-night?
Wilt thou be saved? wilt thou be saved? Then why not, O why not to - night?

132 Come Home, Poor Sinner

H. R. Jeffrey, 1885 H. R. Jeffrey, 1885

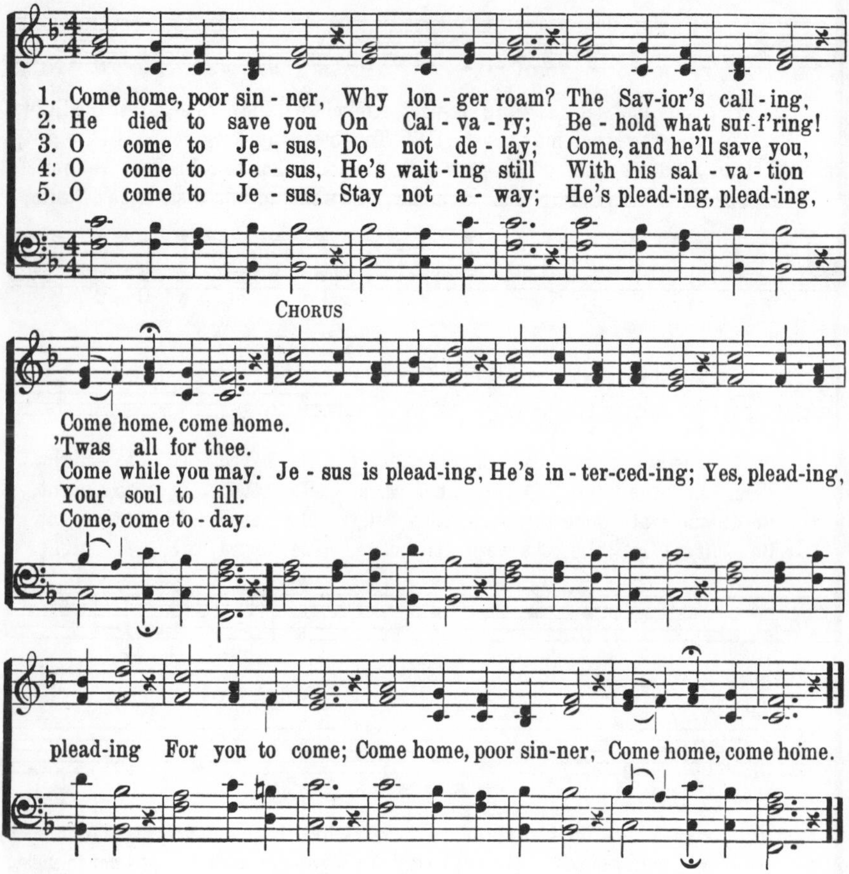

1. Come home, poor sin - ner, Why lon - ger roam? The Sav-ior's call - ing,
Come home, come home.
2. He died to save you On Cal - va - ry; Be - hold what suf-f'ring!
'Twas all for thee.
3. O come to Je - sus, Do not de - lay; Come, and he'll save you,
Come while you may.
4. O come to Je - sus, He's wait - ing still With his sal - va - tion
Your soul to fill.
5. O come to Je - sus, Stay not a - way; He's plead-ing, plead-ing,
Come, come to - day.

CHORUS

Je - sus is plead-ing, He's in - ter-ced-ing; Yes, plead-ing, plead-ing For you to come; Come home, poor sin-ner, Come home, come home.

133 Let Him In

Barney E. Warren, 1900 Barney E. Warren, 1900

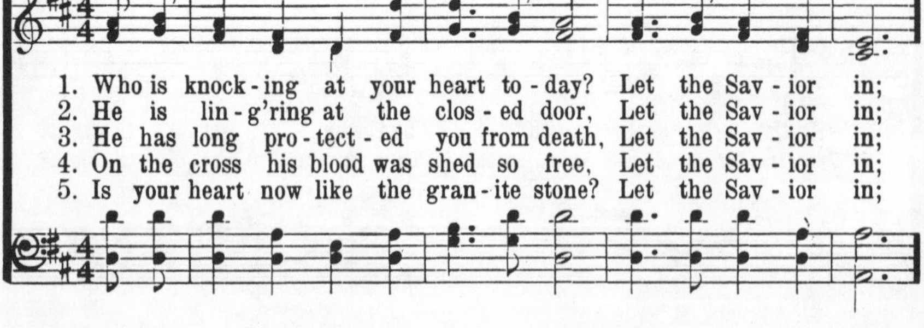

1. Who is knock - ing at your heart to - day? Let the Sav - ior in;
2. He is lin - g'ring at the clos - ed door, Let the Sav - ior in;
3. He has long pro - tect - ed you from death, Let the Sav - ior in;
4. On the cross his blood was shed so free, Let the Sav - ior in;
5. Is your heart now like the gran - ite stone? Let the Sav - ior in;

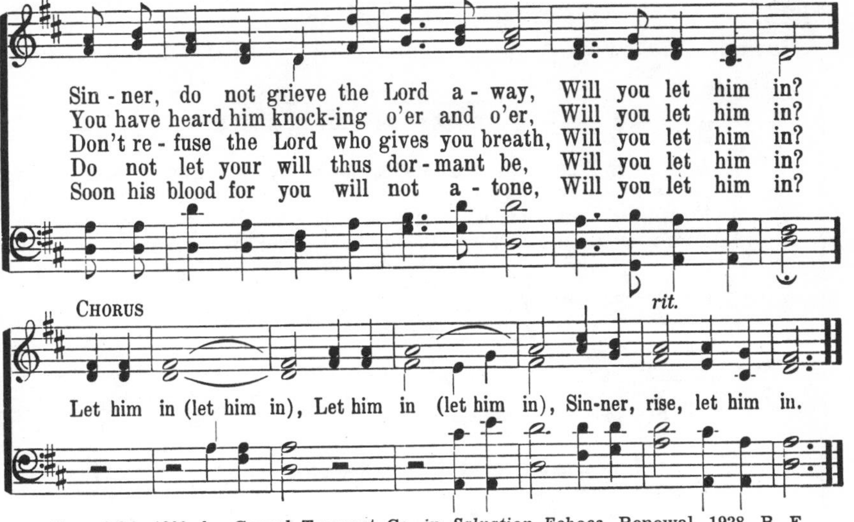
Sin - ner, do not grieve the Lord a - way, Will you let him in?
You have heard him knock-ing o'er and o'er, Will you let him in?
Don't re - fuse the Lord who gives you breath, Will you let him in?
Do not let your will thus dor - mant be, Will you let him in?
Soon his blood for you will not a - tone, Will you let him in?
CHORUS
rit.
Let him in (let him in), Let him in (let him in), Sin-ner, rise, let him in.

Almost Persuaded 134

Philip P. Bliss, 1838-1876 — Philip P. Bliss, 1838-1876

1. "Al - most per-suad - ed" now to be - lieve; "Al - most per-suad - ed"
2. "Al - most per-suad - ed," come, come to - day; "Al - most per-suad - ed,"
3. "Al - most per-suad - ed," har-vest is past! "Al - most per-suad - ed,"

Christ to re - ceive; Seems now some soul to say, "Go, Spir - it,
turn not a - way; Je - sus in - vites you here, An - gels are
doom comes at last! "Al - most" can - not a - vail; "Al - most" is

go thy way, Some more con - ven - ient day On thee I'll call."
lin-g'ring near, Prayers rise from hearts so dear, O wan-d'rer, come.
but to fail! Sad, sad, that bit - ter wail, "Al - most," but lost!

135 He Is Calling

W. Dale Oldham, 1936 W. Dale Oldham, 1936

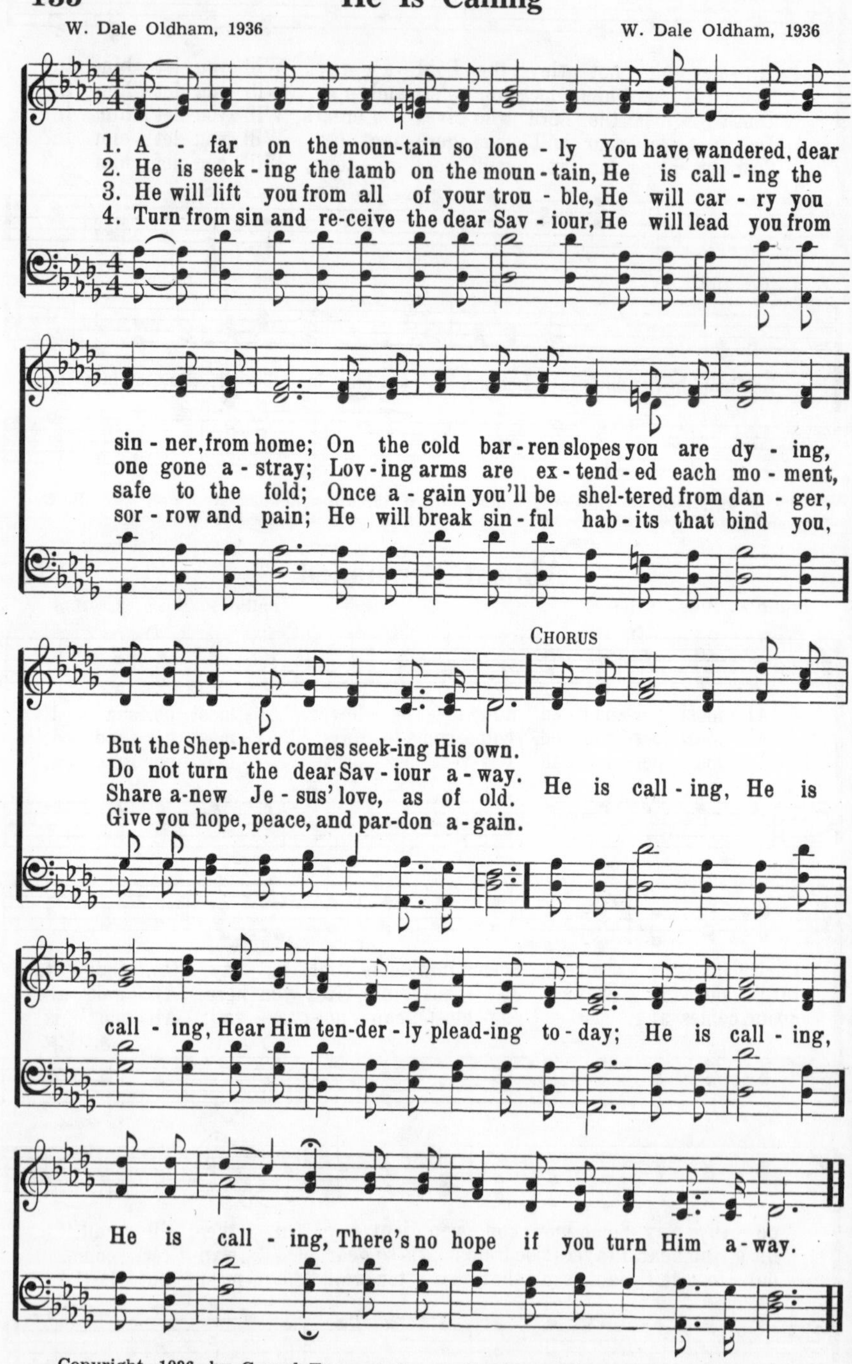
1. A - far on the moun-tain so lone - ly You have wandered, dear sin - ner, from home; On the cold bar - ren slopes you are dy - ing, But the Shep-herd comes seek-ing His own.
2. He is seek - ing the lamb on the moun - tain, He is call - ing the one gone a - stray; Lov - ing arms are ex - tend - ed each mo - ment, Do not turn the dear Sav - iour a - way.
3. He will lift you from all of your trou - ble, He will car - ry you safe to the fold; Once a - gain you'll be shel-tered from dan - ger, Share a-new Je - sus' love, as of old.
4. Turn from sin and re-ceive the dear Sav - iour, He will lead you from sor - row and pain; He will break sin - ful hab - its that bind you, Give you hope, peace, and par-don a - gain.
CHORUS
He is call - ing, He is call - ing, Hear Him ten-der - ly plead-ing to - day; He is call - ing, He is call - ing, There's no hope if you turn Him a - way.

Jesus Is Calling

136

Fanny J. Crosby, 1820-1915

George C. Stebbins, 1846-1945

1. Je - sus is ten - der - ly call - ing thee home— Call - ing to - day,
2. Je - sus is call - ing the wea - ry to rest— Call - ing to - day,
3. Je - sus is wait - ing; O come to Him now— Wait-ing to - day,
4. Je - sus is plead-ing; O list to His voice: Hear Him to - day,
call - ing to - day; Why from the sun - shine of love wilt thou roam
call - ing to - day; Bring Him thy bur - den and thou shalt be blest;
wait - ing to - day; Come with thy sins; at His feet low - ly bow;
hear Him to - day; They who be - lieve on His name shall re - joice;
Far-ther and far-ther a - way?
He will not turn thee a - way.
Come, and no lon - ger de - lay.
Quick-ly a - rise and a - way.
Refrain
Call - - ing to - day, ...
Call - ing, call - ing to - day, to - day,
Call - - - ing to - day, ... Je - - - - sus is
Call - ing, call - ing to - day, to - day; Je - sus is ten - der - ly
call - - - - - ing, Is ten - der - ly call - ing to - day.
call - ing to - day,

137 The Last Call

Eugene A. Reardon, 1907 — D. Otis Teasley, 1907

138 Why Do You Wait?

George F. Root, 1820-1895 — George F. Root, 1820-1895

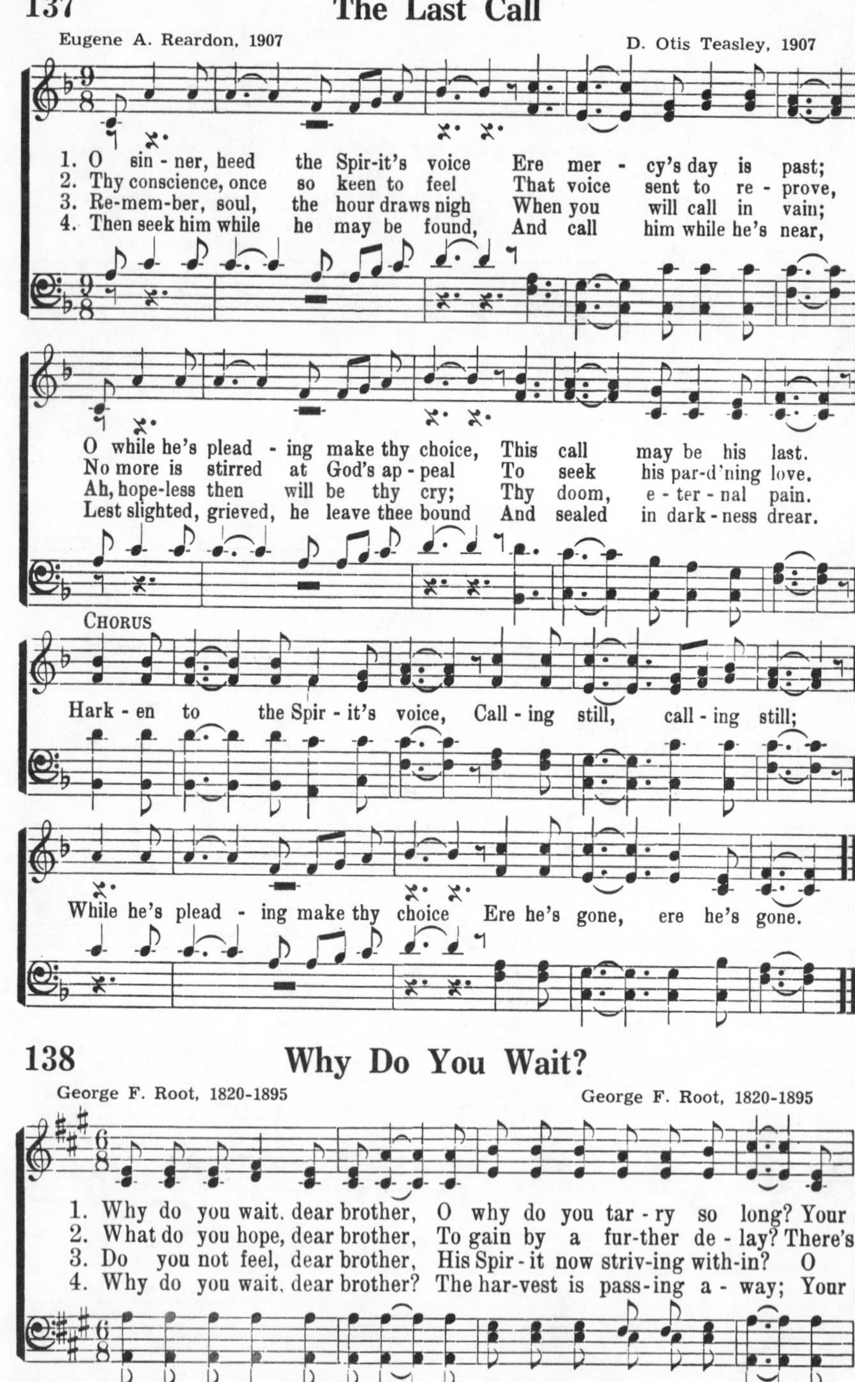

1. O sin - ner, heed the Spir-it's voice Ere mer - cy's day is past;
2. Thy conscience, once so keen to feel That voice sent to re - prove,
3. Re-mem-ber, soul, the hour draws nigh When you will call in vain;
4. Then seek him while he may be found, And call him while he's near,
O while he's plead - ing make thy choice, This call may be his last.
No more is stirred at God's ap - peal To seek his par-d'ning love.
Ah, hope-less then will be thy cry; Thy doom, e - ter - nal pain.
Lest slighted, grieved, he leave thee bound And sealed in dark - ness drear.
CHORUS
Hark - en to the Spir - it's voice, Call - ing still, call - ing still;
While he's plead - ing make thy choice Ere he's gone, ere he's gone.
1. Why do you wait, dear brother, O why do you tar - ry so long? Your
2. What do you hope, dear brother, To gain by a fur-ther de - lay? There's
3. Do you not feel, dear brother, His Spir - it now striv-ing with-in? O
4. Why do you wait, dear brother? The har-vest is pass-ing a - way; Your

Sav - ior is wait - ing to give you A place in his sanc - ti - fied throng.
no one to save you but Je - sus, There's no oth - er way but his way.
why not ac - cept his sal - va - tion, And throw off your bur - den of sin?
Sav - ior is long - ing to bless you, There's danger and death in de - lay.
Chorus.
1
2
Why not? why not? Why not come to him now? now?
Come, Sinner, Come
139
W. E. Witter
H. R. Palmer, 1834-1907
1. While Je - sus whis - pers to you, Come, sin - ner, come! While we are
2. Are you too heav - y - la - den? Come, sin - ner, come! Je - sus will
3. O, hear His ten - der plead-ing, Come, sin - ner, come! Come and re-
pray-ing for you, Come, sin - ner, come! Now is the time to own Him,
bear your bur-den, Come, sin - ner, come! Je - sus will not de-ceive you,
ceive the bless-ing, Come, sin - ner, come! While Je - sus whis-pers to you,
Come, sin-ner, come! Now is the time to know Him, Come, sin-ner, come!
Come, sin-ner, come! Je - sus can now re-ceive you, Come, sin-ner, come!
Come, sin-ner, come! While we are pray-ing for you, Come, sin-ner, come!

140 Give Me Thy Heart

Eliza E. Hewitt, b. 1851 — Annie F. Bourne

1. "Give me thy heart," says the Fa - ther a - bove, No gift so pre-cious to
2. "Give me thy heart," says the Sav - ior of men, Call-ing in mer - cy a-
3. "Give me thy heart," says the Spir - it di - vine, "All that thou hast, to my
Him as our love, Soft - ly He whis-pers wher - ev - er thou art,
gain and a - gain; "Turn now from sin, and from e - vil de - part,
keep - ing re - sign; Grace more a - bound-ing is mine to im - part,
"Grate - ful - ly trust me, and give me thy heart."
Have I not died for thee? give me thy heart."
Make full sur - ren - der and give me thy heart."
Chorus
"Give me thy heart,
p
Give me thy heart," Hear the soft whisper, wher-ev - er thou art; From this dark
world He would draw thee a-part, Speak-ing so ten-der-ly, "Give me thy heart."
rit.

Is Your All on the Altar? 141

Elisha A. Hoffman, 1839-1929 Elisha A. Hoffman, 1839-1929

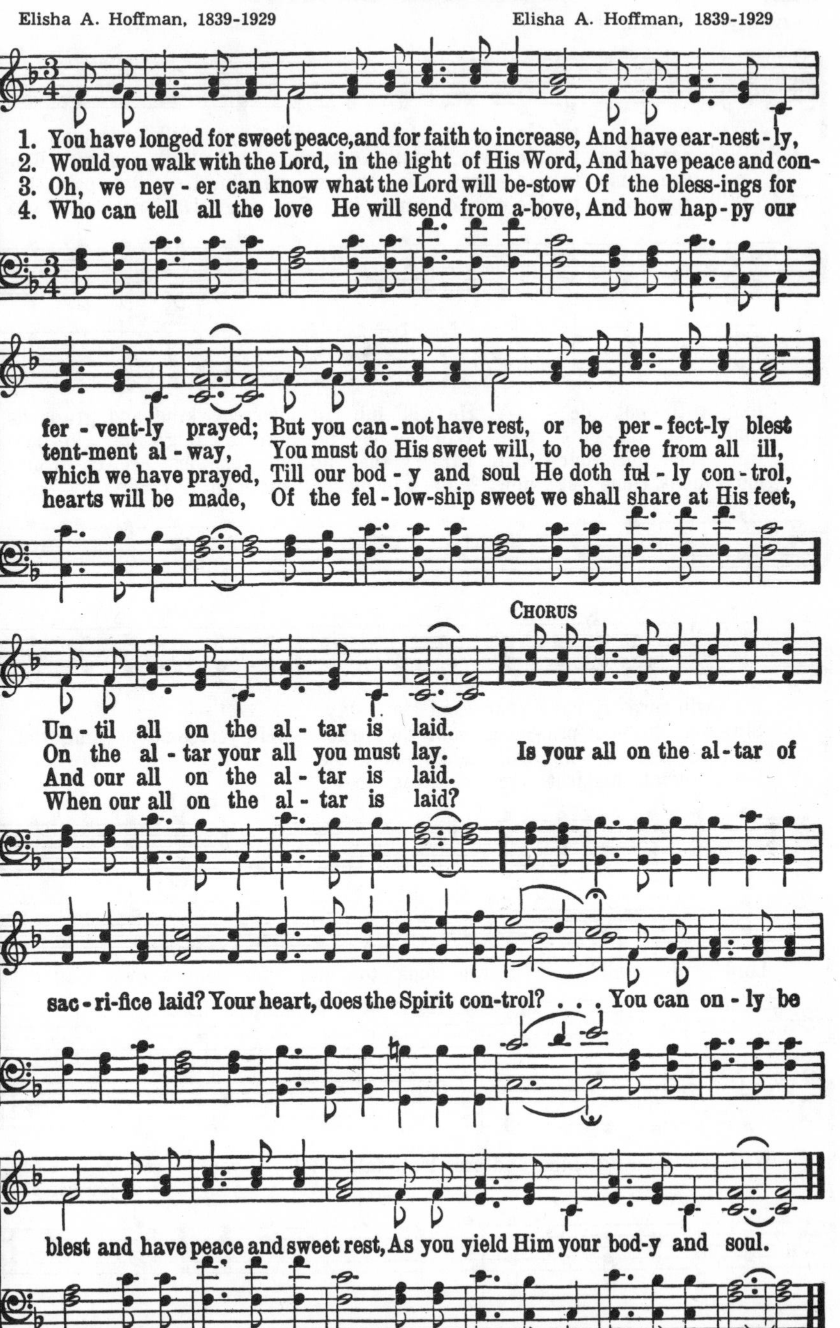
1. You have longed for sweet peace, and for faith to increase, And have ear-nest-ly, fer-vent-ly prayed; But you can-not have rest, or be per-fect-ly blest Un-til all on the al-tar is laid.
2. Would you walk with the Lord, in the light of His Word, And have peace and con-tent-ment al-way, You must do His sweet will, to be free from all ill, On the al-tar your all you must lay.
3. Oh, we nev-er can know what the Lord will be-stow Of the bless-ings for which we have prayed, Till our bod-y and soul He doth ful-ly con-trol, And our all on the al-tar is laid.
4. Who can tell all the love He will send from a-bove, And how hap-py our hearts will be made, Of the fel-low-ship sweet we shall share at His feet, When our all on the al-tar is laid?
CHORUS
Is your all on the al-tar of sac-ri-fice laid? Your heart, does the Spirit con-trol? . . . You can on-ly be blest and have peace and sweet rest, As you yield Him your bod-y and soul.

142 Will You Come?

Barney E. Warren, 1897 Barney E. Warren, 1897

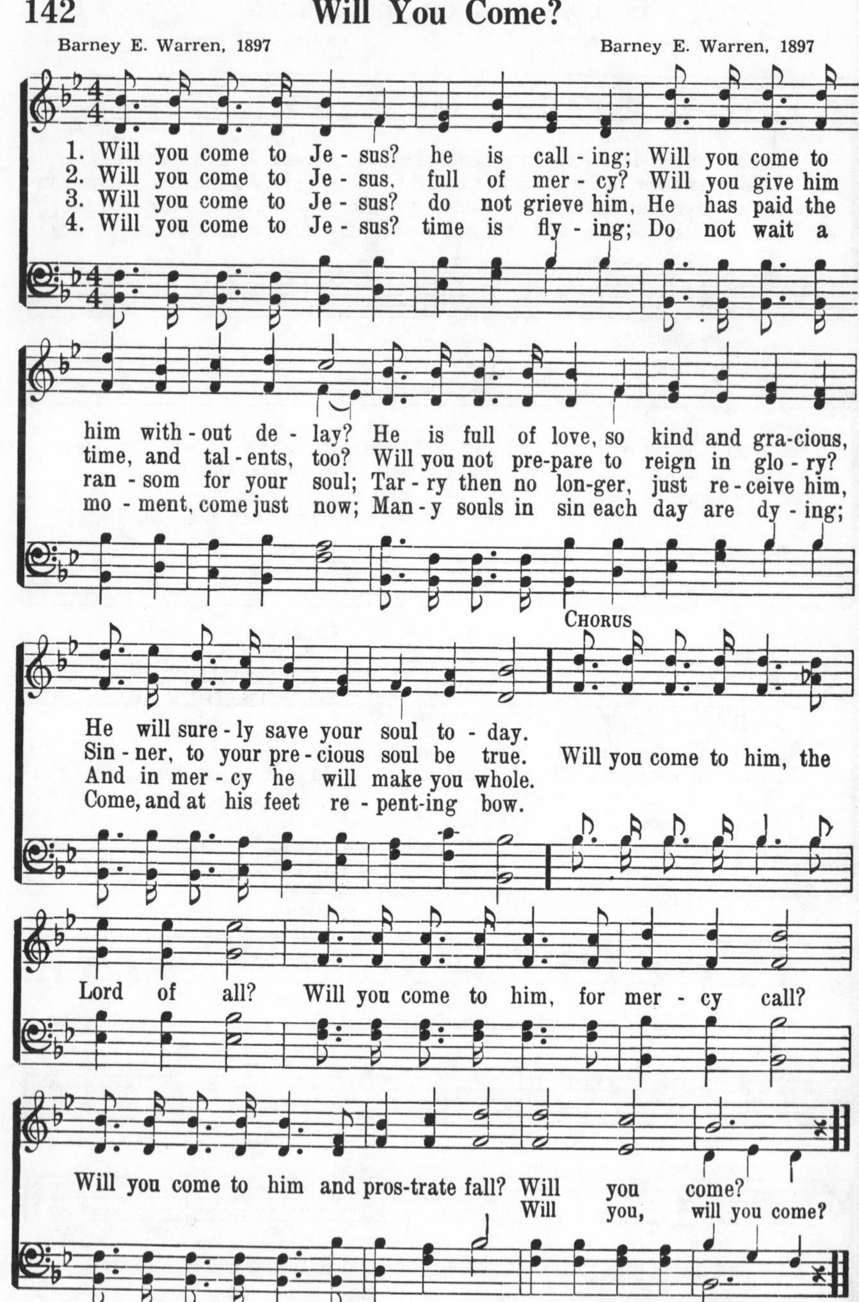
1. Will you come to Je - sus? he is call - ing; Will you come to him with - out de - lay? He is full of love, so kind and gra - cious, He will sure - ly save your soul to - day.
2. Will you come to Je - sus, full of mer - cy? Will you give him time, and tal - ents, too? Will you not pre - pare to reign in glo - ry? Sin - ner, to your pre - cious soul be true.
3. Will you come to Je - sus? do not grieve him, He has paid the ran - som for your soul; Tar - ry then no lon - ger, just re - ceive him, And in mer - cy he will make you whole.
4. Will you come to Je - sus? time is fly - ing; Do not wait a mo - ment, come just now; Man - y souls in sin each day are dy - ing; Come, and at his feet re - pent - ing bow.
CHORUS
Will you come to him, the Lord of all? Will you come to him, for mer - cy call? Will you come to him and pros - trate fall? Will you come?
Will you, will you come?

Softly and Tenderly

143

Will L. Thompson, 1847-1909 — Will L. Thompson, 1847-1909

1. Soft - ly and ten - der - ly Je - sus is call - ing, Call - ing for you and for me, See on the por - tals he's wait - ing and watch-ing, Watch-ing for you and for me.
2. Why should we tar - ry when Je - sus is plead - ing, Plead - ing for you and for me? Why should we lin - ger and heed not his mer - cies, Mer - cies for you and for me?
3. Time is now fleet - ing, the mo - ments are pass - ing, Pass - ing from you and from me; Shad-ows are gath - er - ing, death's night is com - ing, Com - ing for you and for me.
4. O for the won - der - ful love he has prom - ised, Prom - ised for you and for me! Tho' we have sinned, he has mer - cy and par - don, Par - don for you and for me.
CHORUS
Come home,...... come home,......
Come home, come home,
cres.
Ye who are wea - ry, come home;.... Ear - nest - ly, ten - der - ly
rit.
p
Je - sus is call - ing, Call - ing, O sin - ner, come home!

144 Only Trust Him

John H. Stockton, 1813-1877 — John H. Stockton, 1813-1877

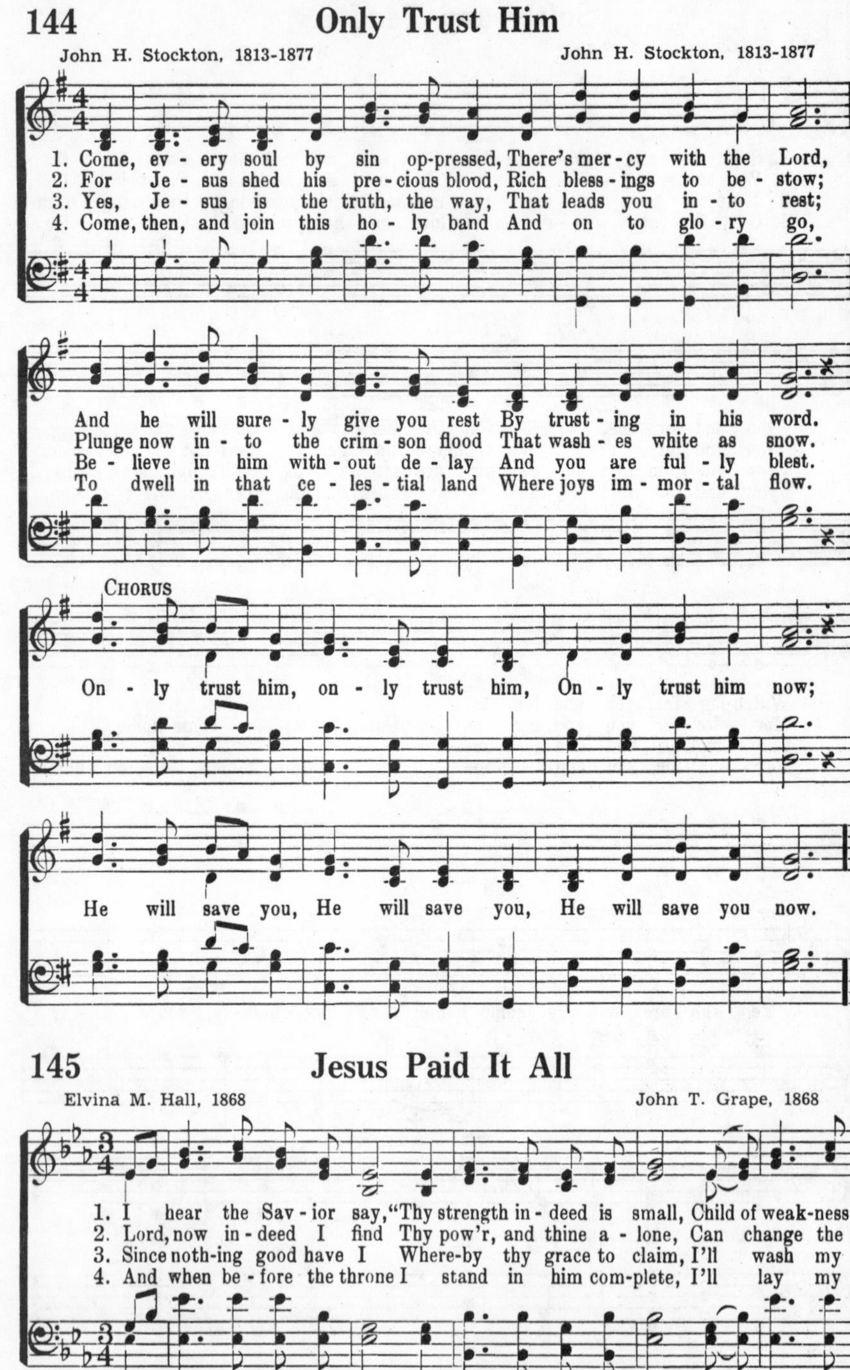
1. Come, ev - ery soul by sin op-pressed, There's mer - cy with the Lord,
2. For Je - sus shed his pre - cious blood, Rich bless - ings to be - stow;
3. Yes, Je - sus is the truth, the way, That leads you in - to rest;
4. Come, then, and join this ho - ly band And on to glo - ry go,
And he will sure - ly give you rest By trust - ing in his word.
Plunge now in - to the crim - son flood That wash - es white as snow.
Be - lieve in him with - out de - lay And you are ful - ly blest.
To dwell in that ce - les - tial land Where joys im - mor - tal flow.
CHORUS
On - ly trust him, on - ly trust him, On - ly trust him now;
He will save you, He will save you, He will save you now.

145 Jesus Paid It All

Elvina M. Hall, 1868 — John T. Grape, 1868

1. I hear the Sav - ior say, "Thy strength in - deed is small, Child of weak-ness,
2. Lord, now in - deed I find Thy pow'r, and thine a - lone, Can change the
3. Since noth-ing good have I Where-by thy grace to claim, I'll wash my
4. And when be - fore the throne I stand in him com-plete, I'll lay my

CHORUS
watch and pray, Find in me thine all in all."
lep - er's spots And melt the heart of stone. Je - sus paid it all,
gar - ments white In the blood of Cal-v'ry's Lamb.
tro - phies down, All down at Je - sus' feet.
All to him I owe; Sin had left a crim-son stain: He washed it white as snow.
I Hear Thy Welcome Voice
146
Lewis Hartsough, 1828-1872
Lewis Hartsough, 1828-1872
1. I hear thy wel-come voice That calls me, Lord, to thee For cleans-ing
2. Tho' com-ing weak and vile, Thou dost my strength assure; Thou dost my
3. 'Tis Je - sus calls me on To per - fect faith and love, To per - fect
4. All hail, a - ton-ing blood! All hail, re-deem-ing grace! All hail, the
in thy pre-cious blood That flowed on Cal-va - ry.
vile-ness ful-ly cleanse, Till spot-less all and pure. I am com - ing, Lord,
hope, and peace, and trust, For earth and heav'n a-bove.
gift of Christ our Lord, Our Strength and Righteousness!
CHORUS
Com-ing now to thee! Wash me, cleanse me in the blood That flowed on Cal-va-ry

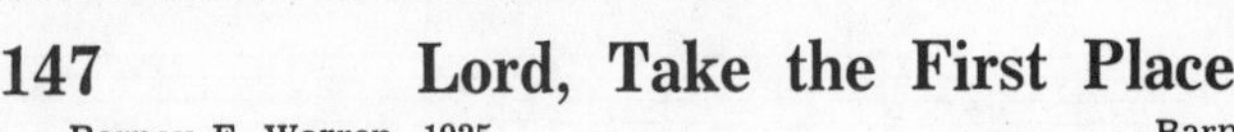

147 Lord, Take the First Place

Barney E. Warren, 1925 — Barney E. Warren, 1925

Not too fast

1. I yield to thee, Sav - ior, for - sak - ing my all, From sin - ful things
2. O come, gen - tle Spir - it, don't leave me, I pray, From thee I will
3. I can - not be lost, Lord, for thee I will live, For - give - ness, O
4. The joy - bells of heav - en will ring in my soul, My Sav - ior, Re-

now I will part; To thee I sur - ren - der, for mer - cy I call,
nev - er de - part; I come to thee now, for I can - not de - lay,
Sav - ior, im - part; If I will con - fess thou wilt free - ly for - give,
deem - er, thou art; To thee I sur - ren - der, wilt thou make me whole?

Come, take the first place in my heart.
Lord, take the first place in my heart.
And take the first place in my heart.
Take now the first place in my heart.

Chorus

O take the first place in my heart (my heart), O take the first place in my heart (my heart); I o - pen the door, Come in, I im - plore; Lord, take the first place in my heart (my heart).

Jesus, I Come 148

W. T. Sleeper, c. 1840-1920 George C. Stebbins, 1846-1945

1. Out of my bond-age, sor-row and night, Je-sus, I come, Je-sus, I come;
2. Out of my shame-ful fail-ure and loss, Je-sus, I come, Je-sus, I come;
3. Out of un-rest and ar-ro-gant pride, Je-sus, I come, Je-sus, I come;
4. Out of the fear and dread of the tomb, Je-sus, I come, Je-sus, I come;
In-to Thy free-dom, glad-ness and light, Je-sus, I come to Thee;
In-to the glo-rious gain of Thy cross, Je-sus, I come to Thee;
In-to Thy bless-ed will to a-bide, Je-sus, I come to Thee;
In-to the joy and light of Thy home, Je-sus, I come to Thee;
Out of my sick-ness in-to Thy health, Out of my want and in-to Thy wealth,
Out of earth's sorrows in-to Thy balm, Out of life's storms and in-to Thy calm,
Out of my-self to dwell in Thy love, Out of de-spair in-to rap-tures a-bove,
Out of the depths of ru-in un-told, In-to the peace of Thy sheltering fold,
Out of my sin and in-to Thy-self, Je-sus, I come to Thee.
Out of dis-tress to ju-bi-lant psalm, Je-sus, I come to Thee.
Up-ward for aye on wings like a dove, Je-sus, I come to Thee.
Ev-er Thy glo-rious face to be-hold, Je-sus, I come to Thee.

149 Take Me as I Am

Eliza H. Hamilton — John H. Stockton, 1813-1877

1. Je - sus, my Lord, to thee I cry, Un - less thou help me, I must die;
2. Help-less I am, and full of guilt, But yet thy blood for me was spilt;
3. No prep - a - ra - tion can I make, My best re - solves I on - ly break;
4. I thirst, I long to know thy love, Thy full sal - va - tion I would prove;

O bring thy free sal - va - tion nigh And take me as I am.
And thou canst make me what thou wilt, But take me as I am.
Yet save me for thine own name's sake, And take me as I am.
But since to thee I can - not move, O take me as I am.

REFRAIN

Take me as I am,........ Take me as I am;........ O
Take me, take me as I am, Take me, take me as I am;

bring thy free sal - va - tion nigh And take me as I am.

150 Pass Me Not

Fanny J. Crosby, 1820-1915 — William Howard Doane, 1832-1915

1. Pass me not, O gen - tle Sav - ior, Hear my hum - ble cry; While on oth - ers
2. Let me at a throne of mer - cy Find a sweet re - lief; Kneel-ing there in
3. Trust-ing on - ly in Thy mer - it, Would I seek Thy face; Heal my wounded,
4. Thou the Spring of all my com - fort, More than life to me, Whom have I on

CHORUS

Thou art call-ing, Do not pass me by.
deep con-tri-tion, Help my un-be-lief. Sav-ior, Sav-ior, Hear my humble
bro-ken spir-it, Save me by Thy grace.
earth beside Thee? Whom in Heav'n but Thee?

cry; While on oth-ers Thou art call-ing, Do not pass me by.

Lord, I'm Coming Home 151

William J. Kirkpatrick, 1838-1921 William J. Kirkpatrick, 1838-1921

1. I've wan-dered far a-way from God, Now I'm com-ing home,
The paths of sin too long I've trod, Lord, I'm com-ing home.

2. I've wast-ed man-y pre-cious years, Now I'm com-ing home;
I now re-pent with bit-ter tears, Lord, I'm com-ing home.

3. I've tired of sin and stray-ing, Lord, Now I'm com-ing home;
I'll trust Thy love, be-lieve Thy word, Lord, I'm com-ing home.

4. My soul is sick, my heart is sore, Now I'm com-ing home;
My strength re-new, my hope re-store, Lord, I'm com-ing home.

FINE

D. S.—*O-pen wide Thine arms of love, Lord, I'm com-ing home.*

CHORUS

Com-ing home, com-ing home, Nev-er-more to roam,

D. S.

152 Just as I Am

Charlotte Elliott, 1789-1871 William B. Bradbury, 1816-1868

1. Just as I am, with-out one plea, But that thy blood was shed for me,
2. Just as I am, and wait-ing not To rid my soul of one dark blot,
3. Just as I am, thou wilt re-ceive, Wilt wel-come, par-don, cleanse, relieve;
4. Just as I am, thy love unknown Hath bro-ken ev-ery bar-rier down;
And that thou bidd'st me come to thee—O Lamb of God, I come, I come!
To thee, whose blood can cleanse each spot, O Lamb of God, I come, I come!
Be-cause thy prom-ise I be-lieve, O Lamb of God, I come, I come!
Now, to be thine, yea, thine a-lone, O Lamb of God, I come, I come!

153 I Am Coming to the Cross

William McDonald, 1820-1901 William G. Fischer, 1835-1912

1. I am com-ing to the cross; I am poor and weak and blind;
2. Here I give my all to thee, Friends and time, and earth-ly store;
3. In the prom-is-es I trust, Now I feel the blood ap-plied;
4. Je-sus comes, he fills my soul! Per-fect-ed in love I am;
I am count-ing all but dross, I shall full sal-va-tion find.
Soul and bod-y, thine to be, Whol-ly thine for-ev-er-more.
I am pros-trate in the dust, I with Christ am cru-ci-fied.
I am ev-ery whit made whole, Glo-ry, glo-ry to the Lamb!
CHORUS–I am trust-ing, Lord, in thee, Dear Lamb of Cal-va-ry;
D.C. for Chorus
Hum-bly at thy cross I bow, Je-sus saves me, saves me now.

I Believe Jesus Saves

William McDonald, 1820-1901

Joseph P. Webster, 1819-1875

1. I am com-ing to Je-sus for rest, Rest such as the pu-ri-fied know; My soul is a-thirst to be blest, To be washed and made whit-er than snow.
2. In com-ing, my sin I de-plore, My weak-ness and pov-er-ty show; I long to be saved ev-er-more, To be washed and made whit-er than snow.
3. To Je-sus I give up my all, Ev-ery treas-ure and i-dol I know; For his full-ness of bless-ing I call, Till his blood wash-es whit-er than snow.
4. I am trust-ing in Je-sus a-lone, Trusting now his sal-va-tion to know; And his blood doth so full-y a-tone, I am washed and made whit-er than snow.

CHORUS

I be-lieve Je-sus saves, (I be-lieve Je-sus saves,)
And his blood wash-es whit-er than snow; (yes, whit-er than snow;)
I be-lieve Je-sus saves, (I be-lieve Je-sus saves,)
And his blood wash-es whit-er than snow.

155 I Am Coming, Lord, to Thee

Barney E. Warren, 1911 Barney E. Warren, 1911

1. I am com-ing, Lord, to thee with my bro - ken heart; I am com - ing, Lord, to thee for rest: Wilt thou hear my hum - ble plea, bid my sins de - part? O re - lieve me, Sav - ior, I'm op-pressed.
2. I am com-ing, Lord, to thee with re - lent - ing will, I will glad - ly lay my bur - den down; I will con - se - crate to thee and thy law ful - fill, I will bear the cross, and wear a crown.
3. I am com-ing, Lord, to thee, and with an - guish riv'n, I am wea - ry, worn and tired of sin; Lord, I press my ur - gent plea, may I be for - giv'n? While I knock, O Sav - ior, let me in.
4. I am com-ing, Lord, to thee with an ach - ing breast, And I know that thou wilt hear my cry; I will leave the paths of sin, for my heart's dis-tressed, Save me, or I per - ish, Lord, and die.
5. I am com-ing, Lord, to thee, for I'm sick and sore, Do not turn from me thy smil - ing face; Lord, for mer - cy now I call, I will sin no more, Wilt thou hear and save me by thy grace?
CHORUS
I am com-ing, Lord, to thee, wilt thou hear my hum - ble plea? I am

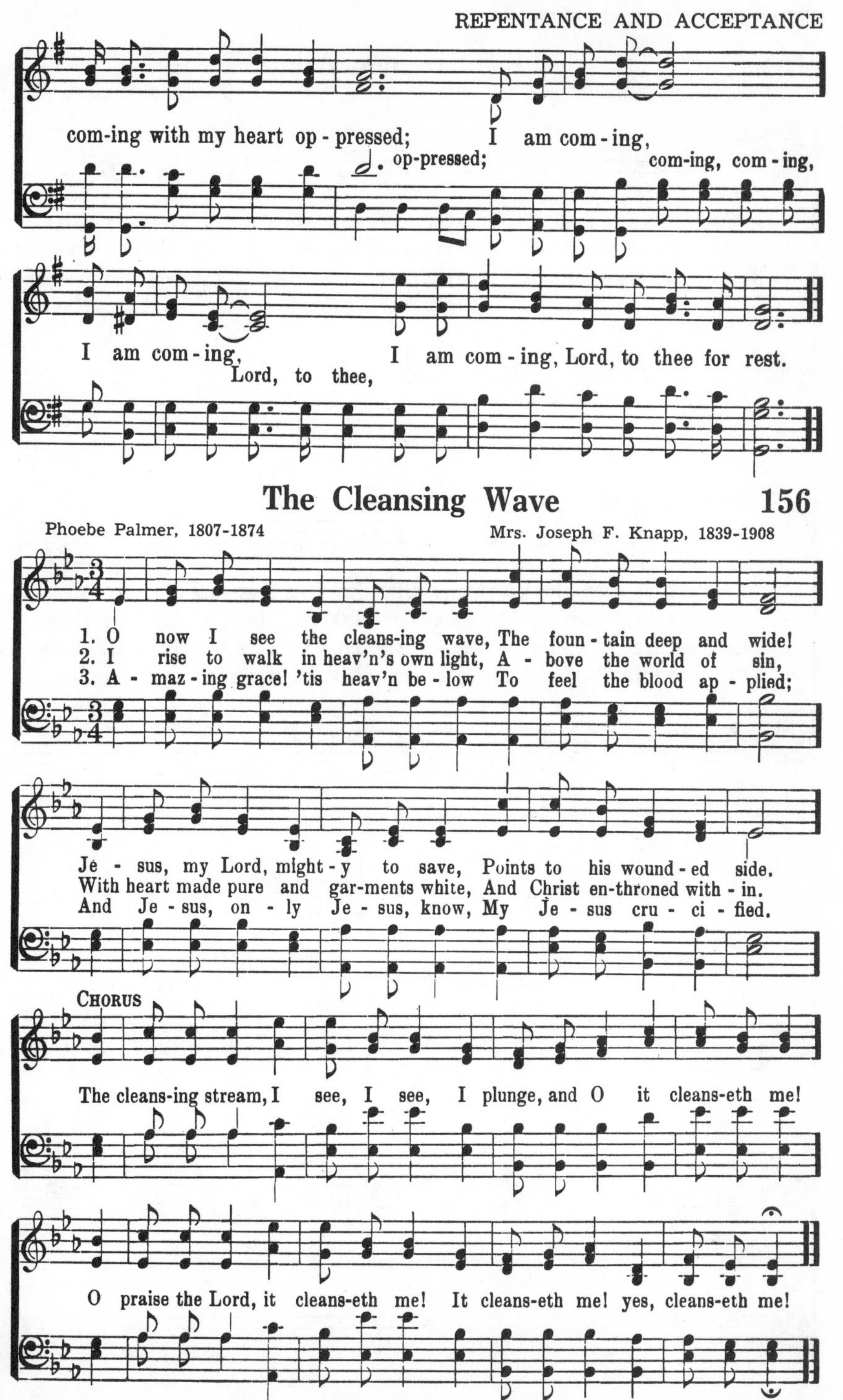
com-ing with my heart op - pressed; I am com - ing,
op-pressed; coming, com - ing,
I am com - ing, I am com - ing, Lord, to thee for rest.
Lord, to thee,
The Cleansing Wave 156
Phoebe Palmer, 1807-1874
Mrs. Joseph F. Knapp, 1839-1908
1. O now I see the cleans-ing wave, The foun - tain deep and wide!
2. I rise to walk in heav'n's own light, A - bove the world of sin,
3. A - maz - ing grace! 'tis heav'n be - low To feel the blood ap - plied;
Je - sus, my Lord, might - y to save, Points to his wound - ed side.
With heart made pure and gar-ments white, And Christ en-throned with - in.
And Je - sus, on - ly Je - sus, know, My Je - sus cru - ci - fied.
Chorus
The cleans-ing stream, I see, I see, I plunge, and O it cleans-eth me!
O praise the Lord, it cleans-eth me! It cleans-eth me! yes, cleans-eth me!

157 I Surrender All

J. W. Van Deventer W. S. Weeden

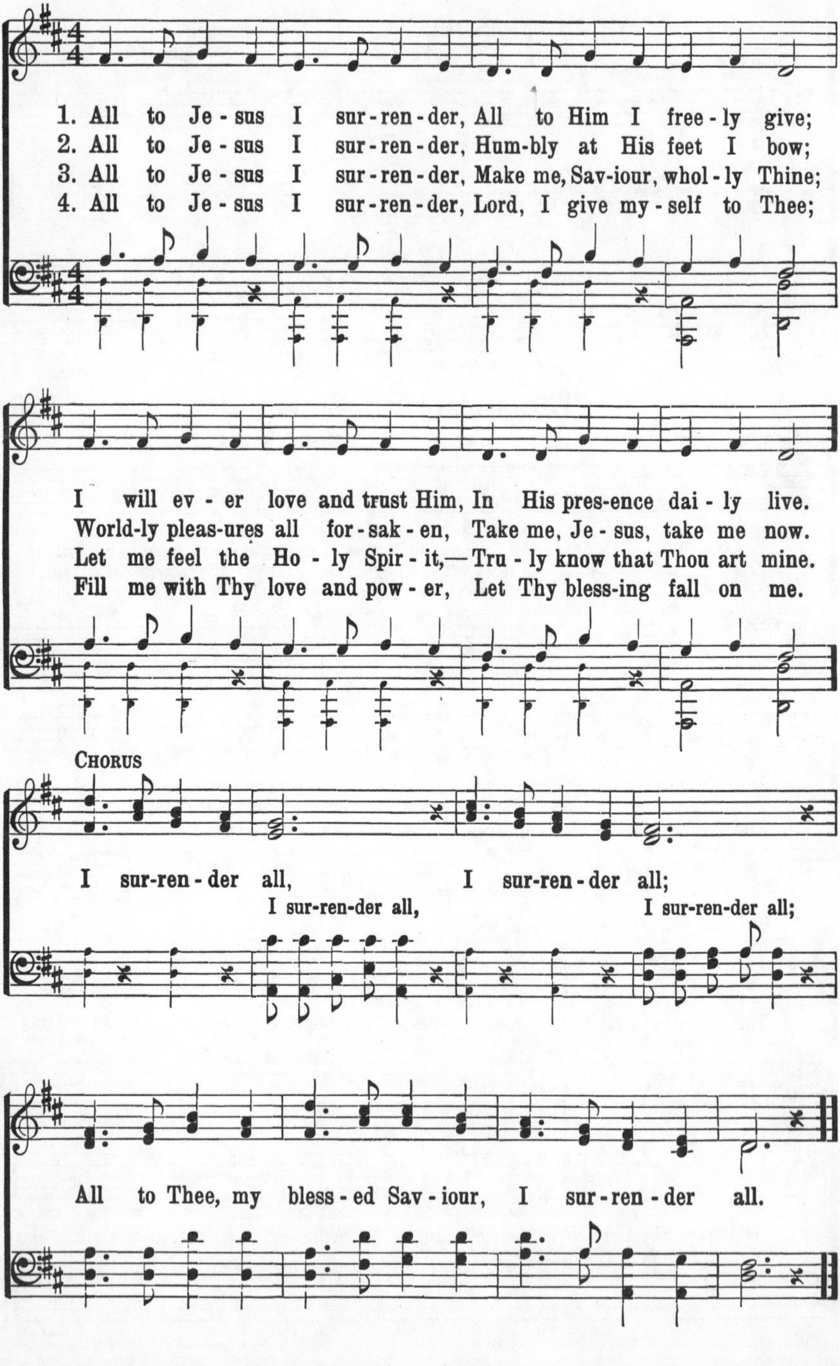

1. All to Je - sus I sur - ren - der, All to Him I free - ly give;
2. All to Je - sus I sur - ren - der, Hum-bly at His feet I bow;
3. All to Je - sus I sur - ren - der, Make me, Sav-iour, whol - ly Thine;
4. All to Je - sus I sur - ren - der, Lord, I give my - self to Thee;

I will ev - er love and trust Him, In His pres-ence dai - ly live.
World-ly pleas-ures all for - sak - en, Take me, Je - sus, take me now.
Let me feel the Ho - ly Spir - it,—Tru - ly know that Thou art mine.
Fill me with Thy love and pow - er, Let Thy bless-ing fall on me.

CHORUS

I sur-ren - der all, I sur-ren - der all;
I sur-ren-der all, I sur-ren-der all;

All to Thee, my bless - ed Sav - iour, I sur - ren - der all.

Whiter than Snow

158

James Nicholson, 19th century — William G. Fischer, 1835-1912

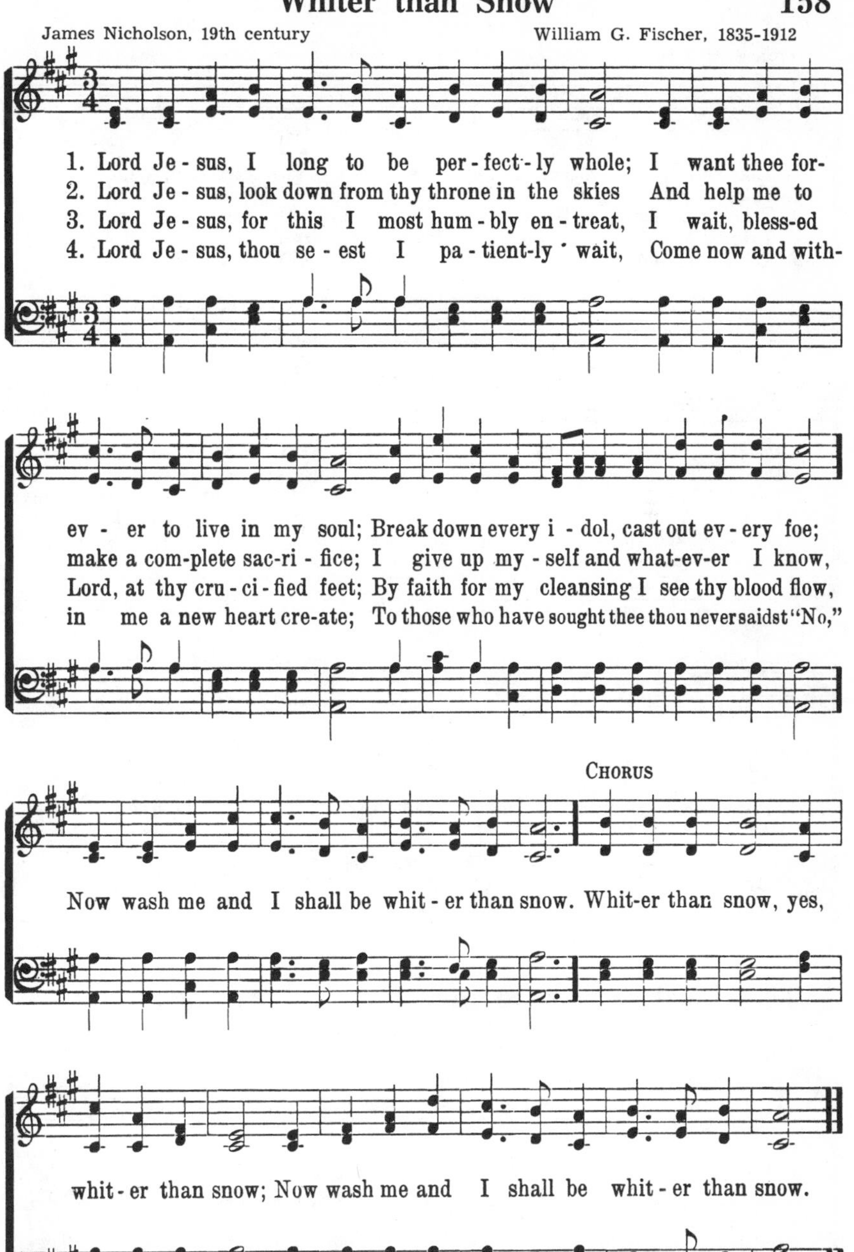
1. Lord Je - sus, I long to be per - fect - ly whole; I want thee for - ev - er to live in my soul; Break down every i - dol, cast out ev - ery foe; Now wash me and I shall be whit - er than snow.
2. Lord Je - sus, look down from thy throne in the skies And help me to make a com-plete sac-ri - fice; I give up my - self and what-ev-er I know,
3. Lord Je - sus, for this I most hum - bly en - treat, I wait, bless-ed Lord, at thy cru - ci - fied feet; By faith for my cleansing I see thy blood flow,
4. Lord Je - sus, thou se - est I pa - tient-ly wait, Come now and with - in me a new heart cre-ate; To those who have sought thee thou never saidst "No,"
CHORUS
Whit-er than snow, yes, whit - er than snow; Now wash me and I shall be whit - er than snow.

159 Take My Life, and Let It Be

HENDON. 7.7.7.7.7.

Frances R. Havergal, 1836-1879 — H. A. Caesar Malan, 1787-1864

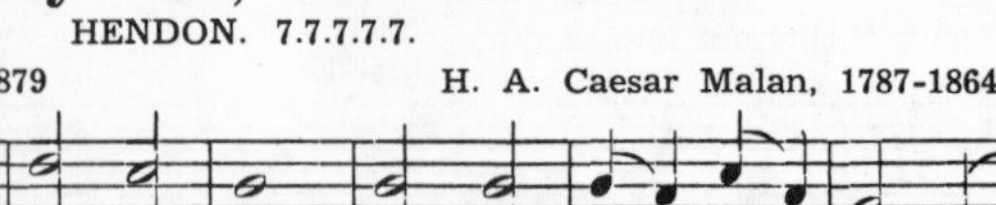

1. Take my life, and let it be Con - se - crat - ed, Lord, to
2. Take my feet, and let them be Swift and beau - ti - ful for
3. Take my lips, and let them be Filled with mes - sag - es from
4. Take my will and make it thine; It shall be no lon - ger
5. Take my love, my Lord, I pour At thy feet its treas - ure-

thee; Take my hands, and let them move At the im - pulse
thee; Take my voice, and let me sing Al - ways, on - ly,
thee; Take my sil - ver and my gold, Not a mite would
mine; Take my heart, it is thine own, It shall be thy
store; Take my - self, and I will be, Ev - er, on - ly,

of thy love, At the im - pulse of thy love.
for my King, Al - ways, on - ly, for my King.
I with - hold, Not a mite would I with - hold.
roy - al throne, It shall be thy roy - al throne.
all for thee, Ev - er, on - ly, all for thee. A - MEN.

160 Lord, Speak to Me, That I May Speak

CANONBURY. L.M.

Frances R. Havergal, 1836-1879 — Robert Schumann, 1810-1856

1. Lord, speak to me, that I may speak In liv - ing ech - oes of Thy tone;
2. Oh! teach me, Lord, that I may teach The precious things Thou dost im-part;
3. Oh! give Thine own sweet rest to me, That I may speak with soothing pow'r
4. Oh! fill me with Thy ful-ness, Lord, Un-til my ver - y heart o'er-flow
5. Oh! use me, Lord, use e - ven me, Just as Thou wilt, and when, and where;

As Thou has sought, so let me seek The err-ing chil-dren lost and lone.
And wing my words, that they may reach The hidden depths of many a heart.
A word in sea-son, as from Thee, To wea-ry ones in needful hour.
In kindling thought and glowing word, Thy love to tell, Thy praise to show.
Un - til Thy blessed face I see, Thy rest, Thy joy, Thy glo-ry share. A-men.
Have Thine Own Way, Lord!
161
Adelaide A. Pollard, 1860-1934
George C. Stebbins, 1846-1945
Slowly
1. Have Thine own way, Lord! Have Thine own way!.. Thou art the
2. Have Thine own way, Lord! Have Thine own way!.. Search me and
3. Have Thine own way, Lord! Have Thine own way!.. Wound-ed and
4. Have Thine own way, Lord! Have Thine own way!.. Hold o'er my
Pot - ter; I am the clay... Mould me and make me Aft - er Thy
try me, Mas-ter, to - day!... Whit - er than snow, Lord, Wash me just
wea - ry, Help me, I pray!. Pow - er—all pow - er—Sure - ly is
be - ing Ab - so - lute sway!. Fill with Thy Spir - it Till all shall
will,... While I am wait - ing, Yield - ed and still...
now,... As in Thy pres - ence Hum - bly I bow...
Thine! Touch me and heal me, Sav - ior di - vine!..
see.... Christ on - ly, al - ways, Liv - ing in me!....

162 Consecration

Mildred E. Howard, 1907 — Andrew L. Byers, 1907

1. Since Je - sus gave his life for me Should I not give him mine?
I'm con - se - crat - ed, Lord, to thee, I shall be whol - ly thine.

2. I care not where my Lord di-rects, His pur - pose I'll ful - fill;
I know he ev - ery one pro-tects Who does his ho - ly will.

3. Tho' he may call a - cross the sea, With Je - sus I will go,
And tell the lost of love so free, Till all his pow'r may know.

4. My home and friends are dear to me, Yet he is dear - er still;
In my af - fec - tion first he'll be, And first his right - eous will.

5. My all, O Lord, to thee I give, Ac - cept it as thine own;
For thee a - lone I'll ev - er live, My heart shall be thy throne.

CHORUS

My life, O Lord, I give to thee, My tal - ents, time and all; I'll serve thee, Lord, and faith-ful be, I'll hear thy faintest call. . . . A - MEN.
faint-est call.

I'll Live for Him 163

R. E. Hudson, 1843-1901 C. R. Dunbar

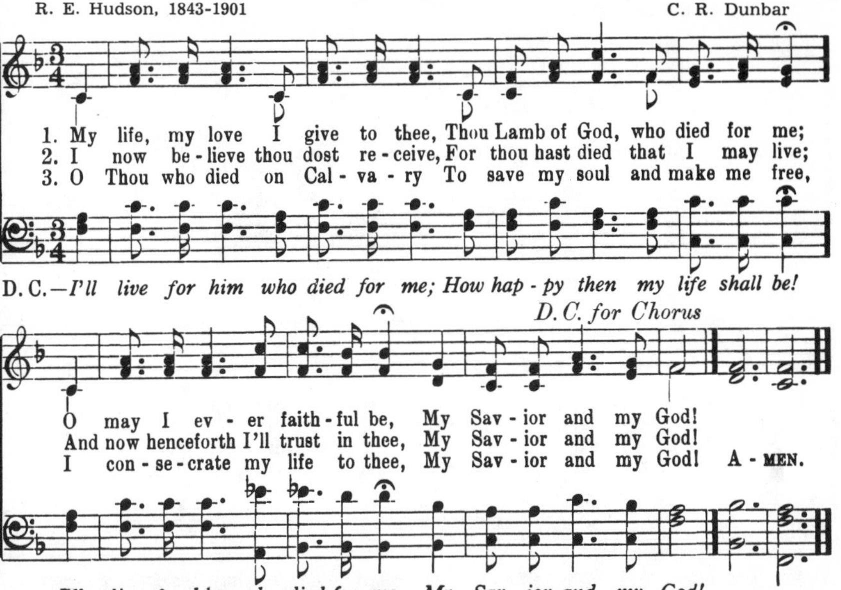
1. My life, my love I give to thee, Thou Lamb of God, who died for me;
2. I now be - lieve thou dost re - ceive, For thou hast died that I may live;
3. O Thou who died on Cal - va - ry To save my soul and make me free,
D. C.—I'll live for him who died for me; How hap - py then my life shall be!
D. C. for Chorus
O may I ev - er faith - ful be, My Sav - ior and my God!
And now henceforth I'll trust in thee, My Sav - ior and my God!
I con - se - crate my life to thee, My Sav - ior and my God! A - MEN.
I'll live for him who died for me, My Sav - ior and my God!

Where He Leads Me 164

E. W. Blandly J. S. Norris

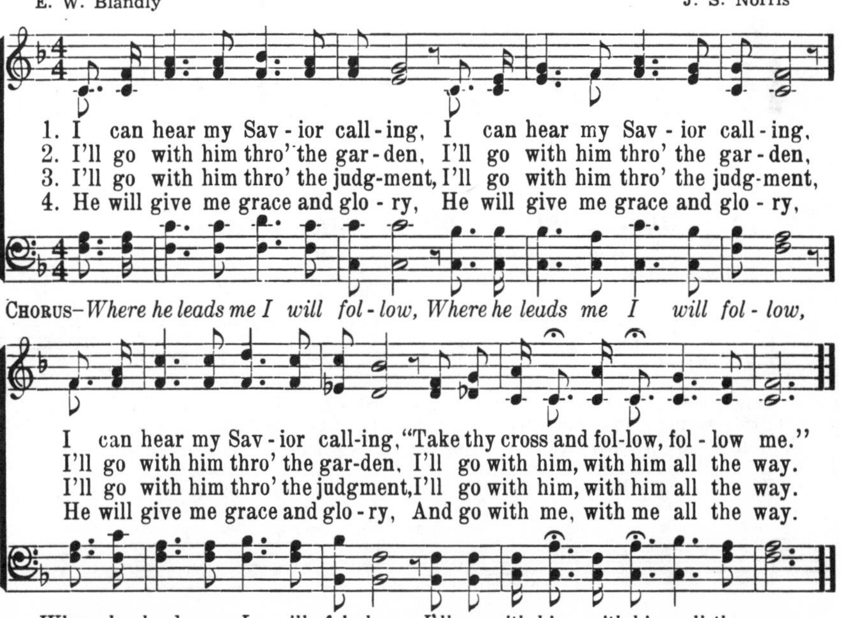
1. I can hear my Sav - ior call - ing, I can hear my Sav - ior call - ing,
2. I'll go with him thro' the gar - den, I'll go with him thro' the gar - den,
3. I'll go with him thro' the judg-ment, I'll go with him thro' the judg-ment,
4. He will give me grace and glo - ry, He will give me grace and glo - ry,
CHORUS—Where he leads me I will fol - low, Where he leads me I will fol - low,
I can hear my Sav - ior call-ing, "Take thy cross and fol-low, fol - low me."
I'll go with him thro' the gar-den, I'll go with him, with him all the way.
I'll go with him thro' the judgment, I'll go with him, with him all the way.
He will give me grace and glo - ry, And go with me, with me all the way.
Where he leads me I will fol - low, I'll go with him, with him, all the way.

165 A Living Sacrifice

Lucena C. Byrum, 1921 — Henry C. Clausen, 1922

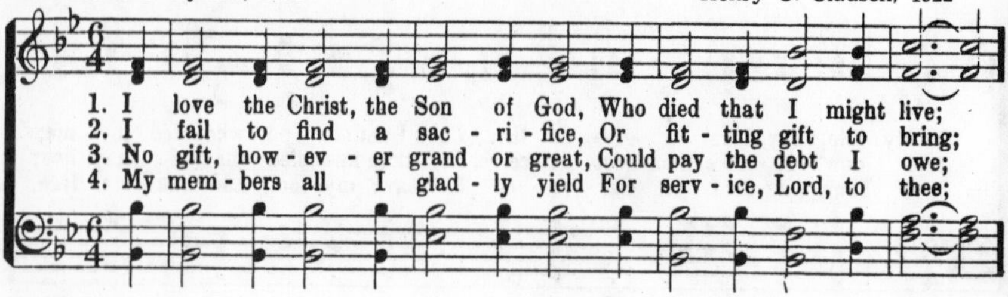

1. I love the Christ, the Son of God, Who died that I might live;
2. I fail to find a sac - ri - fice, Or fit - ting gift to bring;
3. No gift, how - ev - er grand or great, Could pay the debt I owe;
4. My mem - bers all I glad - ly yield For serv - ice, Lord, to thee;

I would my grat - i - tude ex - press, A gift un - to him give.
Earth's treas-ures have too lit - tle worth To of - fer to my King.
I bring my - self, my life, my all, A liv - ing gift be - stow.
To bear the bless - ed gos - pel light, That oth - ers Christ may see.

FINE.

D S.—*Let self be slain, let Je - sus reign With - in my heart al - way.*

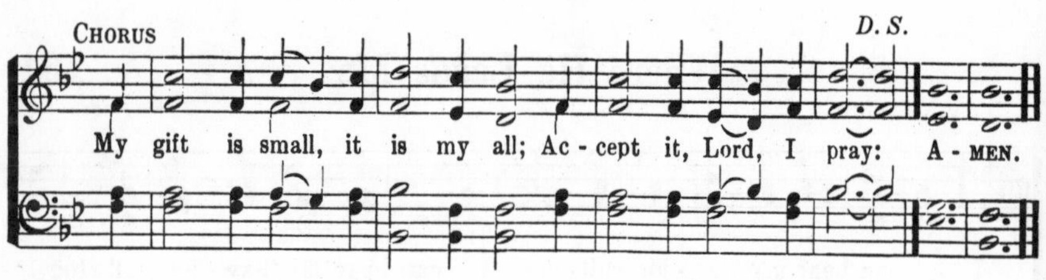
CHORUS
D. S.
My gift is small, it is my all; Ac - cept it, Lord, I pray: A - MEN.

166 How Shall I Follow Him I Serve?

FEDERAL STREET. L.M.

Josiah Conder, 1824 — Henry K. Oliver, 1800-1885

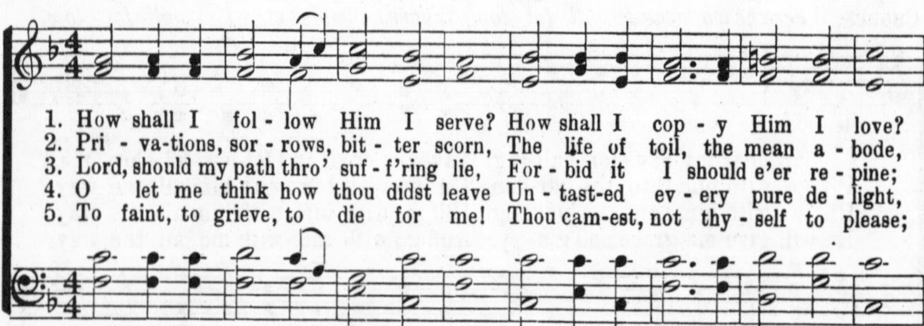
1. How shall I fol - low Him I serve? How shall I cop - y Him I love?
2. Pri - va-tions, sor - rows, bit - ter scorn, The life of toil, the mean a - bode,
3. Lord, should my path thro' suf - f'ring lie, For - bid it I should e'er re - pine;
4. O let me think how thou didst leave Un - tast-ed ev - ery pure de - light,
5. To faint, to grieve, to die for me! Thou cam-est, not thy - self to please;

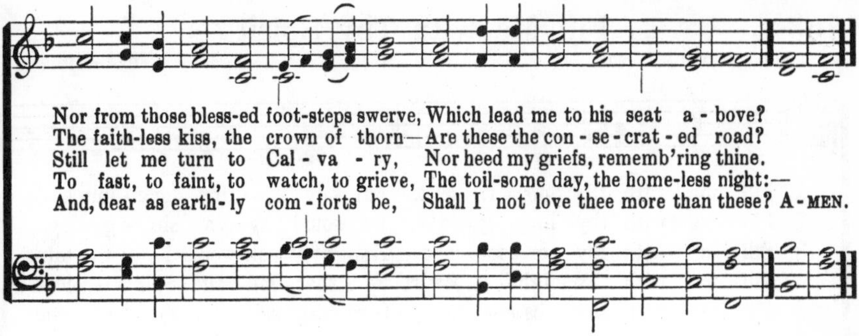

Nor from those bless-ed foot-steps swerve, Which lead me to his seat a - bove?
The faith-less kiss, the crown of thorn—Are these the con - se - crat - ed road?
Still let me turn to Cal - va - ry, Nor heed my griefs, rememb'ring thine.
To fast, to faint, to watch, to grieve, The toil-some day, the home-less night:—
And, dear as earth - ly com - forts be, Shall I not love thee more than these? A - MEN.

With Thy Spirit Fill Me 167

Oswald J. Smith

B. D. Ackley, b. 1872

Legato

1. Lord, pos - sess me now, I pray, Make me whol - ly Thine to - day;
Glad - ly do I own Thy sway, With Thy spir - it fill me.
2. Lord, I yield my - self to Thee, All I am or hope to be
Now and thru e - ter - ni - ty, With Thy spir - it fill me.
3. Lord, com - mis - sion me, I pray! Souls are dy - ing ev - 'ry day;
Help me lead them in Thy way, With Thy spir - it fill me.

CHORUS

With Thy spir - it fill me, With Thy spir - it fill me;
Make me whol - ly Thine, I pray, With Thy spir - it fill me.

168 Fill Me with Thy Spirit

Daniel S. Warner, 1893 — Andrew L. Byers, 1918

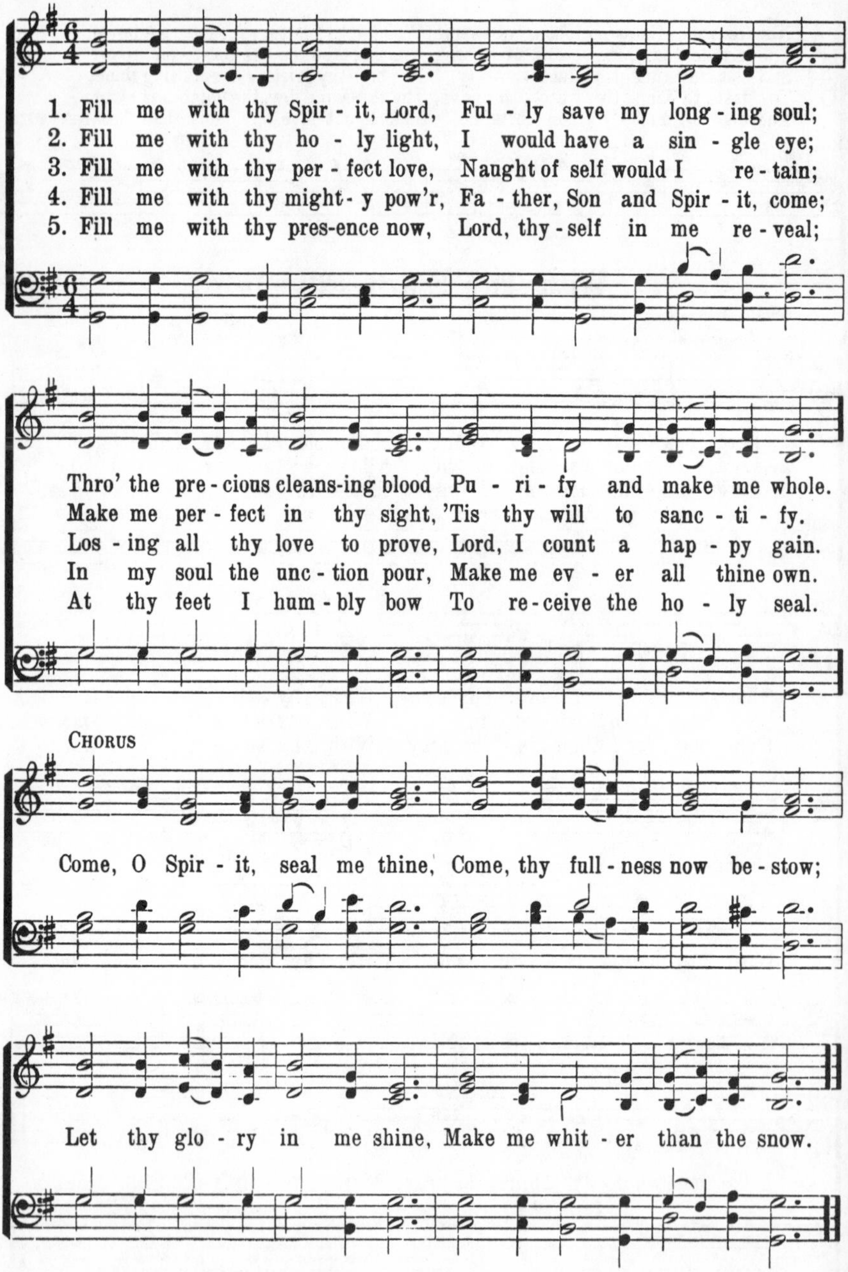

1. Fill me with thy Spir - it, Lord, Ful - ly save my long - ing soul;
2. Fill me with thy ho - ly light, I would have a sin - gle eye;
3. Fill me with thy per - fect love, Naught of self would I re - tain;
4. Fill me with thy might - y pow'r, Fa - ther, Son and Spir - it, come;
5. Fill me with thy pres-ence now, Lord, thy - self in me re - veal;

Thro' the pre - cious cleans-ing blood Pu - ri - fy and make me whole.
Make me per - fect in thy sight, 'Tis thy will to sanc - ti - fy.
Los - ing all thy love to prove, Lord, I count a hap - py gain.
In my soul the unc - tion pour, Make me ev - er all thine own.
At thy feet I hum - bly bow To re - ceive the ho - ly seal.

CHORUS

Come, O Spir - it, seal me thine, Come, thy full - ness now be - stow;
Let thy glo - ry in me shine, Make me whit - er than the snow.

Draw Thou My Soul, O Christ 169

ST. EDMUND. 6.4.6.4.6.6.6.4.

Lucy Larcom, 1826-1893 | Arthur S. Sullivan, 1842-1900

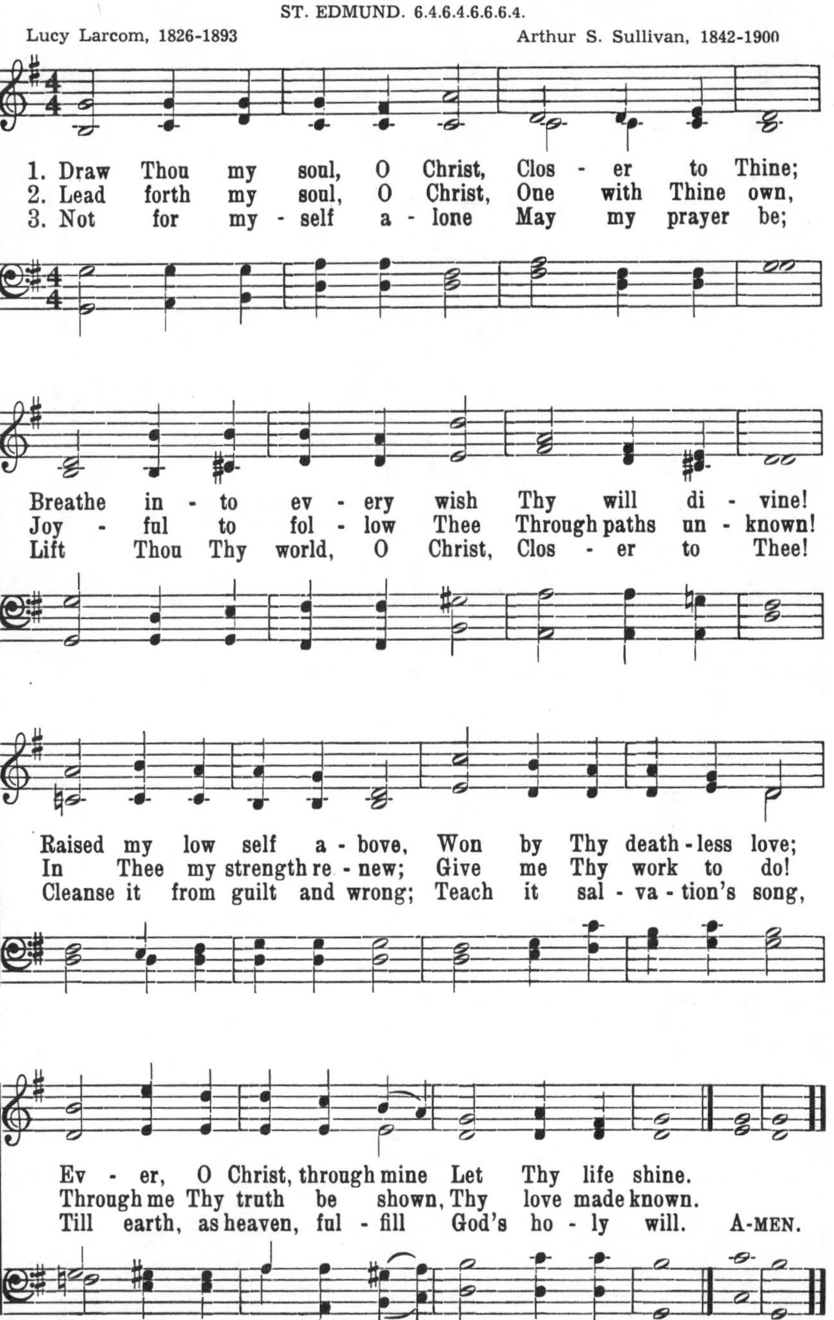
1. Draw Thou my soul, O Christ, Clos - er to Thine;
2. Lead forth my soul, O Christ, One with Thine own,
3. Not for my - self a - lone May my prayer be;
Breathe in - to ev - ery wish Thy will di - vine!
Joy - ful to fol - low Thee Through paths un - known!
Lift Thou Thy world, O Christ, Clos - er to Thee!
Raised my low self a - bove, Won by Thy death - less love;
In Thee my strength re - new; Give me Thy work to do!
Cleanse it from guilt and wrong; Teach it sal - va - tion's song,
Ev - er, O Christ, through mine Let Thy life shine.
Through me Thy truth be shown, Thy love made known.
Till earth, as heaven, ful - fill God's ho - ly will. A-MEN.

170 I'll Go Where You Want Me to Go

Mary Brown — Carrie E. Rounsefell

1. It may not be on the mountain's height, Or o - ver the storm-y sea;
It may not be at the bat-tle's front My Lord will have need of me;
But if by a still, small voice He calls To paths I do not know,
I'll answer, dear Lord, with my hand in Thine, I'll go where you want me to go.

2. Per-haps to-day there are lov-ing words Which Jesus would have me speak;
There may be now, in the paths of sin, Some wand'rer whom I should seek.
O Sav-ior, if Thou wilt be my Guide, Tho' dark and rug-ged the way,
My voice shall ech-o the mes-sage sweet, I'll say what you want me to say.

3. There's surely somewhere a low-ly place In earth's har-vest-fields so wide,
Where I may la-bor thro' life's short day For Je-sus, the Cru-ci-fied.
So, trust-ing my all un-to Thy care, I know Thou lov-est me!
I'll do Thy will with a heart sin-cere, I'll be what you want me to be.

FINE

D. S.–*I'll say what you want me to say, dear Lord, I'll be what you want me to be.*

REFRAIN

I'll go where you want me to go, dear Lord, O'er mountain, or plain, or sea;

D. S.

Yielded to Thee

171

Haldor Lillenas, 1924 — Richard Hainsworth, 1924

1. Yield-ed to thee, Ho-ly Spir-it di-vine, Hence-forth thy will shall for-ev-er be mine; Since I sur-ren-dered com-plete-ly to thee Thou art a-bid-ing for-ev-er with me.

2. Yield-ed to thee, thou dost cleanse me from sin, Mak-ing me pure and ho-ly with-in; Yield-ed to thee, thou dost purge me from dross, Now with re-joic-ing I car-ry my cross.

3. Yield-ed to thee, all my self-ish de-sires Per-ished one day 'mid the Pen-te-cost fires; Yield-ed to thee, now thy im-age shall be Stamped and en-grav-en for-ev-er on me.

CHORUS

Yield-ed to thee, ful-ly yield-ed to thee, Noth-ing with-held, thou art reign-ing in me; All on the al-tar, My faith shall not fal-ter, I'm yielded to thee, Lord, yielded to thee. A-MEN.

172 Fill Me Now

Elwood H. Stokes, 1815-1895 John R. Sweney, 1837-1899

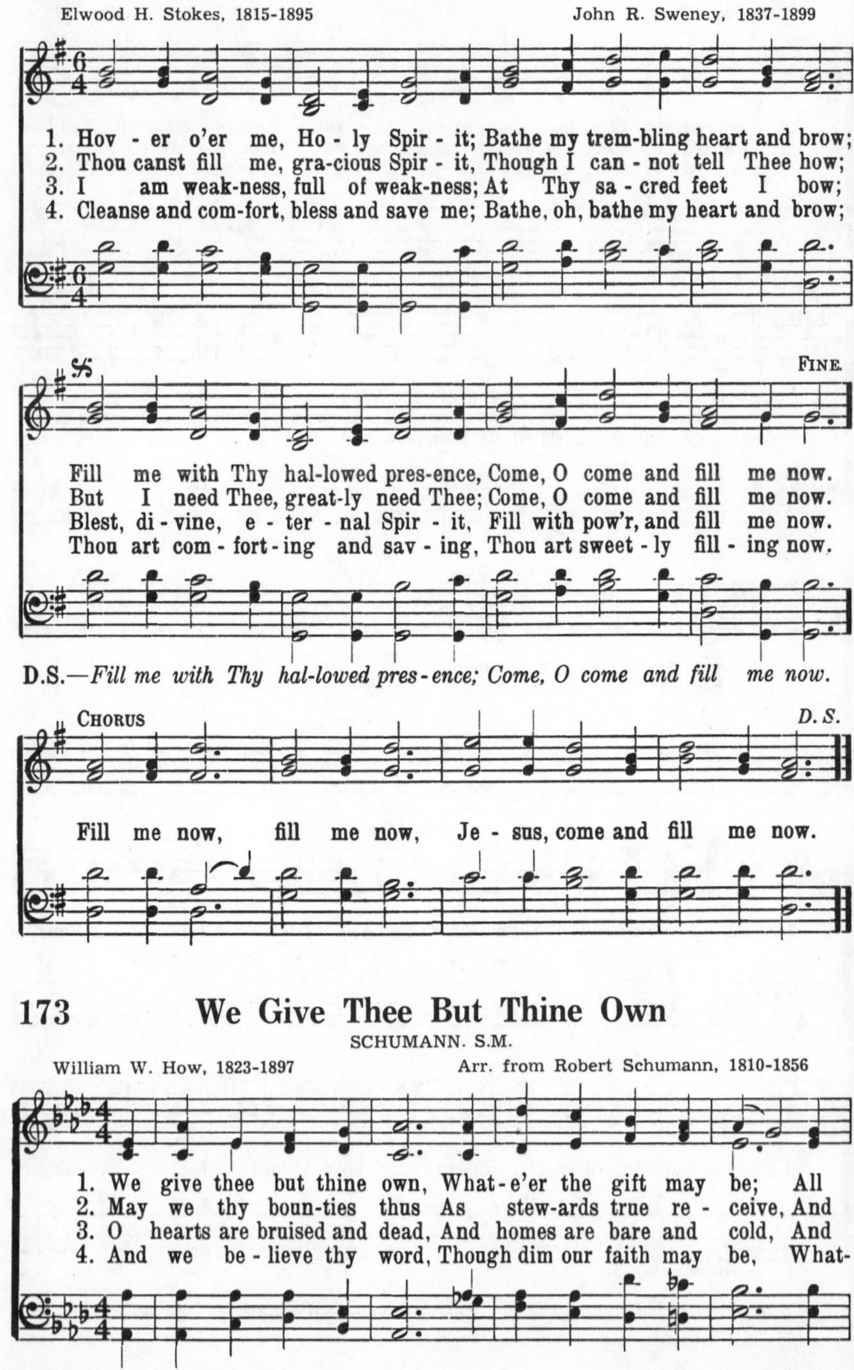
1. Hov - er o'er me, Ho - ly Spir - it; Bathe my trem-bling heart and brow;
2. Thou canst fill me, gra-cious Spir - it, Though I can - not tell Thee how;
3. I am weak-ness, full of weak-ness; At Thy sa - cred feet I bow;
4. Cleanse and com-fort, bless and save me; Bathe, oh, bathe my heart and brow;
FINE.
Fill me with Thy hal-lowed pres-ence, Come, O come and fill me now.
But I need Thee, great-ly need Thee; Come, O come and fill me now.
Blest, di - vine, e - ter - nal Spir - it, Fill with pow'r, and fill me now.
Thou art com - fort - ing and sav - ing, Thou art sweet - ly fill - ing now.
D.S.—Fill me with Thy hal-lowed pres - ence; Come, O come and fill me now.
CHORUS
D. S.
Fill me now, fill me now, Je - sus, come and fill me now.

173 We Give Thee But Thine Own

SCHUMANN. S.M.

William W. How, 1823-1897 Arr. from Robert Schumann, 1810-1856

1. We give thee but thine own, What - e'er the gift may be; All
2. May we thy boun-ties thus As stew-ards true re - ceive, And
3. O hearts are bruised and dead, And homes are bare and cold, And
4. And we be - lieve thy word, Though dim our faith may be, What-

that we have is thine a - lone, A trust, O Lord, from thee.
glad - ly as thou bless - est us, To thee our first - fruits give.
lambs for whom the Shep-herd bled Are stray-ing from the fold.
e'er for thine we do, O Lord, We do it un - to thee. A - MEN.
Transformed
174
Mrs. F. G. Burroughs
B. D. Ackley, b. 1872
1. Dear Lord, take up my tan-gled strands, Where we have wrought in vain,
2. Touch Thou the sad, dis - cord - ant keys Of ev - 'ry troub - led breast,
3. Where bro - ken vows in frag-ments lie— The toll of wast - ed years,—
4. Take all the fail - ures, each mis-take Of our poor, hu - man ways,
That by the skill of Thy dear hands Some beau - ty may re - main.
And change to peace-ful har - mo - nies The sigh - ings of un - rest.
Do Thou make whole a-gain, we cry, And give a song for tears.
Then, Sav - ior, for Thine own dear sake, Make them show forth Thy praise.
CHORUS
Transformed by grace di-vine, The glo - - ry shall be Thine;
Trans-formed
The glo - ry
To Thy most ho - ly will, O Lord, We now our all re - sign.

175 He Wants His Way in Thee

Charles W. Naylor, 1918 — Henry C. Clausen, 1918

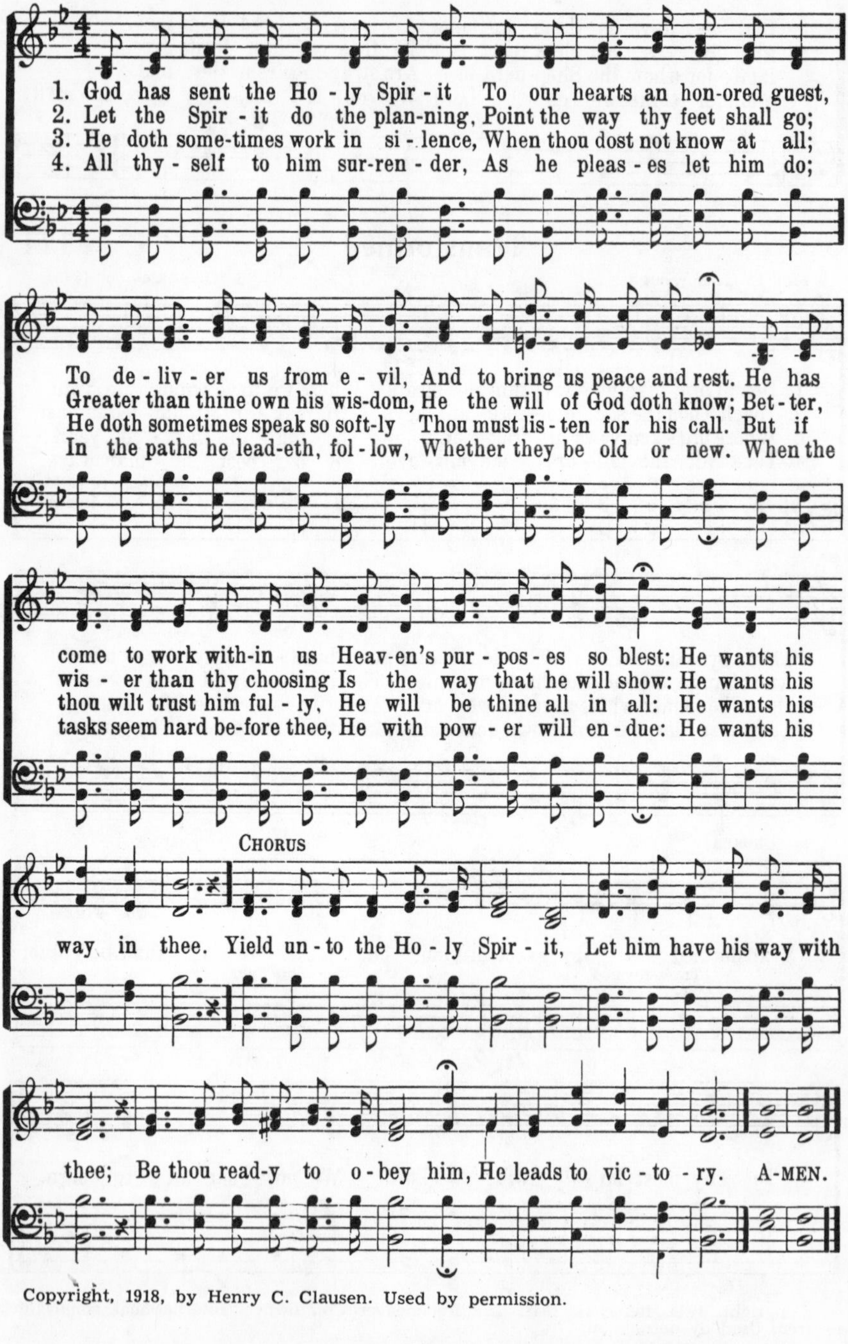

1. God has sent the Ho - ly Spir - it To our hearts an hon-ored guest,
2. Let the Spir - it do the plan-ning, Point the way thy feet shall go;
3. He doth some-times work in si - lence, When thou dost not know at all;
4. All thy - self to him sur-ren - der, As he pleas - es let him do;

To de - liv - er us from e - vil, And to bring us peace and rest. He has
Greater than thine own his wis-dom, He the will of God doth know; Bet - ter,
He doth sometimes speak so soft-ly Thou must lis - ten for his call. But if
In the paths he lead-eth, fol - low, Whether they be old or new. When the

come to work with-in us Heav-en's pur - pos - es so blest: He wants his
wis - er than thy choosing Is the way that he will show: He wants his
thou wilt trust him ful - ly, He will be thine all in all: He wants his
tasks seem hard be-fore thee, He with pow - er will en - due: He wants his

way in thee.

CHORUS

Yield un - to the Ho - ly Spir - it, Let him have his way with
thee; Be thou read-y to o - bey him, He leads to vic - to - ry. A-MEN.

His Way with Thee 176

Cyrus S. Nusbaum
Cyrus S. Nusbaum
1. Would you live for Je - sus, and be al - ways pure and good? Would you walk with him with - in the nar - row road? Would you have him bear your bur - den, car - ry all your load? Let him have his way with thee.
2. Would you have him make you free, and fol - low at his call? Would you know the peace that comes by giv - ing all? Would you have him save you, so that you need nev-er fall? Let him have his way with thee.
3. Would you in his king-dom find a place of con-stant rest? Would you prove him true in prov - i - den - tial test? Would you in his serv - ice la - bor al - ways at your best? Let him have his way with thee.
CHORUS
His pow'r can make you what you ought to be; His blood can cleanse your heart and make you free; His love can fill your soul, and you will see, 'Twas best for him to have his way with thee. A - MEN.
rit.

177 Only for Thee
Eliza A. Walker
William A. Ogden, 1841-1897
1. Bless - ed Sav - ior, I would live On - ly for thee, for thee (for thee);
2. All my spir - it's deep de - sire, On - ly for thee, for thee (for thee);
3. In my joys would I re - joice, On - ly for thee, for thee (for thee);
4. All my smiles and all my tears, On - ly for thee, for thee (for thee);
Use the tal - ents thou dost give, On - ly for thee, for thee.
All my pow'rs of mind as - pire, On - ly for thee, for thee.
In my choic - es make my choice, On - ly for thee, for thee.
All my youth and rip - er years, On - ly for thee, for thee.
CHORUS
All for Christ who died for me; Paid the debt to set me free;
Now, and thro' e - ter - ni - ty, On - ly for thee, for thee (for thee). A - MEN.
178 Breathe on Me, Breath of God
TRENTHAM. S.M.
Edwin Hatch, 1835-1889
Robert Jackson, 1843-1914
1. Breathe on me, Breath of God, Fill me with life a - new,
2. Breathe on me, Breath of God, Un - til my heart is pure,
3. Breathe on me, Breath of God, Till I am whol - ly Thine,
4. Breathe on me, Breath of God; So shall I nev - er die,

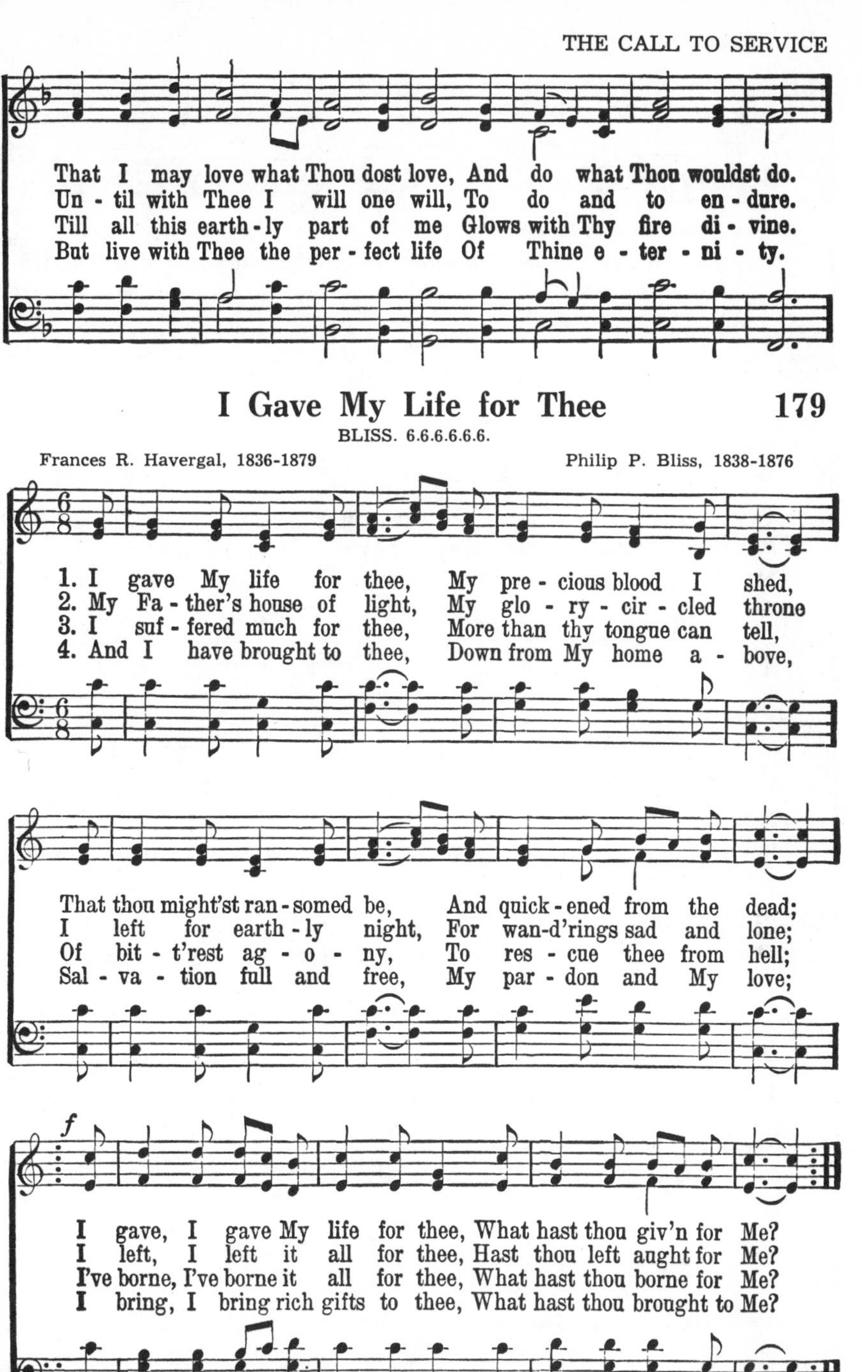
That I may love what Thou dost love, And do what Thou wouldst do.
Un - til with Thee I will one will, To do and to en - dure.
Till all this earth - ly part of me Glows with Thy fire di - vine.
But live with Thee the per - fect life Of Thine e - ter - ni - ty.
I Gave My Life for Thee
179
BLISS. 6.6.6.6.6.6.
Frances R. Havergal, 1836-1879
Philip P. Bliss, 1838-1876
1. I gave My life for thee, My pre - cious blood I shed,
2. My Fa - ther's house of light, My glo - ry - cir - cled throne
3. I suf - fered much for thee, More than thy tongue can tell,
4. And I have brought to thee, Down from My home a - bove,
That thou might'st ran - somed be, And quick - ened from the dead;
I left for earth - ly night, For wan-d'rings sad and lone;
Of bit - t'rest ag - o - ny, To res - cue thee from hell;
Sal - va - tion full and free, My par - don and My love;
f
I gave, I gave My life for thee, What hast thou giv'n for Me?
I left, I left it all for thee, Hast thou left aught for Me?
I've borne, I've borne it all for thee, What hast thou borne for Me?
I bring, I bring rich gifts to thee, What hast thou brought to Me?

180 Our Best

S. C. Kirk

Grant Colfax Tullar, 1869-1950

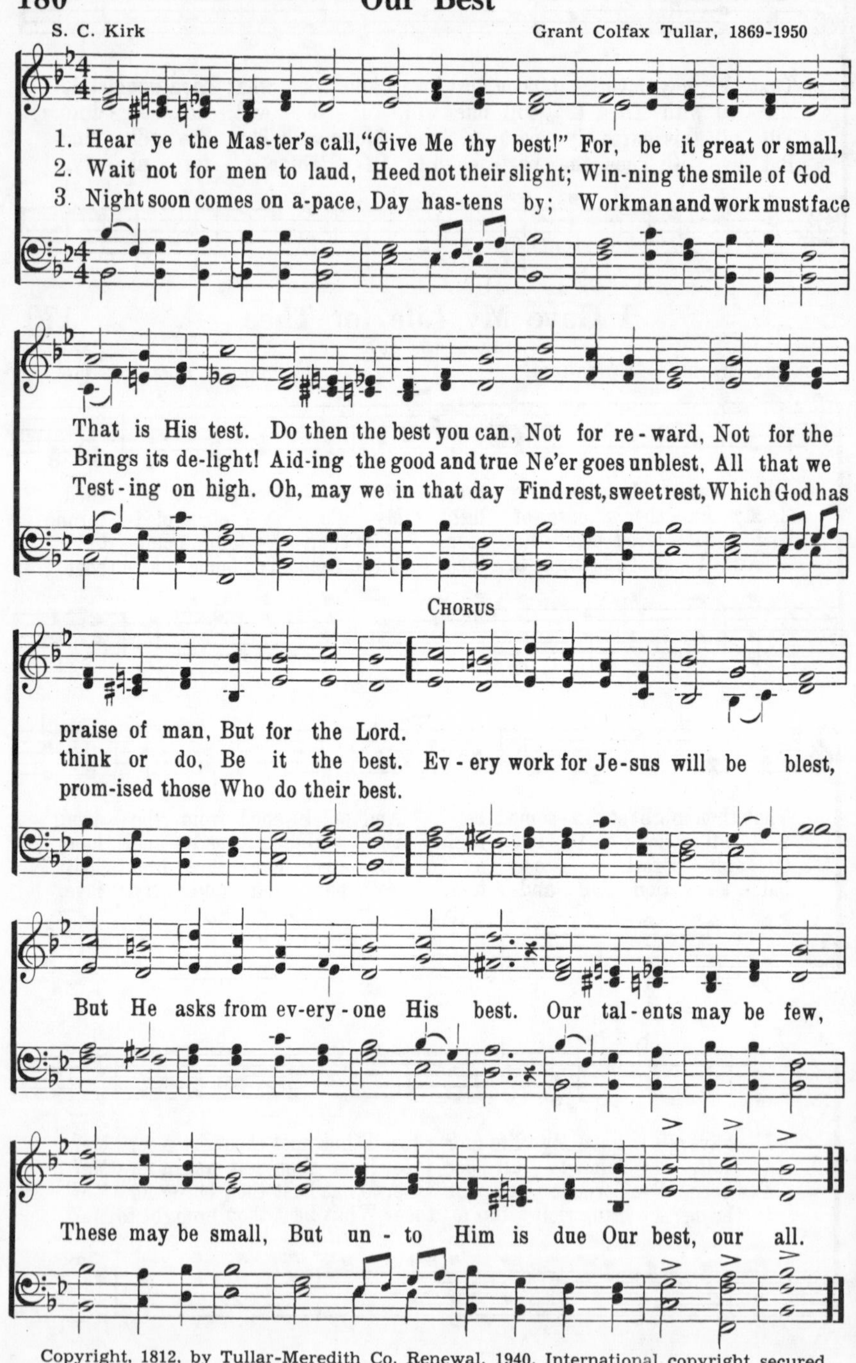
1. Hear ye the Mas-ter's call, "Give Me thy best!" For, be it great or small, That is His test. Do then the best you can, Not for re-ward, Not for the praise of man, But for the Lord.
2. Wait not for men to laud, Heed not their slight; Win-ning the smile of God Brings its de-light! Aid-ing the good and true Ne'er goes unblest, All that we think or do, Be it the best.
3. Night soon comes on a-pace, Day has-tens by; Workman and work must face Test-ing on high. Oh, may we in that day Find rest, sweet rest, Which God has prom-ised those Who do their best.
CHORUS
Ev-ery work for Je-sus will be blest, But He asks from ev-ery-one His best. Our tal-ents may be few, These may be small, But un-to Him is due Our best, our all.

Give of Your Best to the Master 181

Howard B. Grose — Mrs. Charles Barnard, 1830-1869

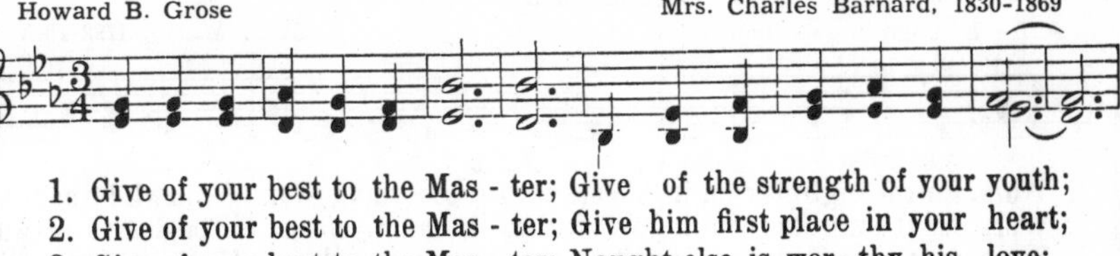
1. Give of your best to the Mas - ter; Give of the strength of your youth;
2. Give of your best to the Mas - ter; Give him first place in your heart;
3. Give of your best to the Mas - ter; Naught else is wor - thy his love;

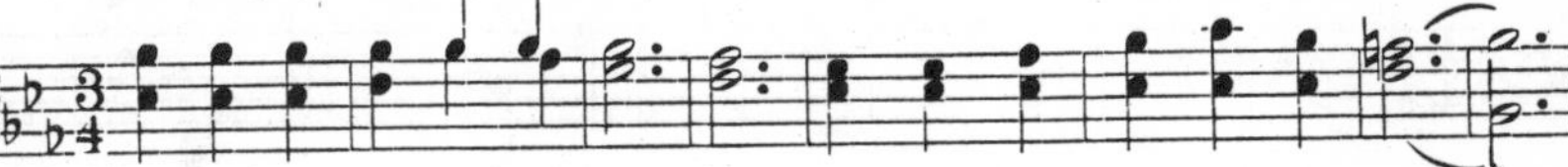
REFRAIN–Give of your best to the Mas - ter; Give of the strength of your youth;

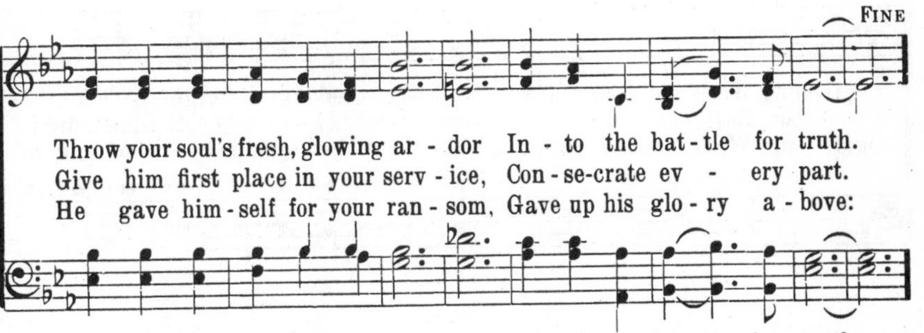
FINE
Throw your soul's fresh, glowing ar - dor In - to the bat - tle for truth.
Give him first place in your serv - ice, Con - se - crate ev - ery part.
He gave him - self for your ran - som, Gave up his glo - ry a - bove:
Clad in sal - va-tion's full ar - mor, Join in the bat - tle for truth.

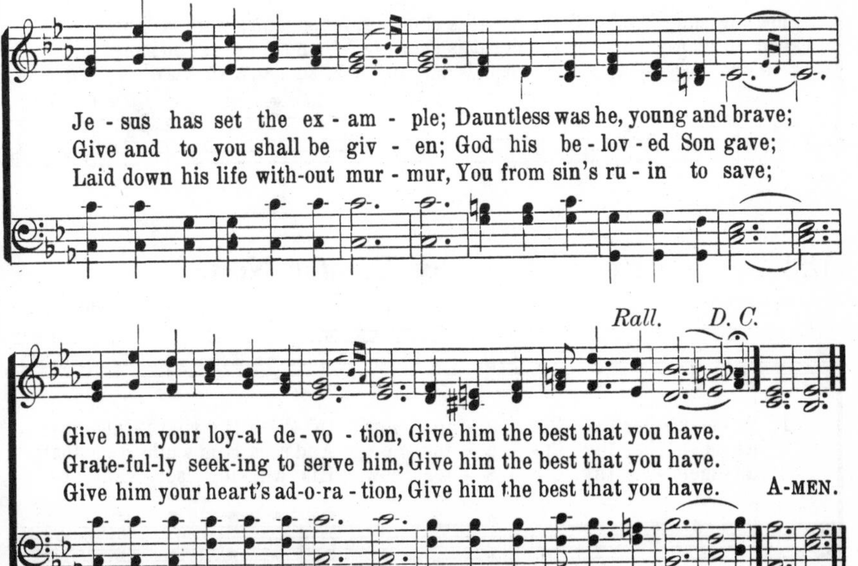
Je - sus has set the ex - am - ple; Dauntless was he, young and brave;
Give and to you shall be giv - en; God his be - lov - ed Son gave;
Laid down his life with-out mur - mur, You from sin's ru - in to save;
Rall. D. C.
Give him your loy-al de - vo - tion, Give him the best that you have.
Grate-ful-ly seek-ing to serve him, Give him the best that you have.
Give him your heart's ad-o-ra - tion, Give him the best that you have.
A-MEN.

182 Work, for the Night Is Coming

WORK SONG. 7.6.7.6.D.

Annie L. Coghill, 1836-1907 — Lowell Mason, 1792-1872

1. Work, for the night is com-ing, Work thro' the morning hours; Work while the dew is
2. Work, for the night is com-ing, Work thro' the sun-ny noon; Fill brightest hours with
3. Work, for the night is com-ing, Un - der the sun - set skies; While their bright tints are

spar-kling, Work 'mid springing flow'rs: Work when the day grows brighter, Work in the
la - bor, Rest comes sure and soon: Give ev - ery fly - ing min - ute Something to
glow - ing, Work, for day-light flies: Work till the last beam fad-eth, Fad - eth to

glow-ing sun; Work, for the night is com-ing, When man's work is done.
keep in store; Work, for the night is com-ing, When man works no more.
shine no more; Work while the night is dark'ning, When man's work is o'er. A-MEN.

183 Remember Thy Creator Now

Unknown — Lola M. Thompson

1. Re - mem - ber thy Cre - a - tor now, In these thy youth - ful days
2. Re - mem - ber thy Cre - a - tor now, And seek Him while He's near;
3. Re - mem - ber thy Cre - a - tor now, His will - ing ser - vant be.

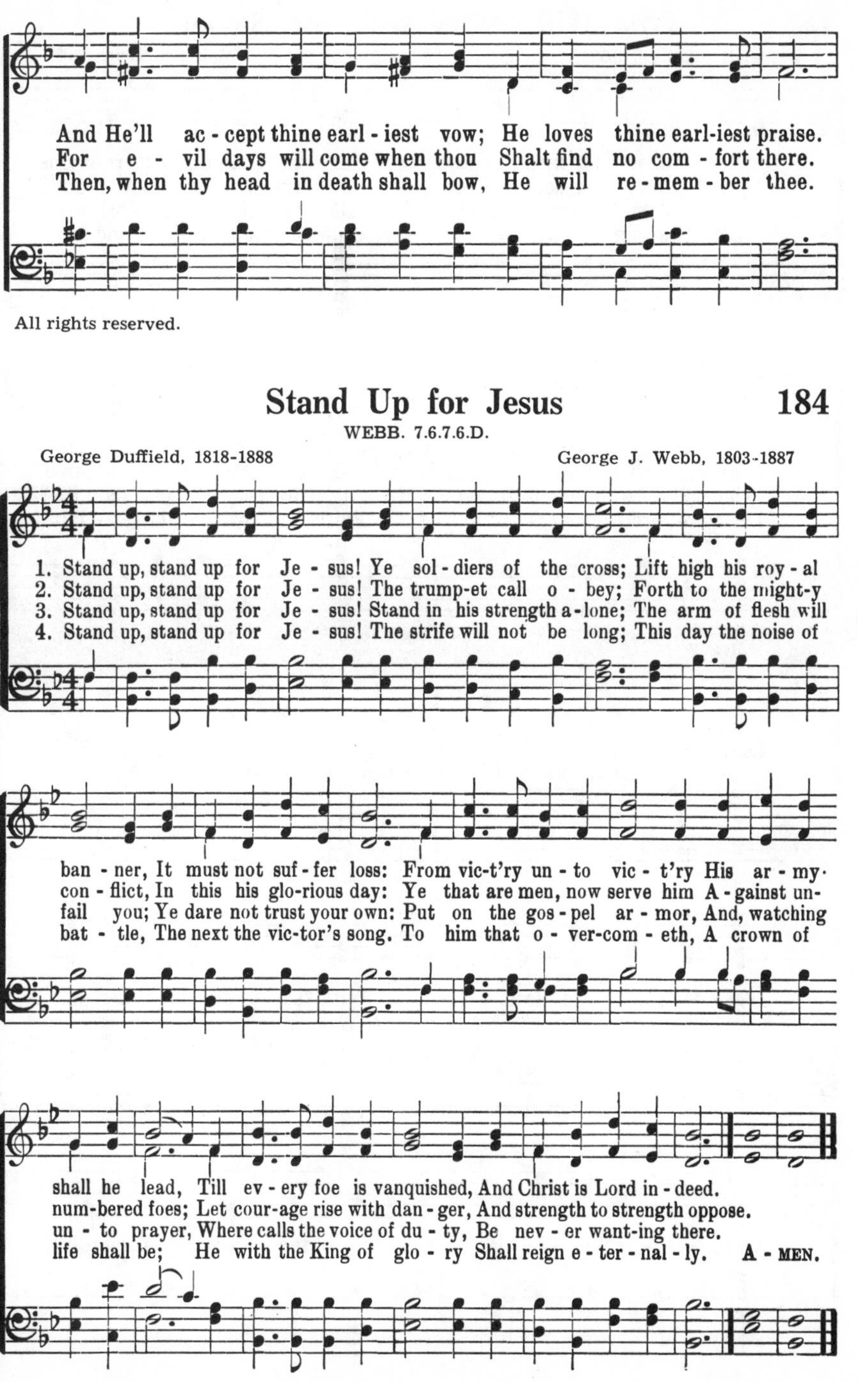
And He'll ac - cept thine earl - iest vow; He loves thine earl-iest praise.
For e - vil days will come when thou Shalt find no com - fort there.
Then, when thy head in death shall bow, He will re - mem - ber thee.
All rights reserved.
Stand Up for Jesus
184
WEBB. 7.6.7.6.D.
George Duffield, 1818-1888
George J. Webb, 1803-1887
1. Stand up, stand up for Je - sus! Ye sol - diers of the cross; Lift high his roy - al
2. Stand up, stand up for Je - sus! The trump-et call o - bey; Forth to the might-y
3. Stand up, stand up for Je - sus! Stand in his strength a - lone; The arm of flesh will
4. Stand up, stand up for Je - sus! The strife will not be long; This day the noise of
ban - ner, It must not suf - fer loss: From vic-t'ry un - to vic - t'ry His ar - my
con - flict, In this his glo-rious day: Ye that are men, now serve him A - gainst un-
fail you; Ye dare not trust your own: Put on the gos - pel ar - mor, And, watching
bat - tle, The next the vic-tor's song. To him that o - ver-com - eth, A crown of
shall he lead, Till ev - ery foe is vanquished, And Christ is Lord in - deed.
num-bered foes; Let cour-age rise with dan - ger, And strength to strength oppose.
un - to prayer, Where calls the voice of du - ty, Be nev - er want-ing there.
life shall be; He with the King of glo - ry Shall reign e - ter - nal - ly. A - MEN.

185 Who Will Suffer with the Savior?

Daniel S. Warner, 1890 — Ludolph Schroeder, 1893

1. Who will suf-fer with the Sav-ior, Take the lit-tle that re-mains
2. Who will of-fer soul and bod-y On the al-tar of our God?
3. O for con-se-crat-ed serv-ice 'Mid the din of Ba-bel strife!
4. Soon the con-flict will be o-ver, Crowns a-wait the firm and pure;
Of the cup of trib-u-la-tion Je-sus drank in dy-ing pains?
Leav-ing self and world-ly mam-mon, Take the path that Je-sus trod?
Who will dare the truth to her-ald At the per-il of his life?
For-ward, brethren, work and suf-fer, Faith-ful to the end en-dure.
CHORUS
Lord, we fel-low-ship thy pas-sion, Glad-ly
Lord, we fel-low-ship thy pas-sion,
suf-fer shame and loss; . . . . . With thy bless-ing pain is
Glad-ly suf-fer loss (shame and loss); With thy bless-ing pain is
pleas-ure, We will glo-ry in thy cross (in thy cross).

Jesus Calls Us 186

GALILEE. 8.7.8.7.

Cecil F. Alexander, 1823-1895 — William H. Jude, 1851-1892

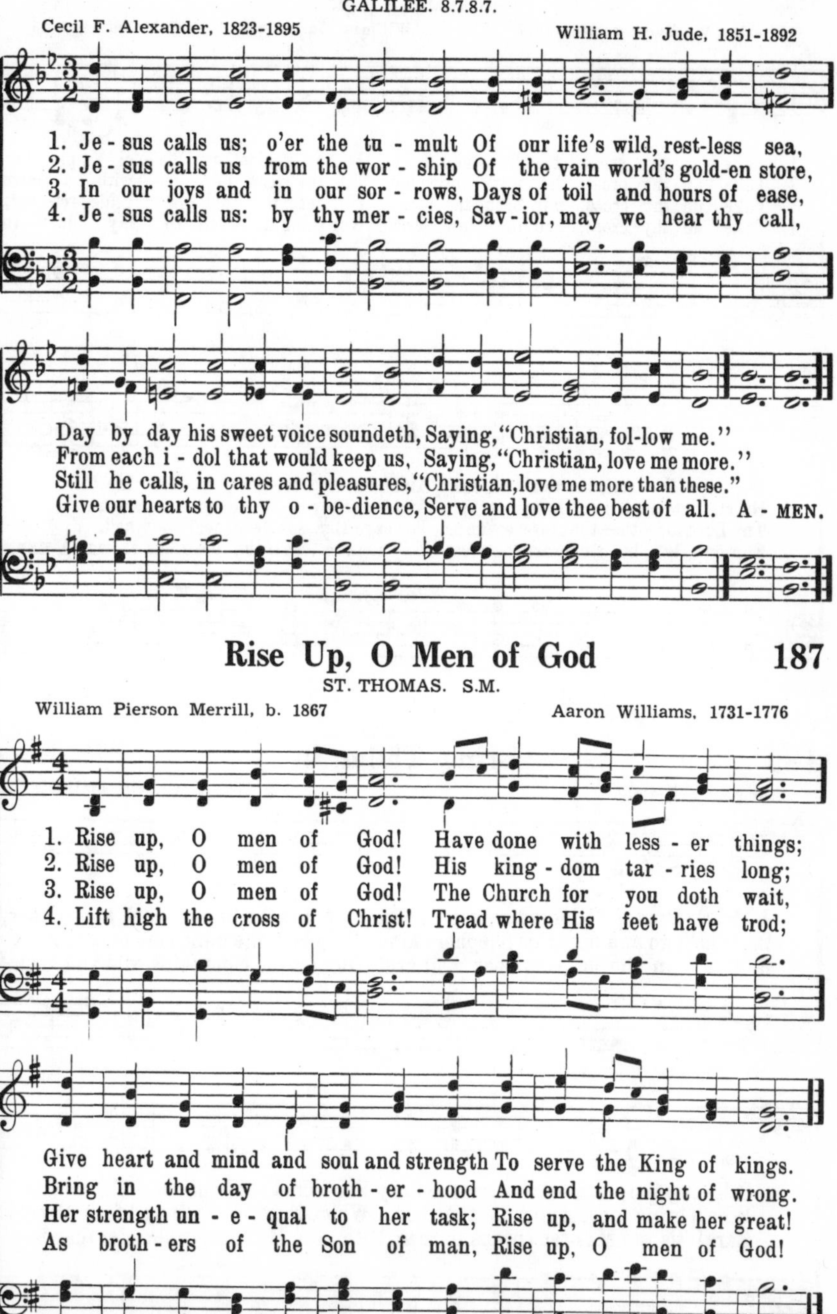
1. Je - sus calls us; o'er the tu - mult Of our life's wild, rest-less sea,
2. Je - sus calls us from the wor - ship Of the vain world's gold-en store,
3. In our joys and in our sor - rows, Days of toil and hours of ease,
4. Je - sus calls us: by thy mer - cies, Sav - ior, may we hear thy call,
Day by day his sweet voice soundeth, Saying, "Christian, fol-low me."
From each i - dol that would keep us, Saying, "Christian, love me more."
Still he calls, in cares and pleasures, "Christian, love me more than these."
Give our hearts to thy o - be-dience, Serve and love thee best of all. A - MEN.
Rise Up, O Men of God 187
ST. THOMAS. S.M.
William Pierson Merrill, b. 1867
Aaron Williams, 1731-1776
1. Rise up, O men of God! Have done with less - er things;
2. Rise up, O men of God! His king - dom tar - ries long;
3. Rise up, O men of God! The Church for you doth wait,
4. Lift high the cross of Christ! Tread where His feet have trod;
Give heart and mind and soul and strength To serve the King of kings.
Bring in the day of broth - er - hood And end the night of wrong.
Her strength un - e - qual to her task; Rise up, and make her great!
As broth - ers of the Son of man, Rise up, O men of God!

Words used by permission of *The Presbyterian Tribune*.

188 "Take Up Thy Cross," the Savior Said

GERMANY. L.M.

Charles W. Everest, 1814-1877 — *William Gardiner's Sacred Melodies,* 1815

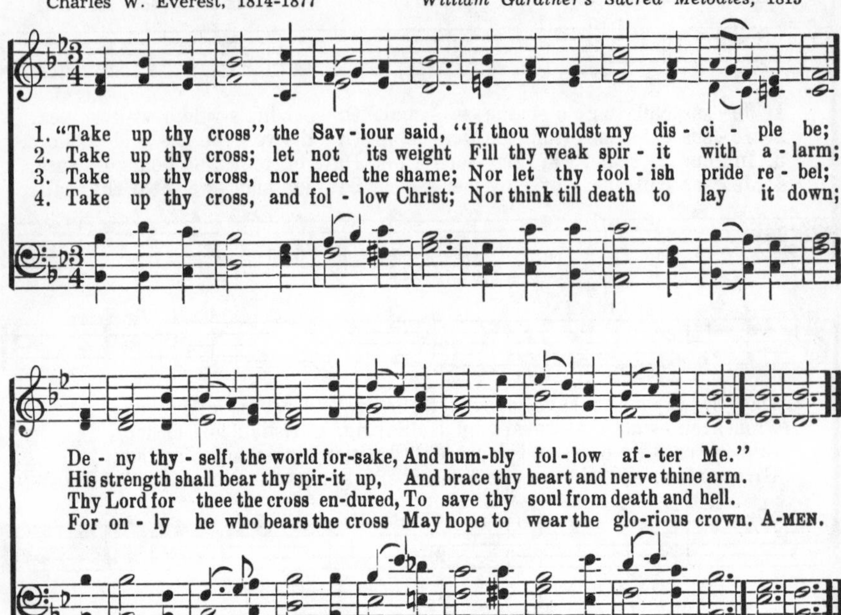
1. "Take up thy cross" the Sav - iour said, "If thou wouldst my dis - ci - ple be;
2. Take up thy cross; let not its weight Fill thy weak spir - it with a - larm;
3. Take up thy cross, nor heed the shame; Nor let thy fool - ish pride re - bel;
4. Take up thy cross, and fol - low Christ; Nor think till death to lay it down;
De - ny thy - self, the world for-sake, And hum-bly fol - low af - ter Me."
His strength shall bear thy spir-it up, And brace thy heart and nerve thine arm.
Thy Lord for thee the cross en-dured, To save thy soul from death and hell.
For on - ly he who bears the cross May hope to wear the glo-rious crown. A-MEN.

189 Bring Them In

Alexcenah Thomas — W. A. Ogden, 1841-1894

1. Hark, 'tis the Shepherd's voice I hear, Out in the des-ert dark and drear,
2. Who'll go and help this Shepherd kind, Help Him the wand'ring ones to find?
3. Out in the des - ert hear their cry, Out on the mountains wild and high,

Call - ing the sheep who've gone a-stray Far from the Shepherd's fold a - way.
Who'll bring the lost ones to the fold, Where they'll be sheltered from the cold?
Hark! 'tis the Mas-ter speaks to thee, "Go find My sheep wher-e'er they be."

Chorus
1
2
Bring them in, Bring them in, Bring them in from the fields of sin;
Bring them in, Bring them in, Bring the wand'ring ones to (Omit)
Je - sus.
I Would Be True
190
PEEK. 11.10.11.10.
Howard Arnold Walter, 1883-1918
Joseph Yates Peek, 1911
1. I would be true, for there are those who trust me; I would be
2. I would be friend of all—the foe, the friend - less; I would be
pure, for there are those who care; I would be strong, for
giv - ing, and for - get the gift; I would be hum - ble,
there is much to suf - fer; I would be brave, for there is much to
for I know my weak-ness; I would look up, and laugh, and love, and
dare, I would be brave, for there is much to dare.
lift, I would look up, and laugh, and love, and lift.

191 "Are Ye Able?" Said the Master

BEACON HILL. Irregular

Earl Marlatt, b. 1892 — Harry S. Mason, b. 1881

1. "Are ye a - ble," said the Mas - ter, "To be cru - ci - fied with Me?"
"Yea," the stur - dy dream-ers an-swered, "To the death we fol - low Thee."

2. "Are ye a - ble," to re-mem - ber, When a thief lifts up his eyes,
That his par-doned soul is wor - thy Of a place in Par - a - dise?

3. "Are ye a - ble," when the shad-ows Close a-round you with the sod,
To be-lieve that spir - it tri-umphs. To com-mend your soul to God?

4. "Are ye a - ble," still the Mas - ter Whispers down e - ter - ni - ty,
And he - ro - ic spir-its an - swer, Now, as then in Gal - i - lee.

REFRAIN

"Lord, we are a - ble," Our spir - its are Thine, Re - mold them; make us like Thee, di - vine: Thy guid - ing ra-diance a - bove us shall be, A bea - con to God, To faith and loy - al - ty.

rit.

The Voice of God Is Calling 192

WEBB. 7.6.7.6.D.

John Haynes Holmes, b. 1879
George J. Webb, 1803-1887
1. The voice of God is call - ing Its sum - mons un - to men;
2. I hear My peo - ple cry - ing In cot and mine and slum;
3. We heed, O Lord, Thy sum - mons, And an - swer, Here are we!
4. From ease and plen - ty save us, From pride of place ab - solve;
As once He spoke in Zi - on, So now He speaks a - gain;
No field or mart is si - lent, No cit - y street is dumb.
Send us up - on Thine er - rand, Let us Thy ser - vants be.
Purge us of low de - sire Lift us to high re - solve.
Whom shall I send to suc - cor My peo - ple in their need,
I see My peo - ple fall - ing In dark-ness and de - spair,
Our strength is dust and ash - es, Our years a pass-ing hour—
Take us, and make us ho - ly, Teach us Thy will and way,
Whom shall I send to loos - en The bonds of shame and greed?
Whom shall I send to shat - ter The fet - ters which they bear?
But Thou canst use our weak-ness, To mag - ni - fy Thy power.
Speak, and be-hold! we an - swer, Com-mand, and we o - bey! A-MEN.

Words used by permission of John Haynes Holmes.

193 I Will Follow Thee

James Lawson, b. 1874 — James Lawson, alt., b. 1874

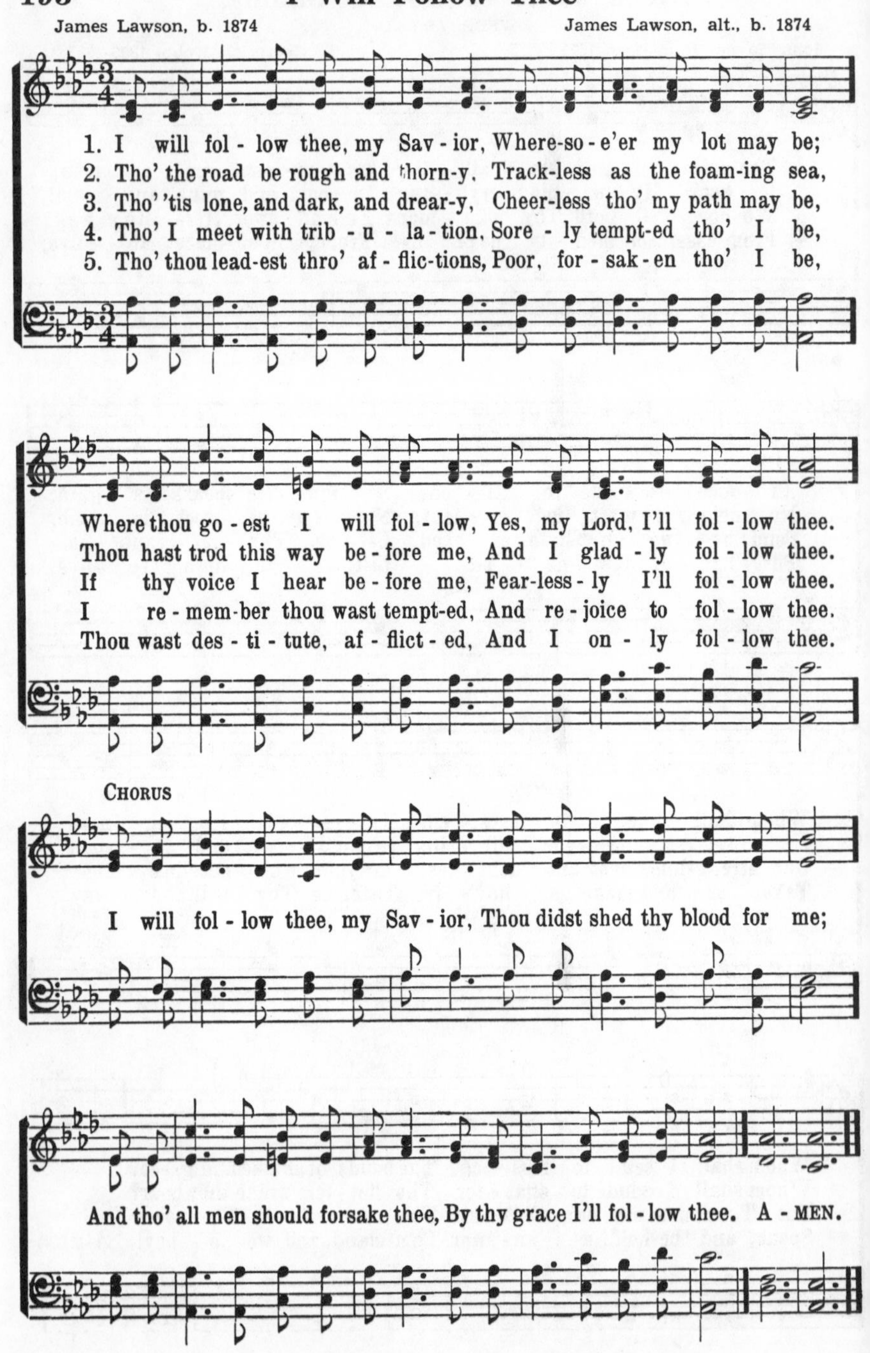
1. I will fol - low thee, my Sav - ior, Where-so - e'er my lot may be;
2. Tho' the road be rough and thorn-y, Track-less as the foam-ing sea,
3. Tho' 'tis lone, and dark, and drear-y, Cheer-less tho' my path may be,
4. Tho' I meet with trib - u - la - tion, Sore - ly tempt-ed tho' I be,
5. Tho' thou lead-est thro' af - flic-tions, Poor, for - sak - en tho' I be,
Where thou go - est I will fol - low, Yes, my Lord, I'll fol - low thee.
Thou hast trod this way be - fore me, And I glad - ly fol - low thee.
If thy voice I hear be - fore me, Fear-less - ly I'll fol - low thee.
I re - mem - ber thou wast tempt-ed, And re - joice to fol - low thee.
Thou wast des - ti - tute, af - flict - ed, And I on - ly fol - low thee.
CHORUS
I will fol - low thee, my Sav - ior, Thou didst shed thy blood for me;
And tho' all men should forsake thee, By thy grace I'll fol - low thee. A - MEN.

Jesus, I My Cross Have Taken 194

ELLESDIE. 8.7.8.7.D.

Henry F. Lyte, 1793-1847

From Wolfgang A. Mozart, 1756-1791
Arr. by Hubert P. Main, 1839-1926

1. Je - sus, I my cross have tak - en, All to leave and fol - low thee;
2. Let the world de-spise and leave me, They have left my Sav - ior, too;
3. Go, then, earth-ly fame and treas-ure! Come, dis - as - ter, scorn and pain!
4. Man may troub-le and dis-tress me, 'Twill but drive me to thy breast;

Nak - ed, poor, de-spised, for - sak - en, Thou from hence my all shalt be:
Hu-man hearts and looks de - ceive me, Thou art not, like them, un - true:
In thy serv - ice pain is pleas-ure; With thy fa - vor loss is gain.
Life with tri - als hard may press me, Heav'n will bring me sweet-er rest.

Per - ish ev - ery fond am - bi - tion, All I've sought, or hoped or known,
And while thou shalt smile up - on me, God of wis - dom, love and might,
I have called thee, "Ab - ba, Fa - ther," I have stayed my heart on thee:
O 'tis not in grief to harm me, While thy love is left to me;

Yet, how rich is my con-di - tion! God and heav'n are still my own.
Foes may hate and friends may shun me, Show thy face and all is bright.
Storms may howl, and clouds may gather, All must work for good to me.
O 'twere not in joy to charm me, Were that joy un-mixed with thee. A-MEN.

195 I've Enlisted in His Service

William J. Henry, 1903 — William J. Henry, 1903

1. I am fight-ing in the ar-my of the Lord, And tho' dan-gers thick-ly
2. And if I should meet with Sa-tan by the way, And his fi-ery darts should
3. Now the world has ceased to be a friend to me, And the ones I most have
4. I shall nev-er tire or give the bat-tle o'er, For the crown-ing day is

round my path-way lie, I shall nev-er faint or fear, for my
thick-ly round me fly; When the shield of faith he sees, then he
loved now pass me by; To my Lord I'll faith-ful be, who has
com-ing by and by; Then thro' all e-ter-ni-ty I shall

Je-sus is so near; I've en-list-ed in his serv-ice till I die.
al-ways quick-ly flees; I've en-list-ed in his serv-ice till I die.
shed his blood for me; I've en-list-ed in his serv-ice till I die.
shout the vic-to-ry; I've en-list-ed in his serv-ice till I die.

CHORUS

I will press the bat-tle on till the vic-to-ry is won And I

reach my crown and man-sion by and by; By the grace of God I know

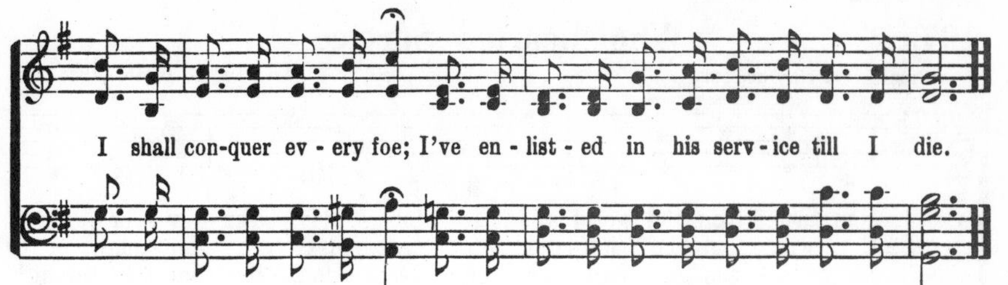
I shall con-quer ev - ery foe; I've en - list - ed in his serv - ice till I die.

Faith of Our Fathers

196

ST. CATHERINE. 8.8.8.8.8.8.

Frederick W. Faber, 1814-1863

Henry F. Hemy, 1818-1888
alt. by James G. Walton, 1821-1905

1. Faith of our fa - thers! liv - ing still In spite of dun-geon, fire and sword:
2. Faith of our fa - thers, we will strive To win all na-tions un - to thee;
3. Faith of our fa - thers! we will love Both friend and foe in all our strife:

O how our hearts beat high with joy Whene'er we hear that glo-rious word!
And thro' the truth that comes from God Mankind shall then in - deed be free.
And preach thee, too, as love knows how, By kind-ly words and vir - tuous life:

Faith of our fa-thers! ho - ly faith! We will be true to thee till death!
Faith of our fa-thers! ho - ly faith! We will be true to thee till death!
Faith of our fa-thers! ho - ly faith! We will be true to thee till death! A-MEN.

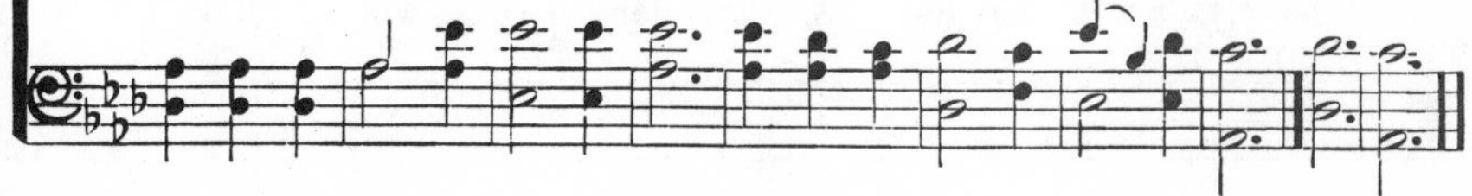

197 Wholehearted Service

Charles W. Naylor, 1925 — Andrew L. Byers, 1925

1. I've turned from the world and its fol - lies, For - ev - er for - sak - en all sin; I've giv - en my - self un - to Je - sus To ev - er and on - ly serve him.
2. I will not be lan - guid or care - less, Or for - mal, or cold, or un - true; But, striv - ing with ear - nest en - deav - or, The will of my Lord I will do.
3. Since Je - sus gave all to re - deem me, Since on - ly through mer - cy I live, It now is my joy and my pur - pose A whole-heart-ed serv - ice to give.
4. O help me, dear Lord, to be read - y The task that thou giv - est to do, Not shrink-ing from la - bor or du - ty, De - vot - ed and faith-ful and true.
CHORUS
I'll put my whole heart in his serv - ice, And do all he ask - eth of me; I mean to live ho - ly and blame - less— A Chris-tian in - deed will I be.

Follow On! 198

William O. Cushing, 1823-1902 | Robert Lowry, 1826-1899

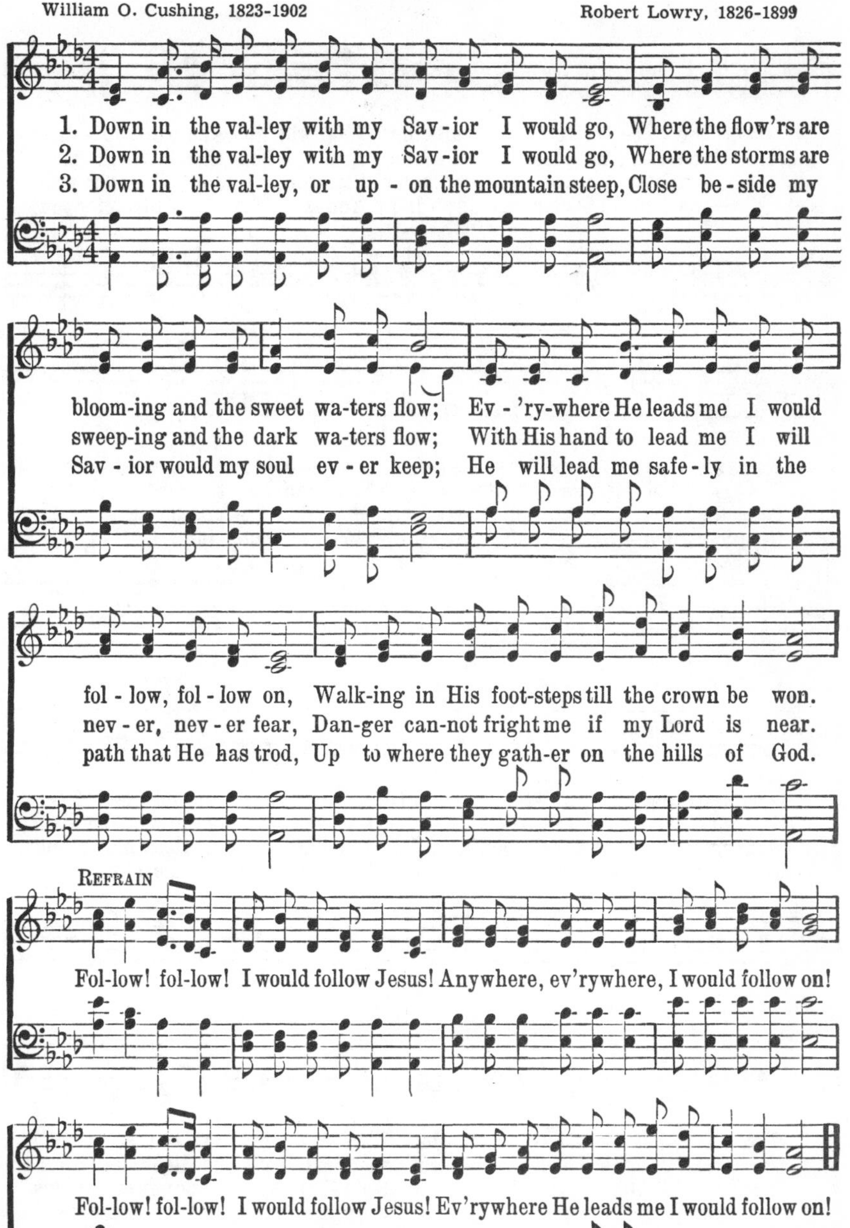
1. Down in the val-ley with my Sav-ior I would go, Where the flow'rs are bloom-ing and the sweet wa-ters flow; Ev-'ry-where He leads me I would fol-low, fol-low on, Walk-ing in His foot-steps till the crown be won.
2. Down in the val-ley with my Sav-ior I would go, Where the storms are sweep-ing and the dark wa-ters flow; With His hand to lead me I will nev-er, nev-er fear, Dan-ger can-not fright me if my Lord is near.
3. Down in the val-ley, or up-on the mountain steep, Close be-side my Sav-ior would my soul ev-er keep; He will lead me safe-ly in the path that He has trod, Up to where they gath-er on the hills of God.
Refrain
Fol-low! fol-low! I would follow Jesus! Anywhere, ev'rywhere, I would follow on!
Fol-low! fol-low! I would follow Jesus! Ev'rywhere He leads me I would follow on!

199 Here Am I, Send Me

Daniel March, 1816-1909 — Franklin E. Belden, b. 1858

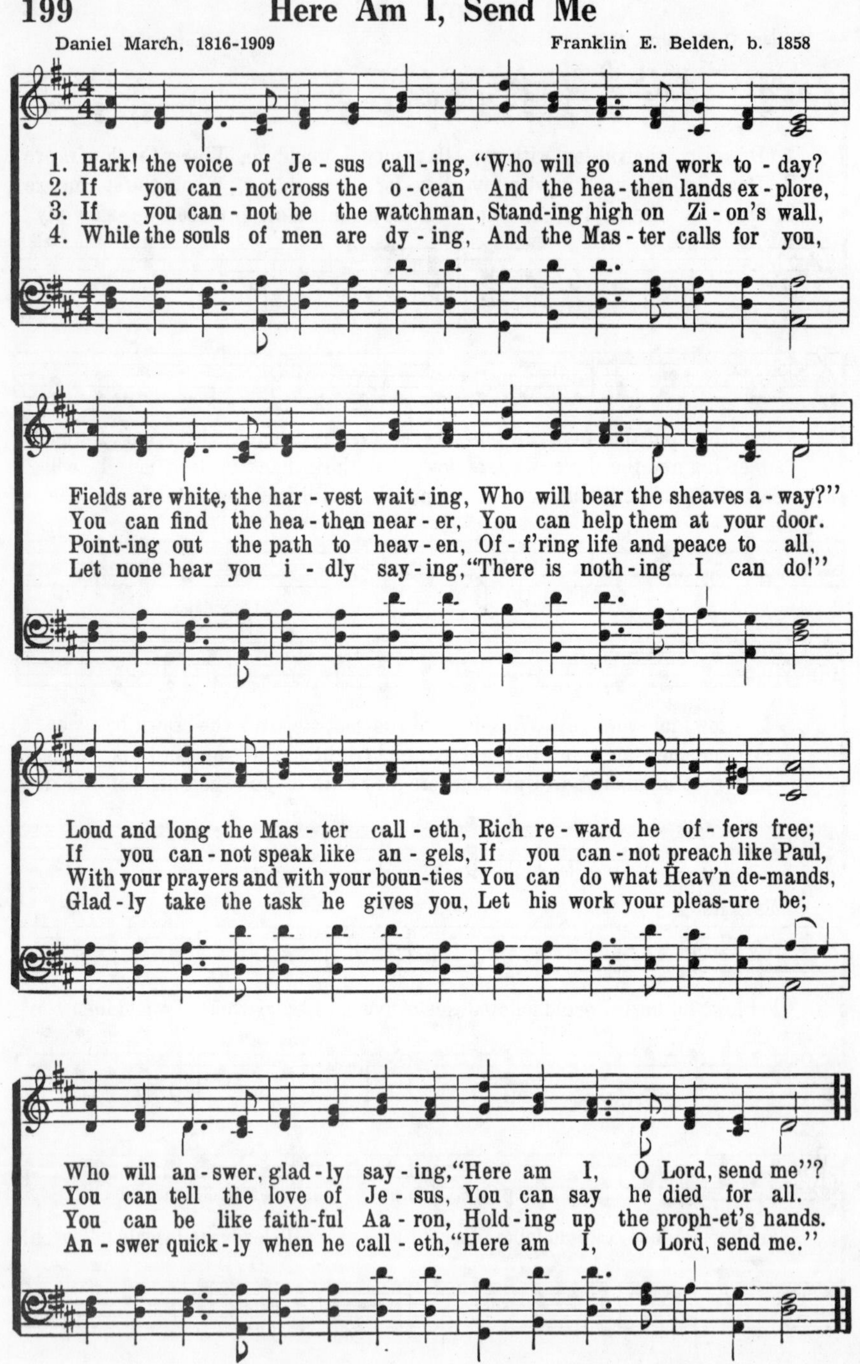
1. Hark! the voice of Je - sus call - ing, "Who will go and work to - day?
2. If you can - not cross the o - cean And the hea - then lands ex - plore,
3. If you can - not be the watchman, Stand-ing high on Zi - on's wall,
4. While the souls of men are dy - ing, And the Mas - ter calls for you,
Fields are white, the har - vest wait - ing, Who will bear the sheaves a - way?"
You can find the hea - then near - er, You can help them at your door.
Point-ing out the path to heav - en, Of - f'ring life and peace to all,
Let none hear you i - dly say - ing, "There is noth - ing I can do!"
Loud and long the Mas - ter call - eth, Rich re - ward he of - fers free;
If you can - not speak like an - gels, If you can - not preach like Paul,
With your prayers and with your boun-ties You can do what Heav'n de-mands,
Glad - ly take the task he gives you, Let his work your pleas-ure be;
Who will an - swer, glad - ly say - ing, "Here am I, O Lord, send me"?
You can tell the love of Je - sus, You can say he died for all.
You can be like faith-ful Aa - ron, Hold-ing up the proph-et's hands.
An - swer quick - ly when he call - eth, "Here am I, O Lord, send me."

Must Jesus Bear the Cross Alone? 200

MAITLAND. C.M.

Thomas Shepherd, 1665-1739, and others — George N. Allen, 1812-1877

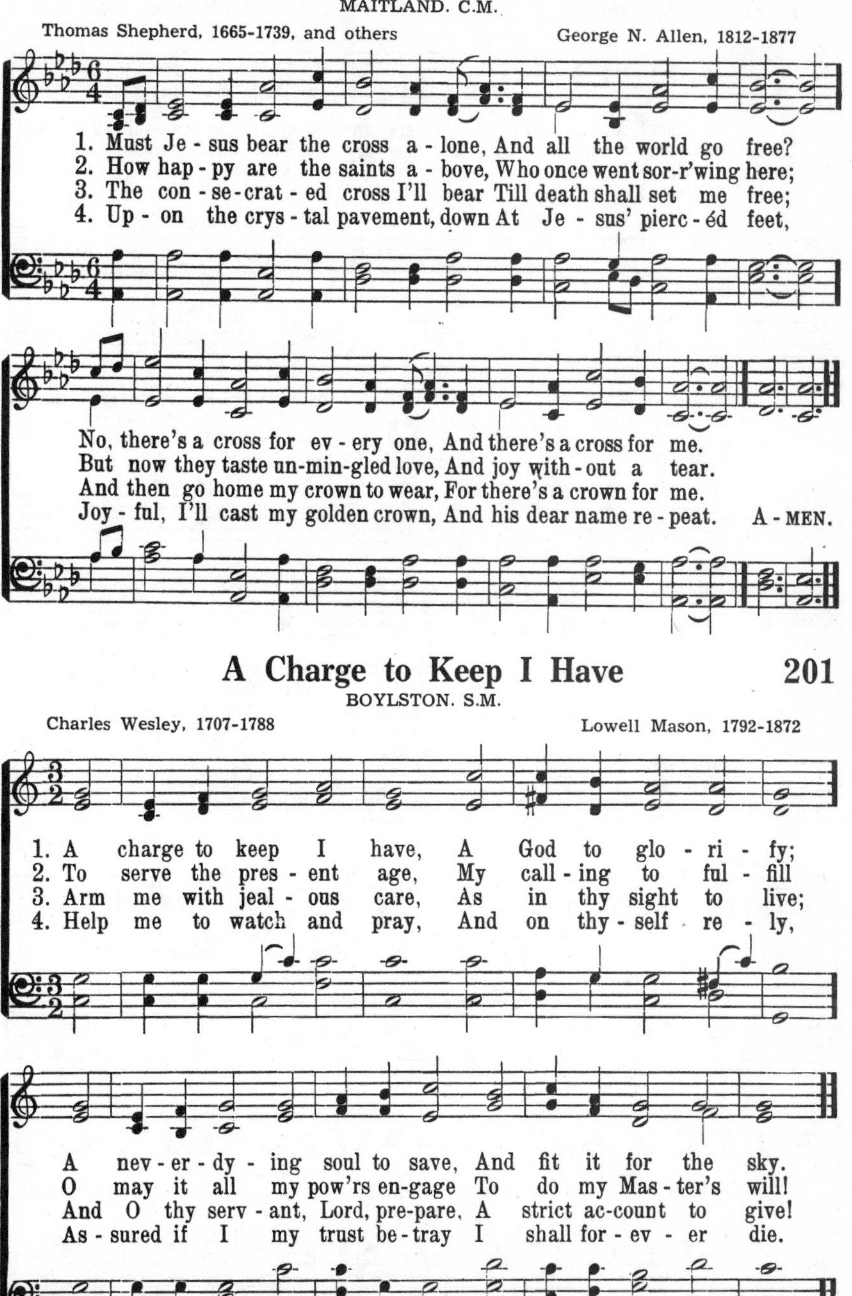
1. Must Je - sus bear the cross a - lone, And all the world go free?
2. How hap - py are the saints a - bove, Who once went sor-r'wing here;
3. The con - se - crat - ed cross I'll bear Till death shall set me free;
4. Up - on the crys - tal pavement, down At Je - sus' pierc - éd feet,
No, there's a cross for ev - ery one, And there's a cross for me.
But now they taste un-min-gled love, And joy with - out a tear.
And then go home my crown to wear, For there's a crown for me.
Joy - ful, I'll cast my golden crown, And his dear name re - peat. A - MEN.

A Charge to Keep I Have 201

BOYLSTON. S.M.

Charles Wesley, 1707-1788 — Lowell Mason, 1792-1872

1. A charge to keep I have, A God to glo - ri - fy;
2. To serve the pres - ent age, My call - ing to ful - fill
3. Arm me with jeal - ous care, As in thy sight to live;
4. Help me to watch and pray, And on thy - self re - ly,
A nev - er - dy - ing soul to save, And fit it for the sky.
O may it all my pow'rs en-gage To do my Mas - ter's will!
And O thy serv - ant, Lord, pre-pare, A strict ac-count to give!
As - sured if I my trust be-tray I shall for - ev - er die.

202 To the Work

Fanny J. Crosby, 1820-1915 William H. Doane, 1832-1915

1. To the work! to the work! we are serv-ants of God, Let us fol-low the path that our Mas-ter has trod; With the balm of his coun-sel our strength to re-new, Let us do with our might what our hands find to do.
2. To the work! to the work! let the hun-gry be fed; To the foun-tain of life let the wea-ry be led; In the cross and its ban-ner our glo-ry shall be, While we her-ald the ti-dings, "Sal-va-tion is free!"
3. To the work! to the work! there is la-bor for all, For the king-dom of dark-ness and er-ror shall fall; And the name of Je-ho-vah ex-alt-ed shall be In the loud-swell-ing cho-rus, "Sal-va-tion is free!"
4. To the work! to the work! in the strength of the Lord, And a robe and a crown shall our la-bor re-ward; When the home of the faith-ful our dwell-ing shall be, And we shout with the ran-somed, "Sal-va-tion is free!"
CHORUS
Toil-ing on, Toil-ing on, toil-ing on, toil-ing on, Toil-ing on, Toil-ing on, toil-ing on; toil-ing on;
Let us hope, and trust, let us watch, and pray, And la-bor till the Mas-ter comes. A-MEN.

Every Hour for Jesus

203

Barney E. Warren, 1900 Barney E. Warren, 1900

1. Ev - ery hour for Je - sus, shall our mot - to be, There is plen - ty of
2. Ev - ery hour for Je - sus, we must work and pray, We should nev - er be
3. Ev - ery hour for Je - sus, and what-e'er we do, We must have his ap-
4. Ev - ery hour for Je - sus, there is work for all, Spend your time in his
work we may do; We may all keep bus - y till the Lord we see,
sloth - ful, or tire; For the time is com-ing, so his word doth say,
prov - al to - day; If we do heart serv-ice with the Lord in view,
serv - ice a - lone; Be ye read - y, wait-ing for his ev - ery call,
CHORUS
Till he comes for his faith - ful few.
When our work shall be tried by fire. Ev - ery hour for the
He will bless us a - long life's way.
Soon he'll say, "'Tis e-nough, come home." Ev - ery hour
Lord, Ev - ery hour for the Lord let us spend; Ev - ery hour for
for the Lord,
Je - sus till he comes a - gain, When the la - bor of life shall end. A - MEN.

204 Together We Go to Make Disciples

Frederick G. Shackleton. 1950 — Frederick G. Shackleton. 1950

1. Christ our might-y Lead-er calls us, "Go, make dis-ci-ples!" What a no-ble task be-falls us: "Go, make dis-ci-ples!"
2. Hear the Great Com-mis-sion sound-ing, "Go, make dis-ci-ples!" Har-vest fields are now a-bound-ing. "Go, make dis-ci-ples!"
3. Sow-ers shall re-joice with reap-ers— "Go, make dis-ci-ples!" All who are their broth-ers' keep-ers, "Go, make dis-ci-ples!"

REFRAIN

To-geth-er we go to make dis-ci-ples for Je-sus our Lord in ev-'ry land; We're reaching the lost for Christ, the Sav-iour, On far-a-way shores and near at hand. To-geth-er we go to tell our neigh-bors The mes-sage of Christ, man's tru-est Friend. All

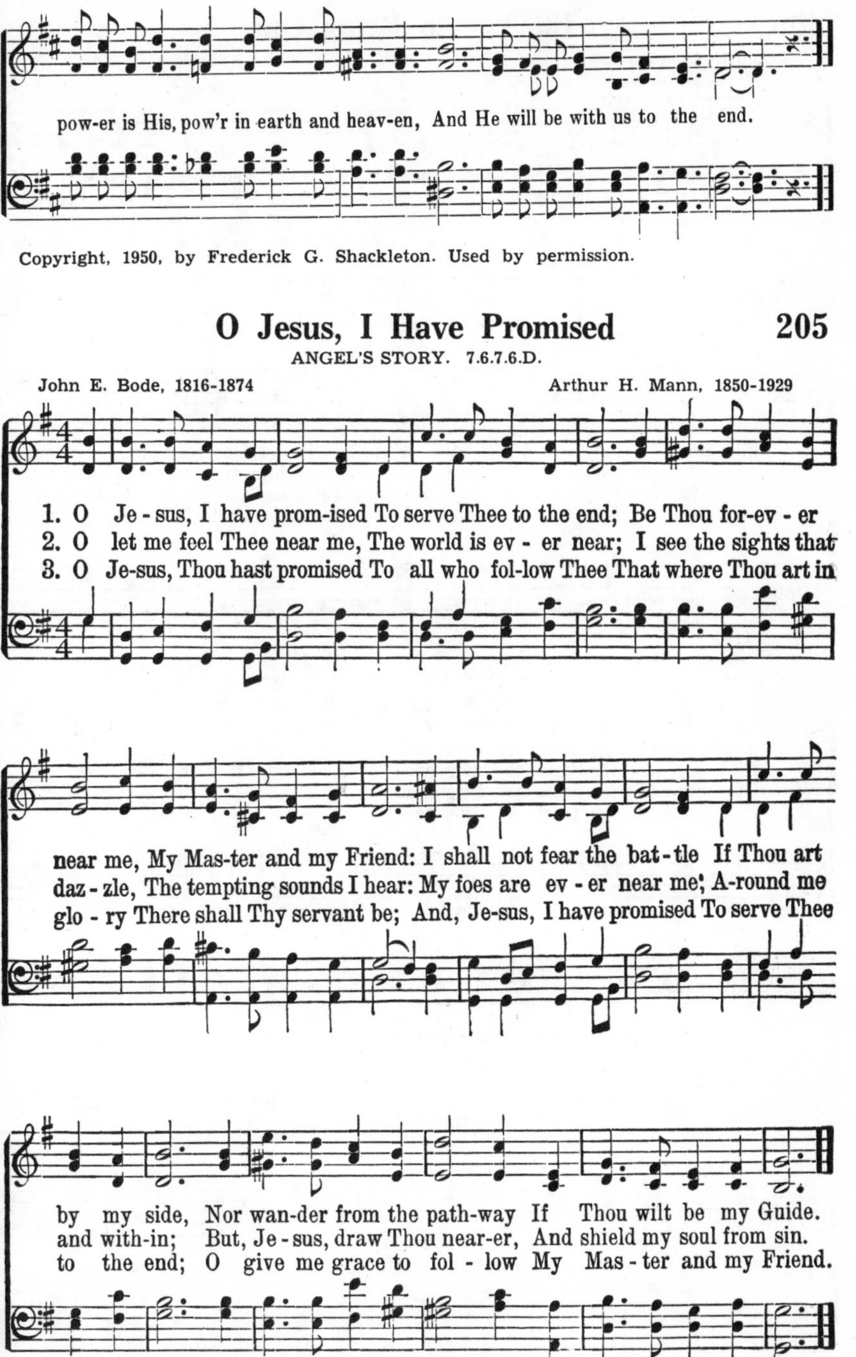
pow-er is His, pow'r in earth and heav-en, And He will be with us to the end.
Copyright, 1950, by Frederick G. Shackleton. Used by permission.
O Jesus, I Have Promised
205
ANGEL'S STORY. 7.6.7.6.D.
John E. Bode, 1816-1874
Arthur H. Mann, 1850-1929
1. O Je - sus, I have prom-ised To serve Thee to the end; Be Thou for-ev - er
2. O let me feel Thee near me, The world is ev - er near; I see the sights that
3. O Je-sus, Thou hast promised To all who fol-low Thee That where Thou art in
near me, My Mas-ter and my Friend: I shall not fear the bat - tle If Thou art
daz - zle, The tempting sounds I hear: My foes are ev - er near me, A-round me
glo - ry There shall Thy servant be; And, Je-sus, I have promised To serve Thee
by my side, Nor wan-der from the path-way If Thou wilt be my Guide.
and with-in; But, Je - sus, draw Thou near-er, And shield my soul from sin.
to the end; O give me grace to fol - low My Mas - ter and my Friend.

206 I'll Try to Bring One

Lizzie DeArmond, 1923 — Andrew L. Byers, 1923

Not too fast
1. I have a dear Sav-ior, the best Friend I know, While dai-ly my life-race I run, I'll try to help oth-ers as on-ward I go, And in-to his keep-ing bring one.
2. So man-y are walk-ing in path-ways of sin, Who glad-ly the e-vil would shun If some one would help them the vic-t'ry to win: I'll try to the Christ to bring one.
3. So man-y grow wea-ry and fall in the fight, Their jour-ney to heav'n just be-gun; Per-haps they are watch-ing my dim lit-tle light, I'll try in his name to bring one.
4. I'll stand in the pres-ence of Je-sus my King Some day when my work is all done: With all of the ran-somed I'll joy-ful-ly sing If un-to my Lord I bring one.
CHORUS
Each soul that we save is a star in our crown, When heaven's glad morning's be-gun; If I can-not do more ere life's sun go-eth down I will bring to the Sav-ior just one.

We Will Work for Jesus 207

Daniel S. Warner, 1893 Andrew L. Byers, 1897

1. We will work for Je - sus and a - dore the plan That ex - alt - eth so a fall - en race, Join - ing with the Sav - ior, do - ing what we can To ex - tend the won-ders of his grace.
2. We will work for Je - sus, all to him we owe; On - ly for his mer - cy we would be Lost in sin for - ev - er; but we tru - ly know That his might - y love has set us free.
3. We will work for Je - sus, we are not our own; Je - sus, we can nev - er i - dle be; Souls a - round us dy - ing, pur-chased for thy throne–We will gath - er all we can for thee.
4. We will work for Je - sus, bless his ho - ly name! Ev - ery-where the rip - ened grain we see; From the ear - ly morn-ing till the day is gone, Je - sus, we will la - bor on for thee.

CHORUS

We will work for Je - sus, We will work for Je - sus, We will work
We will work for Je - sus,
for Je - sus, We will live for him who died for all;
We will work for Je - sus,
yes, for all;

2

work for Je - sus, Till we hear the fi - nal trump - et call.
We will work for Je - sus,

208 Bringing In the Sheaves

Knowles Shaw, 1834-1878 — George A. Minor

1. Sow - ing in the morn - ing, sow-ing seeds of kind - ness, Sow-ing in the noon - tide and the dew - y eve; Wait-ing for the har - vest, and the time of reap-ing, We shall come re - joic - ing, bring-ing in the sheaves.
2. Sow - ing in the sun-shine, sow-ing in the shad - ows, Fear-ing nei - ther clouds nor win-ter's chill - ing breeze; By and by the har - vest, and the la - bor end - ed, We shall come re - joic - ing, bring-ing in the sheaves.
3. Go - ing forth with weep-ing, sow-ing for the Mas - ter, Tho' the loss sus-tained our spir - it oft - en grieves; When our weep - ing's o - ver, He will bid us wel-come, We shall come re - joic - ing, bring-ing in the sheaves.

CHORUS

Bring-ing in the sheaves, bring-ing in the sheaves, We shall come re-joic-ing, bring - ing in the sheaves;
Bring-ing in the sheaves, bring-ing in the sheaves, We shall come re-joic-ing, bring - ing in the sheaves.

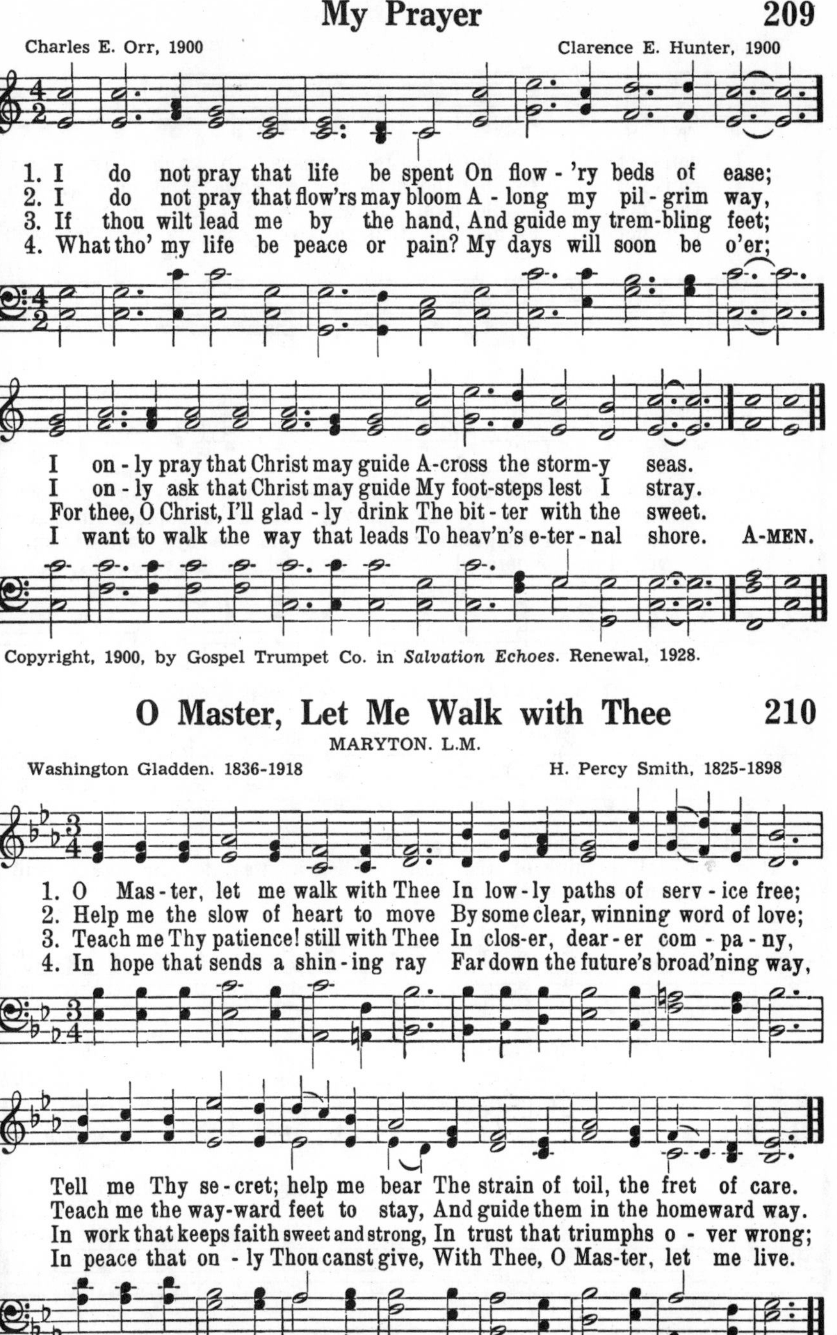
My Prayer 209
Charles E. Orr, 1900
Clarence E. Hunter, 1900
1. I do not pray that life be spent On flow-'ry beds of ease; I on-ly pray that Christ may guide A-cross the storm-y seas.
2. I do not pray that flow'rs may bloom A-long my pil-grim way, I on-ly ask that Christ may guide My foot-steps lest I stray.
3. If thou wilt lead me by the hand, And guide my trem-bling feet; For thee, O Christ, I'll glad-ly drink The bit-ter with the sweet.
4. What tho' my life be peace or pain? My days will soon be o'er; I want to walk the way that leads To heav'n's e-ter-nal shore. A-MEN.
Copyright, 1900, by Gospel Trumpet Co. in Salvation Echoes. Renewal, 1928.
O Master, Let Me Walk with Thee 210
MARYTON. L.M.
Washington Gladden. 1836-1918
H. Percy Smith, 1825-1898
1. O Mas-ter, let me walk with Thee In low-ly paths of serv-ice free; Tell me Thy se-cret; help me bear The strain of toil, the fret of care.
2. Help me the slow of heart to move By some clear, winning word of love; Teach me the way-ward feet to stay, And guide them in the homeward way.
3. Teach me Thy patience! still with Thee In clos-er, dear-er com-pa-ny, In work that keeps faith sweet and strong, In trust that triumphs o-ver wrong;
4. In hope that sends a shin-ing ray Far down the future's broad'ning way, In peace that on-ly Thou canst give, With Thee, O Mas-ter, let me live.

211 I Cannot Be Idle

William J. Henry, 1897 William J. Henry, 1897

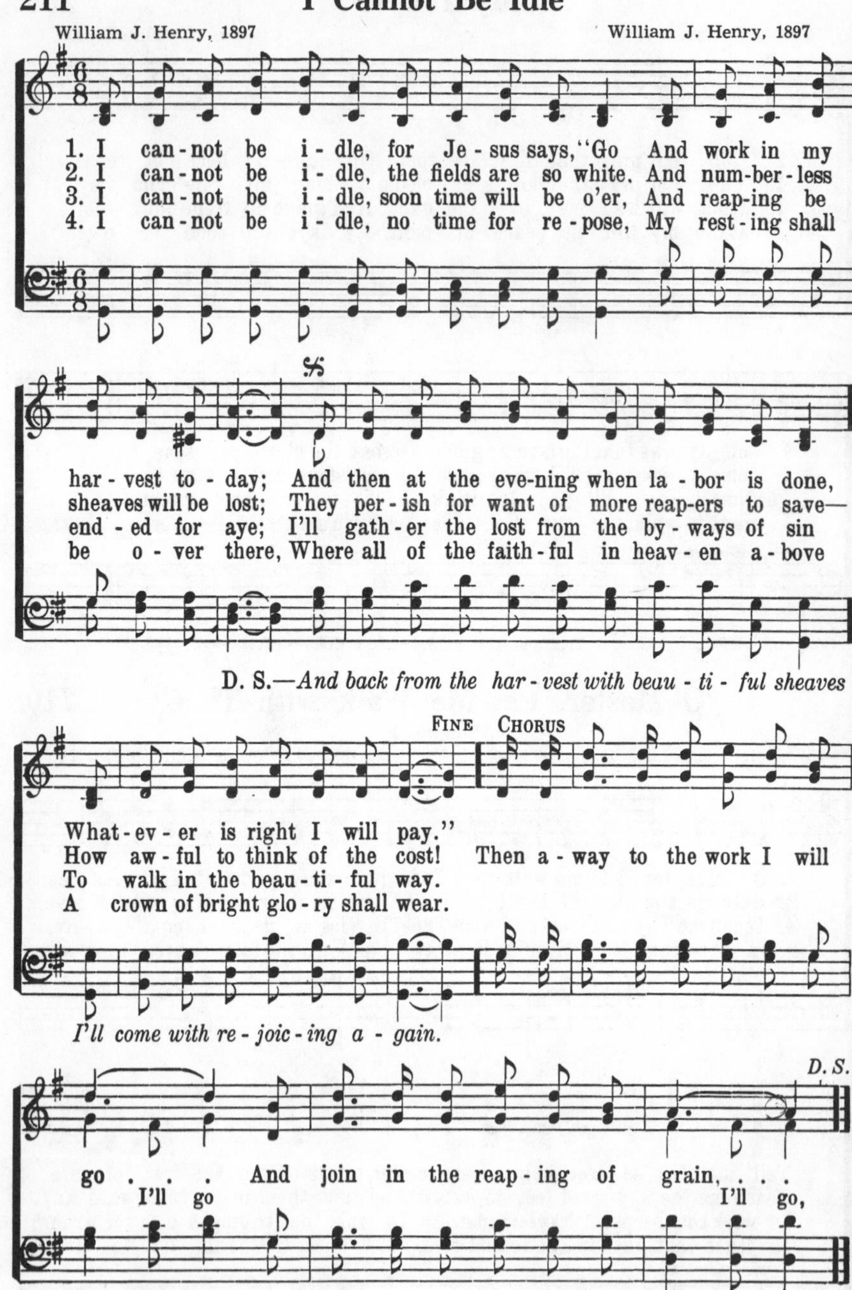
1. I can-not be i-dle, for Je-sus says, "Go And work in my har-vest to-day; And then at the eve-ning when la-bor is done, What-ev-er is right I will pay."
2. I can-not be i-dle, the fields are so white, And num-ber-less sheaves will be lost; They per-ish for want of more reap-ers to save— How aw-ful to think of the cost!
3. I can-not be i-dle, soon time will be o'er, And reap-ing be end-ed for aye; I'll gath-er the lost from the by-ways of sin To walk in the beau-ti-ful way.
4. I can-not be i-dle, no time for re-pose, My rest-ing shall be o-ver there, Where all of the faith-ful in heav-en a-bove A crown of bright glo-ry shall wear.
D. S.—And back from the har-vest with beau-ti-ful sheaves I'll come with re-joic-ing a-gain.
FINE
CHORUS
Then a-way to the work I will go . . . I'll go And join in the reap-ing of grain, . . . I'll go,
D. S.

Every Hour of the Passing Day 212

D. Otis Teasley, 1907 — D. Otis Teasley, 1907

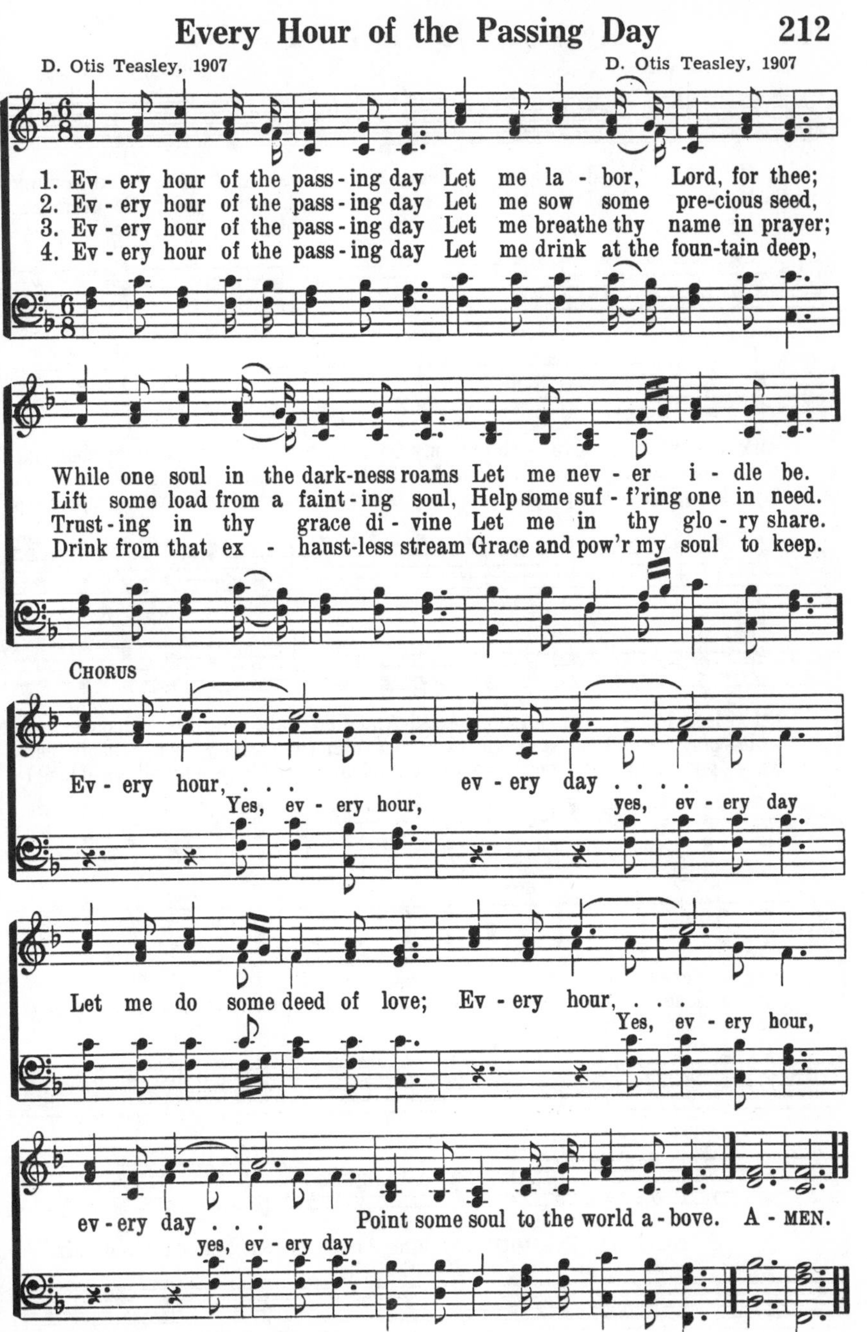
1. Ev - ery hour of the pass - ing day Let me la - bor, Lord, for thee;
2. Ev - ery hour of the pass - ing day Let me sow some pre-cious seed,
3. Ev - ery hour of the pass - ing day Let me breathe thy name in prayer;
4. Ev - ery hour of the pass - ing day Let me drink at the foun-tain deep,
While one soul in the dark-ness roams Let me nev - er i - dle be.
Lift some load from a faint - ing soul, Help some suf - f'ring one in need.
Trust - ing in thy grace di - vine Let me in thy glo - ry share.
Drink from that ex - haust-less stream Grace and pow'r my soul to keep.
CHORUS
Ev - ery hour, . . . ev - ery day . . . .
Yes, ev - ery hour, yes, ev - ery day
Let me do some deed of love; Ev - ery hour, . . .
Yes, ev - ery hour,
ev - ery day . . . Point some soul to the world a - bove. A - MEN.
yes, ev - ery day

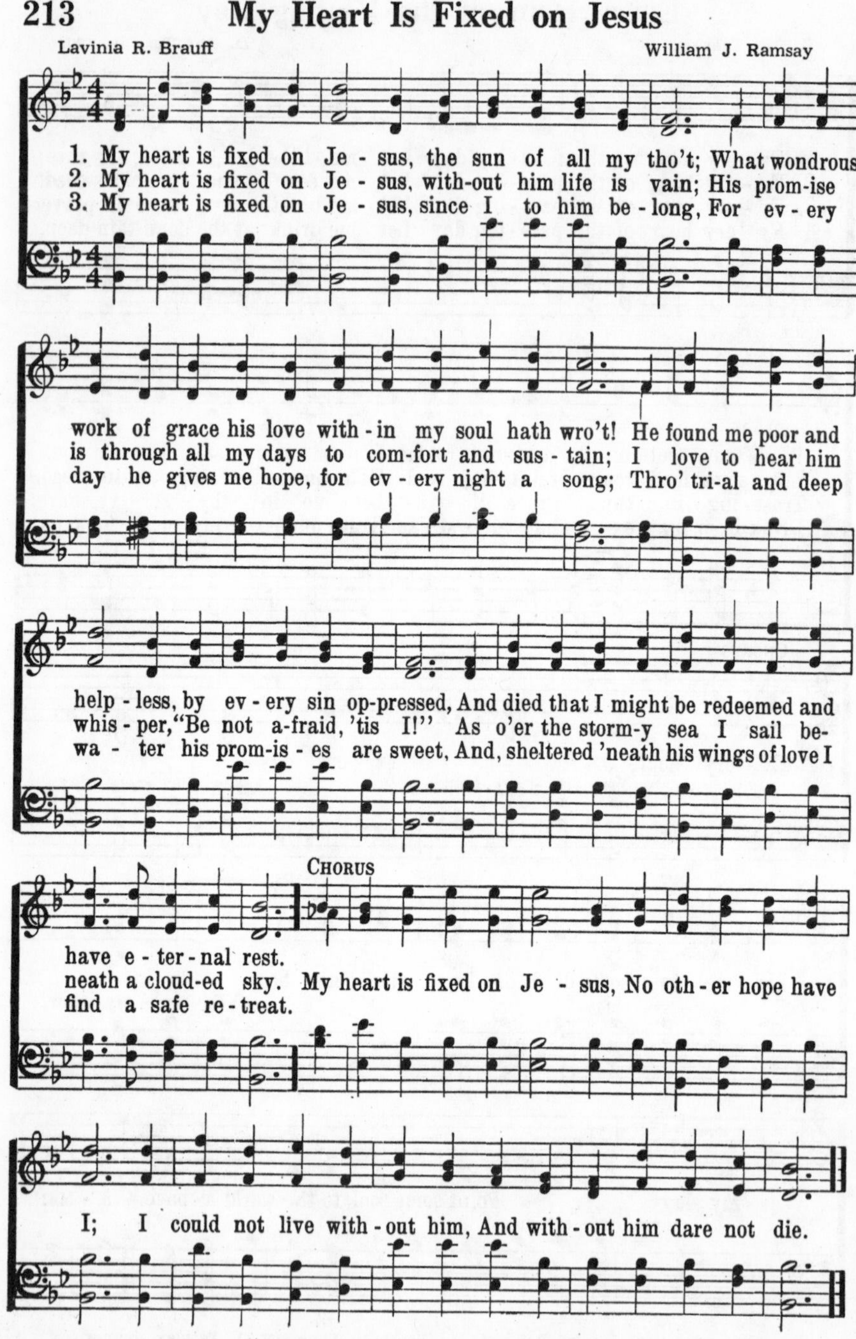
213
My Heart Is Fixed on Jesus
Lavinia R. Brauff
William J. Ramsay
1. My heart is fixed on Je - sus, the sun of all my tho't; What wondrous
2. My heart is fixed on Je - sus, with-out him life is vain; His prom-ise
3. My heart is fixed on Je - sus, since I to him be - long, For ev - ery
work of grace his love with - in my soul hath wro't! He found me poor and
is through all my days to com-fort and sus - tain; I love to hear him
day he gives me hope, for ev - ery night a song; Thro' tri-al and deep
help - less, by ev - ery sin op-pressed, And died that I might be redeemed and
whis - per, "Be not a-fraid, 'tis I!" As o'er the storm-y sea I sail be-
wa - ter his prom-is - es are sweet, And, sheltered 'neath his wings of love I
have e - ter - nal rest.
neath a cloud-ed sky.
find a safe re - treat.
CHORUS
My heart is fixed on Je - sus, No oth - er hope have
I; I could not live with - out him, And with - out him dare not die.

Let the Fire Fall on Me

William J. Henry, b. 1869
William J. Henry, b. 1869
1. Lord, I would be whol - ly thine, I would do thy will di - vine, From the
2. I would have suf - fi - cient grace Ev - ery foe to brave - ly face, And an
3. Ho - ly Spir - it from a - bove, Fill my long - ing soul with love, Till the
4. In the king-dom I would stay, There to la - bor night and day, An - y
world and sin and self I would be free; On the al - tar now I lie, And with
o - ver-com - er ev - er-more to be; That I well may fill my place, And that
Mas - ter's im - age all in me may see; Make me gen - tle, true and kind, Meek of
way and an - y-where thy will may be; But that I may do my best, And that
all my heart I cry, Let the ho - ly fire from heav - en fall on me.
I may win the race, Let the ho - ly fire from heav - en fall on me.
heart and hum - ble mind, Let the ho - ly fire from heav - en fall on me.
oth - ers may be blest, Let the ho - ly fire from heav - en fall on me.
FINE
D. S.—ho - ly fire from heav - en fall on me.
CHORUS
Let the fire fall on me, Let the fire fall on me;
Let the fire fall on me, Let the fire fall on me;
D. S.
The fire of Pen - te - cost, con - sum - ing sin and dross, Let the A - MEN.

215 Like a Rock in the Billows

Barney E. Warren, 1900
Barney E. Warren, 1900
1. Like a rock in the bil - lows I would sta - ble be Till the
2. Like a rock in the bil - lows I would nev - er yield To the
3. Like a rock in the bil - lows of a boil - ing sea, When its
4. Like a rock in the bil - lows I would fear - less stand And de-
storm is o - ver - past; For I long to har - bor, Lord, with thee
wild and an - gry wave; I would cling to Christ, my sun and shield,
wa - ters leap and foam, I would rest se - cure, my Lord, in thee
fy the threat-'ning blast; For the Sav - ior holds me by the hand
In my heav'n-ly home at last.
For his pow'r a - lone can save.
Till the trump - et calls me home.
Till the rag - ing storm is past.
CHORUS
If I trust in Je - sus and o-
bey his word, If I lean up - on his breast, If I keep low
down at his feet, I know He will give me peace and rest.

By Thy Blessed Word Obeying 216

Daniel S. Warner, 1842-1895 — Andrew L. Byers, 1870-1952

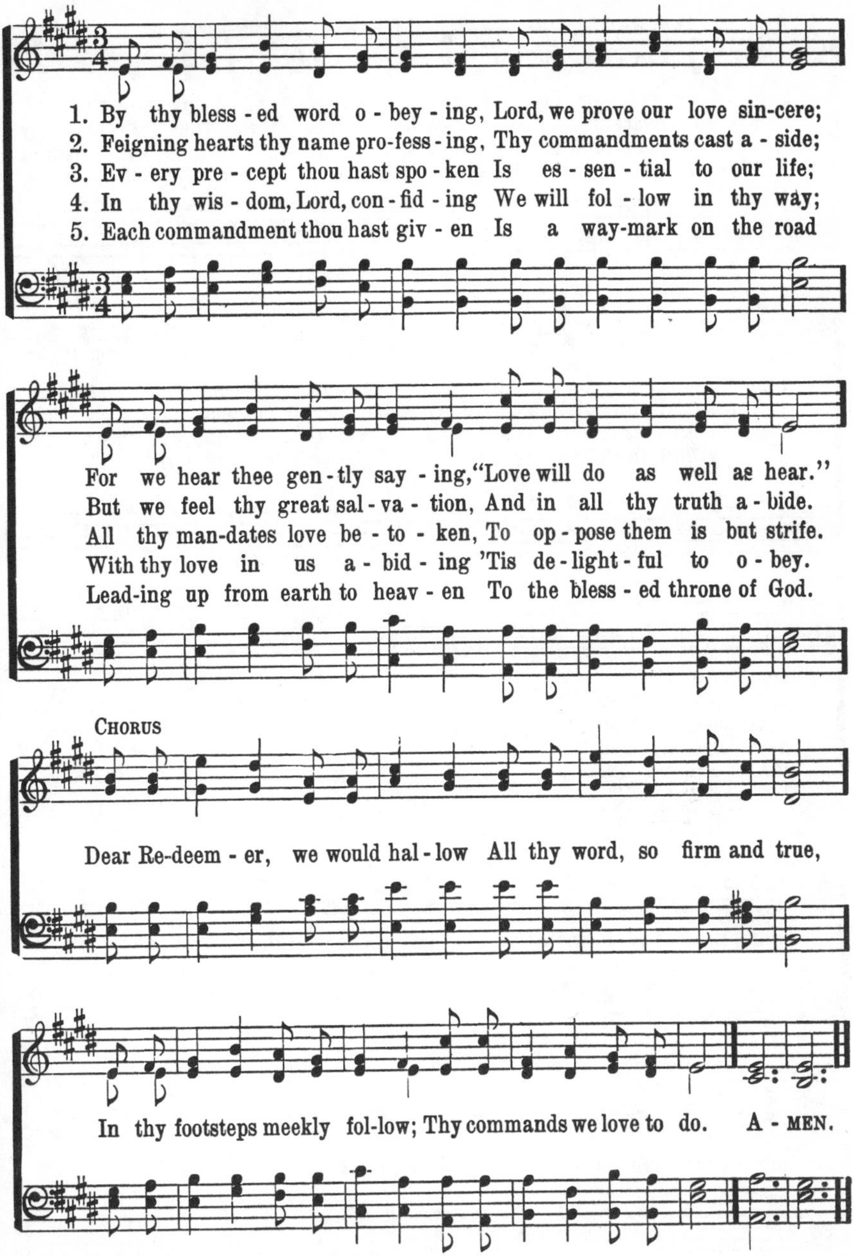

1. By thy bless - ed word o - bey - ing, Lord, we prove our love sin-cere;
2. Feigning hearts thy name pro-fess - ing, Thy commandments cast a - side;
3. Ev - ery pre - cept thou hast spo - ken Is es - sen - tial to our life;
4. In thy wis - dom, Lord, con - fid - ing We will fol - low in thy way;
5. Each commandment thou hast giv - en Is a way-mark on the road

For we hear thee gen - tly say - ing, "Love will do as well as hear."
But we feel thy great sal - va - tion, And in all thy truth a - bide.
All thy man-dates love be - to - ken, To op - pose them is but strife.
With thy love in us a - bid - ing 'Tis de - light - ful to o - bey.
Lead-ing up from earth to heav - en To the bless - ed throne of God.

CHORUS

Dear Re-deem - er, we would hal - low All thy word, so firm and true,

In thy footsteps meekly fol-low; Thy commands we love to do. A - MEN.

217 My Heart Says Amen

Charles W. Naylor, 1904 — Clarence E. Hunter, 1907

1. I have yield - ed my - self to thy serv - ice, And thy pres-ence my
2. All the heart-ties of earth may be sun - dered, So that I may thy
3. Tho' my plans and my hopes may seem blight-ed, I will love thee and
4. When I pass to that heav - en - ly coun - try, And my soul with its
bos - om doth fill; O my Sav - ior, I haste to o - bey thee, And my
pur - pose ful - fill; Help me glad - ly sub - mit and not mur - mur, Ev - er
trust in thee still, For I know all is well that thou do - est, And my
glo - ry doth thrill, This for - ev - er shall be my re - joic - ing, That my
heart says a - men to thy will.
say - ing a - men to thy will.
heart says a - men to thy will.
heart said a - men to thy will.
CHORUS
Yes, my heart says a - men to thy
will, Lord, And I know that thou lov - est me still, While I bow low in
hum - ble sub-mis - sion, And my heart says a-men to thy will. A - MEN.

I'm Going On 218

Charles W. Naylor, 1918 — Andrew L. Byers, 1918

1. I mean to go right on Until the crown is won; I mean to fight the fight of faith Till life on earth is done. I'll nevermore turn back, Defeat I shall not know, For God will give me victory If onward I shall go.
2. Should opposition come, Should foes obstruct my way, Should persecution's fires be lit As in the ancient day; With Jesus by my side, His peace within my soul, No matter if the battle's hot, I mean to win the goal.
3. I see a shining crown Awaiting over there, I see a mansion all prepared And decked with beauties rare: Shall that which intervenes Deprive me of my right? Nay, on I'll go until I reach That city of delight.
4. Then forward let us go, Our hearts with love aflame, Our snowy banner borne aloft, Inscribed with Jesus' name. The hosts of evil flee, And heaven's open gates Invite me now to hasten where Eternal glory waits.
CHORUS
I'm going on, going on, going on, I'm going on, going on, going on, Unto the final triumph I'm going, going, going on; going, going on; going on.

219 On to the Goal

Charles W. Naylor, 1874-1950 Andrew L. Byers, 1870-1952

1. Turn - ing thy face from all the past, On to the goal keep press - ing;
2. Nev - er mind what the oth - ers do, On to the goal keep press - ing;
3. For - ward and up - ward, faint - ing not, On to the goal keep press - ing;
4. Je - sus a crown holds out to thee, On to the goal keep press - ing;
All of the weights from off thee cast, On to the goal keep press - ing.
They can - not run the race for you, On to the goal keep press - ing.
Bear - ing what - ev - er falls thy lot, On to the goal keep press - ing.
Heav - en - ly glo - ry thine shall be, On to the goal keep press - ing.
See in the dis - tance there a - rise Glo - ri - ous man - sions in the skies,
Whether they run or turn a - side, Wheth-er in sin they still a - bide,
Trust in the Lord for strength to - day, "He is my help - er," bold - ly say,
Hap - pi - ness that no tongue can tell, Ev - er to prais - es shall im - pel,
Wait - ing for thee— a won-drous prize— On to the goal keep press - ing.
Fix - ing thine eyes on him who died, On to the goal keep press - ing.
An - gels will guard thee on thy way, On to the goal keep press - ing.
Safe in his pres - ence thou shalt dwell, On to the goal keep press - ing.
CHORUS
On, on, on to the goal! Je - sus will add his bless - ing:
On to the goal, will add his bless - ing:

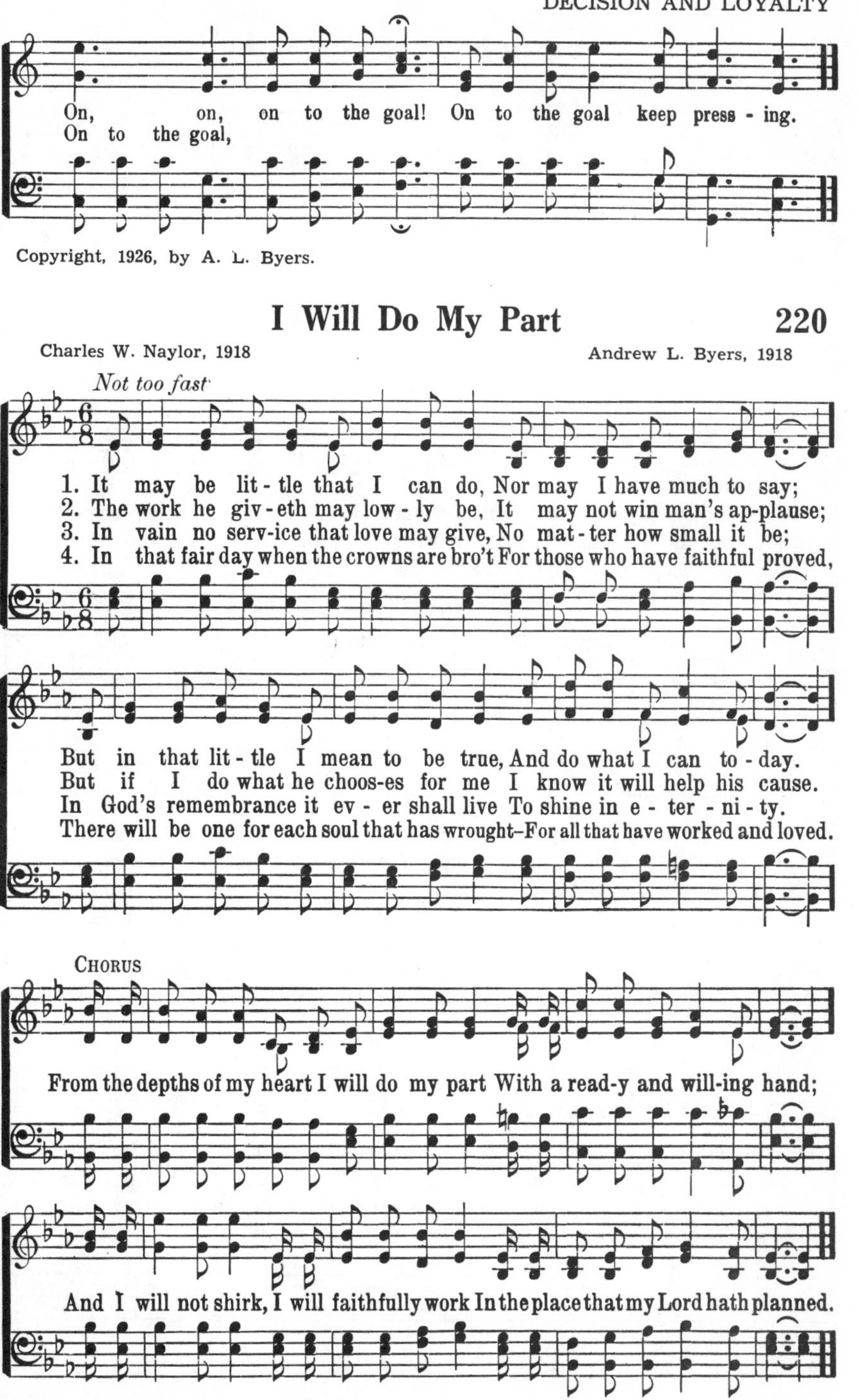
On, on, on to the goal! On to the goal keep press - ing.
On to the goal,
Copyright, 1926, by A. L. Byers.
I Will Do My Part
220
Charles W. Naylor, 1918
Andrew L. Byers, 1918
Not too fast
1. It may be lit - tle that I can do, Nor may I have much to say;
2. The work he giv - eth may low - ly be, It may not win man's ap-plause;
3. In vain no serv-ice that love may give, No mat - ter how small it be;
4. In that fair day when the crowns are bro't For those who have faithful proved,
But in that lit - tle I mean to be true, And do what I can to - day.
But if I do what he choos-es for me I know it will help his cause.
In God's remembrance it ev - er shall live To shine in e - ter - ni - ty.
There will be one for each soul that has wrought–For all that have worked and loved.
Chorus
From the depths of my heart I will do my part With a read-y and will-ing hand;
And I will not shirk, I will faithfully work In the place that my Lord hath planned.

221 Forward, Ever Forward

Charles W. Naylor, 1924 — Andrew L. Byers, 1924

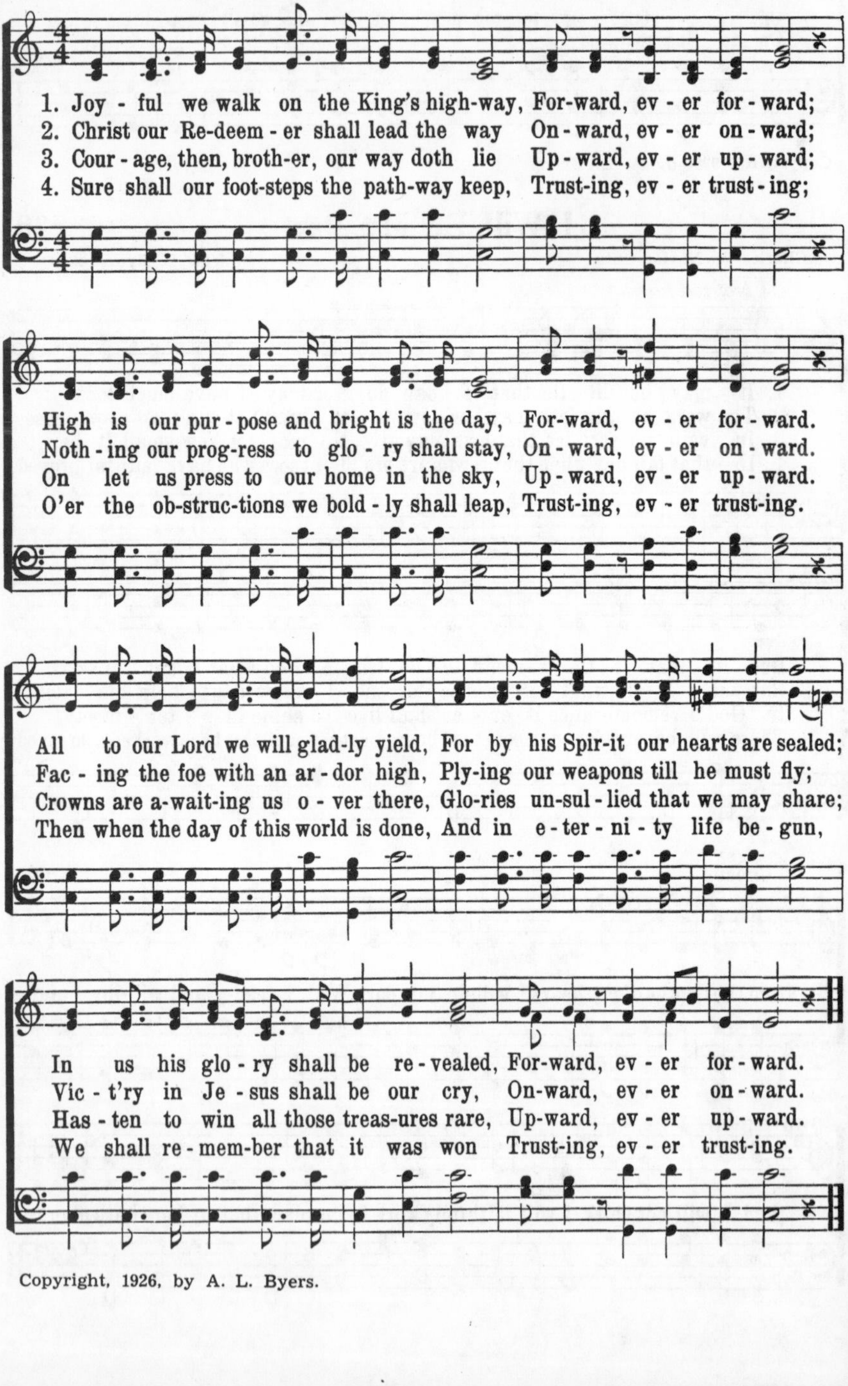

1. Joy - ful we walk on the King's high-way, For-ward, ev - er for - ward;
2. Christ our Re-deem - er shall lead the way On - ward, ev - er on - ward;
3. Cour - age, then, broth-er, our way doth lie Up - ward, ev - er up - ward;
4. Sure shall our foot-steps the path-way keep, Trust-ing, ev - er trust - ing;

High is our pur - pose and bright is the day, For-ward, ev - er for - ward.
Noth - ing our prog-ress to glo - ry shall stay, On - ward, ev - er on - ward.
On let us press to our home in the sky, Up - ward, ev - er up - ward.
O'er the ob-struc-tions we bold - ly shall leap, Trust-ing, ev - er trust-ing.

All to our Lord we will glad-ly yield, For by his Spir-it our hearts are sealed;
Fac - ing the foe with an ar - dor high, Ply-ing our weapons till he must fly;
Crowns are a-wait-ing us o - ver there, Glo-ries un-sul - lied that we may share;
Then when the day of this world is done, And in e - ter - ni - ty life be - gun,

In us his glo - ry shall be re - vealed, For-ward, ev - er for - ward.
Vic - t'ry in Je - sus shall be our cry, On-ward, ev - er on - ward.
Has - ten to win all those treas-ures rare, Up-ward, ev - er up - ward.
We shall re - mem-ber that it was won Trust-ing, ev - er trust-ing.

Am I a Soldier of the Cross? 222

ARLINGTON. C.M.

Isaac Watts, 1674-1748 | From Thomas A. Arne, 1710-1778

1. Am I a sol - dier of the cross, A fol-low'r of the Lamb?
2. Must I be car - ried to the skies On flow-'ry beds of ease
3. Are there no foes for me to face? Must I not stem the flood?
4. Sure I must fight, if I would reign; In-crease my cour - age, Lord;

And shall I fear to own his cause, Or blush to speak his name?
While oth-ers fought to win the prize, And sailed thro' bloody seas?
Is this vile world a friend to grace To help me on to God?
I'll bear the toil, en-dure the pain, Sup-port - ed by thy word. A - MEN.

My Soul, Be on Thy Guard 223

LABAN. S.M.

George Heath, 1750-1822 | Lowell Mason, 1792-1872

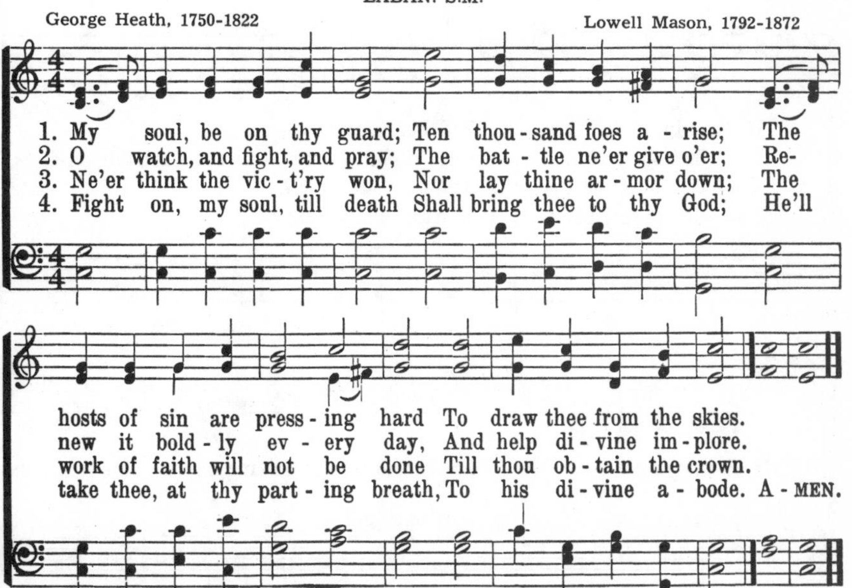
1. My soul, be on thy guard; Ten thou - sand foes a - rise; The
2. O watch, and fight, and pray; The bat - tle ne'er give o'er; Re-
3. Ne'er think the vic - t'ry won, Nor lay thine ar - mor down; The
4. Fight on, my soul, till death Shall bring thee to thy God; He'll
hosts of sin are press - ing hard To draw thee from the skies.
new it bold - ly ev - ery day, And help di - vine im - plore.
work of faith will not be done Till thou ob - tain the crown.
take thee, at thy part - ing breath, To his di - vine a - bode. A - MEN.

224 Onward, Christian Soldiers

ST. GERTRUDE. 6.5.6.5.D. with Refrain

Sabine Baring-Gould, 1834-1924 — Arthur S. Sullivan, 1842-1900

1. On - ward, Christian sol-diers, Marching as to war, With the cross of Je - sus
2. Like a might-y ar - my Moves the church of God: Brothers, we are tread-ing
3. Crowns and thrones may perish, Kingdoms rise and wane, But the church of Je - sus
4. On - ward, then, ye peo - ple, Join our hap-py throng, Blend with ours your voic-es

Go - ing on be-fore! Christ, the roy-al Mas-ter, Leads a - gainst the foe:
Where the saints have trod: We are not di - vid - ed, All one bod - y we,
Con - stant will re-main; Gates of hell can nev - er 'Gainst that church pre-vail;
In the tri-umph song,–"Glory, laud, and hon-or Un - to Christ the King!"

For-ward in - to bat - tle See his banners go.
One in hope and doc-trine, One in char-i - ty.
We have Christ's own promise, And that cannot fail.
This thro' countless a - ges Men and an-gels sing.

REFRAIN

Onward, Christian sol-diers, March-ing as to war, With the cross of Je - sus Go-ing on be-fore! A-MEN.

Victory Through Grace 225

Sallie Martin

John R. Sweney, 1837-1899

1. Con-quer-ing now and still to con - quer, Rid-eth a King in his might,
2. Con-quer-ing now and still to con - quer, Who is this won-der - ful King?
3. Con-quer-ing now and still to con - quer, Je - sus, thou Rul - er of all,
Lead - ing the hosts of all the faith - ful In - to the midst of the fight.
Whence are the ar - mies which he lead - eth, While of his glo - ry they sing?
Thrones and their scep-ters all shall per - ish, Crowns and their splendor shall fall;
See them with cour - age ad - vanc - ing, Clad in their bril - liant ar - ray,
He is our Lord and Re - deem - er, Sav - ior and Mon-arch di - vine;
Yet shall the ar - mies thou lead - est, Faith-ful and true to the last,
FINE
Shout-ing the name of their Lead - er, Hear them ex - ult - ing - ly say:
They are the stars that for - ev - er Bright in his king-dom will shine.
Find in thy man-sions e - ter - nal Rest, when their war - fare is past.
D.S.—Yet to the true and the faith - ful Vic - t'ry is prom-ised through grace.
CHORUS
D. S.
Not to the strong is the bat - tle, Not to the swift is the race, A - MEN.

226 The Army of the Lord

Barney E. Warren, 1926 Barney E. Warren, 1926

1. In the ho - ly ar-my we've en - list - ed, Now the ban-ner of the cross we bear;
2. We will push the fight o'er land and o - cean, And a - cross the des-ert plains of sin;
3. Hear the tramping of the count-less mil - lions, Hear the bat-tle's might-y thun-ders roar;
All the forc - es of the wrong re - sist - ed Caus - es right to tri-umph ev - ery-where.
We will give the cause our true de - vo - tion, Till for truth and righteousness we win.
Hear the great Commander of the ar - my Sound the or-ders loud from shore to shore:
We will fol-low where our Cap-tain lead - eth, We will fight a-gainst the sul - len foe,
We're ar-rayed in all the gos - pel ar - mor, Brave-ly on-ward we will ev - er go,
"Go ye in - to all the world, I'm with you, Take the for-tress-es of sin to - day,
We will stand to-geth-er, then we'll con - quer; Cer - tain vic - to - ry is ours, we know.
Till we put to flight the hosts of e - vil, Thro' our Lead-er we'll sub-due the foe.
Charge the en - e - my, com-pel sur - ren - der, Wear the victor's crown thro' endless day."
CHORUS
We are march - ing on to cer - tain vic - to - ry, In the

hot - test fight is where we love to be; Let the bat - tle rage o'er
ev - ery land and sea—'Tis the ar - my of the Lord. A - MEN.

Lead On, O King Eternal 227

LANCASHIRE. 7.6.7.6.D.

Ernest W. Shurtleff. 1862-1917 Henry Smart, 1813-1879

1. Lead on, O King E - ter-nal, The day of march has come; Henceforth in fields of
2. Lead on, O King E - ter-nal, Till sin's fierce war shall cease, And ho-li-ness shall
3. Lead on, O King E - ter-nal, We fol-low, not with fears; For gladness breaks like

con-quest Thy tents shall be our home. Thro' days of prep - a - ra - tion Thy
whis - per The sweet A - men of peace; For not with swords loud clashing, Nor
morn - ing Where'er Thy face ap-pears; Thy cross is lift - ed o'er us; We

grace has made us strong, And now, O King E-ter - nal, We lift our bat-tle song.
roll of stir-ring drums; With deeds of love and mercy, The heav'nly kingdom comes.
jour - ney in its light: The crown awaits the conquest; Lead on, O God of might.

228 Onward, All Ye People

Barney E. Warren, 1867-1951 — Barney E. Warren, 1867-1951

1. On-ward all ye peo-ple, Conq-'ring as you go; In the strength of Jesus,
2. On-ward all ye peo-ple, Cries the ris-en Lord; Ripened fields are waiting,
3. On-ward all ye peo-ple, Steadfast keep your eyes, On the goal of vic-t'ry,
4. On-ward all ye peo-ple, To the world that waits, Near the rolling o-ceans,

March a-gainst the foe, Raise the roy-al stand-ard, Where our Captain leads,
Work with one ac-cord, Gath-er in the har-vest, From the hill and plain,
Which be-fore you lies, Hear the songs of tri-umph, Sound o'er hill and dale,
Thru the mountain gates, Hungry souls are cry-ing, For the "Bread of Life,"

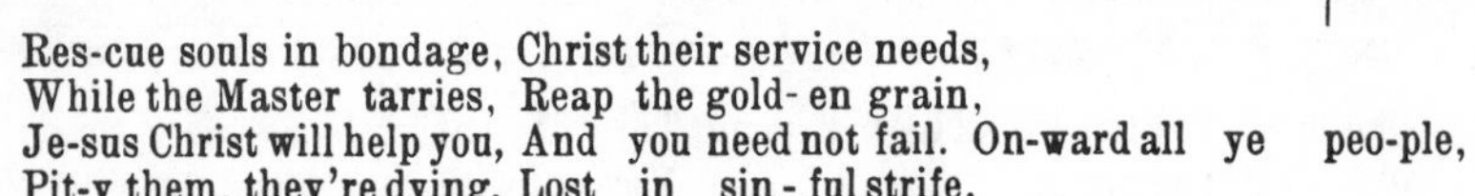

Res-cue souls in bondage, Christ their service needs,
While the Master tarries, Reap the gold-en grain,
Je-sus Christ will help you, And you need not fail. On-ward all ye peo-ple,
Pit-y them, they're dying, Lost in sin-ful strife.

Work for God to-day; Keep good hope and cour-age All a-long the way.

Jesus Saves

Priscilla J. Owens, 1829-c. 1899

William J. Kirkpatrick, 1838-1921

1. We have heard the joy - ful sound: Je - sus saves! Je - sus saves!
2. Waft it on the roll - ing tide; Je - sus saves! Je - sus saves!
3. Sing a - bove the bat - tle strife, Je - sus saves! Je - sus saves!
4. Give the winds a might - y voice, Je - sus saves! Je - sus saves!
Spread the ti - dings all a - round: Je - sus saves! Je - sus saves!
Tell to sin - ners far and wide: Je - sus saves! Je - sus saves!
By His death and end - less life, Je - sus saves! Je - sus saves!
Let the na - tions now re - joice,— Je - sus saves! Je - sus saves!
Bear the news to ev - 'ry land, Climb the steeps and cross the waves;
Sing, ye is - lands of the sea; Ech - o back, ye o - cean caves;
Sing it soft - ly thro' the gloom, When the heart for mer - cy craves;
Shout sal - va - tion full and free; High - est hills and deep - est caves;
On - ward!—'tis our Lord's com - mand; Je - sus saves! Je - sus saves!
Earth shall keep her ju - bi - lee: Je - sus saves! Je - sus saves!
Sing in tri - umph o'er the tomb,— Je - sus saves! Je - sus saves!
This our song of vic - to - ry,— Je - sus saves! Je - sus saves!

230 Soldiers of Christ, Arise

DIADEMATA. S.M.D.

Charles Wesley, 1707-1788 — George J. Elvey, 1816-1893

1. Sol - diers of Christ, a - rise, And put your ar - mor on,
2. Stand then in His great might, With all His strength en - dued,
3. Leave no un-guard - ed place, No weak-ness of the soul,
Strong in the strength which God sup-plies Thru His e - ter - nal Son;
And take, to arm you for the fight, The pan - o - ply of God;
Take ev - 'ry vir - tue, ev - 'ry grace, And for - ti - fy the whole.
Strong in the Lord of hosts, And in His might - y pow'r,
That hav - ing all things done, And all your con - flicts past,
From strength to strength go on, Wres - tle and fight and pray,
Who in the strength of Je - sus trusts Is more than con-quer - or.
Ye may o'er-come thru Christ a - lone, And stand en-tire at last.
Tread all the pow'rs of dark-ness down, And win the well-fought day.

Truehearted, Wholehearted 231

Frances B. Havergal, 1836-1879 George C. Stebbins, 1846-1945

1. True-hearted, whole-hearted, faith-ful and loy - al, King of our lives, by Thy grace we will be; Un-der the standard ex - alt - ed and roy - al, Strong in Thy strength we will bat-tle for Thee.
2. True-hearted, whole-hearted, full - est al - le-giance Yielding henceforth to our glo - ri - ous King; Val-iant en-deav-or and lov - ing o-be-dience, Free - ly and joy - ous - ly now would we bring.
3. True-hearted, whole-hearted, Sav - ior all - glo-rious! Take Thy great pow-er and reign there a - lone, O - ver our wills and af-fec-tions vic-to-rious, Free - ly sur-ren-dered and whol-ly Thine own.
CHORUS
Peal out the watch-word! si - lence it nev-er! Song of our spir-its, re - joic - ing and free; Peal out the watch-word! loy - al for - ev - er, King of our lives, by Thy grace we will be.
Peal out the watch-word! si - lence it nev-er! Song of our spir - its, re - joic-ing and free; Peal out the watch-word! loy - al for - ev - er, King of our lives, by Thy grace we will be.

232 Songs of Victory

H. R. Jeffrey, 1885 H. R. Jeffrey, 1885

1. Songs of vic - to - ry bring - ing Un - to the Lord most high;
2. Songs of vic - to - ry ev - er Shall be our hearts' de - light;
3. Songs of vic - to - ry sound - ing, Go forth to all the world,
4. Songs of vic - to - ry blend - ing With all the heav'n - ly throng;

While vic - to - ry we are sing - ing, Let all the saints draw nigh:
We'll sing of de - feat, no, nev - er— Sing vic - t'ry with all our might.
From shore to shore re - sound - ing, With gos - pel truths un - furled;
A cho - rus that has no end - ing, It is the vic - tor's song.

For there can be no fail - ure While Je - sus leads the van,
We'll raise our voic - es high - er, Up - on the bat - tle field;
Go, sing - ing of the Sav - ior, Send forth an ear - nest call;
We'll sing and shout for - ev - er Glad songs of vic - to - ry;

And vic - to - ry! vic - to - ry! vic - to - ry! Is heard on ev - ery hand.
Our vic - to - ry draw - eth nigh - er When Christ shall be re - vealed.
O sin - ner, seek his fa - vor, 'Tis of - fered un - to all.
We'll sing of Christ our Sav - ior Thro' all e - ter - ni - ty.

CHORUS

Vic - t'ry shall be the cho - rus, Vic - t'ry our watch-word and song;

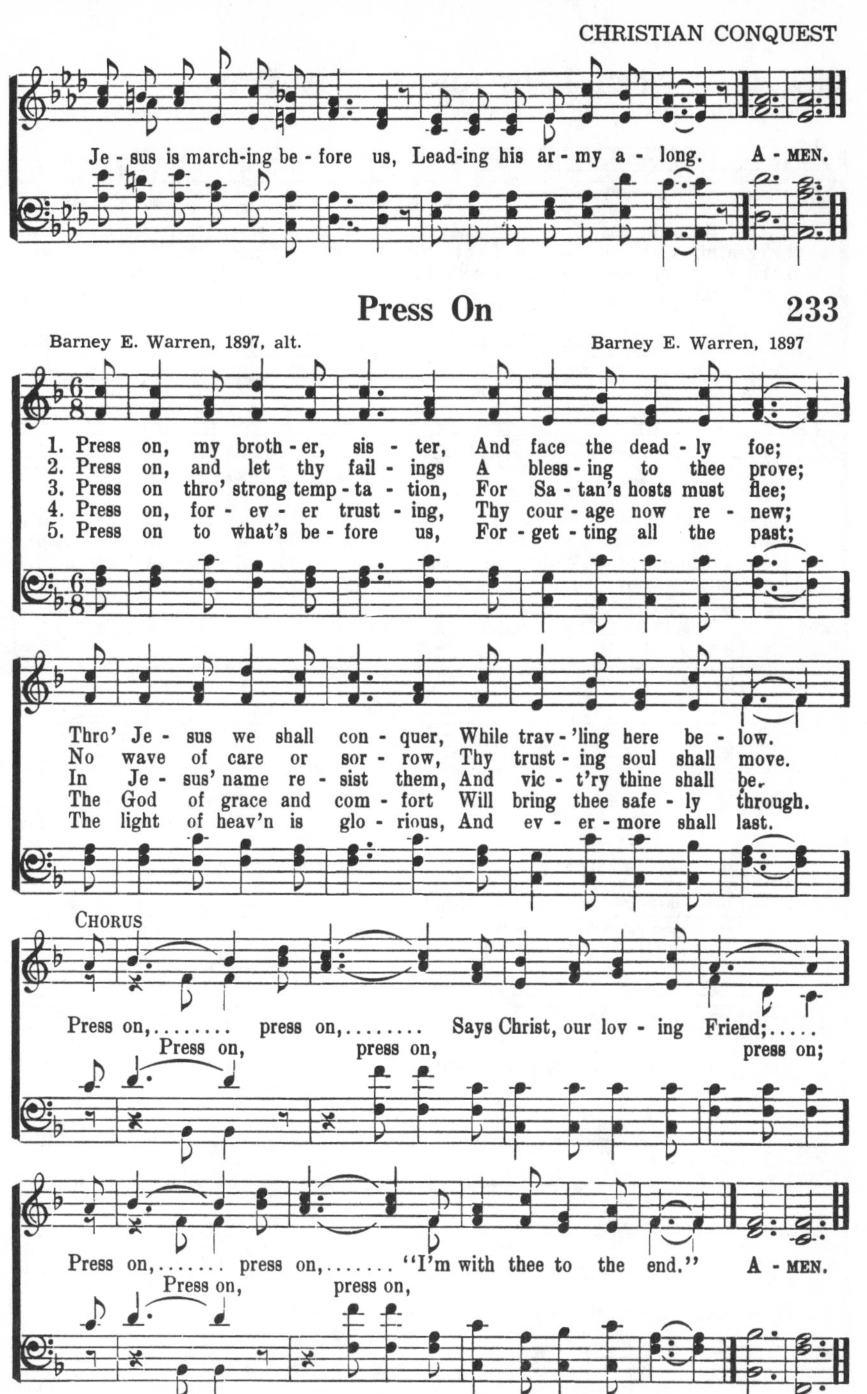
Je - sus is march-ing be - fore us, Lead-ing his ar - my a - long. A - MEN.
Press On
233
Barney E. Warren, 1897, alt.
Barney E. Warren, 1897
1. Press on, my broth - er, sis - ter, And face the dead - ly foe;
2. Press on, and let thy fail - ings A bless - ing to thee prove;
3. Press on thro' strong temp - ta - tion, For Sa - tan's hosts must flee;
4. Press on, for - ev - er trust - ing, Thy cour - age now re - new;
5. Press on to what's be - fore us, For - get - ting all the past;
Thro' Je - sus we shall con - quer, While trav - 'ling here be - low.
No wave of care or sor - row, Thy trust - ing soul shall move.
In Je - sus' name re - sist them, And vic - t'ry thine shall be.
The God of grace and com - fort Will bring thee safe - ly through.
The light of heav'n is glo - rious, And ev - er - more shall last.
CHORUS
Press on,........ press on,........ Says Christ, our lov - ing Friend;.....
Press on, press on, press on;
Press on,....... press on,....... "I'm with thee to the end." A - MEN.
Press on, press on,

234 When Jesus Answers My Prayer

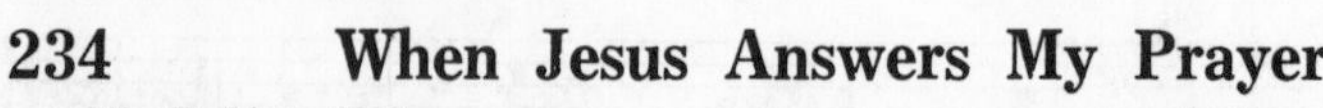

Otto F. Linn, 1923 — Andrew L. Byers, 1923

1. Tho' the night has been long and my tri-als se-vere, And heav-y my burdens of care; As the mists of the morn-ing they all dis-ap-pear When Je-sus an-swers my prayer.
2. Then my faith that is tried by the an-guish and pain Of af-flic-tions so heav-y to bear Is re-ward-ed at last by a won-der-ful gain When Je-sus an-swers my prayer.
3. Ev-er for-ward I press with my cour-age re-newed And a faith that no foe can im-pair; With self and a world of al-lure-ment sub-dued, When Je-sus an-swers my prayer.
4. O the vic-t'ry is won, and the glo-ry di-vine, More pre-cious than jew-els most rare, Brings a lin-ger-ing glow o'er this spir-it of mine When Je-sus an-swers my prayer.

CHORUS

When Je-sus an-swers my prayer, ... an-swers, answers my prayer,
When Je-sus an-swers my prayer: .... an-swers, an-swers my prayer:
O the rap-ture that thrills, the glo-ry that fills, When Je-sus an-swers my prayer! A-MEN.

More than a Conqueror 235

D. Otis Teasley, 1906 D. Otis Teasley, 1906

1. More than a con-quer-or Thro' the might-y God, More than a con-quer-or By the cleans-ing blood; Kept by a pow'r di-vine, Walk-ing in the light, More than a con-quer-or, Reign-ing day and night.
2. More than a con-quer-or By the liv-ing Lord, More than a con-quer-or, Stand-ing on his word; Mine is the vic-to-ry, Hap-py on the way, More than a con quer-or Till my dy-ing day.
3. More than a con-quer-or In the bat-tle's din, More than a con-quer-or O-ver ev-ery sin; Read-y to meet the Lord At the trump-et call, More than a con-quer-or, Vic-tor o-ver all.
4. More than a con-quer-or While I live be-low, More than a con-quer-or O-ver ev-ery foe; And by the grace of God Ev-er shall I be More than a con-quer-or Thro' e-ter-ni-ty.
CHORUS
More, more, more, More than con-quer-or Thro' my Lord;
More than a con-quer-or, more, yes, more, More, yes, more than con-quer-or, More than vic-tor thro' my Lord;
More, more, more, More than a con-quer-or, Standing on his word. A-MEN.
More than a conqueror, more, yes, more,

236 Stand by the Cross

D. Otis Teasley, 1907 | D. Otis Teasley, 1907

1. Stand by the cross when the morn - ing sun Beams on your way so
2. Stand by the cross till the day is done, Firm to the end and
3. Stand by the cross like a sol - dier strong; Fear - less - ly face the
4. Stand by the cross till the Lord re - turns, Faith - ful thro' life's last
bright; (so bright; O) Stand by the cross till the shad - ows fall,
true; (and true; O) Trust when the bat - tle is rag - ing wild,
foe; (the foe; O) Soon shall the ar - my of night re - cede
test; (last test; O) Soon we shall hear from his bless - ed lips,
Soon we shall tri-umph for God and right.
For there is wait-ing a crown for you.
Back from the morn-ing's tri - um - phant glow.
"Lay down your ar - mor and be at rest."
CHORUS
Stand by the cross, sol - dier,
Stand,
stand,
Vic - t'ry will come by and by;
stand by the cross, sol - dier, Stand,
stand by the cross;
Stand by the cross, sol-dier, stand,
And we'll con-quer though we die.
A-MEN.
Stand,
stand by the cross,

Press the Battle On 237

Charles W. Naylor and Barney E. Warren, 1900 — Barney E. Warren, 1900

1. For-ward, for-ward is the bat - tle - cry, On - ward, on-ward to our home on high; We will con - quer for the Lord or die, The foe's re - treat-ing, press the bat - tle on.
2. For-ward, for-ward, nev-er faint or fear, Christ our cap-tain is for-ev - er near; Be cou - ra -geous, full of hope and cheer, With full as - sur ance press the bat - tle on.
3. For-ward, for-ward, put the foe to flight, We are bat-tling for the truth and right; We shall tri - umph in Je - ho-vah's might, Then do not fal - ter, press the bat - tle on.
4. For-ward, for-ward, there's a crown be - fore, See it shin - ing on that heav'n-ly shore; We shall wear it when the con - flict's o'er—The prize is wait-ing, press the bat - tle on.
CHORUS
Strength-ened by the might-y pow'r of heav - en, We shall con - quer, we shall con - quer; Till the rag - ing foe a - far is driv - en, Press the bat - tle on. A - MEN.

238 Mine Eyes Have Seen the Glory

Julia Ward Howe, 1819-1910 — John William Steffe, 1852

1. Mine eyes have seen the glo-ry of the com-ing of the Lord; He is tram-pling out the vintage where the grapes of wrath are stored; He hath loosed the fate-ful light-ning of His ter-ri-ble swift sword; His truth is march-ing on.
2. I have seen Him in the watch-fires of a hun-dred circling camps; They have build-ed Him an al-tar in the eve-ning dews and damps; I can read His righteous sen-tence by the dim and flar-ing lamps; His day is march-ing on.
3. He has sound-ed forth the trumpet that shall nev-er sound re-treat; He is sift-ing out the hearts of men be-fore His judg-ment seat. O be swift, my soul, to an-swer Him! be ju-bi-lant, my feet! Our God is march-ing on.
4. In the beau-ty of the lil-ies Christ was born a-cross the sea, With a glo-ry in His bos-om that trans-fig-ures you and me; As He died to make men ho-ly, let us die to make men free; While God is march-ing on.

CHORUS

Glo-ry! glory, hal-le-lu-jah! Glory! glory, hal-le-lu-jah! His truth is marching on.
Glo-ry! glory, hal-le-lu-jah! Glory! glory, hal-le-lu-jah! His day is marching on.
Glo-ry! glory, hal-le-lu-jah! Glory! glory, hal-le-lu-jah! Our God is marching on.
Glo-ry! glory, hal-le-lu-jah! Glory! glory, hal-le-lu-jah! While God is marching on.

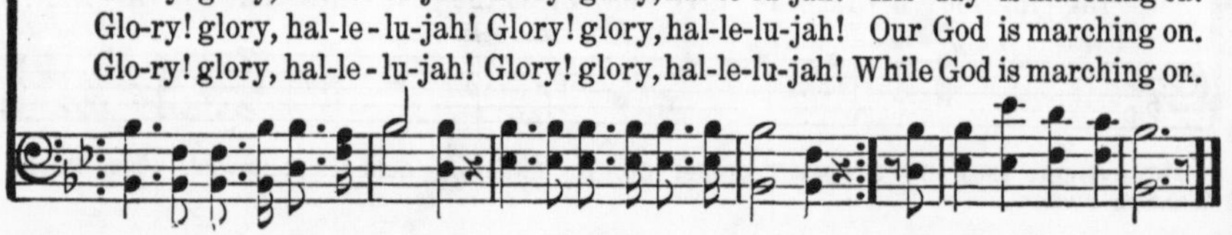

Lift Up Your Heads, Ye Gates of Brass 239

MATERNA. C.M.D.

James Montgomery, 1771-1854 — Samuel A. Ward, 1847-1903

1. Lift up your heads, ye gates of brass, Ye bars of i - ron yield,
2. A ho - ly war those serv-ants wage; Mys - te - rious - ly at strife,
3. Tho' few and small and weak your bands, Strong in your Cap-tain's strength
4. O fear not, faint not, halt not now, In Je - sus' name be strong;

And let the King of Glo - ry pass; The cross is in the field:
The pow'rs of heav'n and hell en-gage For more than death or life.
Go to the con - quest of all lands; All must be his at length.
To him shall all the na - tions bow, And sing with you this song:

That ban - ner, bright-er than the star That leads the train of night,
Ye ar - mies of the liv - ing God, His sac - ra - men - tal host,
Those spoils at his vic - to - rious feet You shall re - joice to lay,
"Up - lift - ed are the gates of brass, The bars of i - ron yield;

Shines on their march, and guides from far His serv-ants to the fight.
Where hal-lowed foot-steps nev - er trod Take your ap-point - ed post.
And lay your-selves, as tro-phies meet, On his great judgment day.
Be - hold the King of Glo - ry pass; The cross hath won the field." A - MEN.

240 Victory

Barney E. Warren, 1897
Barney E. Warren, 1897
1. Hal - le - lu - jah, what a thought—Je - sus full sal - va - tion brought!
2. I am trust - ing in the Lord, I am an - chored on his word,
3. Shout your free - dom ev - ery-where, His e - ter - nal peace de - clare,
4. We will sing it on that shore, When this fleet - ing life is o'er,
Vic - to - ry, vic - to - ry. Let the pow'rs of sin as - sail,
Vic - to - ry, vic - to - ry. I have peace and joy with - in,
Vic - to - ry, vic - to - ry. Let us sing it here be - low,
Vic - to - ry, vic - to - ry. Sing it here, ye ransomed throng,
Vic - to - ry, vic - to - ry.
Heav-en's grace can nev - er fail, Vic - to - ry, vic - to - ry.
Since my heart is free from sin, Vic - to - ry, vic - to - ry.
In the face of ev - ery foe, Vic - to - ry, vic - to - ry.
Start the ev - er - last - ing song, Vic - to - ry, vic - to - ry.
Vic - to - ry, vic - to-ry.
CHORUS
Vic - to - ry,........ yes, vic - to - ry; Hal - le - lu - jah! I am
Vic - to - ry, yes, vic - to - ry;
free, Je - sus gives me vic - to - ry! Glo - ry, glo - - - - ry, hal - le-
Glo - ry, glo - ry,

lu - - jah! He is all..... ..... in all to me.............
Hal - le - lu - jah! He is all, he is all in all to me (all to me).
The Shield of Faith
241
Daniel S. Warner, 1893
Barney E. Warren, 1893
1. Take the shield of faith, my brother, Hold it bold - ly in the light;
2. Faith is might - y and will con - quer, Bind it firm - ly on thy heart;
3. And when trouble specters round thee Come, thy spir - it to de - press,
4. Then put on the ho - ly ar - mor And de - fy the tempting throng;
And its aw - ful burnished glo - ry Will put ev - ery foe to flight.
On the hot - test field of bat - tle Thou shalt quench the vil - est dart.
Lift the shield of faith a - bound - ing, And thy soul shall calm - ly rest.
O - ver all the foes that gath - er Shout and sing the vic - tor's song.
CHORUS
In the might - y name of Je - sus, Ev - er lift up the shield of faith;
Wield the sword of truth, my brother, Heav'n will crown thy fight of faith. A-MEN.

242 Be an Overcomer

Charles W. Naylor, 1907 Andrew L. Byers, 1907

1. Be an o - ver - com - er, on - ly cow - ards yield When the foe they
2. Be an o - ver - com - er, he who stands with you Is a Might - y
3. Be an o - ver - com - er, you are heav - en's heir, And a crown of
4. Be an o - ver - com - er, for - ward bold - ly go, You are strong e-
meet on the bat - tle - field; We are blood-bought princ - es of the
One, who is al - ways true; In the sor - est con - flict you shall
life you may ev - er wear; So with cour - age press the bat - tle
nough if you count it so— Strong e - nough to con-quer through sus-
roy - al host, And must fal - ter not, nor de - sert our post.
win the day, Face the le - gions dark till they flee a - way.
to the gates, Till you gain the prize which in heav - en waits.
tain - ing grace, And to o - ver - come ev - ery foe you face.
CHORUS
O-ver-come,................ O-ver-come;................ In Je-
Never yield a step in the hottest fight, God will send you help from the realms of light;
ho-vah's might put the foe to flight, And the vic-tor's crown you shall wear at last.

I'm on the Winning Side 243

Charles W. Naylor, 1921

Andrew L. Byers, 1922

1. A - long the way of life are man - y foes That dai - ly war a-gainst my soul; But con - stant vic - to - ry My Sav - ior gives to me As I press on to the goal.
2. The bat - tle may be long and hard to win, And Sa-tan's hosts may press me sore; But though I may be tried I'm on the win - ning side, I shall tri - umph ev - er - more.
3. A mul - ti - tude of war-riors of the cross In ser - ried ranks do brave - ly fight; They nev - er shall re - treat, Nor ev - er know de - feat, They are win - ning for the right.
4. With cour-age in my soul I'll do my part, For Je - sus I will loy - al stand; So on the win - ning side Tri - um - phant I a - bide With the faith - ful ho - ly band.
CHORUS
On the win-ning side, I'm on the win - ning side,
On the win - ning side,
I'm on the win - ning side with Je - sus; Though hot may be the fray,
On the win - ning side with Je - sus;
My soul can bold - ly say, I'm on the win - ning side with Je - sus A - MEN.

244 Faith Is the Victory

John H. Yates — Ira D. Sankey, 1840-1908

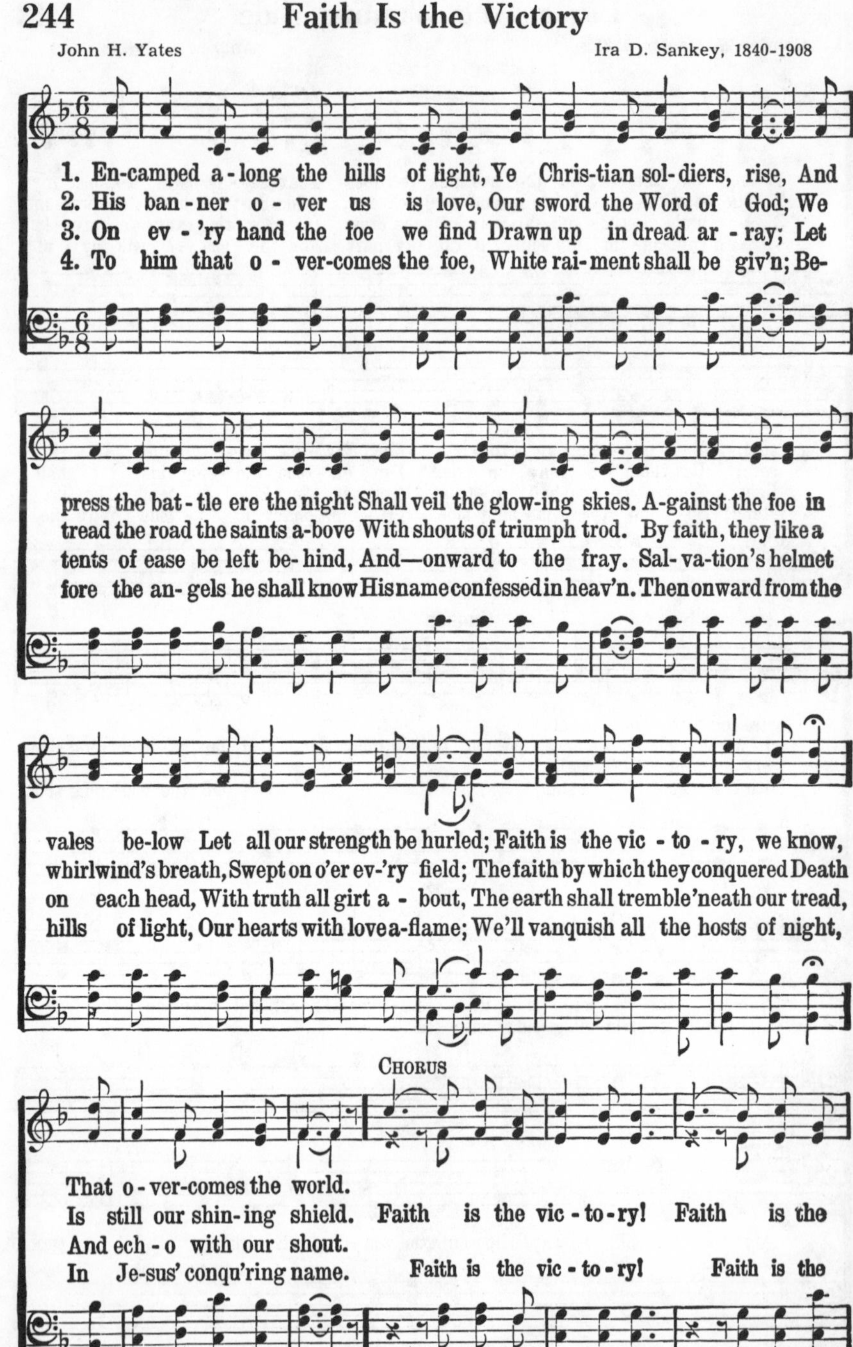
1. En-camped a-long the hills of light, Ye Chris-tian sol-diers, rise, And press the bat-tle ere the night Shall veil the glow-ing skies. A-gainst the foe in vales be-low Let all our strength be hurled; Faith is the vic-to-ry, we know, That o-ver-comes the world.
2. His ban-ner o-ver us is love, Our sword the Word of God; We tread the road the saints a-bove With shouts of triumph trod. By faith, they like a whirlwind's breath, Swept on o'er ev-'ry field; The faith by which they conquered Death Is still our shin-ing shield.
3. On ev-'ry hand the foe we find Drawn up in dread ar-ray; Let tents of ease be left be-hind, And—onward to the fray. Sal-va-tion's helmet on each head, With truth all girt a-bout, The earth shall tremble 'neath our tread, And ech-o with our shout.
4. To him that o-ver-comes the foe, White rai-ment shall be giv'n; Be-fore the an-gels he shall know His name confessed in heav'n. Then onward from the hills of light, Our hearts with love a-flame; We'll vanquish all the hosts of night, In Je-sus' conqu'ring name.
CHORUS
Faith is the vic-to-ry! Faith is the
Faith is the vic-to-ry! Faith is the

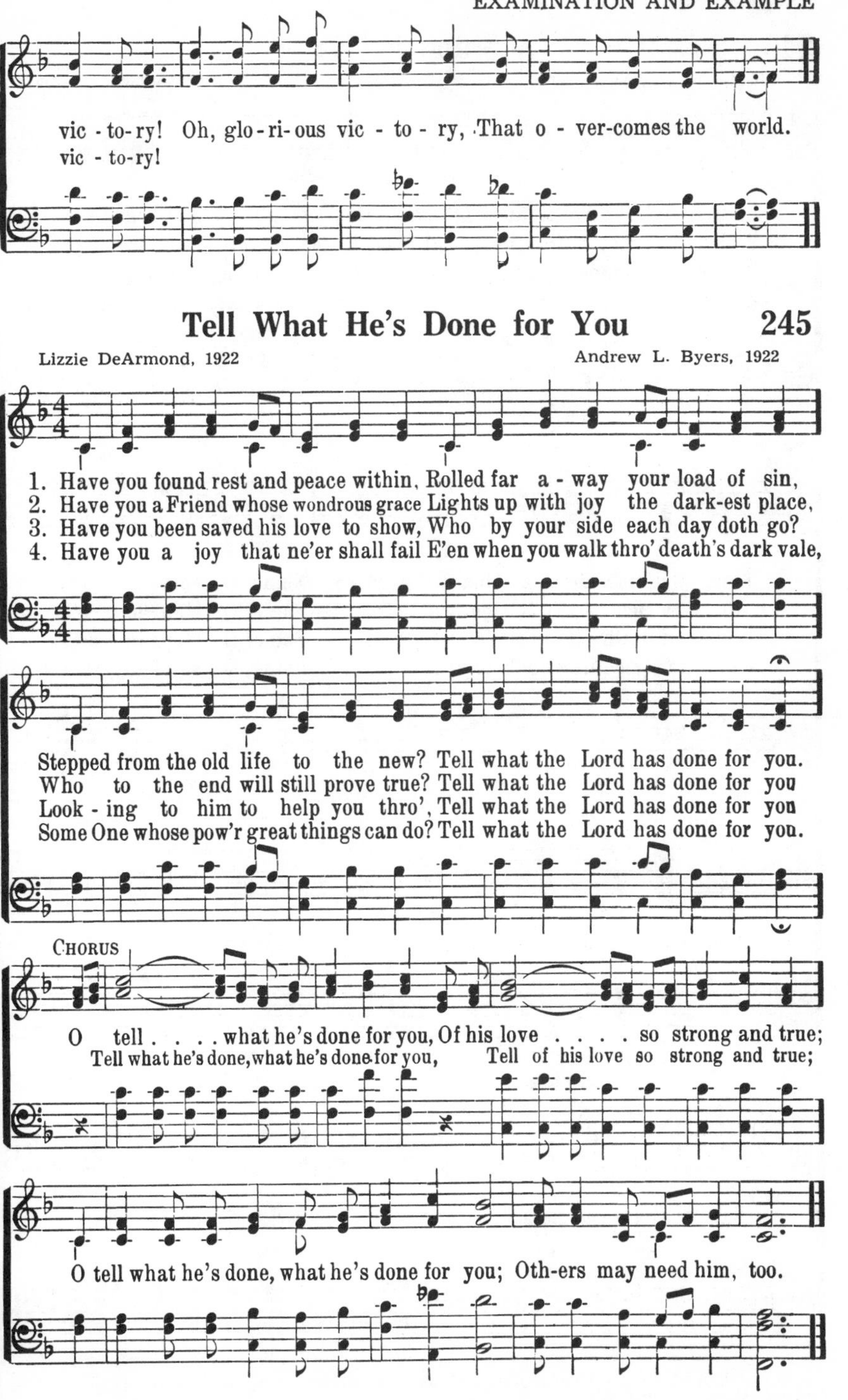
vic - to - ry! Oh, glo - ri - ous vic - to - ry, That o - ver-comes the world.
vic - to - ry!
Tell What He's Done for You
245
Lizzie DeArmond, 1922
Andrew L. Byers, 1922
1. Have you found rest and peace within, Rolled far a - way your load of sin,
2. Have you a Friend whose wondrous grace Lights up with joy the dark-est place,
3. Have you been saved his love to show, Who by your side each day doth go?
4. Have you a joy that ne'er shall fail E'en when you walk thro' death's dark vale,
Stepped from the old life to the new? Tell what the Lord has done for you.
Who to the end will still prove true? Tell what the Lord has done for you
Look - ing to him to help you thro', Tell what the Lord has done for you
Some One whose pow'r great things can do? Tell what the Lord has done for you.
CHORUS
O tell . . . . what he's done for you, Of his love . . . . so strong and true;
Tell what he's done, what he's done for you, Tell of his love so strong and true;
O tell what he's done, what he's done for you; Oth-ers may need him, too.

246 Shine in Me

Charles W. Naylor, c. 1936 W. Dale Oldham, c. 1936

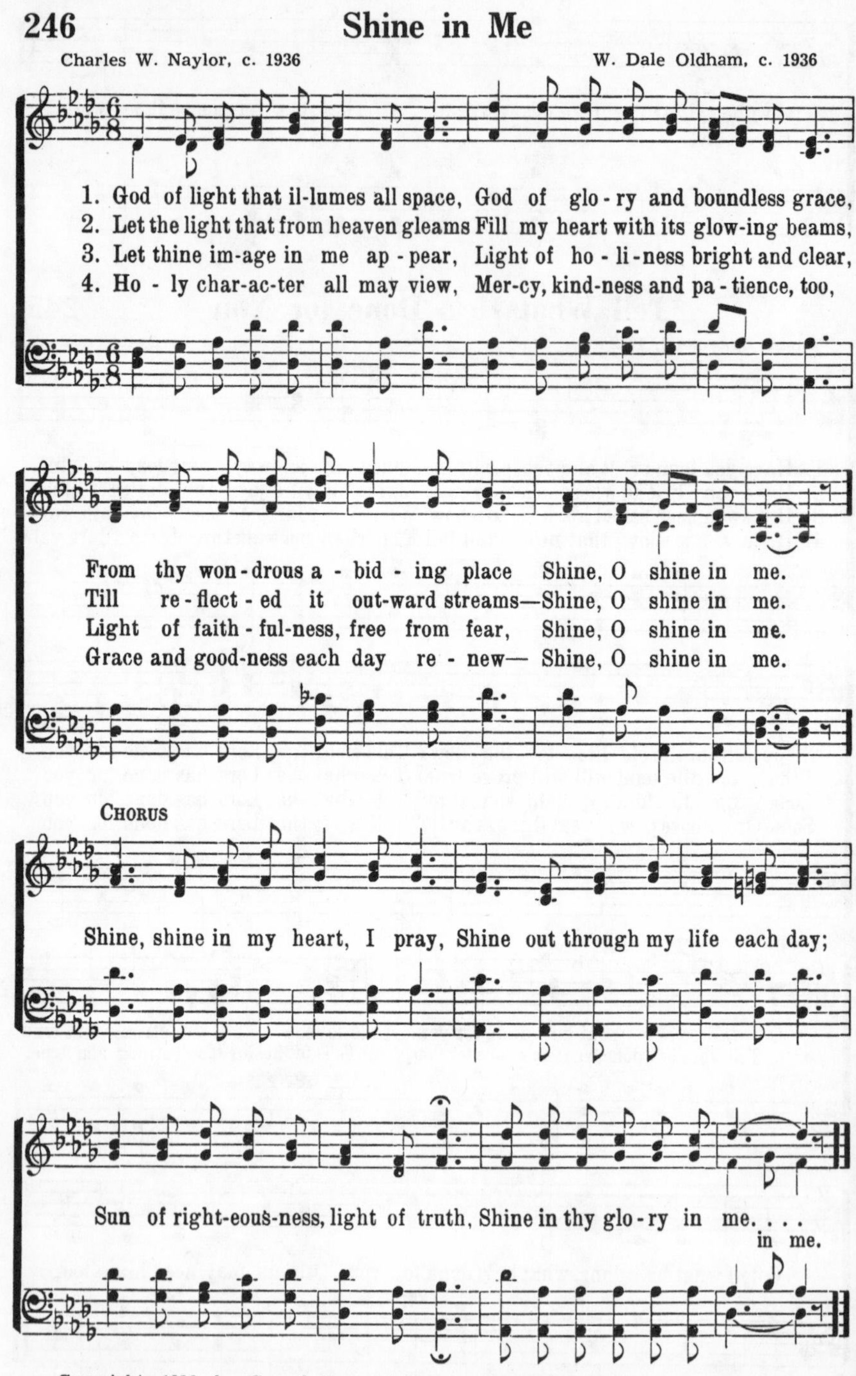
1. God of light that il-lumes all space, God of glo-ry and boundless grace,
2. Let the light that from heaven gleams Fill my heart with its glow-ing beams,
3. Let thine im-age in me ap-pear, Light of ho-li-ness bright and clear,
4. Ho-ly char-ac-ter all may view, Mer-cy, kind-ness and pa-tience, too,
From thy won-drous a-bid-ing place Shine, O shine in me.
Till re-flect-ed it out-ward streams—Shine, O shine in me.
Light of faith-ful-ness, free from fear, Shine, O shine in me.
Grace and good-ness each day re-new— Shine, O shine in me.
CHORUS
Shine, shine in my heart, I pray, Shine out through my life each day;
Sun of right-eous-ness, light of truth, Shine in thy glo-ry in me. . .
in me.

Humble Thyself to Walk with God 247

Johnson Oatman, Jr., 1856-1926

W. J. Rogers, 1909

1. If thou wouldst have the dear Savior from heav-en Walk by thy side from the morn till the e-ven, There is a rule that each day you must fol-low:
2. Just as the Lord in the world's ear-ly a-ges Walked and communed with the proph-ets and sag-es, He will come now if you meet the con-di-tions:
3. Just as the stream finds a bed that is low-ly, So Je-sus walks with the pure and the ho-ly; Cast out thy pride, and in heart-felt con-tri-tion

Hum-ble thy-self to walk with God.

REFRAIN

Hum-ble thy-self and the Lord will draw near thee, Hum-ble thy-self and his pres-ence shall cheer thee: He will not walk with the proud or the scorn-ful, Hum-ble thy-self to walk with God.

248 We Reap as We Sow

Charles W. Naylor, 1907 — Andrew L. Byers, 1907

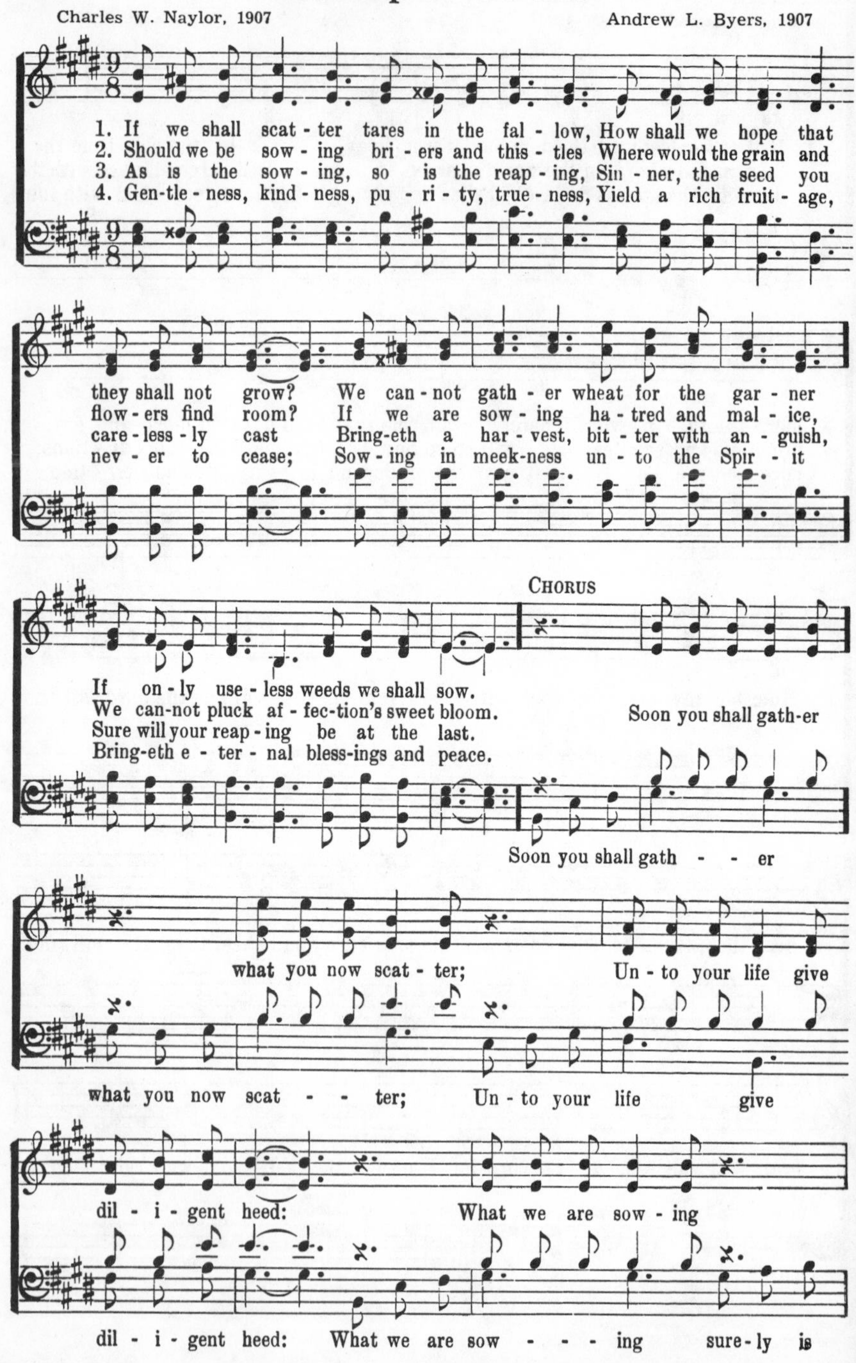
1. If we shall scat - ter tares in the fal - low, How shall we hope that
2. Should we be sow - ing bri - ers and this - tles Where would the grain and
3. As is the sow - ing, so is the reap - ing, Sin - ner, the seed you
4. Gen-tle - ness, kind - ness, pu - ri - ty, true - ness, Yield a rich fruit - age,
they shall not grow? We can - not gath - er wheat for the gar - ner
flow - ers find room? If we are sow - ing ha - tred and mal - ice,
care - less - ly cast Bring-eth a har - vest, bit - ter with an - guish,
nev - er to cease; Sow - ing in meek-ness un - to the Spir - it
If on - ly use - less weeds we shall sow.
We can-not pluck af - fec-tion's sweet bloom.
Sure will your reap - ing be at the last.
Bring-eth e - ter - nal bless-ings and peace.
CHORUS
Soon you shall gath-er
Soon you shall gath - - er
what you now scat - ter; Un - to your life give
what you now scat - - ter; Un - to your life give
dil - i - gent heed: What we are sow - ing
dil - i - gent heed: What we are sow - - - ing sure - ly is

sure - ly is grow - ing, That which we reap shall be as the seed.
grow - - ing, That which we reap shall be as the seed.

Are You Faithful? 249

Charles W. Naylor, 1918 — Andrew L. Byers, 1918

1. Can the Lord count you faith - ful? Is your heart true to - day?
2. Look in the Bi - ble, broth - er, Then at the way you live:
3. Can the dear Sav - ior trust you, Wher-e'er your path may lead,
4. "Faith-ful to death," the mot - to Shines on our ban - ners high;
Is your life pure and ho - ly? What does your con-science say?
Can the Lord as he views you His full ap - prov - al give?
Staunchly to stand, and loy - al? Will you be his in - deed?
Faith-ful to Christ for - ev - er, This is our bat - tle - cry.
CHORUS
Can the Lord count on you to - day? Will you his pure com-mands o - bey—
Ev - er keep stead-fast all the way? Can the Lord count you faith - ful?

250 Are You Adorning the Doctrine?

Charles W. Naylor, 1907 Andrew L. Byers, 1907

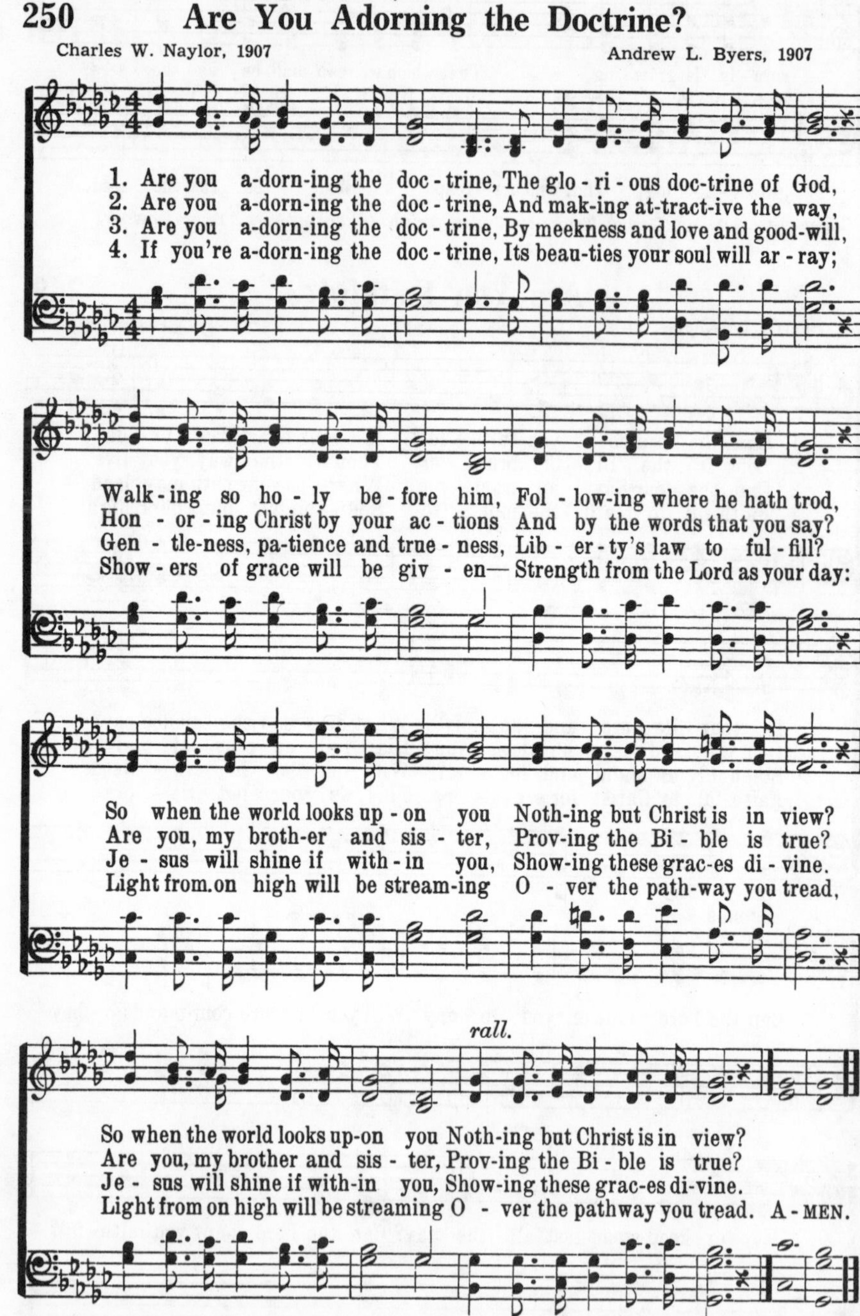
1. Are you a-dorn-ing the doc-trine, The glo-ri-ous doc-trine of God,
2. Are you a-dorn-ing the doc-trine, And mak-ing at-tract-ive the way,
3. Are you a-dorn-ing the doc-trine, By meekness and love and good-will,
4. If you're a-dorn-ing the doc-trine, Its beau-ties your soul will ar-ray;
Walk-ing so ho-ly be-fore him, Fol-low-ing where he hath trod,
Hon-or-ing Christ by your ac-tions And by the words that you say?
Gen-tle-ness, pa-tience and true-ness, Lib-er-ty's law to ful-fill?
Show-ers of grace will be giv-en— Strength from the Lord as your day:
So when the world looks up-on you Noth-ing but Christ is in view?
Are you, my broth-er and sis-ter, Prov-ing the Bi-ble is true?
Je-sus will shine if with-in you, Show-ing these grac-es di-vine.
Light from.on high will be stream-ing O-ver the path-way you tread,
rall.
So when the world looks up-on you Noth-ing but Christ is in view?
Are you, my brother and sis-ter, Prov-ing the Bi-ble is true?
Je-sus will shine if with-in you, Show-ing these grac-es di-vine.
Light from on high will be streaming O-ver the pathway you tread. A-MEN.

We Must Be Holy 251

Daniel S. Warner, 1893 Barney E. Warren, 1893

1. Je - sus has tak - en my load of sin, Such love no
2. Can I be - hold the dear Sav - ior's death And yet with-
3. Rea - son and jus - tice, my debt of love, De - mand that
4. We must be ho - ly as he is pure, For this the
tongue can tell; Then should I not re - sign to him
hold a part? O can I draw one self - ish breath,
I should be, Bod - y and spir - it and all I have,
Sav - ior died; Tal - ents and time and all earth - ly store
My life and all my will?
And not give all my heart?
De - vot - ed, Lord, to thee.
To God be sanc - ti - fied.
CHORUS
Ho - ly, dear breth - ren,
we must be ho - ly, Liv - ing be - fore the throne; Self and pos-
ses - sions, All must be tru - ly Giv - en to God a - lone.

252 Fire in the Soul

Daniel S. Warner, 1887 — Andrew L. Byers, 1918

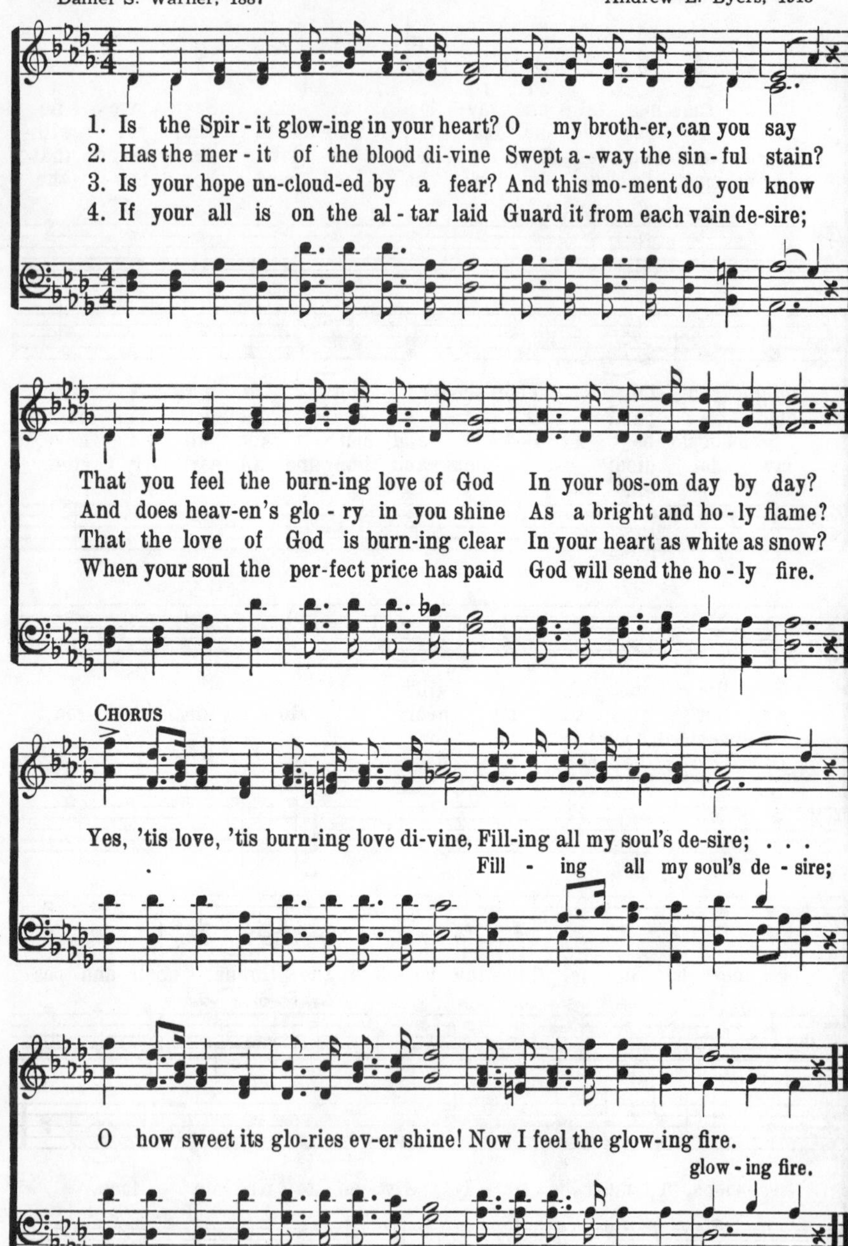
1. Is the Spir - it glow-ing in your heart? O my broth-er, can you say
2. Has the mer - it of the blood di-vine Swept a - way the sin - ful stain?
3. Is your hope un-cloud-ed by a fear? And this mo-ment do you know
4. If your all is on the al - tar laid Guard it from each vain de-sire;
That you feel the burn-ing love of God In your bos-om day by day?
And does heav-en's glo - ry in you shine As a bright and ho - ly flame?
That the love of God is burn-ing clear In your heart as white as snow?
When your soul the per-fect price has paid God will send the ho - ly fire.
CHORUS
Yes, 'tis love, 'tis burn-ing love di-vine, Fill-ing all my soul's de-sire; . . .
Fill - ing all my soul's de - sire;
O how sweet its glo-ries ev-er shine! Now I feel the glow-ing fire.
glow - ing fire.

Are You Building on the Rock? 253

Barney E. Warren, 1897 — Barney E. Warren, 1897

1. Are you build - ing on the Rock e - ter - nal, Or up- on the ev - er - shift - ing sand? Are you go - ing to that home su - per - nal, In that bright and bless - ed heav'n - ly land?
2. Are you build - ing on a strong foun - da - tion, That will stand the storm - y sea of life? 'Mid the surg - ing bil - lows' wild com - mo - tion, Do you con - quer in the rag - ing strife?
3. Are you build - ing on a strong foun - da - tion, That the floods can nev - er sweep a - way? Are you liv - ing in his truth un - shak - en, Read - y for the fi - nal judg - ment day?
4. Are you build - ing on a strong foun - da - tion, That will stand the aw - ful judg - ment shock? Are you ground - ed in his great sal - va - tion, Fas-tened like an an - chor to the Rock?

CHORUS

Are you build - - ing on the Rock? Are you build - - ing on the Rock?
Are you build-ing, build-ing on the Rock? Are you build-ing, build-ing on the Rock?
Are you build - - - ing on the Rock, Or on the sink - ing sand?
Are you build - ing, build-ing on the Rock,

254 Reigning in This Life

Daniel S. Warner, 1842-1895 | Joseph C. Fisher, 1885

1. Do you tri - umph, O my broth-er, O - ver all this world of sin?
2. One we hail as King im-mor-tal, He did earth and hell sub-due;
3. Shall we, then, by sin be hum-bled? Must we yield to an - y foe?
4. O what grace and high pro-mo-tion, That in Je - sus I should be
5. All this life is bliss-ful sun-shine, Earth is sub - ject at our feet;

In each storm of trib - u - la - tion Does your Je - sus reign with-in?
And, be - queath-ing us his glo - ry, We are kings a - noint-ed, too.
No, by heav - en's gift we're reigning O - ver all this world be-low.
Raised from sin to roy - al hon - or, E - ven reign - ing, Lord, with thee!
Heav-en pours its rich-est bless-ings Round our throne of love com-plete.

Chorus

I am reign - ing, sweet-ly reign - ing, Far a - bove . . . .
Reign-ing, sweetly reign-ing, reign-ing in this life, Reign-ing in this life,

this world of strife; . . . . In my bless - - - - ed lov-ing
reign-ing, sweet-ly reign-ing, Reign-ing in this life,

A Song of Joy 255

D. Otis Teasley, 1898 D. Otis Teasley, 1898

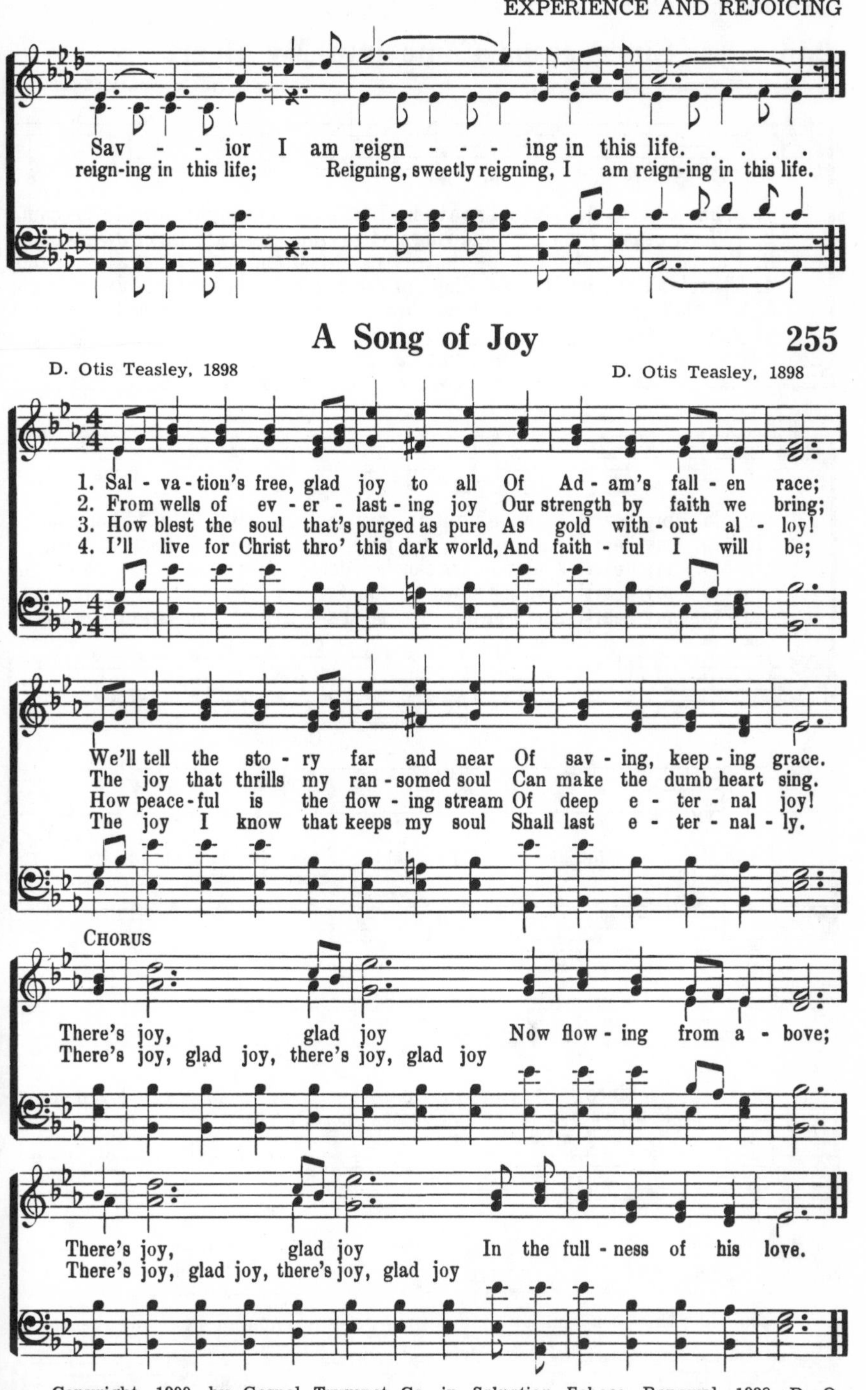
Sav - - ior I am reign - - - ing in this life. . . .
reign-ing in this life; Reigning, sweetly reigning, I am reign-ing in this life.
1. Sal - va - tion's free, glad joy to all Of Ad - am's fall - en race;
2. From wells of ev - er - last - ing joy Our strength by faith we bring;
3. How blest the soul that's purged as pure As gold with - out al - loy!
4. I'll live for Christ thro' this dark world, And faith - ful I will be;
We'll tell the sto - ry far and near Of sav - ing, keep - ing grace.
The joy that thrills my ran - somed soul Can make the dumb heart sing.
How peace - ful is the flow - ing stream Of deep e - ter - nal joy!
The joy I know that keeps my soul Shall last e - ter - nal - ly.
CHORUS
There's joy, glad joy Now flow - ing from a - bove;
There's joy, glad joy, there's joy, glad joy
There's joy, glad joy In the full - ness of his love.
There's joy, glad joy, there's joy, glad joy

256 Since Jesus Came into My Heart
R. H. McDaniel
Charles H. Gabriel, 1856-1932
1. What a won - der - ful change in my life has been wrought Since Je-sus came in - to my heart! I have light in my soul for which long I had sought,
2. I have ceased from my wand'ring and go - ing a-stray, Since Je-sus came in - to my heart! And my sins, which were man-y, are all washed a - way,
3. I'm pos-sessed of a hope that is stead-fast and sure, Since Je-sus came in - to my heart! And no dark clouds of doubt now my path - way ob-scure,
4. There's a light in the val - ley of death now for me, Since Je-sus came in - to my heart! And the gates of the Cit - y be-yond I can see,
5. I shall go there to dwell in that Cit - y, I know, Since Je-sus came in - to my heart! And I'm hap - py, so hap - py, as on - ward I go,
Since Je - sus came in - to my heart!
Chorus
Since Je-sus came in - to my heart,
Since Je - sus came in, came in - to my heart,
Since Je-sus came in - to my heart,
Since Je-sus came in, came in - to my heart,
Floods of joy o'er my soul like the sea bil-lows roll, Since Je - sus came in - to my heart.

I Will Sing the Wondrous Story 257

Francis H. Rowley, 1886 — Peter P. Bilhorn, 1887

1. I will sing the won-drous sto - ry Of the Christ who died for me,
2. I was lost, but Je - sus found me, Found the sheep that went a - stray,
3. I was bruised, but Je - sus healed me; Faint was I from many a fall;
4. Days of dark-ness still come o'er me, Sor - row's paths I oft - en tread,
5. He will keep me till the riv - er Rolls its wa - ters at my feet;
How He left His home in glo - ry For the cross of Cal - va - ry.
Threw His lov - ing arms a-round me, Drew me back in - to His way.
Sight was gone, and fears possessed me, But He freed me from them all.
But the Sav - ior still is with me; By His hand I'm safe - ly led.
Then He'll bear me safe - ly o - ver, Where the loved ones I shall meet.
Chorus
Yes, I'll sing . . . . . the won-drous sto - - - - ry Of the
Yes, I'll sing the won-drous sto - ry
Christ . . . . who died for me, ... Sing it with . . . . the saints in
Of the Christ who died for me, Sing it with
glo - - ry, Gath-ered by . . . . . . the crys-tal sea. . . . .
the saints in glo - ry, Gath-ered by the crys-tal sea.

258 Sunshine in the Soul

Eliza E. Hewitt, b. 1851 — John R. Sweney, 1837-1899

1. There's sun-shine in my soul to-day, More glo-ri-ous and bright
2. There's mu-sic in my soul to-day, A car-ol to the King,
3. There's springtime in my soul to-day, For, when the Lord is near,
4. There's glad-ness in my soul to-day, And hope and praise and love,

Than glows in an-y earth-ly skies, For Je-sus is my light.
And Je-sus, lis-ten-ing, can hear The songs I can-not sing.
The dove of peace sings in my heart, The flow'rs of grace ap-pear.
For bless-ings which He gives me now, For joys "laid up" a-bove.

REFRAIN

O there's sun - - - shine, bless-ed sun - - - shine,
O there's sun-shine in the soul, bless-ed sun-shine in the soul,

When the peace-ful, hap-py mo-ments roll; When
hap-py mo-ments roll;

Je-sus shows His smil-ing face, There is sun-shine in the soul.

Stepping in the Light 259

Eliza E. Hewitt, b. 1851 William J. Kirkpatrick, 1838-1921

1. Try - ing to walk in the steps of the Sav-ior, Try - ing to fol - low our
2. Press-ing more close-ly to Him who is lead-ing, When we are tempted to
3. Walk-ing in foot-steps of gen - tle for-bear-ance, Foot-steps of faith-ful-ness,
4. Try - ing to walk in the steps of the Sav-ior, Up -ward, still upward we'll

Sav - ior and King; Shap - ing our lives by His bless - ed ex - am - ple,
turn from the way; Trust - ing the arm that is strong to de- fend us,
mer - cy and love, Look - ing to Him for the grace free - ly prom- ised,
fol - low our Guide; When we shall see Him, "the King in His beau - ty,"

Hap-py, how hap-py, the songs that we bring.
Hap-py, how hap-py, our prais - es each day.
Hap-py, how hap-py, our jour - ney a - bove.
Hap-py, how hap-py, our place at His side.

CHORUS

How beau-ti-ful to walk in the steps of the Sav - ior, Stepping in the light, Step-ping in the light; How beau - ti - ful to walk in the steps of the Sav - ior, Led in paths of light.

260 I Will Praise Him, Hallelujah!

D. Otis Teasley, 1906 D. Otis Teasley, 1906

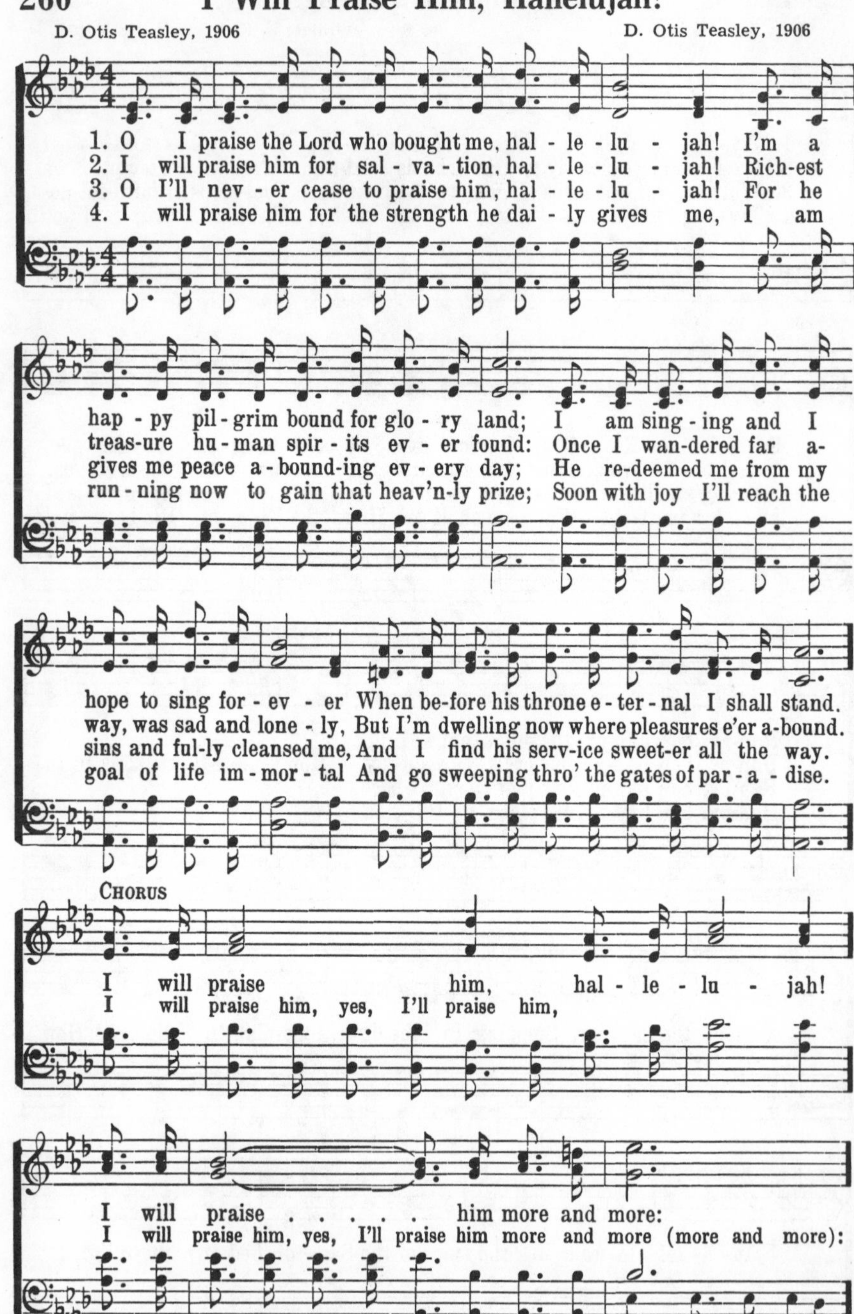
1. O I praise the Lord who bought me, hal - le - lu - jah! I'm a
2. I will praise him for sal - va - tion, hal - le - lu - jah! Rich-est
3. O I'll nev - er cease to praise him, hal - le - lu - jah! For he
4. I will praise him for the strength he dai - ly gives me, I am
hap - py pil - grim bound for glo - ry land; I am sing - ing and I
treas-ure hu - man spir - its ev - er found: Once I wan-dered far a-
gives me peace a - bound-ing ev - ery day; He re-deemed me from my
run - ning now to gain that heav'n-ly prize; Soon with joy I'll reach the
hope to sing for - ev - er When be-fore his throne e - ter - nal I shall stand.
way, was sad and lone - ly, But I'm dwelling now where pleasures e'er a-bound.
sins and ful-ly cleansed me, And I find his serv-ice sweet-er all the way.
goal of life im - mor - tal And go sweeping thro' the gates of par - a - dise.
CHORUS
I will praise him, hal - le - lu - jah!
I will praise him, yes, I'll praise him,
I will praise . . . . . . him more and more:
I will praise him, yes, I'll praise him more and more (more and more):

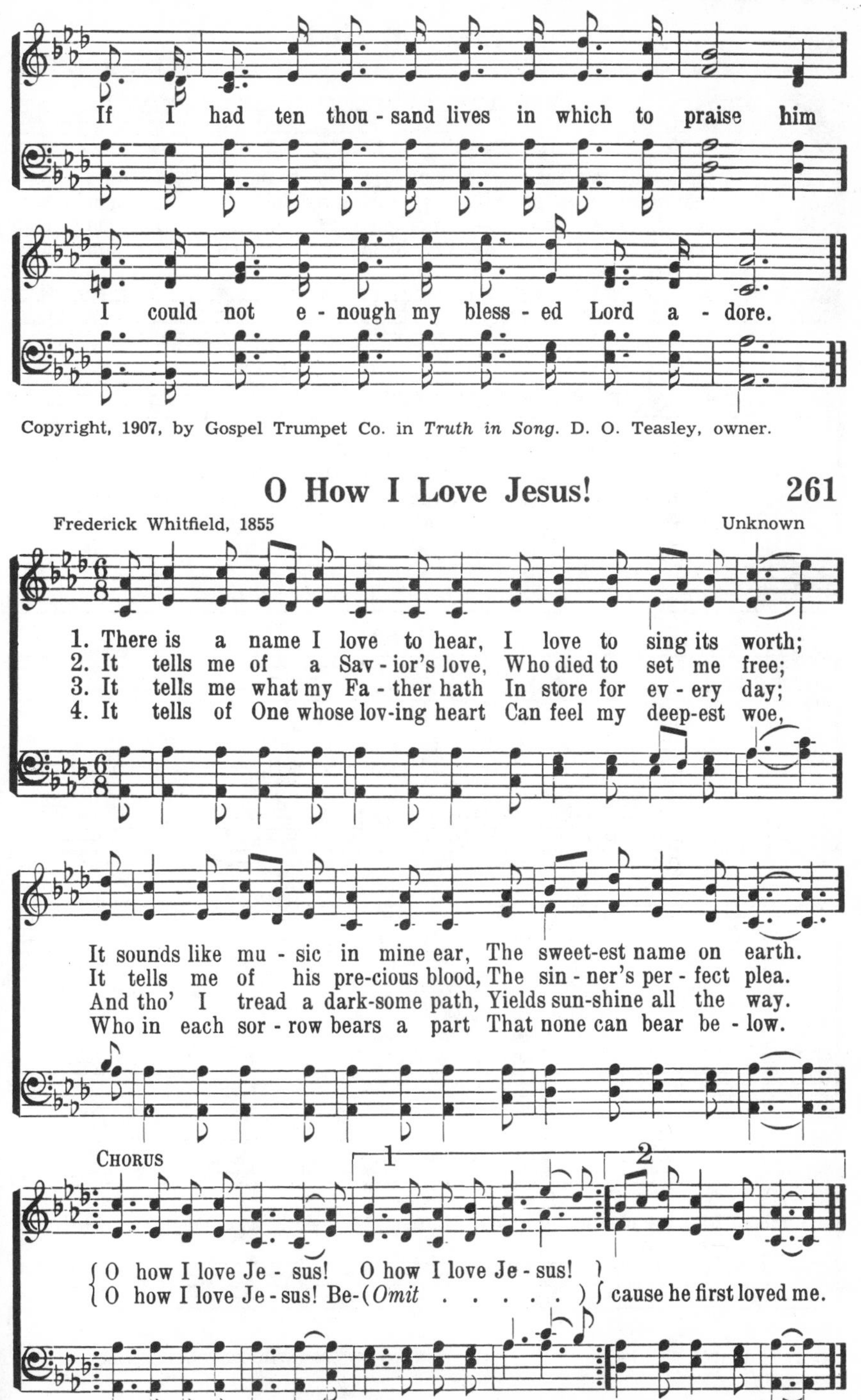
If I had ten thou - sand lives in which to praise him
I could not e - nough my bless - ed Lord a - dore.
Copyright, 1907, by Gospel Trumpet Co. in Truth in Song. D. O. Teasley, owner.
O How I Love Jesus!
261
Frederick Whitfield, 1855
Unknown
1. There is a name I love to hear, I love to sing its worth;
2. It tells me of a Sav - ior's love, Who died to set me free;
3. It tells me what my Fa - ther hath In store for ev - ery day;
4. It tells of One whose lov-ing heart Can feel my deep-est woe,
It sounds like mu - sic in mine ear, The sweet-est name on earth.
It tells me of his pre-cious blood, The sin - ner's per - fect plea.
And tho' I tread a dark-some path, Yields sun-shine all the way.
Who in each sor - row bears a part That none can bear be - low.
CHORUS
O how I love Je - sus! O how I love Je - sus!
O how I love Je - sus! Be-(Omit . . . . .) cause he first loved me.

262 A Child of God

Barney E. Warren, 1907 Barney E. Warren, 1907

1. Praise the Lord! my heart with his love is beam-ing, I am a child of God; Heav-en's gold-en light o-ver me is stream-ing, I am a child of God.
2. Let the saints re-joice with my rap-tured spir-it, I am a child of God; I will tes-ti-fy that the world may hear it,
3. Let a ho-ly life tell the gos-pel sto-ry, I am a child of God; How he fills the soul with his grace and glo-ry,
4. Saved from sin to-day, ev-ery band is riv-en, I am a child of God; Thro' the tests of life I have peace from heav-en,
CHORUS
I am a child of God, ...
I am a child, a child of God,
I am a child of God; . . . .
I am a child, a child of God;
I have washed my robes in the cleans-ing foun-tain, I am a child of God.

All in Jesus

263

Barney E. Warren, 1900 — Barney E. Warren, 1900

Not too slow

1. There is peace and joy in the Lord to - day, More than all in this world of sin;
2. I am blest to - day, I am free in-deed, What a pleas-ure to serve the Lord!
3. Since my cross is gone and my heart is right, O how bless-ed to do his will!
4. All his grace is free as the air we breathe, We may each have a full sup - ply;

There's a hap-py life in the ho - ly way, Praise the Lord, I have en-tered in!
How it fills my soul with de-light to read In his sa - cred and ho - ly word!
Now his yoke is eas - y, his bur-den light, And his Spir - it my soul doth fill.
If we will o - bey and his word be-lieve, He'll pre-pare us to dwell on high.

CHORUS

Praise the Lord, I am free In his love and grace!
Praise the Lord, I'm free, I am free in - deed In his love, his ten - der love and grace!

O his blood reach-es me! I a-bide 'neath his smil-ing face.
O his pre-cious blood reach-es e - ven me!

264 My Redeemer

Philip P. Bliss, 1838-1876 — James McGranahan, 1840-1907

1. I will sing of my Re-deem-er, And His won-drous love to me;
2. I will tell the won-drous sto-ry, How my lost es-tate to save,
3. I will praise my dear Re-deem-er, His tri-um-phant pow'r I'll tell,
4. I will sing of my Re-deem-er, And His heav'n-ly love to me;
On the cru-el cross He suf-fered, From the curse to set me free.
In His bound-less love and mer-cy, He the ran-som free-ly gave.
How the vic-to-ry He giv-eth O-ver sin, and death, and hell.
He from death to life hath bro't me, Son of God with Him to be.
CHORUS
Sing, oh, sing . . . . of my Re-deem-er,
of my Re-deem-er, Sing, oh, sing of my Re-deem-er,
With His blood . . . . He pur-chased me, ...
He pur-chased me, With His blood He pur-chased me,
On the cross . . . . He sealed my par-don,
He sealed my par-don, On the cross He sealed my par-don,

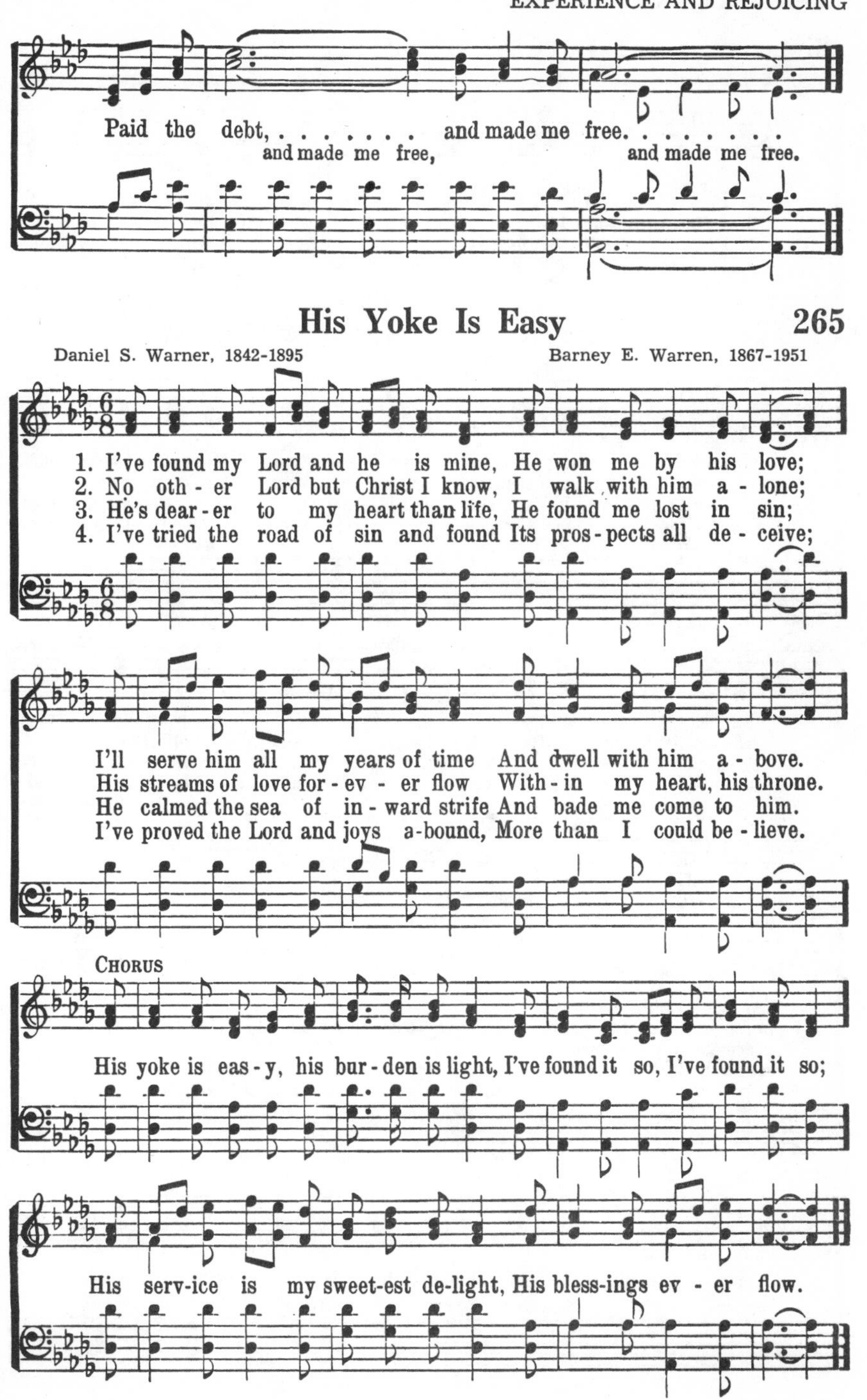
Paid the debt, ... and made me free. . . . .
and made me free, and made me free.
His Yoke Is Easy
265
Daniel S. Warner, 1842-1895
Barney E. Warren, 1867-1951
1. I've found my Lord and he is mine, He won me by his love;
2. No oth - er Lord but Christ I know, I walk with him a - lone;
3. He's dear - er to my heart than life, He found me lost in sin;
4. I've tried the road of sin and found Its pros - pects all de - ceive;
I'll serve him all my years of time And dwell with him a - bove.
His streams of love for - ev - er flow With - in my heart, his throne.
He calmed the sea of in - ward strife And bade me come to him.
I've proved the Lord and joys a-bound, More than I could be - lieve.
CHORUS
His yoke is eas - y, his bur - den is light, I've found it so, I've found it so;
His serv-ice is my sweet-est de-light, His bless-ings ev - er flow.

266 I Love to Serve My Jesus

Barney E. Warren, 1897 Elisha A. Hoffman, 1897

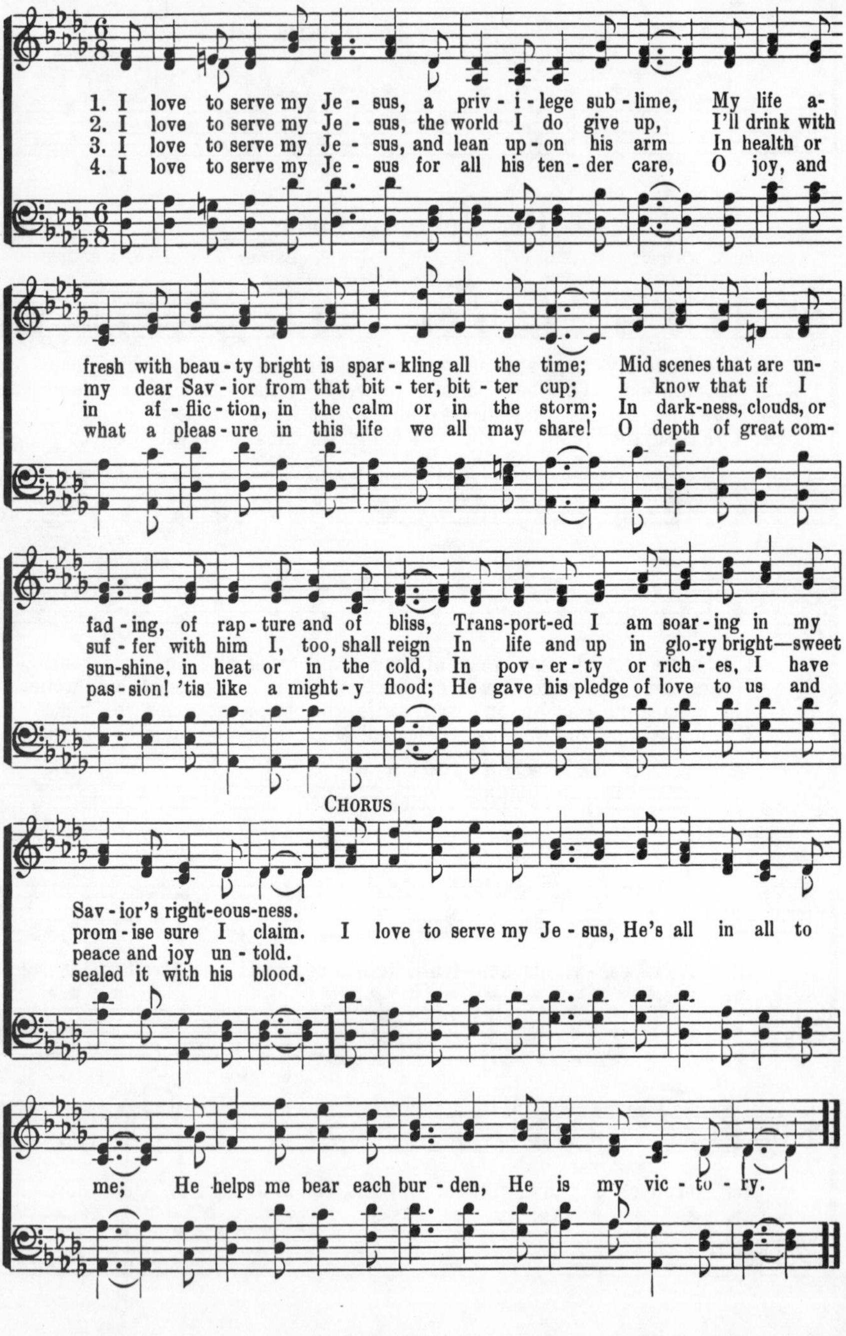

1. I love to serve my Je - sus, a priv - i - lege sub - lime, My life a-
2. I love to serve my Je - sus, the world I do give up, I'll drink with
3. I love to serve my Je - sus, and lean up - on his arm In health or
4. I love to serve my Je - sus for all his ten - der care, O joy, and

fresh with beau - ty bright is spar - kling all the time; Mid scenes that are un-
my dear Sav - ior from that bit - ter, bit - ter cup; I know that if I
in af - flic - tion, in the calm or in the storm; In dark-ness, clouds, or
what a pleas - ure in this life we all may share! O depth of great com-

fad - ing, of rap - ture and of bliss, Trans-port-ed I am soar - ing in my
suf - fer with him I, too, shall reign In life and up in glo-ry bright—sweet
sun-shine, in heat or in the cold, In pov - er - ty or rich - es, I have
pas - sion! 'tis like a might - y flood; He gave his pledge of love to us and

Sav - ior's right-eous-ness.
prom - ise sure I claim.
peace and joy un - told.
sealed it with his blood.

CHORUS

I love to serve my Je - sus, He's all in all to me; He helps me bear each bur - den, He is my vic - to - ry.

What a Dear Friend Is Jesus 267

Lizzie DeArmond, 1923 — Andrew L. Byers, 1923

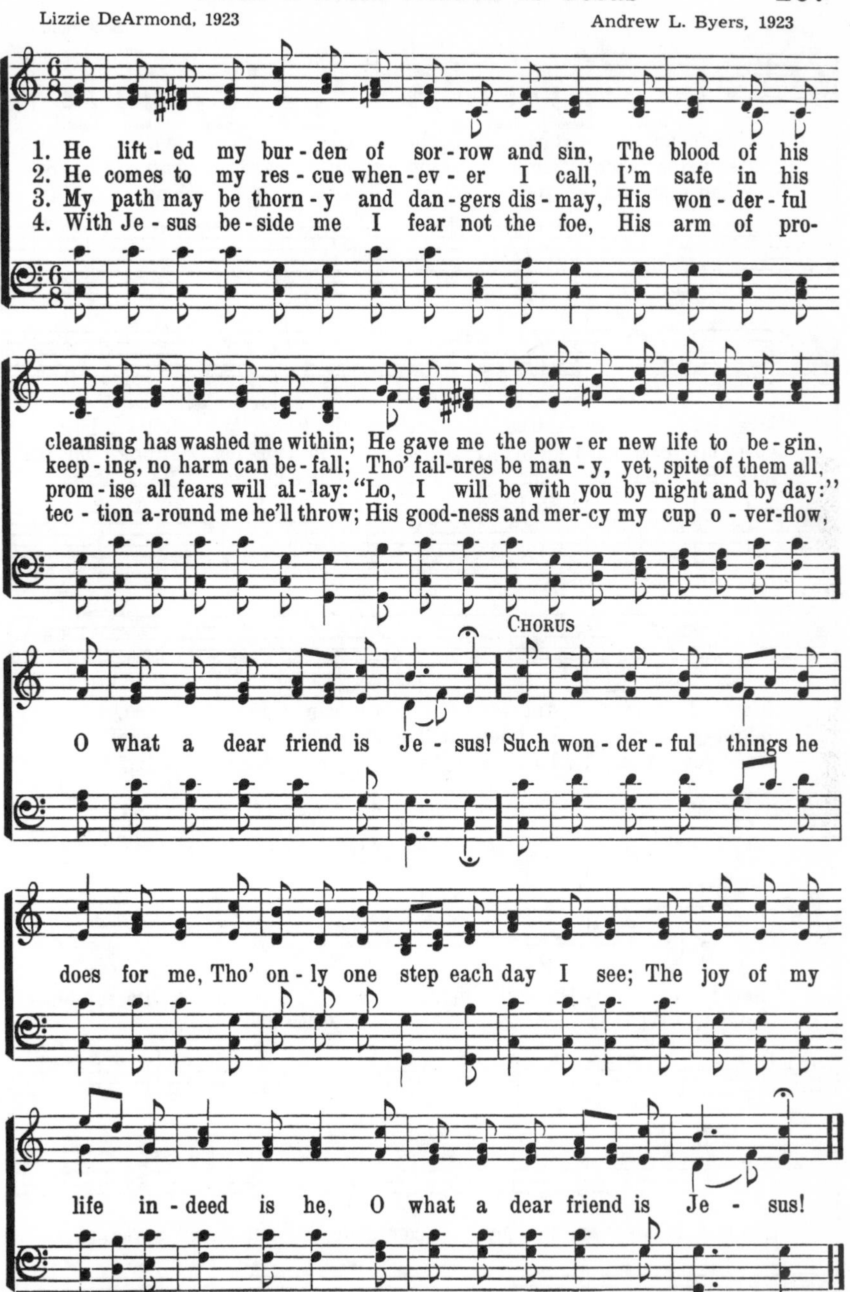
1. He lift-ed my bur-den of sor-row and sin, The blood of his cleansing has washed me within; He gave me the pow-er new life to be-gin,
2. He comes to my res-cue when-ev-er I call, I'm safe in his keep-ing, no harm can be-fall; Tho' fail-ures be man-y, yet, spite of them all,
3. My path may be thorn-y and dan-gers dis-may, His won-der-ful prom-ise all fears will al-lay: "Lo, I will be with you by night and by day:"
4. With Je-sus be-side me I fear not the foe, His arm of pro-tec-tion a-round me he'll throw; His good-ness and mer-cy my cup o-ver-flow,
O what a dear friend is Je-sus!
CHORUS
Such won-der-ful things he does for me, Tho' on-ly one step each day I see; The joy of my life in-deed is he, O what a dear friend is Je-sus!

268 Saved, Saved!

J. P. Scholfield — J. P. Scholfield

1. I've found a friend . . who is all to me, . . . His love is ever true; . . . . I love to tell . . how He lift - ed me, . . And what His grace can do for you. . . .
2. He saves me from . . . ev-'ry sin and harm, . . Se-cures my soul each day; . . . . I'm lean-ing strong on His might-y arm; . . I know He'll guide me all the way. . .
3. When poor and need - y and all a - lone, . . In love He said to me, ... "Come un - to Me . . and I'll lead you home, . . To live with Me e - ter - nal - ly." . . .
CHORUS
Saved . . . . by His pow'r di-vine, Saved . . . . to new life sub-lime!
Saved by His pow'r, Saved to new life,
cres
rit.
Life now is sweet and my joy is com-plete, For I'm Saved, saved, saved!

Love Lifted Me 269

James Rowe, 1865-1933

Howard E. Smith, 1863-1918

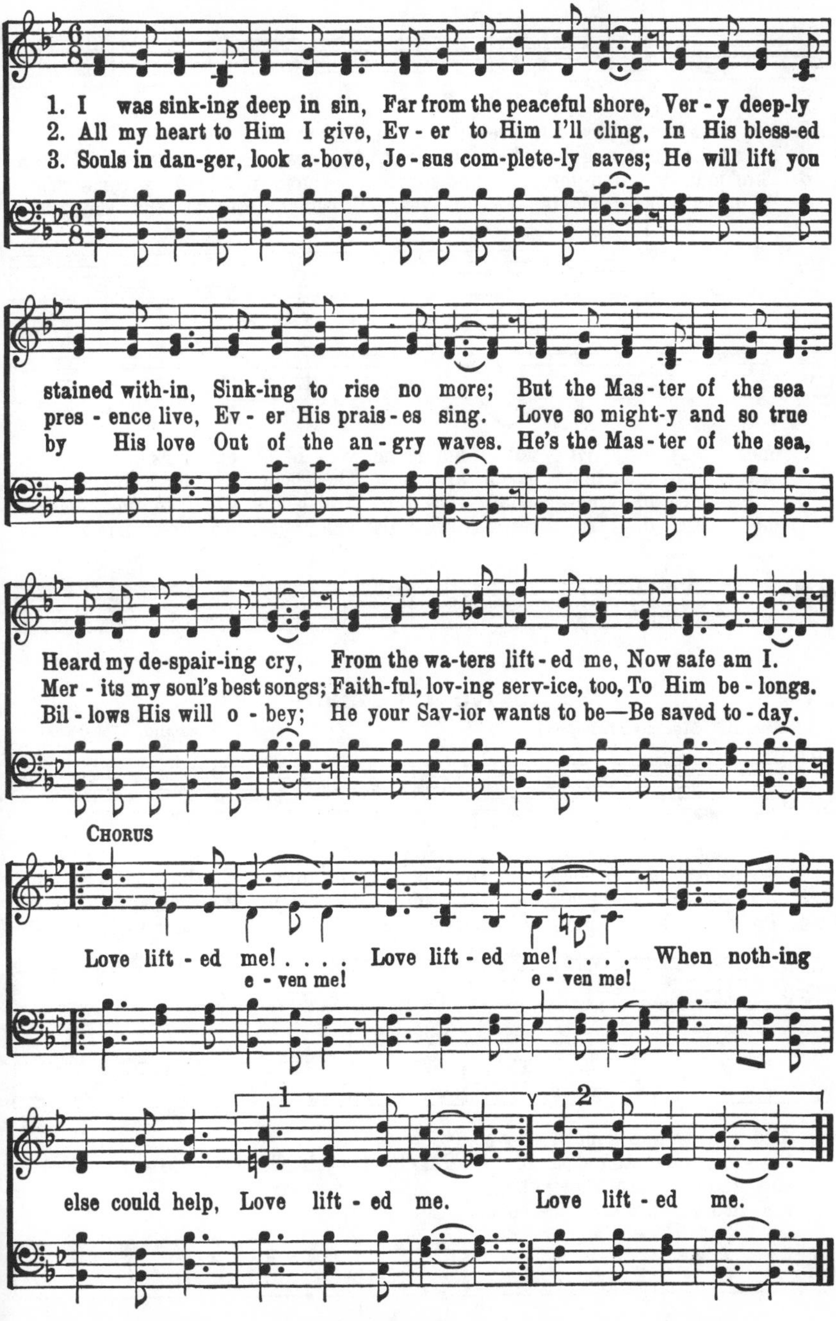

1. I was sink-ing deep in sin, Far from the peaceful shore, Ver - y deep-ly stained with-in, Sink-ing to rise no more; But the Mas - ter of the sea Heard my de-spair-ing cry, From the wa-ters lift - ed me, Now safe am I.

2. All my heart to Him I give, Ev - er to Him I'll cling, In His bless-ed pres - ence live, Ev - er His prais - es sing. Love so might-y and so true Mer - its my soul's best songs; Faith-ful, lov-ing serv-ice, too, To Him be - longs.

3. Souls in dan-ger, look a-bove, Je - sus com-plete-ly saves; He will lift you by His love Out of the an - gry waves. He's the Mas - ter of the sea, Bil - lows His will o - bey; He your Sav-ior wants to be—Be saved to - day.

CHORUS

Love lift - ed me! . . . . Love lift - ed me! . . . .
e - ven me! e - ven me!
When noth-ing else could help, Love lift - ed me. Love lift - ed me.

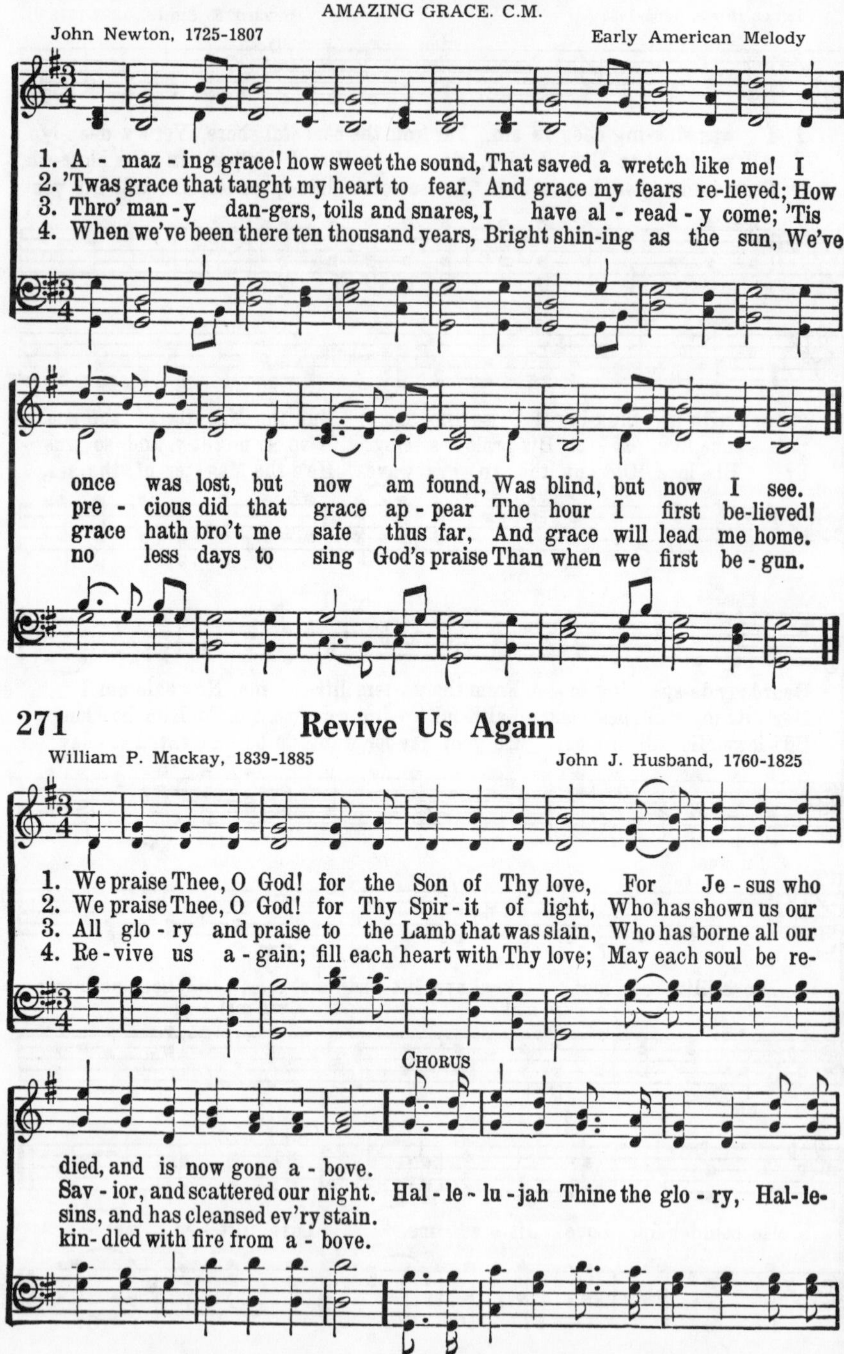
270
Amazing Grace
AMAZING GRACE. C.M.
John Newton, 1725-1807
Early American Melody
1. A - maz - ing grace! how sweet the sound, That saved a wretch like me! I
2. 'Twas grace that taught my heart to fear, And grace my fears re-lieved; How
3. Thro' man - y dan-gers, toils and snares, I have al - read - y come; 'Tis
4. When we've been there ten thousand years, Bright shin-ing as the sun, We've
once was lost, but now am found, Was blind, but now I see.
pre - cious did that grace ap - pear The hour I first be-lieved!
grace hath bro't me safe thus far, And grace will lead me home.
no less days to sing God's praise Than when we first be - gun.
271
Revive Us Again
William P. Mackay, 1839-1885
John J. Husband, 1760-1825
1. We praise Thee, O God! for the Son of Thy love, For Je - sus who
2. We praise Thee, O God! for Thy Spir - it of light, Who has shown us our
3. All glo - ry and praise to the Lamb that was slain, Who has borne all our
4. Re - vive us a - gain; fill each heart with Thy love; May each soul be re-
CHORUS
died, and is now gone a - bove.
Sav - ior, and scattered our night. Hal - le - lu - jah Thine the glo - ry, Hal - le-
sins, and has cleansed ev'ry stain.
kin - dled with fire from a - bove.

lu - jah! a - men; Hal - le - lu - jah! Thine the glo - ry, re - vive us a - gain.
The Half Has Never Been Told
272
Frances R. Havergal, 1836-1879
Ralph E. Hudson, 1843-1901
1. I know I love Thee bet - ter, Lord, Than an - y earth - ly joy.
2. I know that Thou art near - er still Than an - y earth - ly throng,
3. Thou hast put glad - ness in my heart; Then well may I be glad;
4. O Sav - ior, pre - cious Sav - ior mine! What will Thy pres - ence be
For Thou hast giv - en me the peace Which noth - ing can de - stroy.
And sweet - er is the thought of Thee Than an - y love - ly song.
With - out the se - cret of Thy love I could not but be sad.
If such a life of joy can crown Our walk on earth with Thee.
CHORUS
The half has nev - er yet been told, Of love so full and free;
yet been told,
The half has never yet been told, His blood—it cleanseth me.
yet been told,
cleanseth me.
rit.

273 Standing on the Promises

R. Kelso Carter — R. Kelso Carter

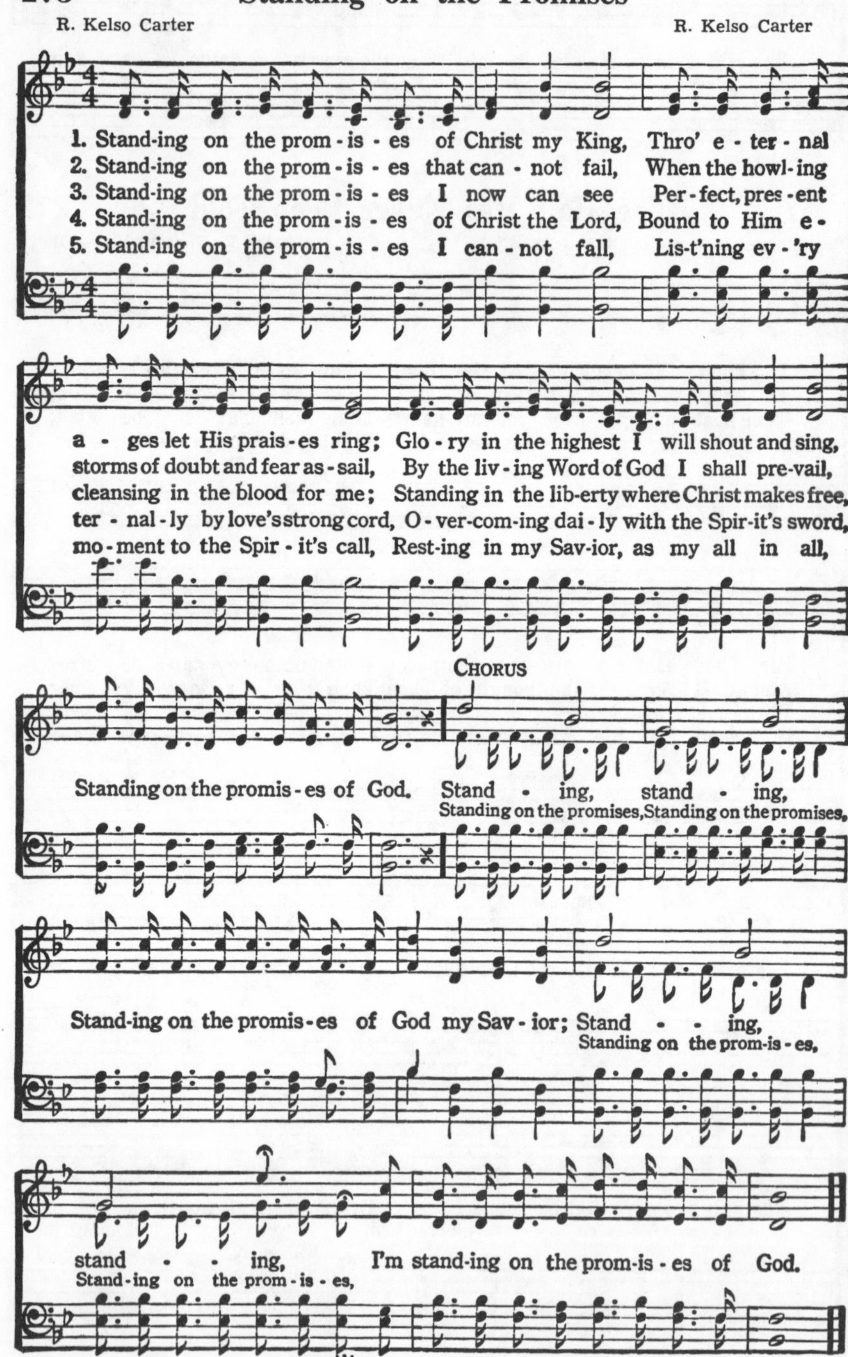
1. Stand-ing on the prom-is-es of Christ my King, Thro' e-ter-nal a-ges let His prais-es ring; Glo-ry in the highest I will shout and sing,
2. Stand-ing on the prom-is-es that can-not fail, When the howl-ing storms of doubt and fear as-sail, By the liv-ing Word of God I shall pre-vail,
3. Stand-ing on the prom-is-es I now can see Per-fect, pres-ent cleansing in the blood for me; Standing in the lib-erty where Christ makes free,
4. Stand-ing on the prom-is-es of Christ the Lord, Bound to Him e-ter-nal-ly by love's strong cord, O-ver-com-ing dai-ly with the Spir-it's sword,
5. Stand-ing on the prom-is-es I can-not fall, Lis-t'ning ev-'ry mo-ment to the Spir-it's call, Rest-ing in my Sav-ior, as my all in all,
Standing on the promis-es of God.
CHORUS
Stand-ing, stand-ing,
Standing on the promises, Standing on the promises,
Stand-ing on the promis-es of God my Sav-ior; Stand-ing,
Standing on the prom-is-es,
stand-ing,
Stand-ing on the prom-is-es,
I'm stand-ing on the prom-is-es of God.

He Keeps Me Singing 274

L. B. Bridgers | L. B. Bridgers

1. There's within my heart a mel - o - dy Je - sus whis-pers sweet and low,
2. All my life was wrecked by sin and strife, Dis-cord filled my heart with pain,
3. Feast - ing on the rich - es of His grace, Resting 'neath His shelt'ring wing,
4. Tho' sometimes He leads thro' waters deep, Tri - als fall a - cross the way,
5. Soon He's com-ing back to wel-come me Far be - yond the star - ry sky;

Fear not, I am with thee, peace, be still, In all of life's ebb and flow.
Je - sus swept across the broken strings, Stirred the slumb'ring chords again.
Al - ways look-ing on His smil - ing face, That is why I shout and sing.
Tho' sometimes the path seems rough and steep, See His footprints all the way.
I shall wing my flight to worlds un-known, I shall reign with Him on high.

CHORUS

Je - sus, Je - sus, Je - sus,— Sweet - est name I know,

Fills my ev - 'ry long - ing, Keeps me sing-ing as I go. A-MEN.

275 I Will Shout His Praise in Glory

P. H. Dingman — John R. Sweney, 1837-1899

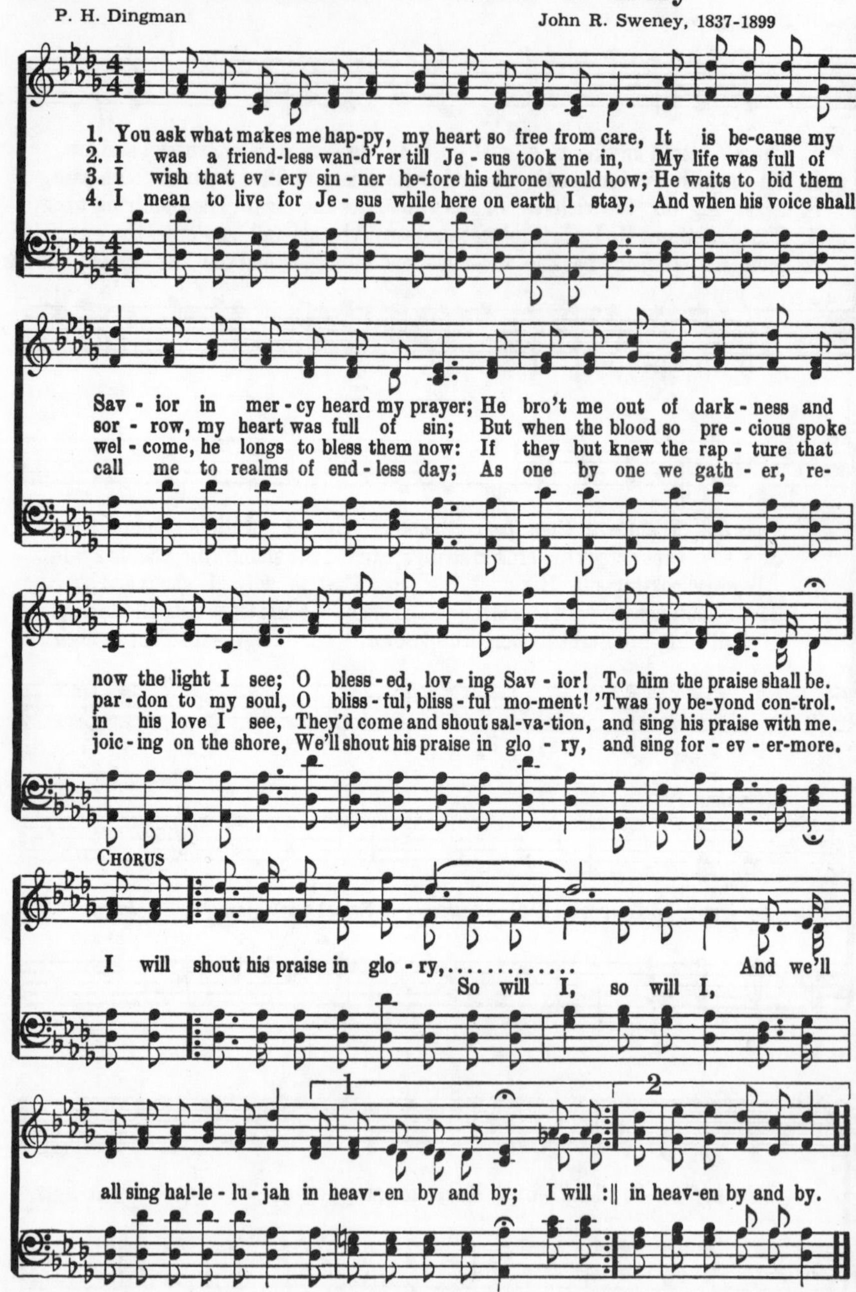
1. You ask what makes me hap-py, my heart so free from care, It is be-cause my Sav - ior in mer - cy heard my prayer; He bro't me out of dark - ness and now the light I see; O bless - ed, lov - ing Sav - ior! To him the praise shall be.
2. I was a friend-less wan-d'rer till Je - sus took me in, My life was full of sor - row, my heart was full of sin; But when the blood so pre - cious spoke par - don to my soul, O bliss - ful, bliss - ful mo-ment! 'Twas joy be-yond con-trol.
3. I wish that ev - ery sin - ner be-fore his throne would bow; He waits to bid them wel - come, he longs to bless them now: If they but knew the rap - ture that in his love I see, They'd come and shout sal-va-tion, and sing his praise with me.
4. I mean to live for Je - sus while here on earth I stay, And when his voice shall call me to realms of end - less day; As one by one we gath - er, re - joic - ing on the shore, We'll shout his praise in glo - ry, and sing for - ev - er-more.
CHORUS
I will shout his praise in glo - ry,............ And we'll
So will I, so will I,
all sing hal-le - lu - jah in heav - en by and by; I will :|| in heav-en by and by.
1
2

I'm Redeemed

Joseph C. Fisher, 1884 — Joseph C. Fisher, 1884

1. I'm re-deemed, I'm re-deemed From the dark-ness of the night That so thick-ly en-vel-oped my soul; In my heart there have gleamed Rays of won-der-ful light, Where the waves of Thy glo-ry now roll.
2. I'm re-deemed by Thy blood, From the pow-er of the grave, And the vic-t'ry I have o-ver death; O that won-der-ful flood! How I felt its pow'r to save, When I plunged in its fath-om-less depth!
3. I'm re-deemed from all sin And I'm walk-ing in the light, And Thy Spir-it il-lu-mines my way; I've no fear now with-in 'For the ter-ror of the night, Nor the ar-row that fli-eth by day.'
4. The re-deemed ones shall walk In the path-way of the just, Which shines bright-er and bright-er each day; They shall sing and shall talk With the bright an-gel-ic host, Where all sor-row and sighs flee a-way.
CHORUS
I'm re-deemed, praise the Lord! I'm re-deemed by the blood of the Lamb; I am
I'm re-deemed, praise the Lord!
saved from all sin, and I'm walk-ing in the light, I'm redeemed by the blood of the Lamb.

277 Joy Unspeakable

Barney E. Warren, 1900 Barney E. Warren, 1900

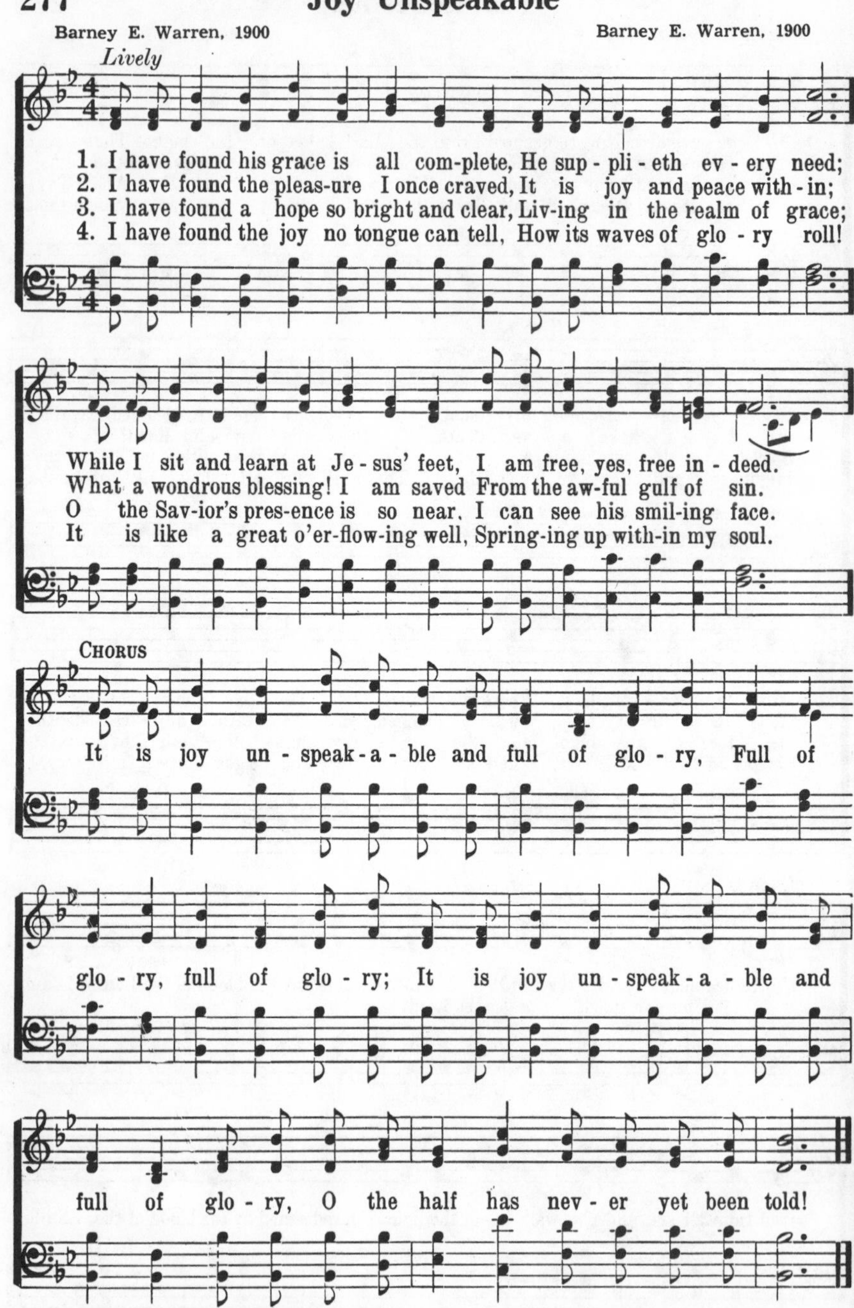
Lively
1. I have found his grace is all com-plete, He sup-pli-eth ev-ery need;
2. I have found the pleas-ure I once craved, It is joy and peace with-in;
3. I have found a hope so bright and clear, Liv-ing in the realm of grace;
4. I have found the joy no tongue can tell, How its waves of glo-ry roll!
While I sit and learn at Je-sus' feet, I am free, yes, free in-deed.
What a wondrous blessing! I am saved From the aw-ful gulf of sin.
O the Sav-ior's pres-ence is so near, I can see his smil-ing face.
It is like a great o'er-flow-ing well, Spring-ing up with-in my soul.
Chorus
It is joy un-speak-a-ble and full of glo-ry, Full of
glo-ry, full of glo-ry; It is joy un-speak-a-ble and
full of glo-ry, O the half has nev-er yet been told!

It Is Truly Wonderful

Barney E. Warren, 1903 — Barney E. Warren, 1903

1. He par - doned my trans - gres - sions, He sanc - ti - fied my soul;
2. He brings me thro' af - flic - tion, He leaves me not a - lone;
3. He pros - pers and pro - tects me, His bless - ings ev - er flow;
4. He keeps me firm and faith - ful, His love I do en - joy;

He hon - ors my con - fes - sions, Since by his blood I'm whole.
He's with me in temp - ta - tion, He keeps me for his own.
He gives me grace and glo - ry, He makes me white as snow.
For this I shall be grate - ful And live in his em - ploy.

CHORUS

It is tru - ly won - der - ful what the Lord has done, It is
tru - ly won - der - ful, It is tru - ly won - der - ful; It is
tru - ly won - der - ful what the Lord has done. Glo - ry to his name!

279 He Lives

A. H. Ackley, 1933 A. H. Ackley, 1933

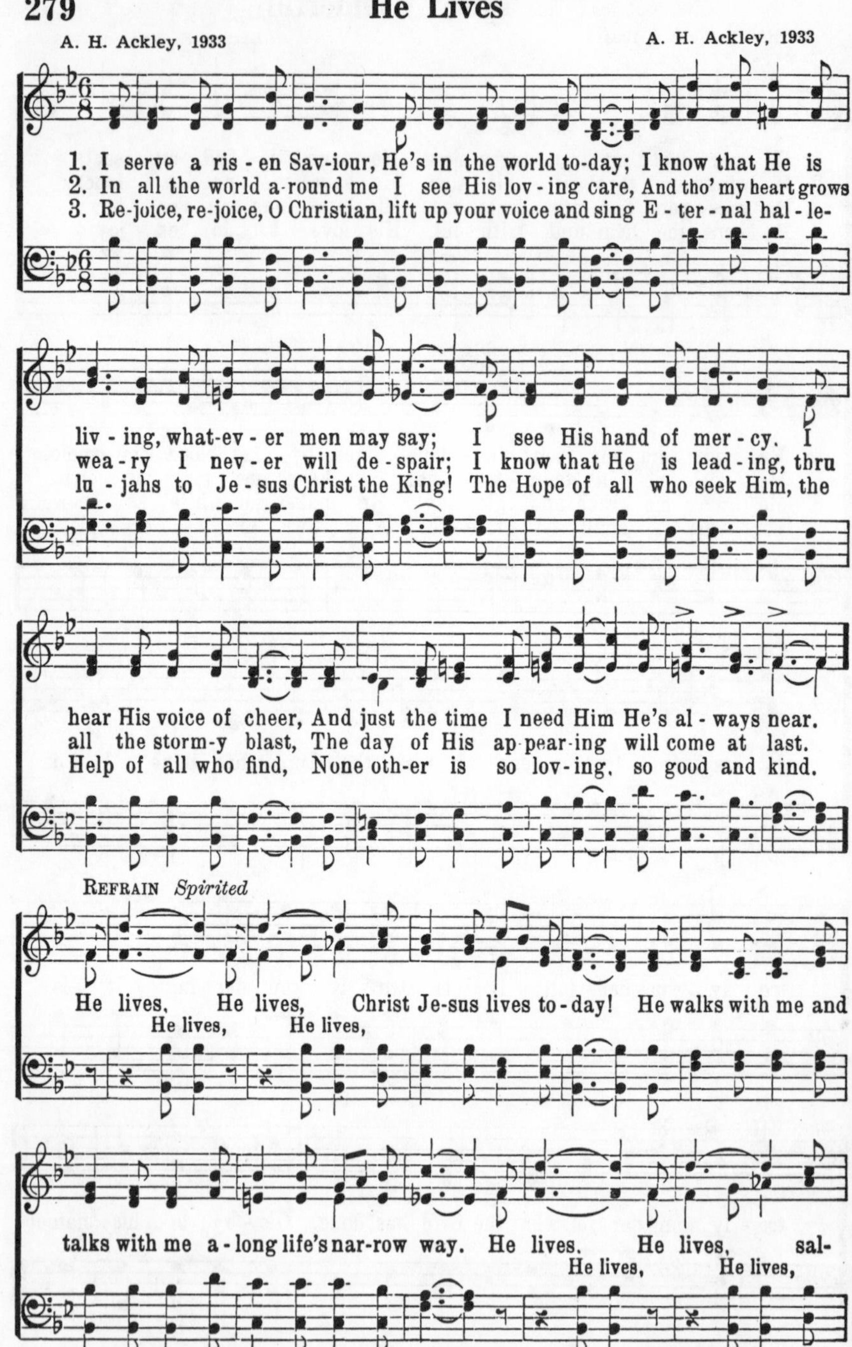
1. I serve a ris - en Sav-iour, He's in the world to-day; I know that He is liv - ing, what-ev - er men may say; I see His hand of mer - cy. I hear His voice of cheer, And just the time I need Him He's al - ways near.
2. In all the world a-round me I see His lov - ing care, And tho' my heart grows wea - ry I nev - er will de - spair; I know that He is lead - ing, thru all the storm-y blast, The day of His ap-pear-ing will come at last.
3. Re-joice, re-joice, O Christian, lift up your voice and sing E - ter - nal hal - le- lu - jahs to Je - sus Christ the King! The Hope of all who seek Him, the Help of all who find, None oth-er is so lov-ing, so good and kind.
REFRAIN Spirited
He lives, He lives, Christ Je-sus lives to-day! He walks with me and talks with me a-long life's nar-row way. He lives, He lives, sal-
He lives, He lives,
He lives, He lives,

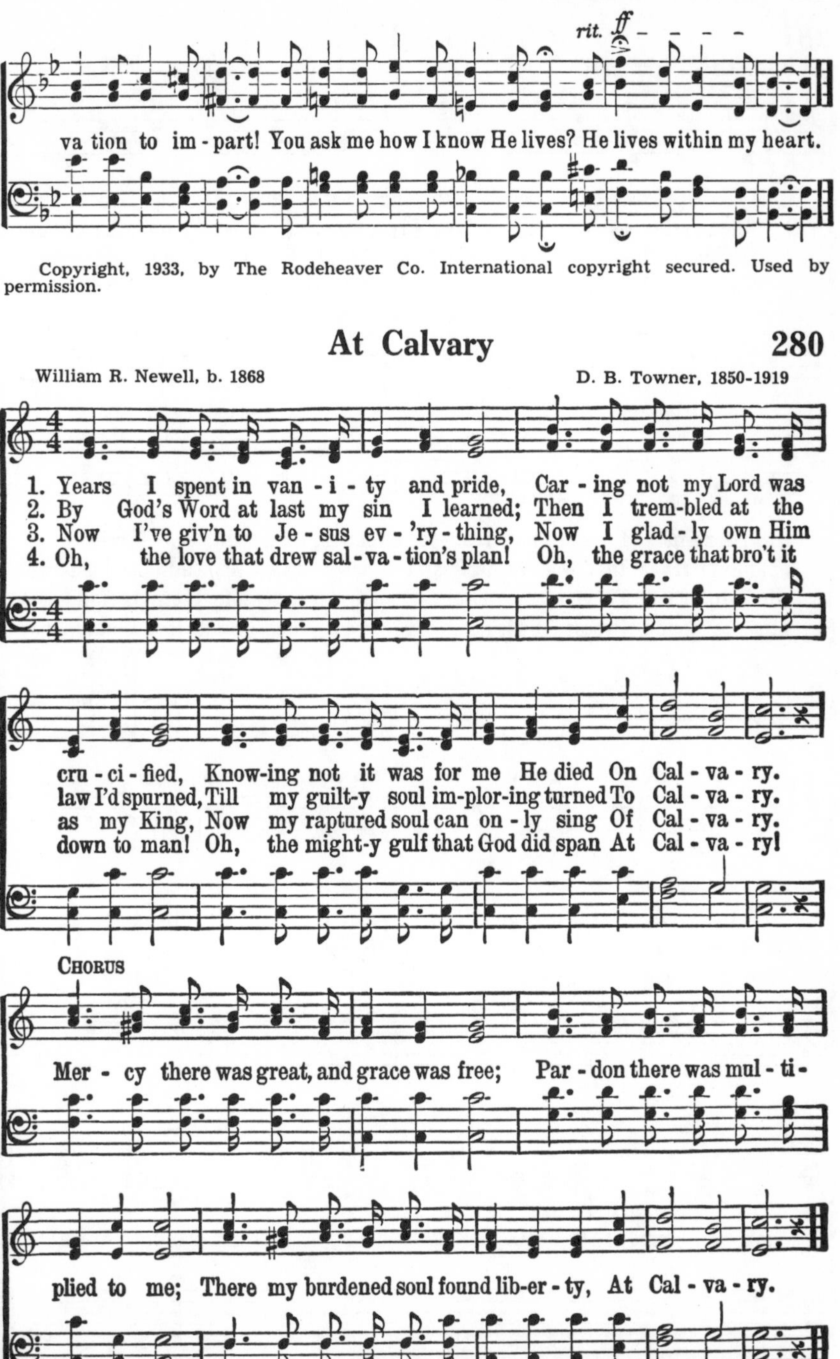
rit. ff
va tion to im-part! You ask me how I know He lives? He lives within my heart.

At Calvary 280

William R. Newell, b. 1868

D. B. Towner, 1850-1919

1. Years I spent in van-i-ty and pride, Car-ing not my Lord was cru-ci-fied, Know-ing not it was for me He died On Cal-va-ry.
2. By God's Word at last my sin I learned; Then I trem-bled at the law I'd spurned, Till my guilt-y soul im-plor-ing turned To Cal-va-ry.
3. Now I've giv'n to Je-sus ev-'ry-thing, Now I glad-ly own Him as my King, Now my raptured soul can on-ly sing Of Cal-va-ry.
4. Oh, the love that drew sal-va-tion's plan! Oh, the grace that bro't it down to man! Oh, the might-y gulf that God did span At Cal-va-ry!
Chorus
Mer-cy there was great, and grace was free; Par-don there was mul-ti-plied to me; There my burdened soul found lib-er-ty, At Cal-va-ry.

281 The Solid Rock

Edward Mote, 1797-1874 William B. Bradbury, 1816-1868

1. My hope is built on nothing less Than Jesus' blood and
2. When darkness veils his lovely face, I rest on his un-
3. His oath, his covenant, his blood, Support me in the
4. When he shall come with trumpet sound, O may I then in

righteousness; I dare not trust the sweetest frame, But wholly lean on
changing grace; In every high and stormy gale My anchor holds with-
whelming flood; When all around my soul gives way He then is all my
him be found Dressed in his righteousness alone, Faultless to stand be-

CHORUS

Jesus' name.
in the veil. On Christ, the solid Rock, I stand; All other ground is
hope and stay.
fore the throne!

sinking sand, All other ground is sinking sand. A-MEN.

Waves of Devotion

282

Barney E. Warren, 1911 — Barney E. Warren, 1911

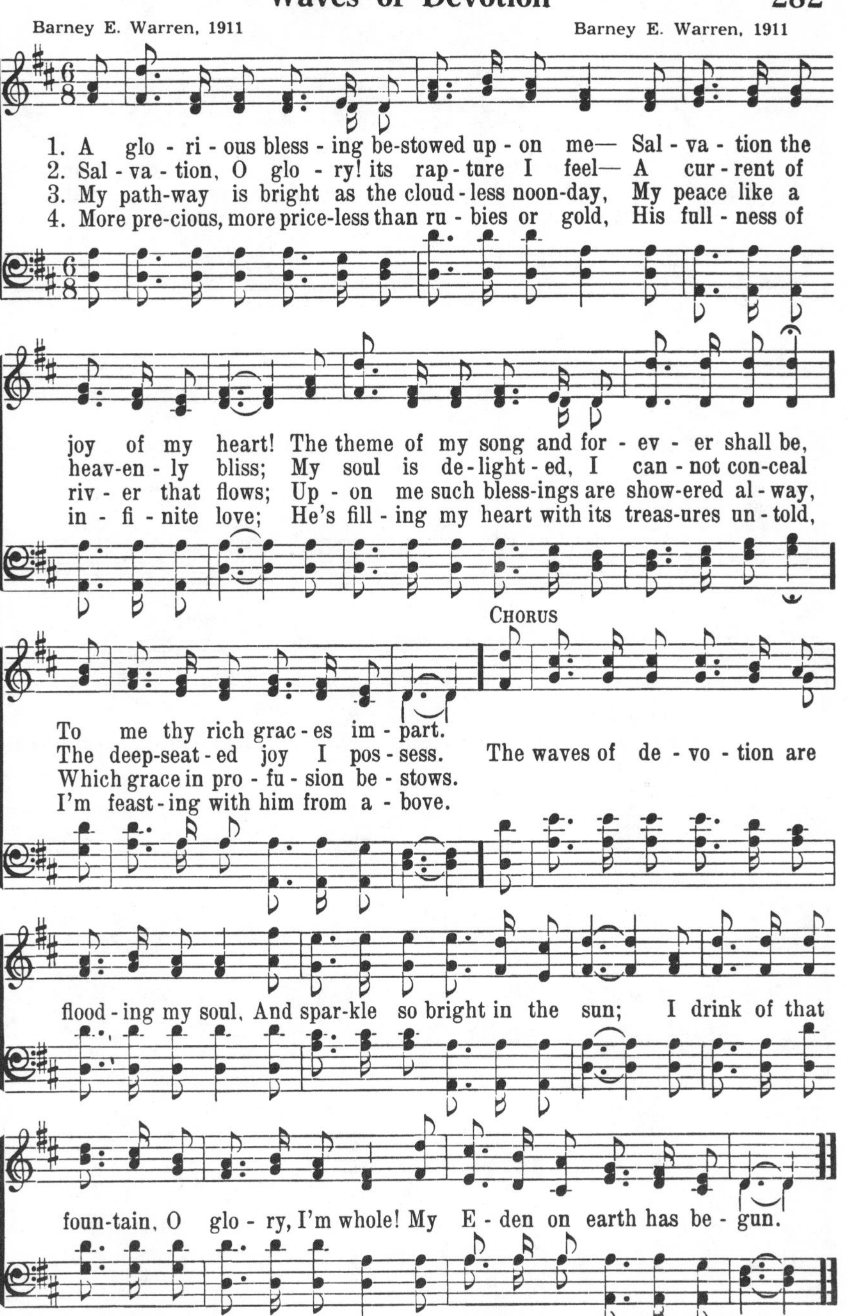
1. A glo - ri - ous bless - ing be-stowed up - on me— Sal - va - tion the joy of my heart! The theme of my song and for - ev - er shall be, To me thy rich grac - es im - part.
2. Sal - va - tion, O glo - ry! its rap - ture I feel— A cur - rent of heav-en - ly bliss; My soul is de - light - ed, I can - not con-ceal The deep-seat - ed joy I pos - sess.
3. My path-way is bright as the cloud - less noon-day, My peace like a riv - er that flows; Up - on me such bless-ings are show-ered al - way, Which grace in pro - fu - sion be - stows.
4. More pre-cious, more price-less than ru - bies or gold, His full - ness of in - fi - nite love; He's fill - ing my heart with its treas-ures un - told, I'm feast - ing with him from a - bove.
CHORUS
The waves of de - vo - tion are flood - ing my soul, And spar-kle so bright in the sun; I drink of that foun-tain, O glo - ry, I'm whole! My E - den on earth has be - gun.

283 Heavenly Sunlight

H. J. Zelley — G. H. Cook

1. Walk-ing in sun - light all of my jour - ney, O - ver the moun-tains, thro' the deep vale; Je - sus has said, I'll nev - er for - sake thee— Prom - ise di - vine that nev - er can fail.
2. Shad-ows a - round me, shad-ows a - bove me Nev-er con - ceal my Sav - ior and Guide; He is the light, in him is no dark-ness, Ev - er I'm walk - ing close to his side.
3. In the bright sun-light, ev - er re - joic - ing, Press-ing my way to man-sions a - bove; Sing-ing his prais - es, glad - ly I'm walk - ing, Walk-ing in sun - light, sun-light of love.
CHORUS
Heav - en - ly sun - light, heav - en - ly sun - light, Flood-ing my soul with glo - ry di - vine: Hal - le - lu - jah, I am re - joic - ing, Sing-ing his prais - es, Je - sus is mine.

He Lifted Me Out

284

Lawrence E. Brooks, c. 1934

Lawrence E. Brooks, c. 1934
Har. by K. Y. Plank

1. I was out on the broad way of sin and de-spair, Crushed 'neath my bur-den of sor-row and care; My constant companions were trou-ble and doubt, Till Je-sus reached down and lift-ed me out.

2. I was wan-d'ring a-far from my Sav-ior and home, Faint-ing and wea-ry in sin did I roam; I need-ed a hand to turn me a-bout, Then Je-sus reached down and lift-ed me out.

3. I was build-ing my home on the dry shift-ing sand, Cast-ing my lot in a cold bar-ren land; "You're doomed now for aye," I heard Sa-tan shout; But Je-sus reached down and lift-ed me out.

4. I have start-ed for heav-en, my heart filled with song, Wan-d'ring is o-ver, my sins all are gone; Thro' Jesus' own blood cleansed within and without, O praise his dear name! he lift-ed me out.

CHORUS

He lift-ed me out of the deep mir-y clay; He set-tled my feet in the strait, narrow way; He lift-ed me up to a heav-en-ly place, And floodeth my soul each day with his grace.

285 The Lord Raised Me

James Rowe, 1865-1933

Hamp Sewell

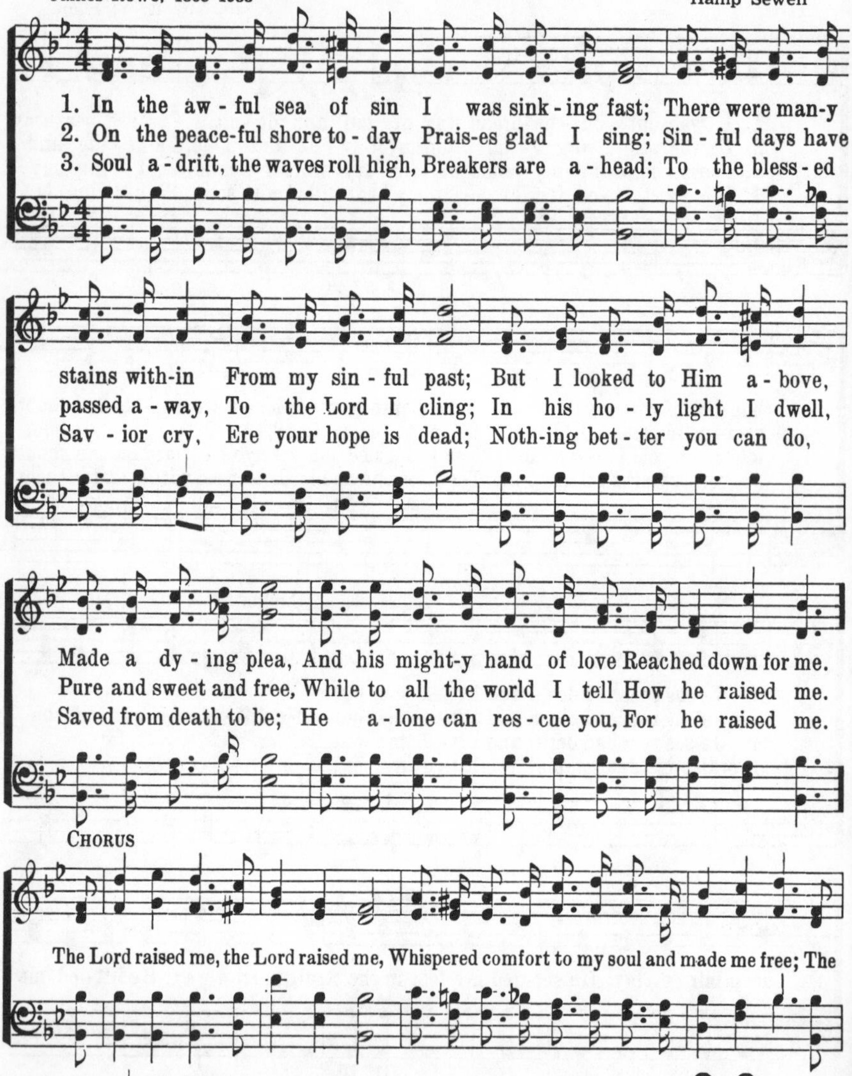

1. In the aw - ful sea of sin I was sink - ing fast; There were man-y stains with-in From my sin - ful past; But I looked to Him a - bove, Made a dy - ing plea, And his might-y hand of love Reached down for me.

2. On the peace-ful shore to - day Prais-es glad I sing; Sin - ful days have passed a - way, To the Lord I cling; In his ho - ly light I dwell, Pure and sweet and free, While to all the world I tell How he raised me.

3. Soul a - drift, the waves roll high, Breakers are a - head; To the bless - ed Sav - ior cry, Ere your hope is dead; Noth-ing bet - ter you can do, Saved from death to be; He a - lone can res - cue you, For he raised me.

CHORUS

The Lord raised me, the Lord raised me, Whispered comfort to my soul and made me free; The Lord raised me, the Lord raised me; When light had fled and hope was dead The Lord raised me.

This Is Why I Love My Savior 286

Daniel S. Warner, 1893 — Barney E. Warren, 1893

1. Shall I tell you why I ceased from fol - ly? Why I turned a - way from sin?
2. Do you ask me why I seek no pleas-ure In the things I once did love?
3. Would you bid me give to all a rea - son Of the hope I now pos - sess?
4. Tho' all men may look on me with won - der At the change that's taken place,
'Twas be-cause the love of my Re-deem - er Ful - ly won my heart to him.
'Tis be-cause I've tast-ed life's pure riv - er, Flow-ing from the throne a-bove.
It is Christ in me the hope of glo - ry, And his per-fect ho - li - ness.
I will walk the downward road no lon - ger; Bless the Lord for sav - ing grace!
CHORUS
This is why . . . I love my Sav - - - - ior, Why I
This is why, why I love my Sav - ior,
love . . . to fol - low him; For he died . . . my soul to
Why I love, love to fol-low him; For he died,
ran - - - som, And he washed me from my sin. . . . . . .
died my soul to ran-som, And he washed me from, he washed me from my sin.

287 There's Music in My Soul

Daniel S. Warner. 1893 — Barney E. Warren, 1893

1. Since I have found my Sav - ior, Bowed to his con - trol, There's ev - er - last - ing mu - sic Ring - ing in my soul.
2. I sing of my Re - deem - er, Hap - py in the way, He sweet - ly tunes the spir - it, Sing - ing all the day.
3. Since I have been trans - lat - ed, Heav - en's an - thems roll In sweet ac - cord with joy - ful Mu - sic in my soul.
4. The an - gels sing in heav - en—Let the prais - es roll: There's mu - sic in cre - a - tion, Mu - sic in my soul.

CHORUS

There is mu - sic in my soul, O there is mu - sic in my soul; 'Tis my glo - ry ev - er sing - ing, "Heav - en's balm has made me whole:" There is mu - sic in my soul, O let the hap - py ti - dings roll! Let it roll (Let it roll), let it roll (let it roll), O there's mu - sic in my soul.

In the Light of God

Daniel S. Warner, 1887

Joshua A. Knight, 1907

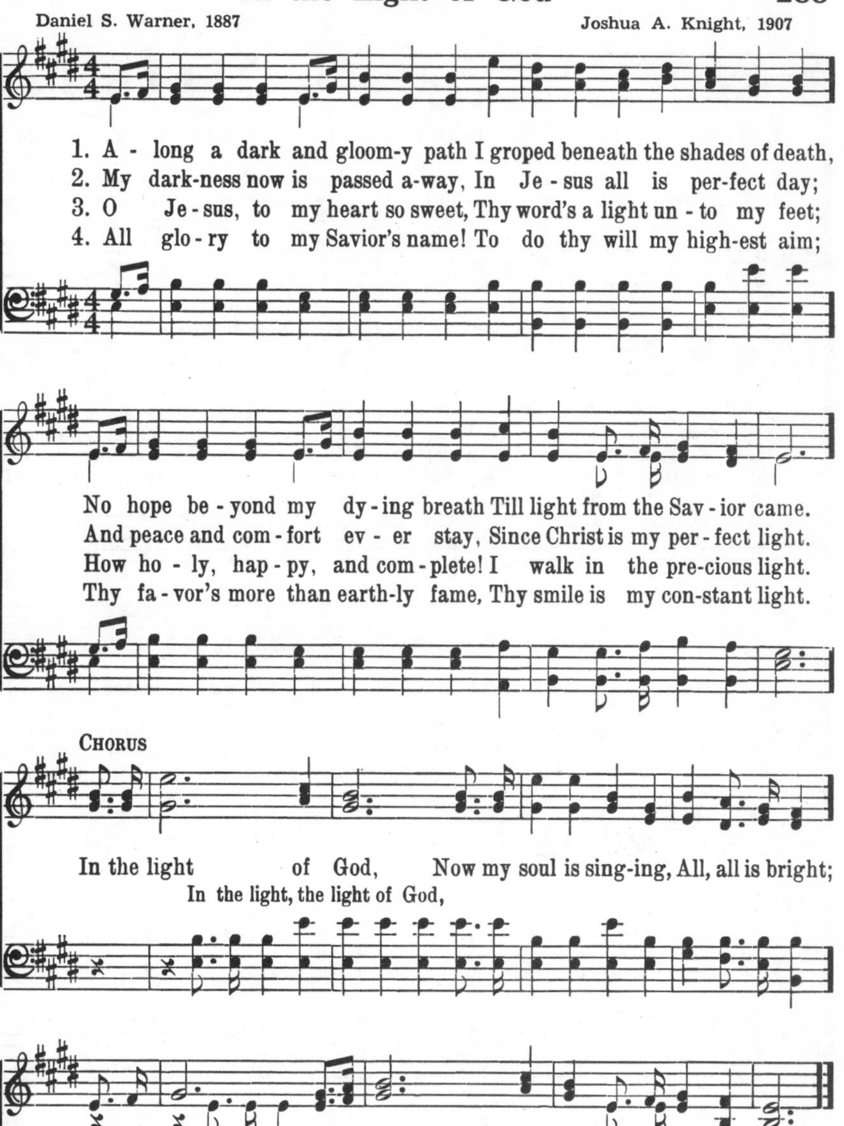
1. A - long a dark and gloom-y path I groped beneath the shades of death,
2. My dark-ness now is passed a-way, In Je - sus all is per-fect day;
3. O Je - sus, to my heart so sweet, Thy word's a light un - to my feet;
4. All glo - ry to my Savior's name! To do thy will my high-est aim;
No hope be - yond my dy - ing breath Till light from the Sav - ior came.
And peace and com - fort ev - er stay, Since Christ is my per - fect light.
How ho - ly, hap - py, and com - plete! I walk in the pre-cious light.
Thy fa - vor's more than earth-ly fame, Thy smile is my con-stant light.
CHORUS
In the light of God, Now my soul is sing-ing, All, all is bright;
In the light, the light of God,
In the light of God, I'm now in the light of God.
In the light, bless-ed light,

289 We're Marching to Zion

Isaac Watts, 1674-1748 Robert Lowry, 1826-1899

1. Come, we that love the Lord, And let our joys be known; Join in a song with sweet ac-cord, Join in a song with sweet ac-cord, And thus sur-round the throne, And thus sur-round the throne.
2. Let those re-fuse to sing Who nev-er knew our God; But chil-dren of the heav'n-ly King, But chil-dren of the heav'n-ly King, May speak their joys a-broad, May speak their joys a-broad.
3. The hill of Zi-on yields A thou-sand sa-cred sweets, Be-fore we reach the heav'n-ly fields, Be-fore we reach the heav'n-ly fields, Or walk the gold-en streets, Or walk the gold-en streets.
4. Then let our songs a-bound, And ev-ery tear be dry; We're march-ing through Im-man-uel's ground, We're march-ing through Im-man-uel's ground To fair-er worlds on high, To fair-er worlds on high.
(1) And thus sur-round the throne, And thus sur-round the throne.
CHORUS
We're march-ing to Zi-on, Beau-ti-ful, beau-ti-ful, Zi-on; We're march-ing up-ward to Zi-on, The beau-ti-ful cit-y of God. A-MEN.
We're march-ing on to Zi-on,
Zi-on, Zi-on,

I've Found It, Lord, in Thee 290

Daniel S. Warner, 1893 — Barney E. Warren, 1893

1. My soul in troub-le roamed Up-on a wea-ry plain,
And, ev-er rest-less, longed A per-fect bliss to gain.

2. Op-pressed with guilt and woe, With fears of hell o'er-cast,
My soul no com-fort knew Un-til I came to Christ.

3. I bore with-in my breast A deep and pain-ful void,
I want-ed in-ward rest, And peace that would a-bide.

4. My fool-ish soul had thought To fill it-self with mold
From earth-ly mines, yet bought No true and last-ing gold.

5. All in this world is dross, Its pleas-ures soon de-cay;
Its hon-ors prove a snare, Its treas-ures fly a-way.

CHORUS

I have found it, Lord, in thee, An ev-er-last-ing store
Of com-fort, joy, and bliss to me: How can I wish for more?

291 The River of Pleasure

Barney E. Warren, 1891 · Andrew L. Byers, 1891

1. O drink of the riv - er of pleas-ure, A deep liv-ing stream of de - light!
'Tis la-den with blessings for - ev - er, It flash-es in heaven's pure light.
2. O drink of the riv - er of pleas-ure, 'Tis sparkling with joy for thy soul;
It flows in the bos - om for - ev - er That's giv-en to Father's con - trol.
3. O drink of the riv - er of pleas-ure, For thee it is flow-ing a - long;
Its source is the boun-te-ous Giv - er, Its mu - sic a sweet, charming song.
4. O drink of the riv - er of pleas-ure, And sure-ly thy spir-it shall know
Thy longing and thirsting are o - ver, Thy blessings for-ev-er shall flow.
CHORUS
O drink . . . of the riv - - er of pleas - - ure and
O drink of the riv - er, drink of the riv - er, O drink of the riv - er of
love, ... I feel . . . . it so deep . . . . in my soul;
pleas-ure and love, I feel it so deep, feel it so deep in my soul;
It glad - - dens the one who is born . . . . from a-
It glad-dens the one, glad-dens the one, it glad - dens the one who is

bove, . . . And mak - - - eth the wound - - - ed heart whole.
born from a-bove, And mak-eth the wounded heart, maketh the wounded heart whole.

Christ Is Mine 292

Charles W. Naylor, 1906 — Barney E. Warren, 1926

1. Christ is mine, my heart's dear treas-ure, Great-er than all earth-ly store;
Filled with his un-told a-bun-dance, Now my heart doth yearn no more.

2. Christ is mine, my hope of glo-ry, An-chor of my trust-ing soul,
Hold-ing fast while in the tem-pest Storm-y waves a-round me roll.

3. Christ, the source of all my pleas-ure, Now in him my soul doth find
Joy un-speak-a-ble, ex-ceed-ing Earth-ly pleas-ures all com-bined.

4. Christ is mine, my lov-ing Sav-ior, For he gave his life for me;
Ran-somed thus from sin-ful bond-age I am his e-ter-nal-ly.

CHORUS

Christ is mine, and ev-ery long-ing Sat-is-fies a-bun-dant-ly;
He's my joy, my hope, my glo-ry, He is all, yes, all to me. A-MEN.

293 There's a Fountain Opened

Joseph C. Fisher, 1883 Joseph C. Fisher, 1883

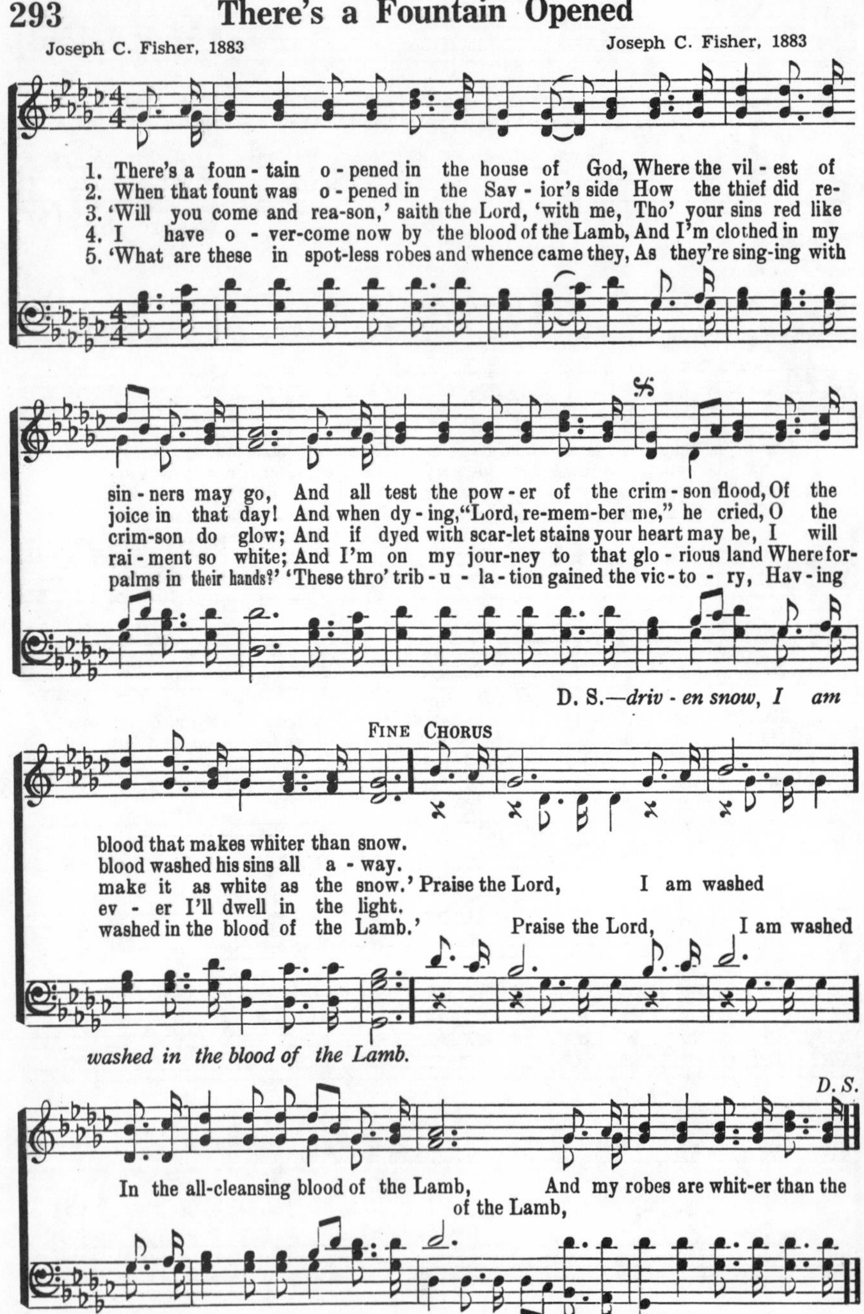
1. There's a foun - tain o - pened in the house of God, Where the vil - est of sin - ners may go, And all test the pow - er of the crim - son flood, Of the blood that makes whiter than snow.
2. When that fount was o - pened in the Sav - ior's side How the thief did re-joice in that day! And when dy - ing, "Lord, re-mem-ber me," he cried, O the blood washed his sins all a - way.
3. 'Will you come and rea-son,' saith the Lord, 'with me, Tho' your sins red like crim-son do glow; And if dyed with scar-let stains your heart may be, I will make it as white as the snow.'
4. I have o - ver-come now by the blood of the Lamb, And I'm clothed in my rai - ment so white; And I'm on my jour-ney to that glo - rious land Where for-ev - er I'll dwell in the light.
5. 'What are these in spot-less robes and whence came they, As they're sing-ing with palms in their hands?' 'These thro' trib - u - la - tion gained the vic - to - ry, Hav-ing washed in the blood of the Lamb.'
D. S.—driv - en snow, I am washed in the blood of the Lamb.
FINE CHORUS
Praise the Lord, I am washed
Praise the Lord, I am washed
In the all-cleansing blood of the Lamb, And my robes are whit-er than the
of the Lamb,
D. S.

Beulah Land

294

Edgar Page Stites, 1876

John R. Sweney, 1837-1899

1. I've reached the land of corn and wine, And all its rich - es free - ly mine; Here shines undimmed one bliss-ful day, For all my night has passed a - way.
2. My Sav-ior comes and walks with me, And sweet com-mun-ion here have we; He gen - tly leads me by his hand, For this is heav-en's bor - der-land.
3. A sweet per-fume up - on the breeze Is borne from ev - er - ver - nal trees, And flow'rs, that nev - er - fad - ing grow Where streams of life for - ev - er flow.
4. The zeph-yrs seem to float to me Sweet sounds of heav-en's mel - o - dy, As an-gels with the white-robed throng Join in the sweet re-demp-tion song.

CHORUS

O Beu-lah Land, sweet Beu-lah Land! As on thy high - est mount I stand, I look a - way a - cross the sea, Where mansions are pre - pared for me, And view the shin - ing glo-ry-shore—My heav'n, my home for - ev - er-more.

295 There Is Joy in the Lord

Barney E. Warren, 1900 — Barney E. Warren, 1900

1. I will sing hal-le-lu-jah, for there's joy in the Lord,
2. I will live for the Sav-ior, I am his ev-er-more,
3. When I come to the por-tals of that land of the blest,
And he fills my heart with rap-ture as I rest on his word;
I am rest-ing in his fa-vor, I am safe and se-cure;
I shall sing with ho-ly an-gels of this rest, hap-py rest;
I will trust in his prom-ise, I will shout I am free,
For the light shin-ing bright-er on my path ev-ery day
I shall dwell there for-ev-er with my Lord and my King,
In my bless-ed lov-ing Sav-ior I have sweet vic-to-ry.
Cheers my hap-py soul with rap-ture as I walk in the way.
And with ev-er-last-ing prais-es make those high arch-es ring.
CHORUS
There is joy in the Lord, there is joy in the Lord; Hal-le-lu-jah, glo-ry,

glo - ry! There is joy in the Lord; There is joy in the Lord, There is
joy in the Lord; Hal-le - lu - jah, glo-ry, glo-ry! There is joy in the Lord.

Unsearchable Riches 296

Fanny J. Crosby, 1820-1915 — John R. Sweney, 1837-1899

1. O the un-search-a - ble rich - es of Christ! Wealth that can nev-er be told;
2. O the un-search-a - ble rich - es of Christ! Who shall their great-ness de - clare?
3. O the un-search-a - ble rich - es of Christ! Free - ly, how free - ly they flow,
4. O the un-search-a - ble rich - es of Christ! Who would not glad - ly en - dure

Rich - es ex - haust-less of mer - cy and grace, Pre-cious, more precious than gold!
Jew - els whose lus - ter our lives may a - dorn, Pearls that the poor-est may wear.
Mak-ing the souls of the faith - ful and true Hap - py wher - ev - er they go!
Tri - als, af - flic-tions, and cross - es on earth, Rich - es like these to se - cure?

FINE

D.S.—*O the un-search-a - ble rich - es of Christ! Precious, more pre-cious than gold!*

CHORUS

Pre - cious, more pre - cious; Wealth that can nev - er be told: A - MEN.

D. S.

297 I Love to Tell the Story

HANKEY. 7.6.7.6.D. with Refrain

Katherine Hankey, 1834-1911 William G. Fischer, 1835-1912

1. I love to tell the Sto - ry Of un - seen things a-bove, Of Je - sus and his
2. I love to tell the Sto - ry! More won-der - ful it seems Than all the gold-en
3. I love to tell the Sto - ry! 'Tis pleas - ant to re - peat What seems, each time I
4. I love to tell the Sto - ry! For those who know it best Seem hun - ger-ing and

glo - ry, Of Je - sus and his love! I love to tell the Sto - ry Be-cause I
fan - cies Of all our gold-en dreams. I love to tell the Sto - ry! It did so
tell it, More won-der - ful - ly sweet. I love to tell the Sto - ry; For some have
thirst-ing To hear it, like the rest. And when in scenes of glo - ry I sing the

know it's true; It sat - is - fies my long-ings As noth - ing else would do.
much for me, And that is just the rea - son, I tell it now to thee.
nev - er heard The mes - sage of sal - va - tion From God's own ho - ly Word.
new, new song 'Twill be the old, old Sto - ry That I have loved so long.

CHORUS

I love to tell the Sto - ry! 'Twill be my theme in glo - ry

To tell the old, old Sto - ry Of Je - sus and his love. A - MEN.

The Child of a King

298

Hattie E. Buell

Arr. from melody by John B. Sumner

1. My Fa - ther is rich in hous - es and lands, He hold - eth the
2. My Fa-ther's own Son, the Sav - ior of men, Once wan-dered o'er
3. I once was an out - cast stran - ger on earth, A sin - ner by
4. A tent or a cot - tage, why should I care? They're build-ing a
wealth of the world in his hands; Of ru - bies and dia-monds, of
earth as the poor-est of them; But now he is reign - ing for-
choice and an al - ien by birth; But I've been a - dopt - ed, my
pal - ace for me o - ver there; Tho' ex - iled from home, yet,
sil - ver and gold His cof - fers are full, he has rich - es un - told.
ev - er on high, And will give me a home in heav'n by and by.
name's written down, An heir to a man - sion, a robe and a crown.
still I may sing: All glo - ry to God, I'm the child of a King!
Refrain
I'm the child of a King, The child of a King; With
ad lib.
Je - sus my Sav - ior I'm the child of a King. A - men.

299 Filled with Grace and Glory

Otto Bolds, 1904 Barney E. Warren, 1907

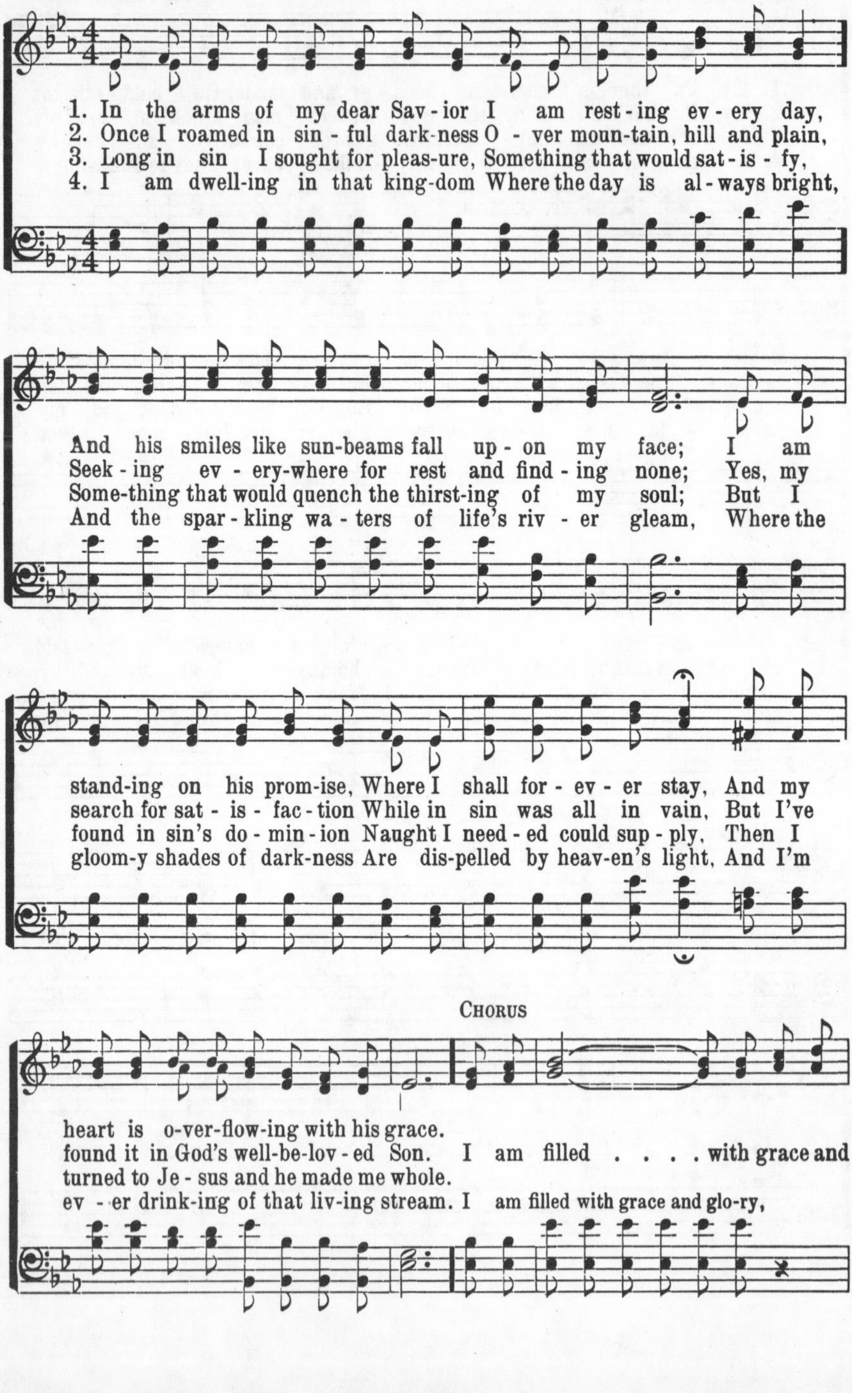

1. In the arms of my dear Sav - ior I am rest - ing ev - ery day,
2. Once I roamed in sin - ful dark - ness O - ver moun - tain, hill and plain,
3. Long in sin I sought for pleas - ure, Something that would sat - is - fy,
4. I am dwell - ing in that king - dom Where the day is al - ways bright,

And his smiles like sun - beams fall up - on my face; I am
Seek - ing ev - ery - where for rest and find - ing none; Yes, my
Some - thing that would quench the thirst - ing of my soul; But I
And the spar - kling wa - ters of life's riv - er gleam, Where the

stand - ing on his prom - ise, Where I shall for - ev - er stay, And my
search for sat - is - fac - tion While in sin was all in vain, But I've
found in sin's do - min - ion Naught I need - ed could sup - ply, Then I
gloom - y shades of dark - ness Are dis - pelled by heav - en's light, And I'm

CHORUS

heart is o - ver - flow - ing with his grace.
found it in God's well - be - lov - ed Son. I am filled . . . . with grace and
turned to Je - sus and he made me whole.
ev - er drink - ing of that liv - ing stream. I am filled with grace and glo - ry,

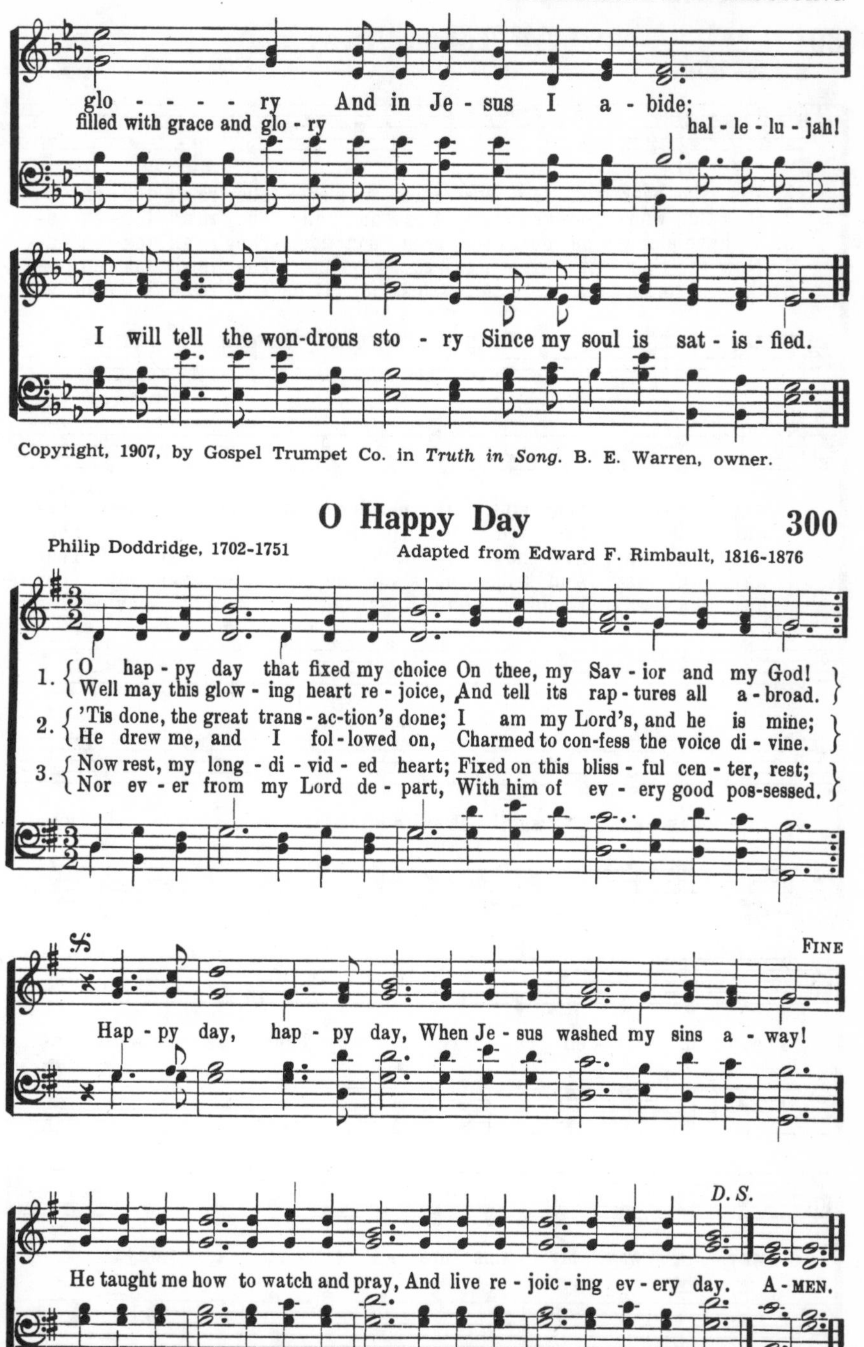
glo - - - - - ry And in Je - sus I a - bide;
filled with grace and glo - ry
hal - le - lu - jah!
I will tell the won-drous sto - ry Since my soul is sat - is - fied.
Copyright, 1907, by Gospel Trumpet Co. in Truth in Song. B. E. Warren, owner.
O Happy Day
300
Philip Doddridge, 1702-1751
Adapted from Edward F. Rimbault, 1816-1876
1. O hap - py day that fixed my choice On thee, my Sav - ior and my God!
Well may this glow - ing heart re - joice, And tell its rap - tures all a - broad.
2. 'Tis done, the great trans - ac-tion's done; I am my Lord's, and he is mine;
He drew me, and I fol - lowed on, Charmed to con-fess the voice di - vine.
3. Now rest, my long - di - vid - ed heart; Fixed on this bliss - ful cen - ter, rest;
Nor ev - er from my Lord de - part, With him of ev - ery good pos-sessed.
FINE
Hap - py day, hap - py day, When Je - sus washed my sins a - way!
D. S.
He taught me how to watch and pray, And live re - joic - ing ev - ery day. A - MEN.

301 All Taken Away

R. Kelso Carter A. A.

1. Did you hear what Je - sus said to me?—"They're all tak - en a-
2. O this won - drous grace so free and full, They're all tak - en a-
3. I have plunged be - neath the crim - son tide, They're all tak - en a-
4. Now the Spir - it wit - ness - es to me They're all tak - en a-
5. So I praise the Lord for sins for-giv'n, They're all tak - en a-
way, a - way; Your sins are par-doned and you are free, They're
way, a - way; Tho' red like crim - son they're now as wool, They're
way, a - way; And now by faith I am pu - ri - fied, They're
way, a - way; And keeps me stand - ing in lib - er - ty, They're
way, a - way; While on - ward press - ing my way to heav'n, They're
all tak - en a - way."
CHORUS
They're all tak - en a - way, a - way,
They're all tak - en a - way, a - way; They're all tak - en a-
way, a - way, My sins are all tak - en a - way.

I Know in My Heart What It Means 302

D. Otis Teasley, 1922 D. Otis Teasley, 1922

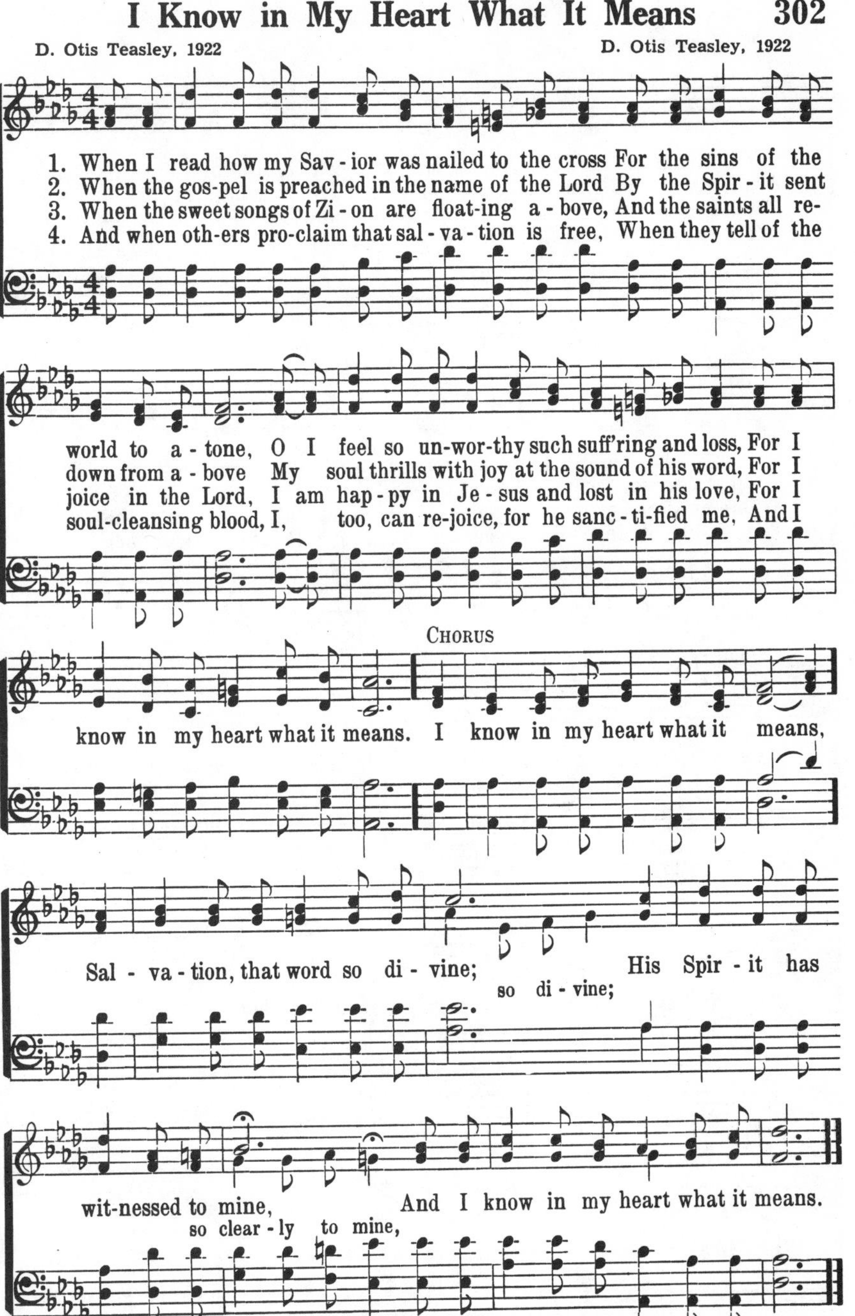
1. When I read how my Sav-ior was nailed to the cross For the sins of the world to a-tone, O I feel so un-wor-thy such suff'ring and loss, For I know in my heart what it means.
2. When the gos-pel is preached in the name of the Lord By the Spir-it sent down from a-bove My soul thrills with joy at the sound of his word, For I
3. When the sweet songs of Zi-on are float-ing a-bove, And the saints all re-joice in the Lord, I am hap-py in Je-sus and lost in his love, For I
4. And when oth-ers pro-claim that sal-va-tion is free, When they tell of the soul-cleansing blood, I, too, can re-joice, for he sanc-ti-fied me, And I
CHORUS
I know in my heart what it means, Sal-va-tion, that word so di-vine; so di-vine; His Spir-it has wit-nessed to mine, so clear-ly to mine, And I know in my heart what it means.

303 We'll Praise the Lord

D. Otis Teasley, 1906 — D. Otis Teasley, 1906

1. We'll praise the Lord for sins for - giv - en, Praise him ev - er - more;
2. We'll praise the Lord for full sal - va - tion, Hearts made pure and free;
3. We'll praise him for a church tri - um-phant Here on earth be - low,
4. We'll praise the Lord that death's dark val - ley Is no lon - ger drear;
Till earth has passed a - way for - ev - er, Christ we will a - dore.
We'll praise him for a blest in - fill - ing, And for vic - to - ry.
Where ev - ery soul is made, in Je - sus, Whit - er than the snow.
The light of love dis - pels the shad - ows, Drives a - way our fear.
CHORUS
We'll tell the sto - ry, And give God glo - ry;
We'll tell the sto - ry all our days, And give God glo - ry, thanks, and praise;
For he has saved us by his blood, And we will sing and praise the Lord;
For he has saved us, And we will praise him;
When like a scroll the sky has vanished, Still we'll praise the Lord. A - MEN.

At the Cross 304

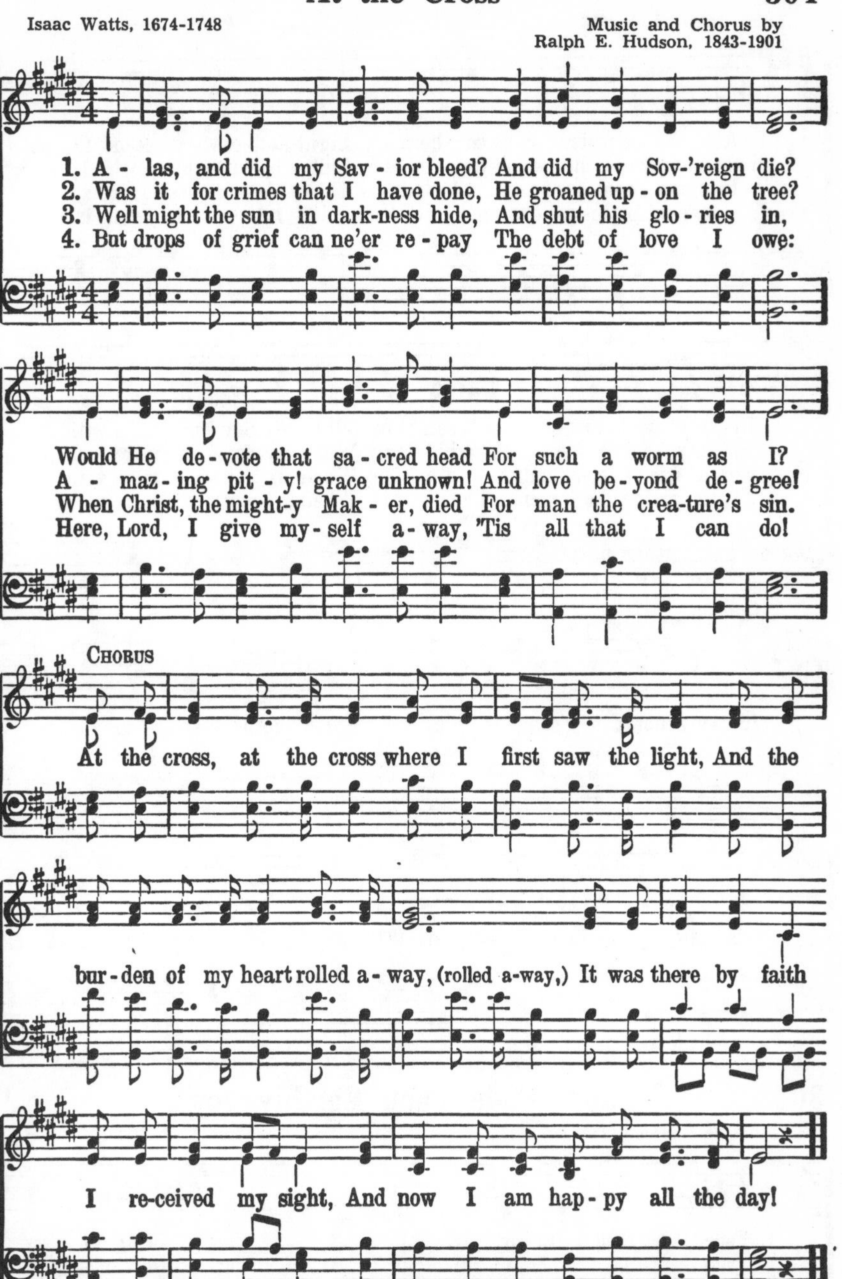
Isaac Watts, 1674-1748
Music and Chorus by
Ralph E. Hudson, 1843-1901
1. A - las, and did my Sav - ior bleed? And did my Sov-'reign die?
2. Was it for crimes that I have done, He groaned up - on the tree?
3. Well might the sun in dark-ness hide, And shut his glo - ries in,
4. But drops of grief can ne'er re - pay The debt of love I owe:
Would He de-vote that sa - cred head For such a worm as I?
A - maz - ing pit - y! grace unknown! And love be - yond de - gree!
When Christ, the might-y Mak - er, died For man the crea-ture's sin.
Here, Lord, I give my - self a - way, 'Tis all that I can do!
Chorus
At the cross, at the cross where I first saw the light, And the
bur - den of my heart rolled a - way, (rolled a-way,) It was there by faith
I re-ceived my sight, And now I am hap - py all the day!

305 When My Savior Talks with Me

Lizzie DeArmond, 1922 — Andrew L. Byers, 1922

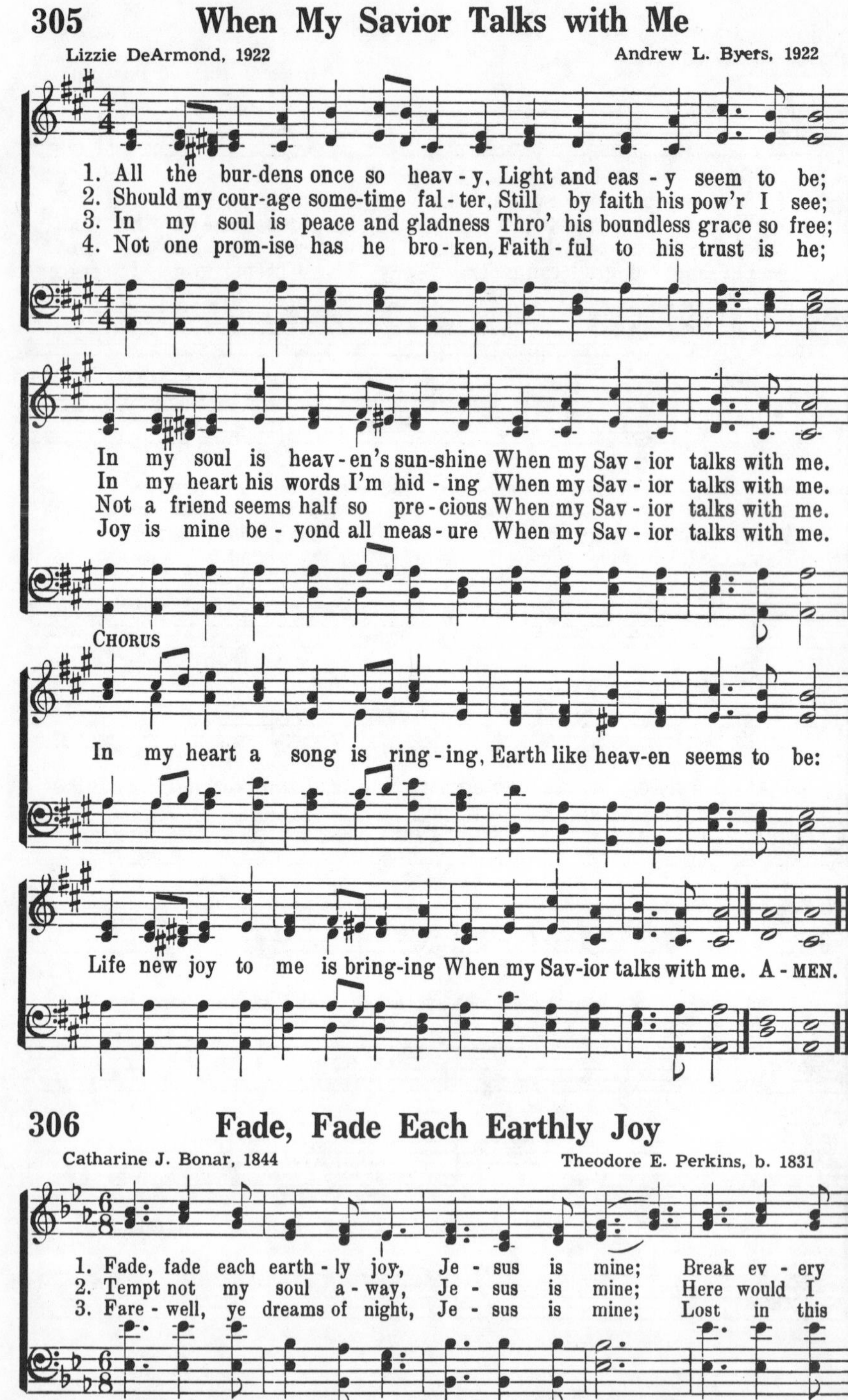
1. All the bur-dens once so heav-y, Light and eas-y seem to be;
2. Should my cour-age some-time fal-ter, Still by faith his pow'r I see;
3. In my soul is peace and gladness Thro' his boundless grace so free;
4. Not one prom-ise has he bro-ken, Faith-ful to his trust is he;
In my soul is heav-en's sun-shine When my Sav-ior talks with me.
In my heart his words I'm hid-ing When my Sav-ior talks with me.
Not a friend seems half so pre-cious When my Sav-ior talks with me.
Joy is mine be-yond all meas-ure When my Sav-ior talks with me.
CHORUS
In my heart a song is ring-ing, Earth like heav-en seems to be:
Life new joy to me is bring-ing When my Sav-ior talks with me. A-MEN.

306 Fade, Fade Each Earthly Joy

Catharine J. Bonar, 1844 — Theodore E. Perkins, b. 1831

1. Fade, fade each earth-ly joy, Je-sus is mine; Break ev-ery
2. Tempt not my soul a-way, Je-sus is mine; Here would I
3. Fare-well, ye dreams of night, Je-sus is mine; Lost in this

ten - der tie, Je - sus is mine. Dark is the wil - der-ness, Earth has no
ev - er stay, Je - sus is mine. Per - ish - ing things of clay Born but for
dawn-ing bright, Je - sus is mine. All that my soul has tried Left but a
rest - ing-place, Je - sus a - lone can bless, Je - sus is mine.
one brief day Pass from my heart a - way; Je - sus is mine.
dis - mal void; Je - sus has sat - is - fied, Je - sus is mine. A - MEN.
Hallelujah! 'Tis Done!
307
Philip P. Bliss, 1838-1876
Philip P. Bliss, 1838-1876
1. 'Tis the prom-ise of God full sal - va - tion to give Un - to him who on
2. Tho' the path-way be lone - ly, and dan - ger-ous, too, Sure - ly Je - sus is
3. Man - y loved ones have I in yon heav - en - ly throng; They are safe now in
4. There's a part in that cho - rus for you and for me, And the theme of our
CHORUS
Je - sus his Son will be - lieve.
a - ble to car - ry me thro'. Hal-le - lu - jah, 'tis done! I be - lieve on the
glo - ry, and this is their song:
prais - es for - ev - er will be:
Son; I am saved by the blood of the Cru - ci - fied One; fied One.
1
2

308 "Whosoever Will"

Philip P. Bliss, 1838-1876 — Philip P. Bliss, 1838-1876

1. "Who-so-ev-er hear - eth," shout, shout the sound! Spread the bless-ed ti-dings
2. Who-so-ev-er com - eth, need not de - lay, Now the door is o - pen,
3. "Who-so-ev-er will," the prom-ise is se - cure; "Who-so-ev - er will," for-
all the world a-round; Tell the joy - ful news wher - ev - er man is found,
en - ter while you may; Je - sus is the true, the on - ly Liv - ing Way:
ev - er must en-dure; "Who-so - ev - er will," 'tis life for - ev - er - more;
CHORUS
"Who-so-ev - er will may come." "Who-so-ev - er will, who - so-ev - er will!"
Send the proc - la - ma - tion o - ver vale and hill; 'Tis a lov - ing
Fa - ther calls the wan-d'rer home: "Who-so - ev - er will may come."

Jesus Loves Even Me

309

Philip P. Bliss, 1838-1876 — Philip P. Bliss, 1838-1876

1. I am so glad that our Fa - ther in heav'n Tells of His love in the Book He has giv'n, Won - der - ful things in the Bi - ble I see; This is the dear - est, that Je - sus loves me.
2. Tho' I for - get Him and wan - der a - way, Still He doth love me wher - ev - er I stray; Back to His dear lov - ing arms would I flee, When I re - mem - ber that Je - sus loves me.
3. Oh, if there's on - ly one song I can sing, When in His beau - ty I see the great King, This shall my song in e - ter - ni - ty be: "Oh, what a won - der that Je - sus loves me."
CHORUS
I am so glad that Je - sus loves me, Je - sus loves me, Je - sus loves me,
I am so glad that Je - sus loves me, Je - sus loves e - ven me.

310 Jesus Is All the World to Me

Will L. Thompson, 1847-1909 Will L. Thompson, 1847-1909

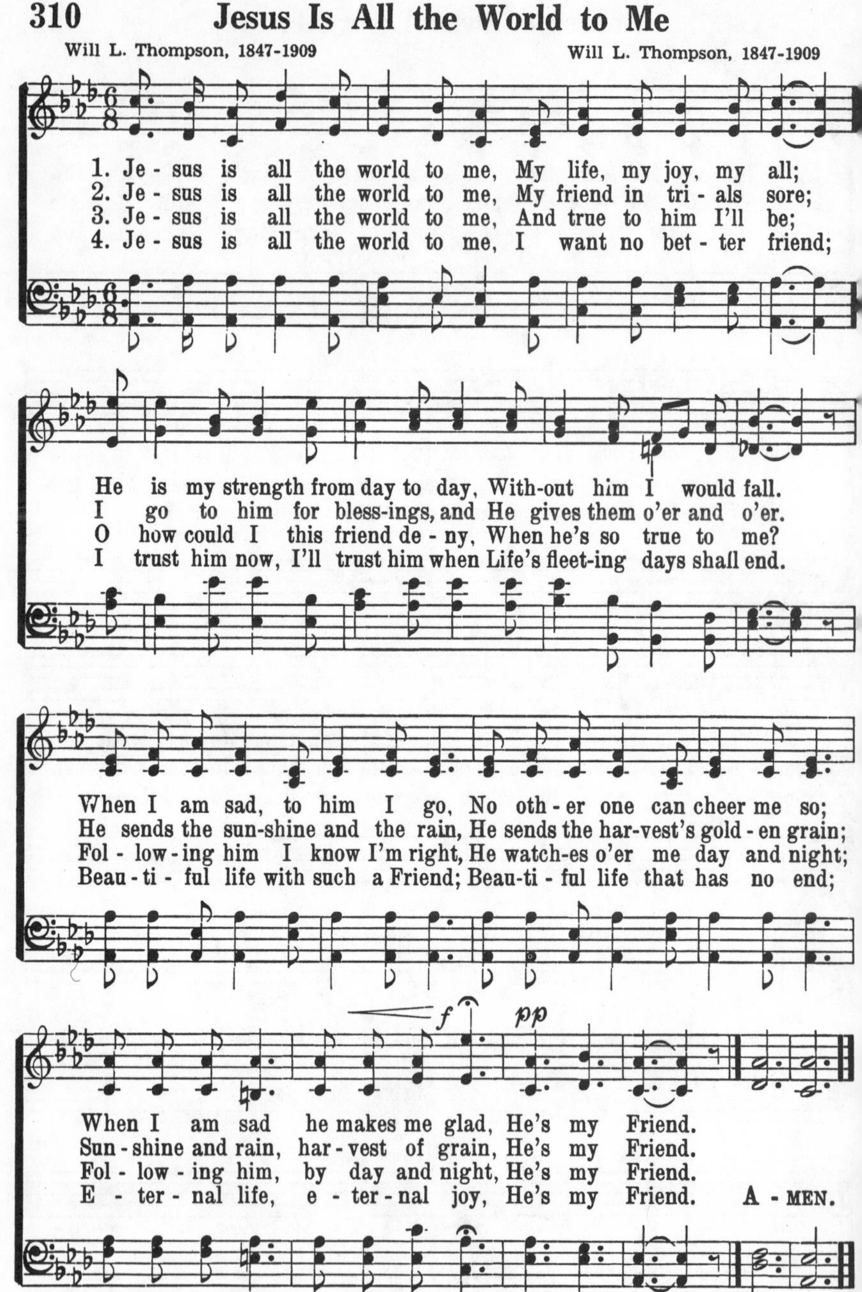
1. Je - sus is all the world to me, My life, my joy, my all;
2. Je - sus is all the world to me, My friend in tri - als sore;
3. Je - sus is all the world to me, And true to him I'll be;
4. Je - sus is all the world to me, I want no bet - ter friend;
He is my strength from day to day, With-out him I would fall.
I go to him for bless-ings, and He gives them o'er and o'er.
O how could I this friend de - ny, When he's so true to me?
I trust him now, I'll trust him when Life's fleet-ing days shall end.
When I am sad, to him I go, No oth - er one can cheer me so;
He sends the sun-shine and the rain, He sends the har-vest's gold - en grain;
Fol - low - ing him I know I'm right, He watch-es o'er me day and night;
Beau - ti - ful life with such a Friend; Beau-ti - ful life that has no end;
f
pp
When I am sad he makes me glad, He's my Friend.
Sun - shine and rain, har - vest of grain, He's my Friend.
Fol - low - ing him, by day and night, He's my Friend.
E - ter - nal life, e - ter - nal joy, He's my Friend.
A - MEN.

There Is Joy in the Service 311

Daniel S. Warner, 1893 — Barney E. Warren, 1893

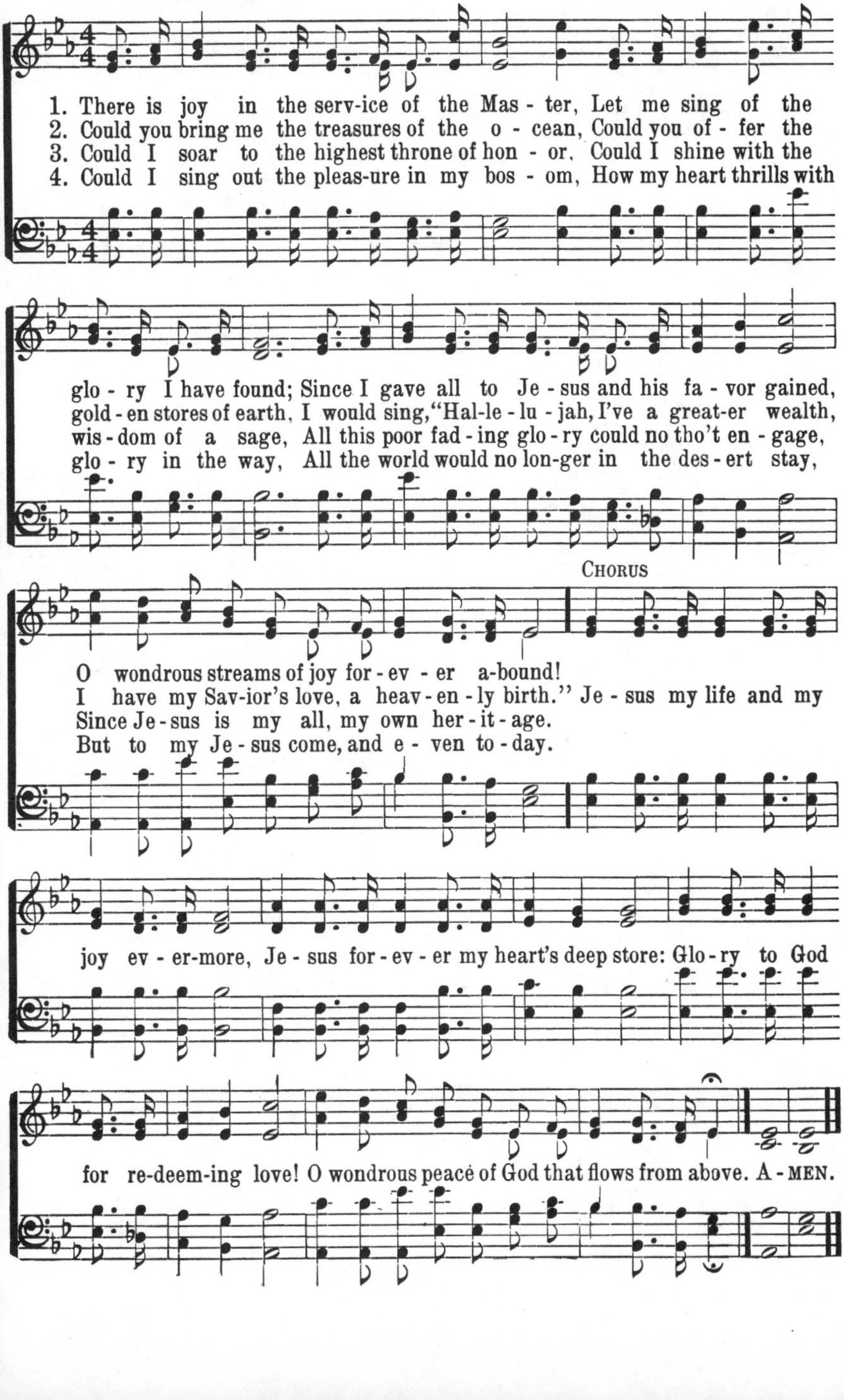

1. There is joy in the serv-ice of the Mas - ter, Let me sing of the glo - ry I have found; Since I gave all to Je - sus and his fa - vor gained, O wondrous streams of joy for - ev - er a-bound!
2. Could you bring me the treasures of the o - cean, Could you of - fer the gold - en stores of earth, I would sing, "Hal-le - lu - jah, I've a great-er wealth, I have my Sav-ior's love, a heav - en - ly birth."
3. Could I soar to the highest throne of hon - or, Could I shine with the wis - dom of a sage, All this poor fad - ing glo - ry could no tho't en - gage, Since Je - sus is my all, my own her - it - age.
4. Could I sing out the pleas-ure in my bos - om, How my heart thrills with glo - ry in the way, All the world would no lon-ger in the des - ert stay, But to my Je - sus come, and e - ven to - day.

CHORUS

Je - sus my life and my joy ev - er-more, Je - sus for - ev - er my heart's deep store: Glo - ry to God for re-deem-ing love! O wondrous peace of God that flows from above. A - MEN.

312 River of Peace

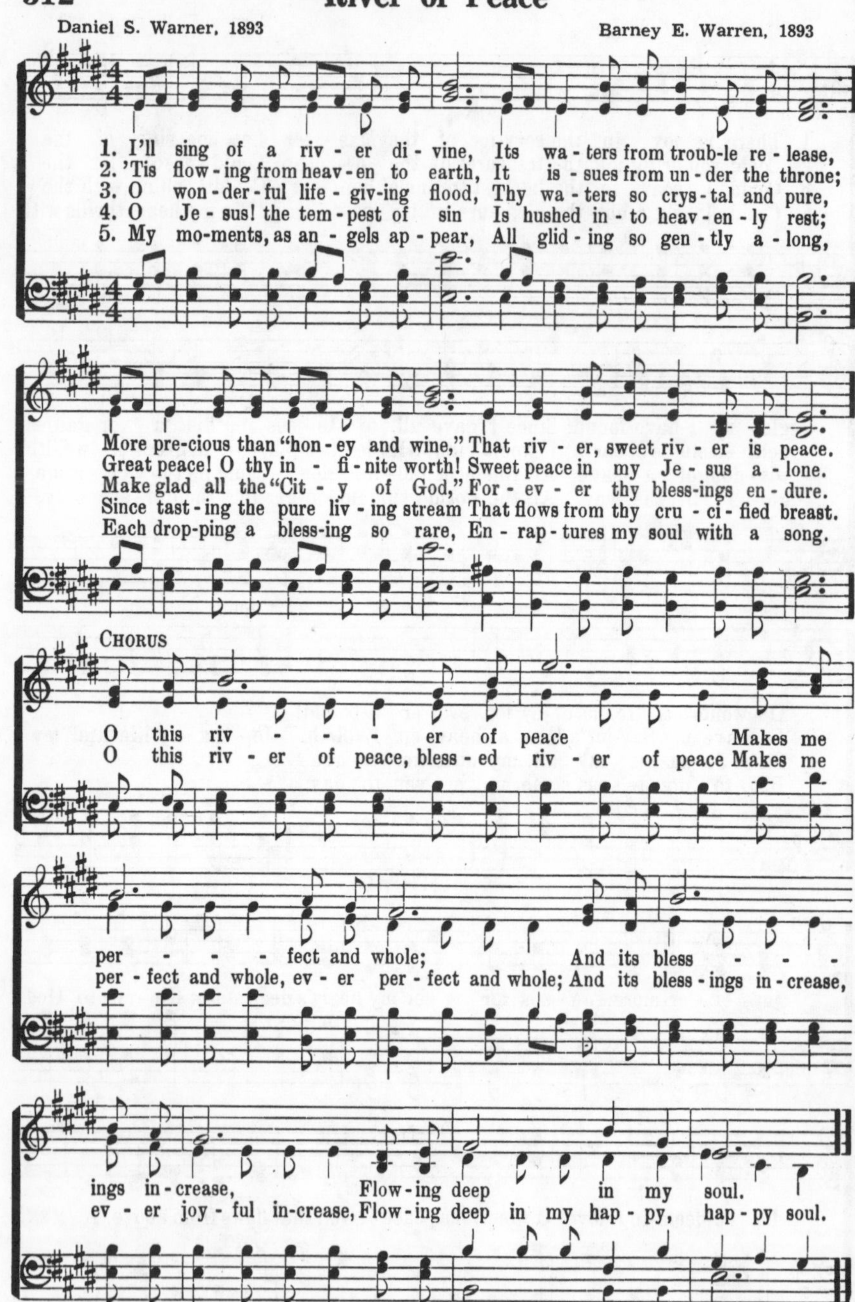
Daniel S. Warner, 1893
Barney E. Warren, 1893
1. I'll sing of a riv - er di - vine, Its wa - ters from troub-le re - lease,
2. 'Tis flow - ing from heav - en to earth, It is - sues from un - der the throne;
3. O won - der - ful life - giv - ing flood, Thy wa - ters so crys - tal and pure,
4. O Je - sus! the tem - pest of sin Is hushed in - to heav - en - ly rest;
5. My mo-ments, as an - gels ap - pear, All glid - ing so gen - tly a - long,
More pre-cious than "hon - ey and wine," That riv - er, sweet riv - er is peace.
Great peace! O thy in - fi - nite worth! Sweet peace in my Je - sus a - lone.
Make glad all the "Cit - y of God," For - ev - er thy bless-ings en - dure.
Since tast - ing the pure liv - ing stream That flows from thy cru - ci - fied breast.
Each drop-ping a bless-ing so rare, En - rap - tures my soul with a song.
CHORUS
O this riv - - - er of peace Makes me
O this riv - er of peace, bless - ed riv - er of peace Makes me
per - - - fect and whole; And its bless - - -
per - fect and whole, ev - er per - fect and whole; And its bless - ings in - crease,
ings in - crease, Flow - ing deep in my soul.
ev - er joy - ful in - crease, Flow - ing deep in my hap - py, hap - py soul.

My Soul Is Satisfied 313

Daniel S. Warner, 1893, alt. Barney E. Warren, 1893

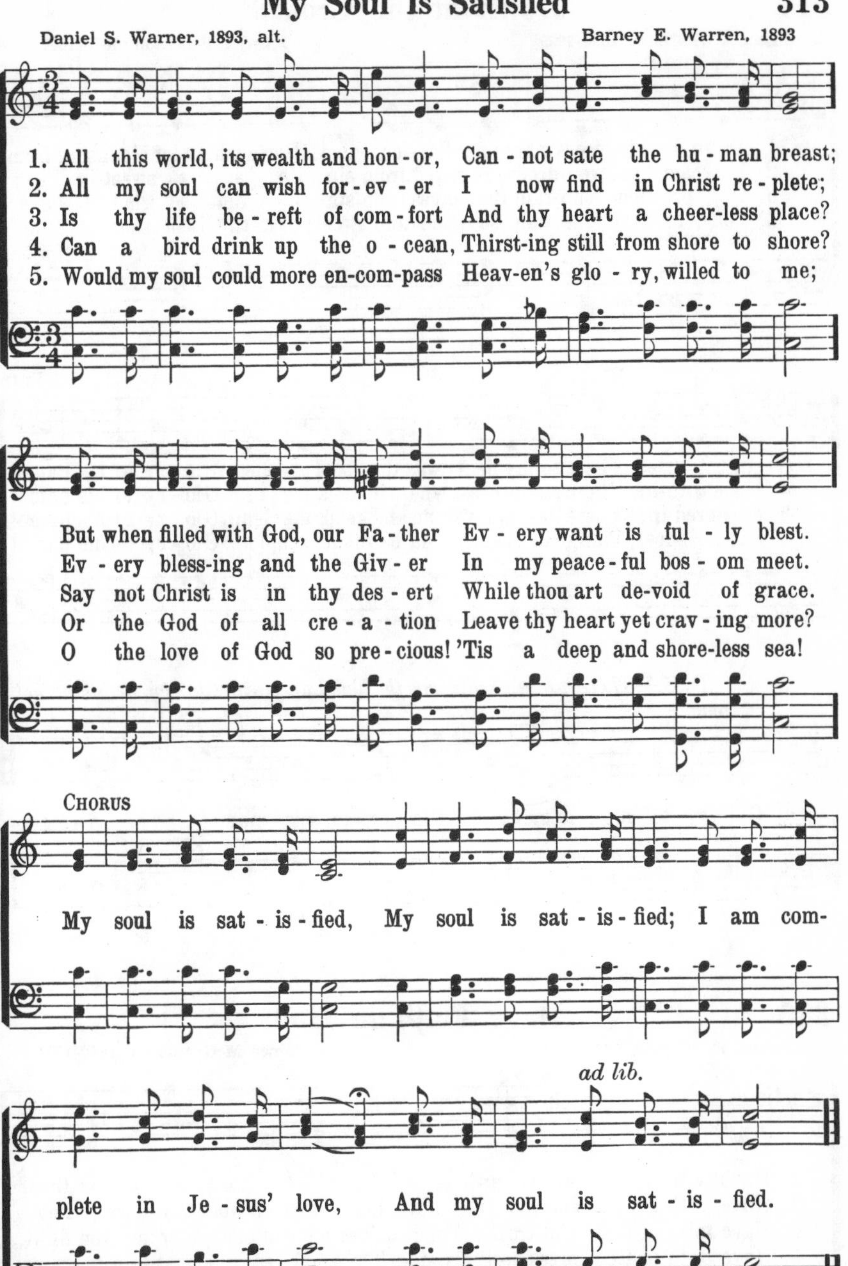
1. All this world, its wealth and hon-or, Can-not sate the hu-man breast;
2. All my soul can wish for-ev-er I now find in Christ re-plete;
3. Is thy life be-reft of com-fort And thy heart a cheer-less place?
4. Can a bird drink up the o-cean, Thirst-ing still from shore to shore?
5. Would my soul could more en-com-pass Heav-en's glo-ry, willed to me;
But when filled with God, our Fa-ther Ev-ery want is ful-ly blest.
Ev-ery bless-ing and the Giv-er In my peace-ful bos-om meet.
Say not Christ is in thy des-ert While thou art de-void of grace.
Or the God of all cre-a-tion Leave thy heart yet crav-ing more?
O the love of God so pre-cious! 'Tis a deep and shore-less sea!
Chorus
My soul is sat-is-fied, My soul is sat-is-fied; I am com-
ad lib.
plete in Je-sus' love, And my soul is sat-is-fied.

314 Down at the Cross

Elisha A. Hoffman, 1839-1929 — John H. Stockton, 1813-1877

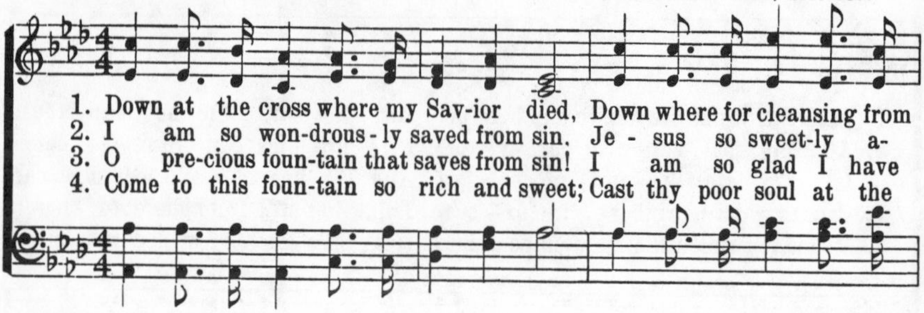

1. Down at the cross where my Sav-ior died, Down where for cleansing from
2. I am so won-drous-ly saved from sin. Je - sus so sweet-ly a-
3. O pre-cious foun-tain that saves from sin! I am so glad I have
4. Come to this foun-tain so rich and sweet; Cast thy poor soul at the

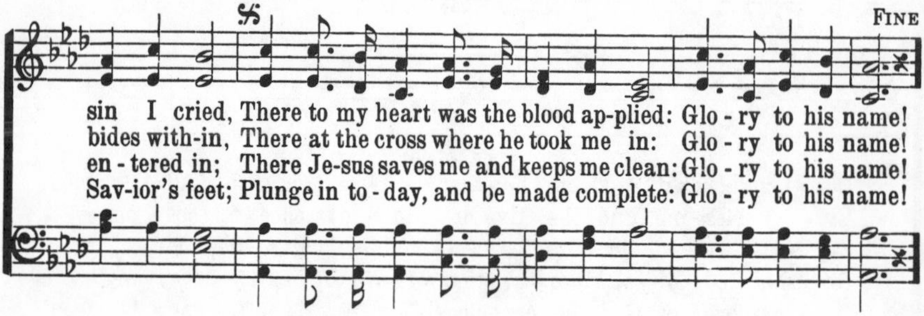

FINE

sin I cried, There to my heart was the blood ap-plied: Glo - ry to his name!
bides with-in, There at the cross where he took me in: Glo - ry to his name!
en - tered in; There Je-sus saves me and keeps me clean: Glo - ry to his name!
Sav-ior's feet; Plunge in to - day, and be made complete: Glo - ry to his name!

D. S.—*There to my heart was the blood ap-plied, Glo - ry to his name!*

CHORUS — *D. S.*

Glo - ry to his name! . . Glo - ry to his name! . . A - MEN.

315 Have Faith in God

Daniel W. Whittle, 1840-1901 — James McGranahan, 1840-1907

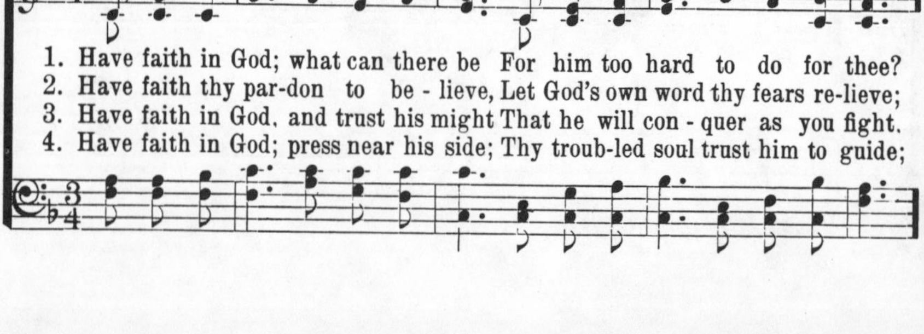

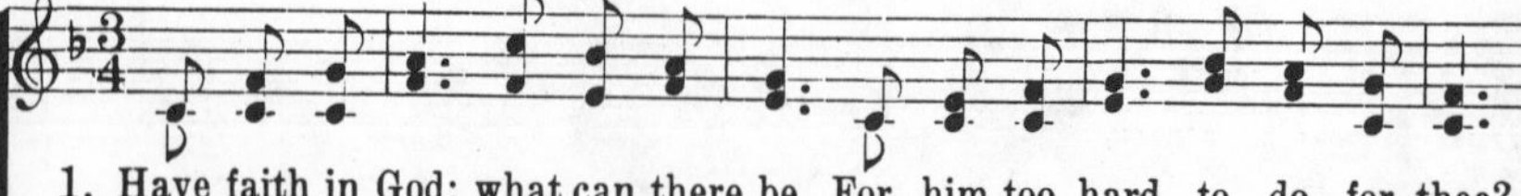

1. Have faith in God; what can there be For him too hard to do for thee?
2. Have faith thy par-don to be - lieve, Let God's own word thy fears re-lieve;
3. Have faith in God, and trust his might That he will con - quer as you fight.
4. Have faith in God; press near his side; Thy troub-led soul trust him to guide;

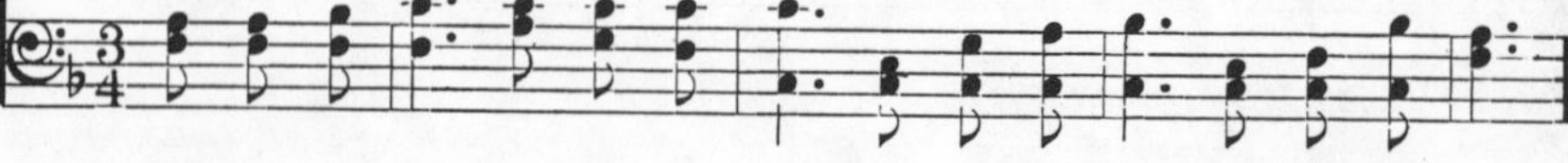

He gave his Son; now all is free; Have faith, have faith in God.
Have faith the Spir-it to re-ceive; Have faith, have faith in God.
And give the tri-umph to the right; Have faith, have faith in God.
In life, in death, what-e'er be-tide, Have faith, have faith in God. A-MEN.
If Thou Wilt Know the Fountain Deep 316
Daniel S. Warner, 1893
Barney E. Warren, 1893
1. If thou wilt know the foun-tain deep Of sweet un-bro-ken rest,
2. The gift of faith no lim-it knows Save God's un-bound-ed word;
3. Stay not in fee-ble un-be-lief When God com-mands be strong;
4. I can do all in Je-sus' name, Thus sings the faith of God;
The rest of faith thy soul shall keep, He that be-lieves is ev-er blest.
It tri-umphs o'er its gi-ant foes And glo-ri-fies the bless-ed Lord.
Be strong in him, the word be-lieve, And shout the o-ver-com-er's song.
It sings, and hills of troub-le flee, It rides tri-um-phant on the flood.
CHORUS
Put on thy strength, O Zi-on, rise, And fix thy trust a-bove the skies;
Move out on faith's al-might-y plane, Thro' him that loved us dare to reign.

317 "Great Is Thy Faithfulness"

Thomas O. Chisholm, b. 1866 — William M. Runyan, b. 1870

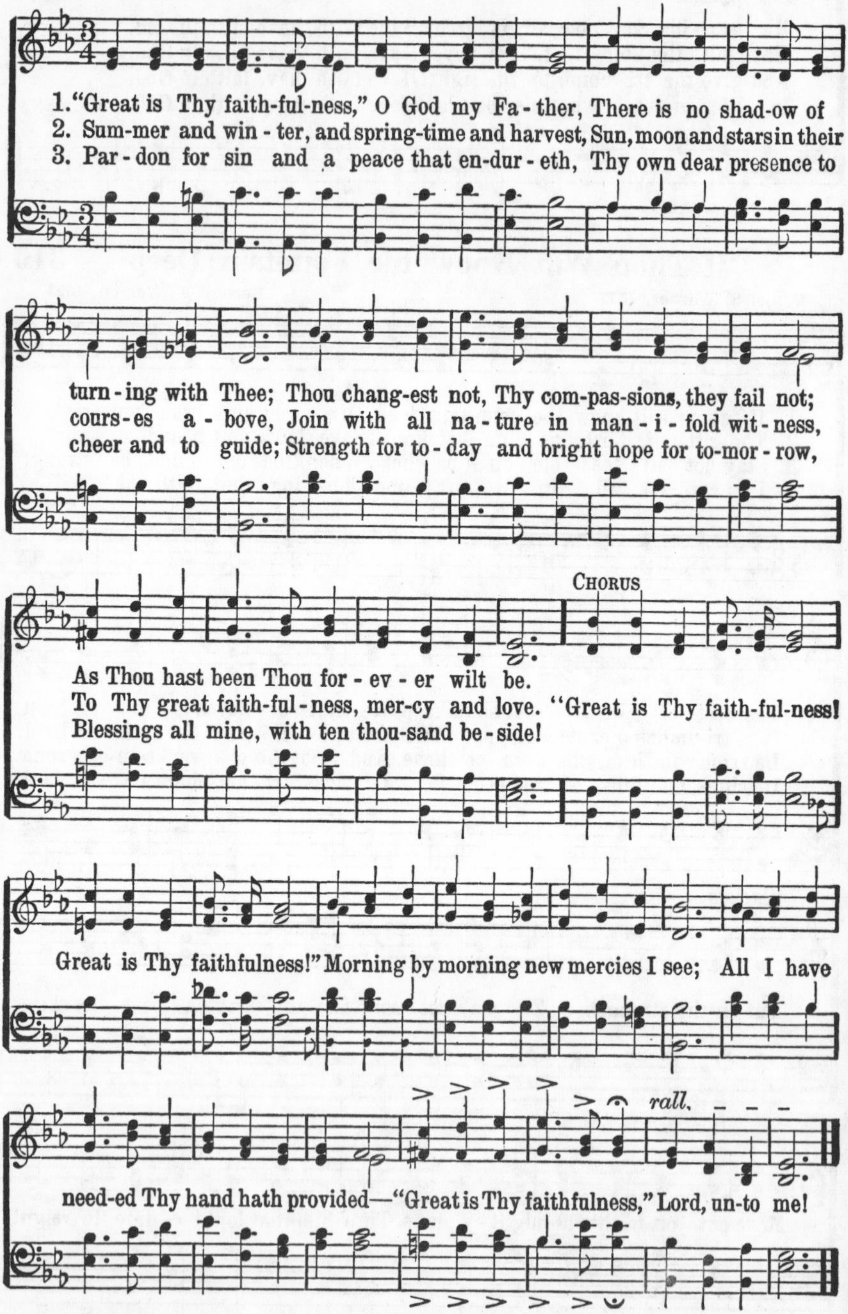

1. "Great is Thy faith-ful-ness," O God my Fa - ther, There is no shad-ow of
2. Sum-mer and win - ter, and spring-time and harvest, Sun, moon and stars in their
3. Par - don for sin and a peace that en-dur - eth, Thy own dear presence to

turn - ing with Thee; Thou chang-est not, Thy com-pas-sions, they fail not;
cours - es a - bove, Join with all na - ture in man - i - fold wit - ness,
cheer and to guide; Strength for to - day and bright hope for to-mor - row,

As Thou hast been Thou for - ev - er wilt be.
To Thy great faith-ful - ness, mer-cy and love.
Blessings all mine, with ten thou-sand be - side!

CHORUS

"Great is Thy faith-ful-ness! Great is Thy faithfulness!" Morning by morning new mercies I see; All I have need-ed Thy hand hath provided—"Great is Thy faithfulness," Lord, un-to me!

rall.

I Know Whom I Have Believed 318

Daniel W. Whittle, 1840-1901 James McGranahan, 1840-1907

Moderato
1. I know not why God's won-drous grace To me He hath made known,
2. I know not how this sav - ing faith To me He did im - part,
3. I know not how the Spir - it moves, Con-vinc-ing men of sin,
4. I know not what of good or ill May be re-served for me,
5. I know not when my Lord may come, At night or noon-day fair,
Nor why un - wor - thy—Christ in love Re-deemed me for His own.
Nor how be - liev - ing in His Word Wrought peace within my heart.
Re - veal - ing Je - sus thro' the Word, Cre - at - ing faith in Him.
Of wea - ry ways or gold - en days, Be - fore His face I see.
Nor if I walk the vale with Him, Or "meet Him in the air."
Chorus
But "I know whom I have be - liev - ed, and am per-suad-ed that He is
a - ble To keep that which I've committed Un - to Him a-gainst that day."

319 I Know

Charles W. Naylor, 1919 — Andrew L. Byers, 1919

1. I know on whom my faith is fixed, I know in whom I trust;
I know that Christ a - bides in me, And all his ways are just.

2. Let scoff - ers scoff, let scorn-ers sneer, My heart is full of peace;
They can - not take the joy I feel, Nor make my hope to cease.

3. They can - not quench the fire of love That burns with-in my breast,
Nor break that ten - der fel - low-ship That makes my life so blest.

4. They can - not bring a - gain the sins The blood has washed a - way,
Nor make my heart like stone once more, Nor turn to night my day.

5. I know God is, I know his word Un - fail - ing meets each test;
I calm - ly face a hos - tile world, With soul and mind at rest.

CHORUS

I know . . . on whom my faith is fixed, His mer-cy has set me free;
I know — set me free;
I know . . . . that he will safe - ly keep, And his love is sweet to me.
yes, I know

The Faithfulness of God 320

Barney E. Warren, 1893 Barney E. Warren, 1893

1. O look at the faith-ful-ness of Christ our Lord, How he saves and keeps the soul! Who trusts in his maj-es-ty and stand-eth on his word Shall be safe while the bil-lows roll.
2. The Lord in his faith-ful-ness be-stows on us Life and breath, yea, and all things; But great-er his sav-ing grace and gift of right-eous-ness, O what peace, love and joy it brings!
3. Be-hold all the u-ni-verse that he hath made, See the twin-kling worlds on high; A-lone on his fi-at are these star-ry heav-ens stayed, Then we know he can nev-er lie.
4. His word is e-ter-nal and shall ev-er stand, It can nev-er pass a-way; By it were the heav-ens made, the sea and all the land, And its pow'r is the same to-day.
Chorus
O trust in God, O trust . . . . in God,
Trust in the faithfulness and love of God, Trust in the faithfulness and love of God,
O trust in God, O trust in the faith-ful God!
Trust in the faith-ful-ness and love of God,

321 Blessed Assurance

Fanny J. Crosby, 1820-1915
Mrs. Joseph F. Knapp, 1839-1908
1. Bless-ed as - sur - ance, Je - sus is mine! O what a fore - taste of glo - ry di - vine! Heir of sal - va - tion, pur-chase of God, Born of his Spir - it, washed in his blood.
2. Per - fect sub - mis - sion, per-fect de - light, Vi-sions of rap - ture now burst on my sight; An - gels de-scend-ing bring from a - bove Ech - oes of mer - cy, whis-pers of love.
3. Per - fect sub - mis - sion, all is at rest, I in my Sav - ior am hap-py and blest; Watching and waiting, look-ing a - bove, Filled with his good-ness, lost in his love.
CHORUS
This is my sto - ry, this is my song, Prais - ing my Sav - ior all the day long; This is my sto - ry, this is my song, Prais-ing my Sav - ior all the day long.

It Is Well with My Soul 322

Horatio G. Spafford, 1828-1888 Philip P. Bliss, 1838-1876

1. When peace like a riv - er at - tend - eth my way, When
2. Though Sa - tan should buf - fet, though tri - als should come, Let
3. My sin— O the bliss of this glo - ri-ous thought!—My
4. And, Lord, haste the day when the faith shall be sight, The
sor - rows like sea - bil - lows roll, What - ev - er my lot, thou hast
this blest as - sur - ance con - trol, That Christ hath re - gard - ed my
sin, not in part but the whole, Is nailed to his cross and I
clouds be rolled back as a scroll, The trump shall re - sound, and the
taught me to say, "It is well, it is well with my soul."
help - less es - tate And hath shed his own blood for my soul.
bear it no more; Praise the Lord, praise the Lord, O my soul!
Lord shall de - scend; "E - ven so"— it is well with my soul.
CHORUS
It is well . . . . with my soul, . . . It is well, it is well with my soul.
It is well with my soul,

323 How Firm a Foundation

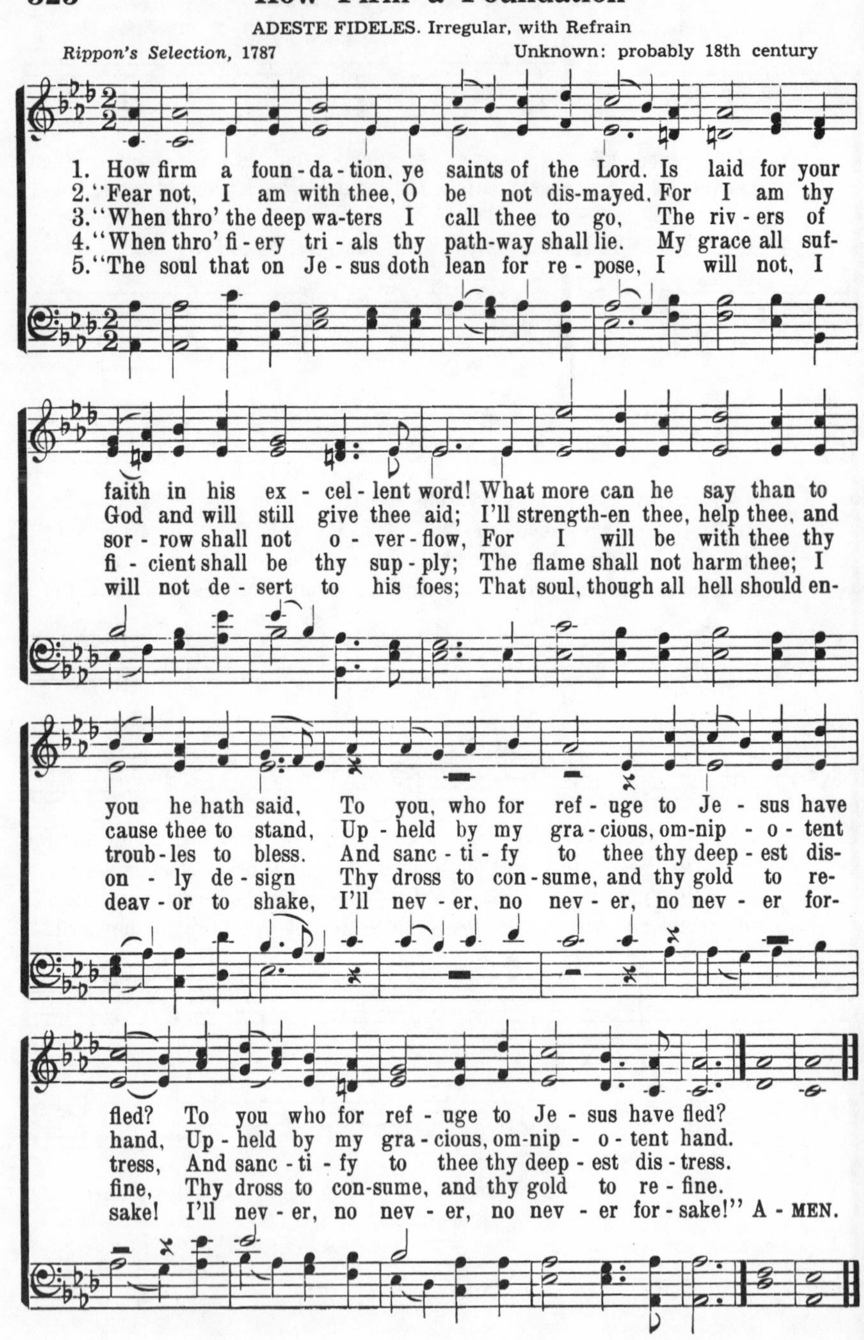
ADESTE FIDELES. Irregular, with Refrain
Rippon's Selection, 1787
Unknown: probably 18th century
1. How firm a foun-da-tion, ye saints of the Lord. Is laid for your
2."Fear not, I am with thee, O be not dis-mayed, For I am thy
3."When thro' the deep wa-ters I call thee to go, The riv-ers of
4."When thro' fi-ery tri-als thy path-way shall lie. My grace all suf-
5."The soul that on Je-sus doth lean for re-pose, I will not, I
faith in his ex-cel-lent word! What more can he say than to
God and will still give thee aid; I'll strength-en thee, help thee, and
sor-row shall not o-ver-flow, For I will be with thee thy
fi-cient shall be thy sup-ply; The flame shall not harm thee; I
will not de-sert to his foes; That soul, though all hell should en-
you he hath said, To you, who for ref-uge to Je-sus have
cause thee to stand, Up-held by my gra-cious, om-nip-o-tent
troub-les to bless. And sanc-ti-fy to thee thy deep-est dis-
on-ly de-sign Thy dross to con-sume, and thy gold to re-
deav-or to shake, I'll nev-er, no nev-er, no nev-er for-
fled? To you who for ref-uge to Je-sus have fled?
hand, Up-held by my gra-cious, om-nip-o-tent hand.
tress, And sanc-ti-fy to thee thy deep-est dis-tress.
fine, Thy dross to con-sume, and thy gold to re-fine.
sake! I'll nev-er, no nev-er, no nev-er for-sake!" A-MEN.

I Am the Lord's

Charles W. Naylor, 1902 — D. Otis Teasley, 1902

1. Wheth-er I live or die, Wheth-er I wake or sleep,
2. When with a - bun - dant store Or in deep pov - er - ty,
3. When I am safe at home Or in a for - eign land,
4. Noth - ing shall sep - a - rate From his un - bound-ed love,
Wheth-er up - on the land Or on the storm - y deep;
And when the world may smile Or it may frown on me;
When on an ice - bound shore Or on a sun - lit strand;
Nei - ther in depths be - low Nor in the heights a - bove;
When 'tis se - rene and calm Or when the wild winds blow,
When it shall help me on Or shall ob - struct my way,
When on the moun-tain height Or in the val - ley low,
And in the years to come He will a - bide with me;
rit.
I shall not be a - fraid— I am the Lord's, I know.
Still shall my heart re - joice— I am the Lord's to - day.
Still doth he care for me— I am the Lord's, I know.
I am the Lord's, I know, For all e - ter - ni - ty.

325 He Is with Me Still

Charles W: Naylor, 1902

Charles W. Naylor, 1902
D. Otis Teasley, 1902

1. Tho' I walk in ways un-known I am nev-er left a-lone,
2. When the rag-ing storm-winds blow And the clouds are hang-ing low,
3. 'Mid the bus-y cares of life, In the bat-tle's rag-ing strife,
For the Lord will not for-sake me while I do his will;
When the waves are beat-ing on me and the night is chill,
When a-round my soul are gath-ered all the hosts of ill,
But what-ev-er may be-tide, He is walk-ing by my side,
Then his pres-ence in the storm Qui-ets all my soul's a-larm,
Then a voice so sweet and clear Whis-pers words of love and cheer,
And by this I know he loves me still.
And I know that he is with me still.
And I know that he is with me still.
CHORUS
He . . . . is with me
He is with me,
still,
he is with me still,
He . . . . is with me still;
He is with me, he is with me still;

In the sun-shine or the shad-ow, He is with me still.
He is with me, with me still.

I'll Follow with Rejoicing 326

Charles W. Naylor, 1874-1950 — Andrew L. Byers, 1870-1952

1. The fu-ture lies un-seen a-head, It holds I know not what;
But still I know I need not dread, For Je-sus fail-eth not.

2. Doth he not know what I shall meet Up-on life's rug-ged way?
Will he not guide my halt-ing feet, Lest from the path I stray?

3 No mat-ter how things look to me, Nor if they threat-en sore;
I know my way pre-pared shall be, For Christ leads on be-fore.

4. The glo-ry of e-ter-nal dawn Shines from his smil-ing face;
So trust-ing him I fol-low on, With heart made strong by grace.

CHORUS

I'll fol-low him with re-joic-ing, With re-joic-ing, re-joic-ing;
I'll fol-low him, I'll fol-low him, With re-joic-ing I will fol-low him;
I know he safe-ly will lead me To my e-ter-nal home.
I know he safe-ly will lead me on

327 That's Enough for Me

William J. Henry, b. 1869

Wm. J. Henry, b. 1869
Andrew L. Byers, 1870-1952

1. When my sky is clear and bright, When I find it dark as night;
2. When my heart is filled with joy, When the foe would fain de-stroy,
3. When I'm pressed with toil and care, When the cross seems hard to bear,
4. When I part with loved ones here, When I'm tempt-ed death to fear,

Just to trust and do the right, That's e-nough for me.
If I'm in my Lord's em-ploy, That's e-nough for me.
Just the grace of God to share, That's e-nough for me.
Just to know my Lord is near, That's e-nough for me.

CHORUS

That's e-nough for me, . . . That's e-nough for me; . . .
e-nough for me, e-nough for me;

Just to trust and do the right,
If I'm in my Lord's em-ploy, That's e-nough for me. . . .
Just the grace of God to share, e-nough for me.
Just to know my Lord is near,

By Faith and Not by Sight

328

Clara M. Brooks, c. 1907

Andrew L. Byers, 1870-1952

1. Fol-low-ing Je-sus from day to day, Gen-tly he leads me a-long the way;
2. Je - sus has purchased me for his own, Sweetly he reigns in my heart, his throne;
3. Seek-ing to en - ter the holiest place, Bold-ly I came to the throne of grace;
4. When I was held in affliction's chain, Suf-fer-ing much from disease and pain,
5. Soon I shall has-ten my Lord to meet, And in his like-ness I'll stand complete,
E'er will I trust him, all foes de-spite, By faith and not by sight.
Par - don he grant-ed and washed me white, By faith and not by sight.
Sanc - ti - fied whol-ly, he's my de-light, By faith and not by sight.
Je - sus then touched me and healed me quite, By faith and not by sight.
Where with the ransomed in heav-en's light My faith is lost in sight.
Chorus
Walk-ing with Je-sus I'm in the light, Walking with Je - sus in robes of white,
Walk-ing with Je - sus my way is bright, By faith and not by sight.

329 I Know My Name Is There

Daniel S. Warner, 1893 — Barney E. Warren, 1893

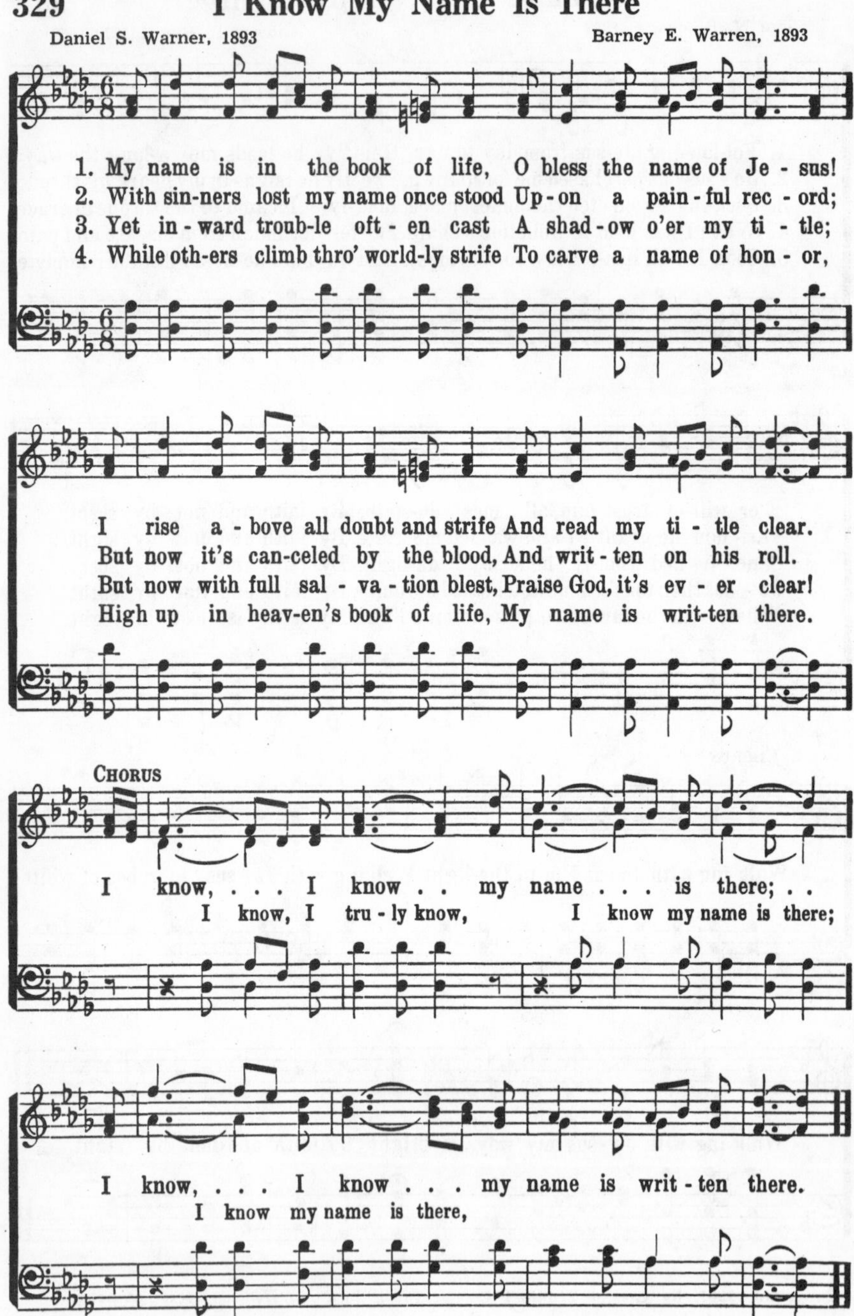
1. My name is in the book of life, O bless the name of Je - sus!
2. With sin-ners lost my name once stood Up-on a pain-ful rec - ord;
3. Yet in-ward troub-le oft - en cast A shad-ow o'er my ti - tle;
4. While oth-ers climb thro' world-ly strife To carve a name of hon - or,
I rise a - bove all doubt and strife And read my ti - tle clear.
But now it's can-celed by the blood, And writ - ten on his roll.
But now with full sal - va - tion blest, Praise God, it's ev - er clear!
High up in heav-en's book of life, My name is writ-ten there.
CHORUS
I know, . . . I know . . my name . . . is there; . .
I know, I tru - ly know, I know my name is there;
I know, . . . I know . . . my name is writ - ten there.
I know my name is there,

We Have a Hope 330

William G. Schell, 1893 William G. Schell, 1893

1. Have we an - y hope with-in us of a life be-yond the grave, In the fair and ver - nal lands? Do we know that when our earth-ly house by death shall be dissolved We've a house not made with hands?
2. Bless - ed hope we have with-in us is an an - chor to the soul, It is both stead - fast and sure; It is found - ed on the prom - is - es of Fa-ther's written word, And 'twill ev - er - more en - dure.
3. Since we've walked the strait and narrow way our path has ev - er shone Brighter, bright-er, day by day; Hope with-in our hearts as-sures us it is bet - ter far-ther on, It is bright-er all the way.
4. Life will end in joy - ful sing-ing, "I have fought a faith-ful fight," Then we'll lay our ar - mor down; And our spir - its freed from earth-ly ties shall take their hap-py flight To pos - sess a star - ry crown.
CHORUS
We have a hope with- in our souls, Brighter than the per-fect day: God has giv - en us his Spir - it. And we want the world to hear it. All our doubts are passed a - way.

331 Let Not Your Heart Be Troubled

Barney E. Warren, 1900 — Barney E. Warren, 1900

1. Let not your wea - ry heart be troub - led, Be - lieve in
God, be - lieve in me; In Fa-ther's house are man - y man - sions, I
will pre - pare a place for thee.

2. Let not your peace and calm as - sur - ance Be ruf - fled
by the storms of life, But, sol - dier - like, with firm en - dur - ance, Just
glo - ry in the ho - ly strife.

3. Let not your hope be dimmed with doubt - ing, Let not life's
bur-dens foil your grace; But in each con - flict vic - t'ry shout-ing, As
one who runs to win a race.

CHORUS

Let not . . . . your heart be troub - led, Let not . . . . your heart be troub - led, Let not . . . . your heart be troub - led, Nor let it be a - fraid.
(Let not your heart be troubled, Let not your heart be troub - led, Let not your heart be troub - led,)

rit.

Trust and Obey 332

James H. Sammis, d. 1919 D. B. Towner, 1850-1919

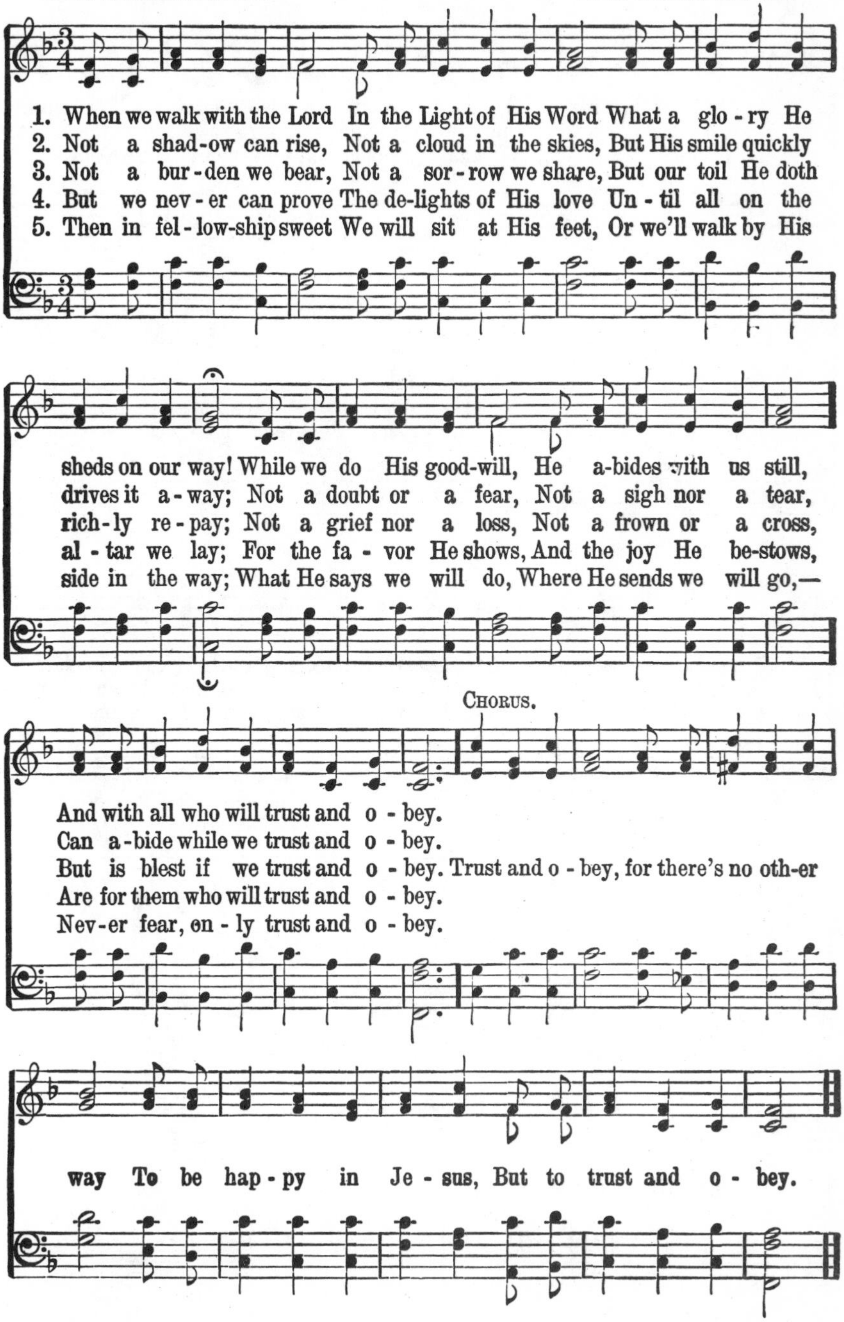

1. When we walk with the Lord In the Light of His Word What a glo - ry He
2. Not a shad-ow can rise, Not a cloud in the skies, But His smile quickly
3. Not a bur-den we bear, Not a sor-row we share, But our toil He doth
4. But we nev-er can prove The de-lights of His love Un - til all on the
5. Then in fel-low-ship sweet We will sit at His feet, Or we'll walk by His

sheds on our way! While we do His good-will, He a-bides with us still,
drives it a-way; Not a doubt or a fear, Not a sigh nor a tear,
rich-ly re-pay; Not a grief nor a loss, Not a frown or a cross,
al - tar we lay; For the fa - vor He shows, And the joy He be-stows,
side in the way; What He says we will do, Where He sends we will go,—

And with all who will trust and o - bey.
Can a-bide while we trust and o - bey.
But is blest if we trust and o - bey.
Are for them who will trust and o - bey.
Nev-er fear, on - ly trust and o - bey.

CHORUS.

Trust and o - bey, for there's no oth-er way To be hap-py in Je - sus, But to trust and o - bey.

333 Under His Wings

William O. Cushing, 1823-1902 — Ira D. Sankey, 1840-1908

1. Un - der His wings I am safe - ly a - bid - ing; Tho' the night
2. Un - der His wings, what a ref - uge in sor - row! How the heart
3. Un - der His wings, O what pre-cious en - joy - ment! There will I
deep - ens and tem - pests are wild, Still I can trust Him; I
yearn-ing - ly turns to His rest! Oft - en when earth has no
hide till life's tri - als are o'er; Shel-tered, pro - tect - ed, no
know He will keep me; He has re-deemed me, and I am His child.
balm for my heal-ing, There I find com-fort, and there I am blest.
e - vil can harm me; Rest-ing in Je - sus I'm safe ev - er - more.
CHORUS
Un-der His wings, un-der His wings, Who from His love can sev - er?
Un-der His wings my soul shall a - bide, Safe-ly a - bide for - ev - er.

All the Way My Savior Leads Me 334

Fanny J. Crosby, 1820-1915 Robert Lowry, 1826-1899

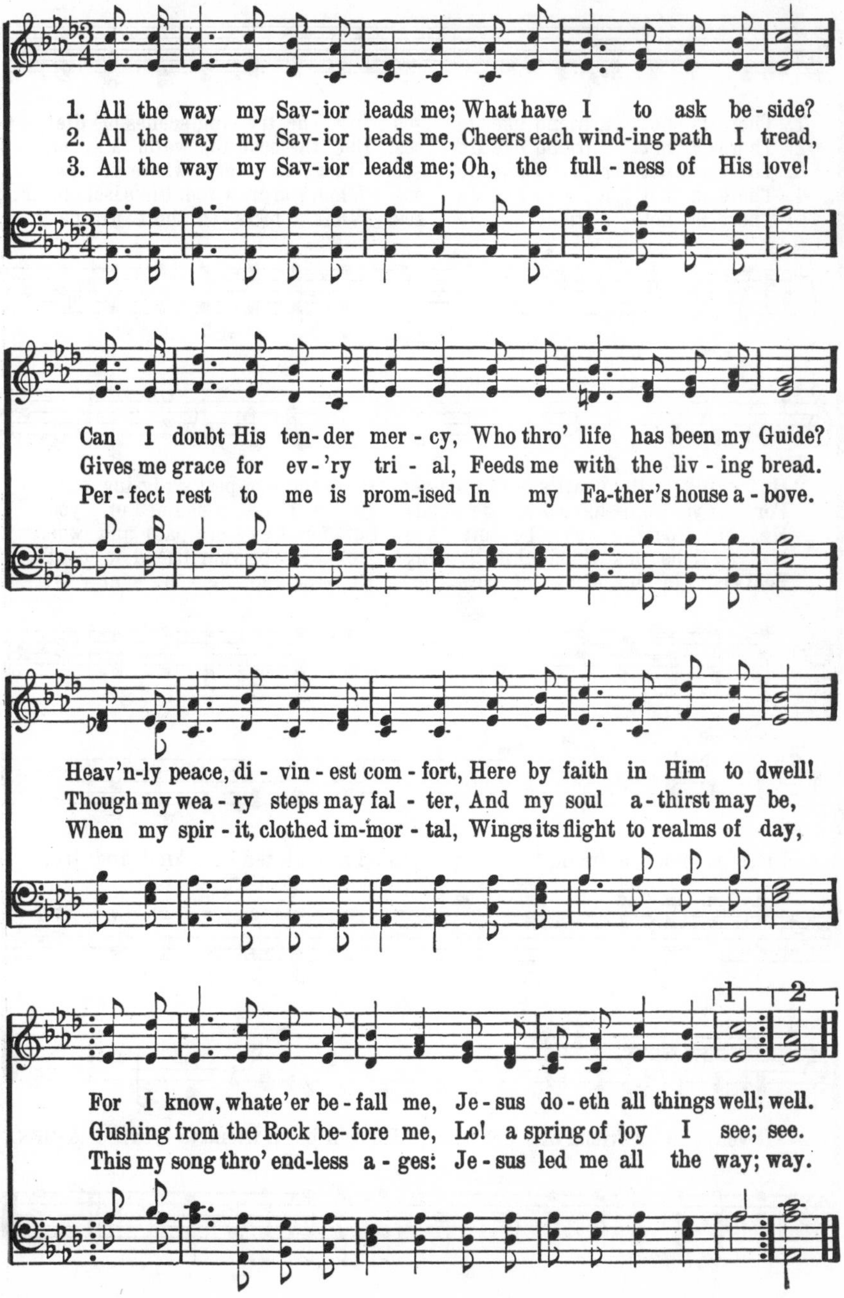

1. All the way my Sav-ior leads me; What have I to ask be-side?
2. All the way my Sav-ior leads me, Cheers each wind-ing path I tread,
3. All the way my Sav-ior leads me; Oh, the full-ness of His love!

Can I doubt His ten-der mer-cy, Who thro' life has been my Guide?
Gives me grace for ev-'ry tri-al, Feeds me with the liv-ing bread.
Per-fect rest to me is prom-ised In my Fa-ther's house a-bove.

Heav'n-ly peace, di-vin-est com-fort, Here by faith in Him to dwell!
Though my wea-ry steps may fal-ter, And my soul a-thirst may be,
When my spir-it, clothed im-mor-tal, Wings its flight to realms of day,

For I know, whate'er be-fall me, Je-sus do-eth all things well; well.
Gushing from the Rock be-fore me, Lo! a spring of joy I see; see.
This my song thro' end-less a-ges: Je-sus led me all the way; way.

335 No Friend like Jesus

Mrs. H. A. Hendricks | D. Otis Teasley, 1903

1. There is not a friend like Je - sus In the try - ing scenes of life:
2. There is not a friend like Je - sus: Bid the scoff-ing world a - dieu;
3. There is not a friend like Je - sus: Trust him ev-ery - where you go;
4. There is not a friend like Je - sus When you draw your life's last breath;
5. There is not a friend like Je - sus: What a bless - ed tho't to be

He can hear the heart's faint whis-per, Calm the tem-pest's rag-ing strife.
For if you're a-shamed of Je - sus He will be a-shamed of you.
He has trod the way be - fore you, Suf - fered ev - ery pain and woe.
If you'll be his friend while liv - ing, He will be your friend in death.
Fold - ed in his arms of pow - er Ev - er in e - ter - ni - ty!

CHORUS

There is not a friend like Je - sus, Pa-tient, ten - der, kind and true:

If you'll be a friend of Je - sus, He will be a friend to you. A-MEN.

Christ the Friend We Need

336

Daniel S. Warner, 1893

Barney E. Warren, 1893

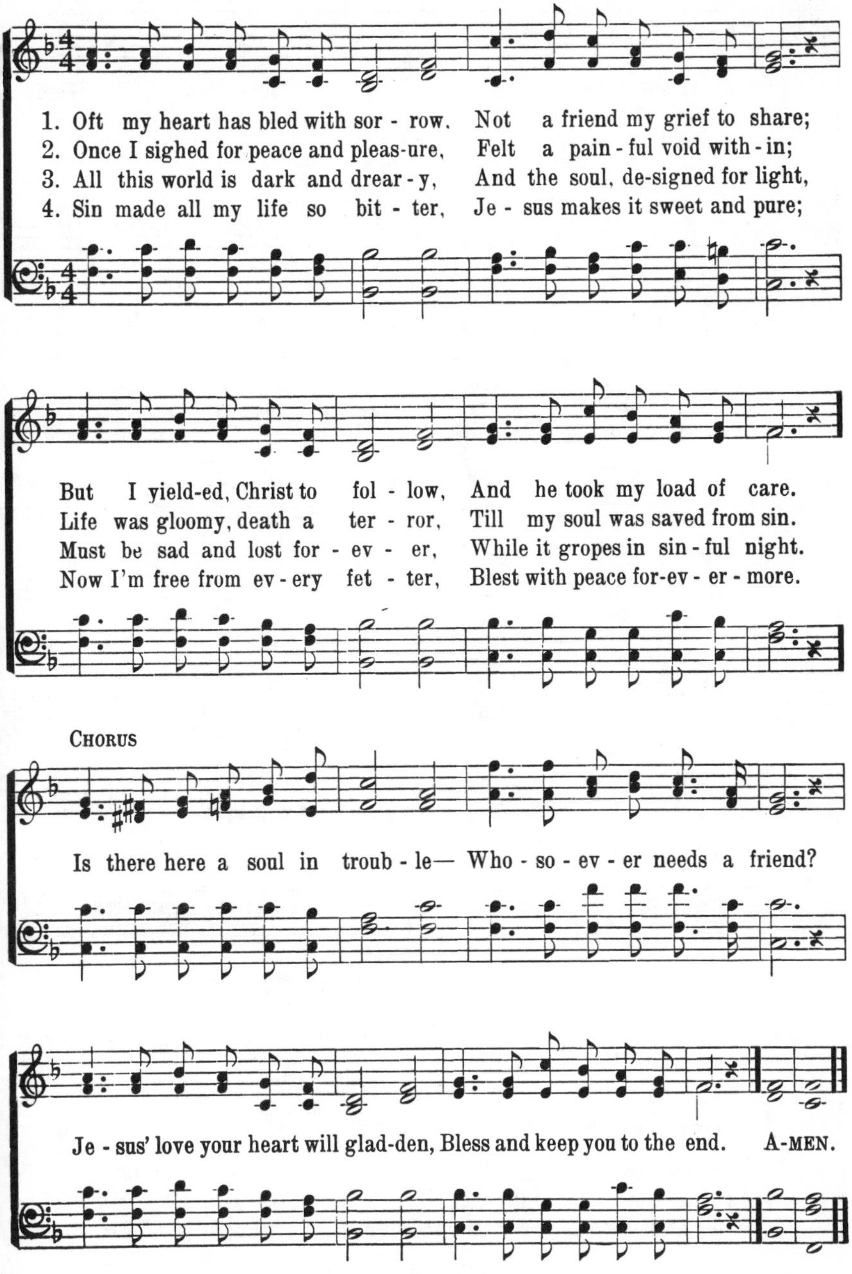

1. Oft my heart has bled with sor - row. Not a friend my grief to share;
2. Once I sighed for peace and pleas-ure, Felt a pain - ful void with - in;
3. All this world is dark and drear - y, And the soul, de-signed for light,
4. Sin made all my life so bit - ter, Je - sus makes it sweet and pure;

But I yield-ed, Christ to fol - low, And he took my load of care.
Life was gloomy, death a ter - ror, Till my soul was saved from sin.
Must be sad and lost for - ev - er, While it gropes in sin - ful night.
Now I'm free from ev - ery fet - ter, Blest with peace for-ev - er - more.

CHORUS

Is there here a soul in troub - le— Who - so - ev - er needs a friend?

Je - sus' love your heart will glad-den, Bless and keep you to the end. A-MEN.

337 'Tis So Sweet to Trust in Jesus

Louisa M. R. Stead — William J. Kirkpatrick, 1838-1921

1. 'Tis so sweet to trust in Je - sus, Just to take Him at His Word;
2. O how sweet to trust in Je - sus, Just to trust His cleans-ing blood;
3. Yes, 'tis sweet to trust in Je - sus, Just from sin and self to cease;
4. I'm so glad I learned to trust Thee, Pre-cious Je - sus, Sav - ior, Friend;
Just to rest up - on His prom-ise; Just to know, "Thus saith the Lord."
Just in sim - ple faith to plunge me 'Neath the heal - ing, cleans-ing flood!
Just from Je - sus sim - ply tak - ing Life and rest, and joy and peace.
And I know that Thou art with me, Wilt be with me to the end.
CHORUS
Je - sus, Je - sus, how I trust Him! How I've proved Him o'er and o'er!
p
Je - sus, Je - sus, pre - cious Je - sus! O for grace to trust Him more!

338 Jesus, Savior, Pilot Me

PILOT. 7.7.7.7.7.7.

Edward Hopper, 1816-1888 — John E. Gould, 1822-1875

1. Je - sus, Sav - ior, pi - lot me O - ver life's tem-pes-tuous sea;
2. As a moth - er stills her child Thou canst hush the o - cean wild;
3. When at last I near the shore, And the fear - ful break-ers roar

Un-known waves be-fore me roll. Hid - ing rock and treach'rous shoal;
Bois-t'rous waves o - bey thy will When thou say'st to them, "Be still."
'Twixt me and the peace-ful rest, Then, while lean-ing on thy breast,
Chart and com-pass came from thee: Je - sus, Sav - ior, pi - lot me.
Won-drous Sov'reign of the sea, Je - sus, Sav - ior, pi - lot me.
May I hear thee say to me, "Fear not, I will pi - lot thee." A-MEN.
Ever Lead Me
339
Barney E. Warren, 1897
Barney E. Warren, 1897
1. Out on this dark world, Sav - ior, am I; Be thou my help - er,
2. Hope of my heart, Lord, Strength of my soul, Guide thou my foot-steps
3. Calm thou the wild storm, Clear up the way; Keep me from fall - ing
O hear my cry! Thou art my por - tion, All is in thee; O let thy
Safe to the goal. My help and for - tress, Lord, thou wilt be; O let thy
By night and day. Trav-'ling to glo - ry, Walk-ing with thee; O let thy
REFRAIN pp
might-y hand ev - er lead me!
might-y hand ev - er lead me! Wilt thou lead me by thy hand? A-MEN.
might-y hand ev - er lead me!

340 I Will Be with Thee

Daniel S. Warner, 1842-1895 — Andrew L. Byers, 1870-1952

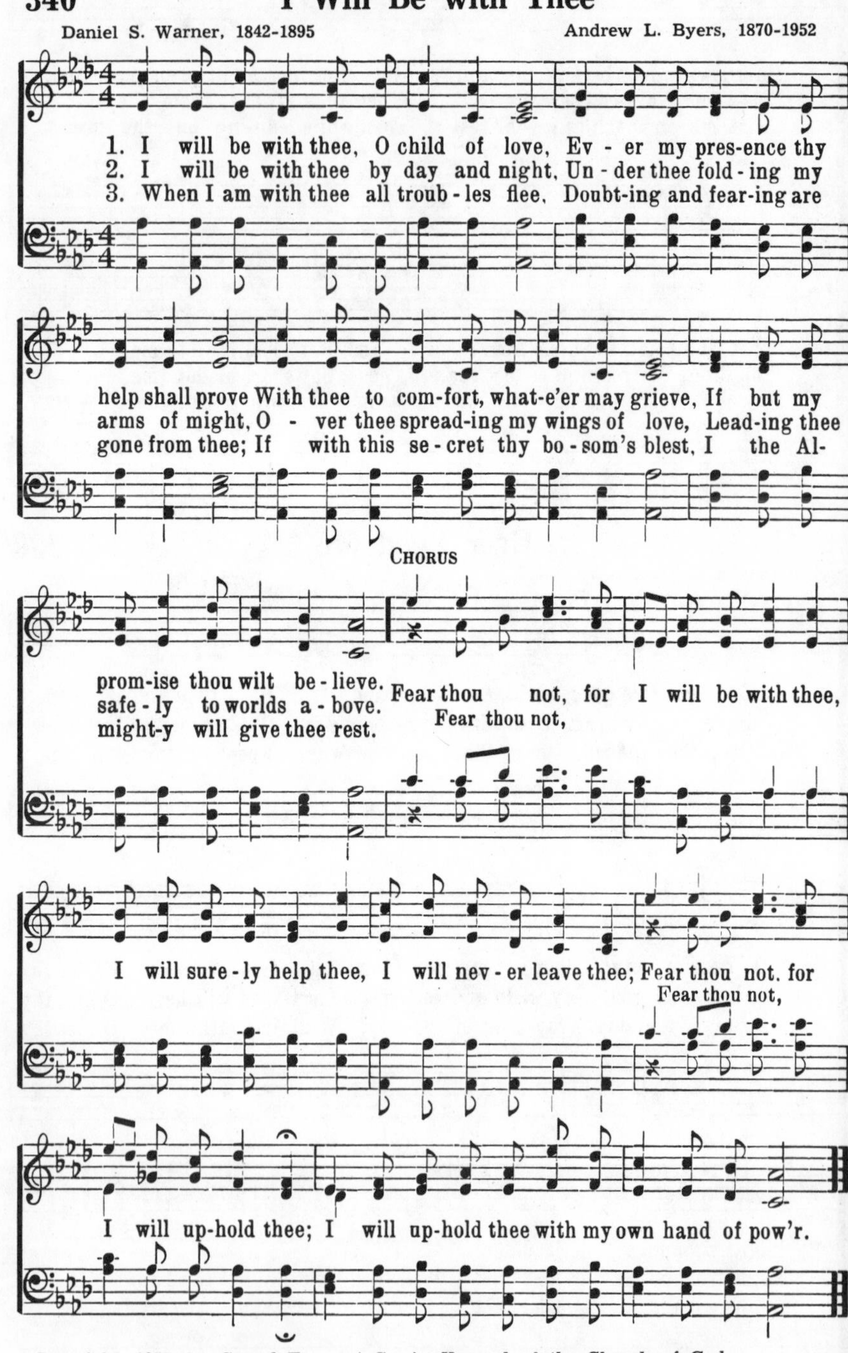
1. I will be with thee, O child of love, Ev - er my pres-ence thy help shall prove With thee to com-fort, what-e'er may grieve, If but my prom-ise thou wilt be - lieve.
2. I will be with thee by day and night, Un - der thee fold - ing my arms of might, O - ver thee spread-ing my wings of love, Lead-ing thee safe - ly to worlds a - bove.
3. When I am with thee all troub - les flee, Doubt-ing and fear-ing are gone from thee; If with this se - cret thy bo - som's blest, I the Al-might-y will give thee rest.
CHORUS
Fear thou not, for I will be with thee,
Fear thou not,
I will sure - ly help thee, I will nev - er leave thee; Fear thou not, for
Fear thou not,
I will up-hold thee; I will up-hold thee with my own hand of pow'r.

The Lord Our Shepherd 341

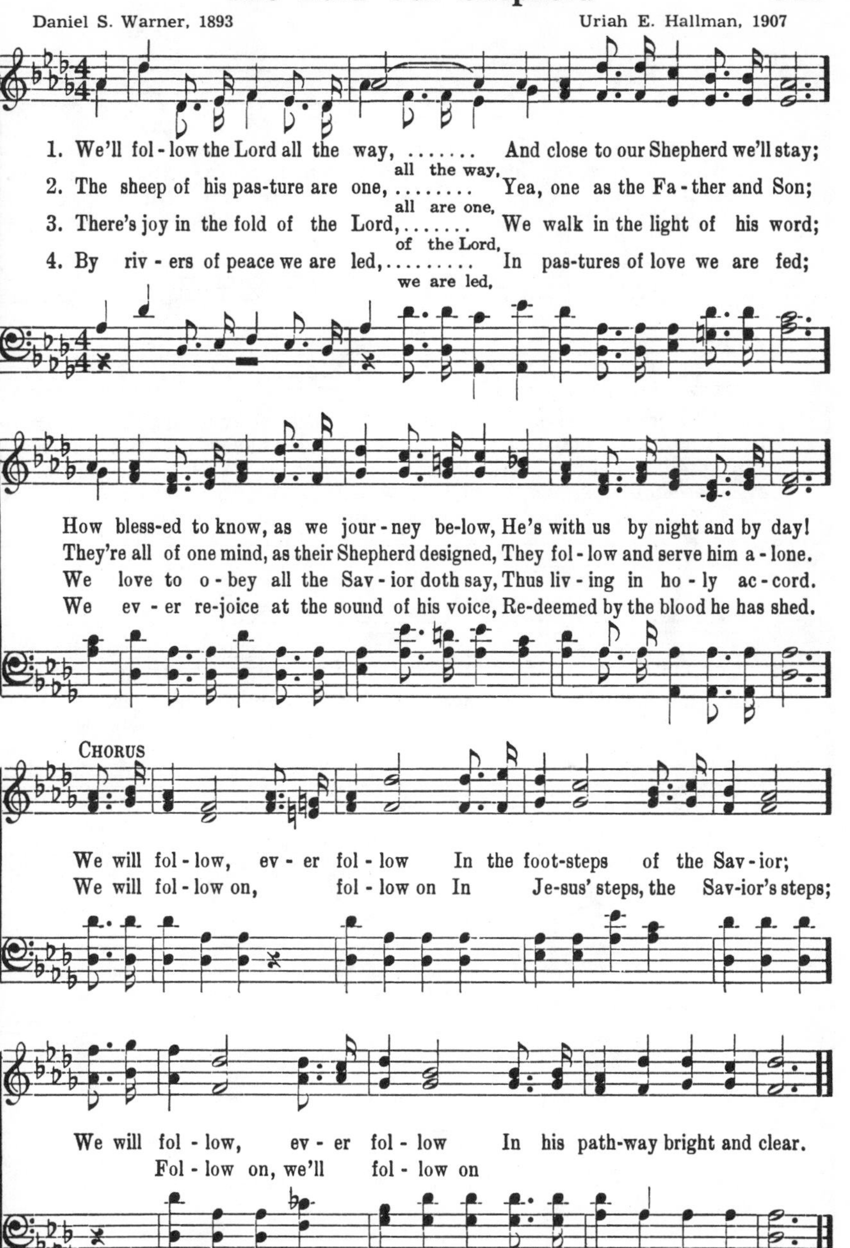
Daniel S. Warner, 1893
Uriah E. Hallman, 1907
1. We'll fol-low the Lord all the way, ... And close to our Shepherd we'll stay;
all the way,
2. The sheep of his pas-ture are one, ... Yea, one as the Fa-ther and Son;
all are one,
3. There's joy in the fold of the Lord, ... We walk in the light of his word;
of the Lord,
4. By riv-ers of peace we are led, ... In pas-tures of love we are fed;
we are led,
How bless-ed to know, as we jour-ney be-low, He's with us by night and by day!
They're all of one mind, as their Shepherd designed, They fol-low and serve him a-lone.
We love to o-bey all the Sav-ior doth say, Thus liv-ing in ho-ly ac-cord.
We ev-er re-joice at the sound of his voice, Re-deemed by the blood he has shed.
CHORUS
We will fol-low, ev-er fol-low In the foot-steps of the Sav-ior;
We will fol-low on, fol-low on In Je-sus' steps, the Sav-ior's steps;
We will fol-low, ev-er fol-low In his path-way bright and clear.
Fol-low on, we'll fol-low on

342 The Hollow of His Mighty Hand

Barney E. Warren, 1897
Revised, 1926

Barney E. Warren, 1897
Revised, 1926

1. I have left all sin's do - min - ion, I am free, I shall ev - er keep the Lord's command; Trusting him in glad sub - mis - sion I shall be
2. When the cares of life be - set, I'll on - ward go, And for Je - sus I will firm - ly stand; He has prom-ised he will shield me from the foe,
3. He'll be with me on the bless - ed ho - ly way, Till at last I join the an - gel band; And from sin - ful things he'll keep me ev - ery day
4. When the Lord of glo - ry wipes a - way my tears, O - ver on the ev - er-shin-ing strand, I will praise his name who kept me thro' the years
In the hol - low of his might - y hand.
CHORUS
In the hol - low of his might - y hand, In the hol - low of his might-y hand; By the Ho - ly Spir - it's pow'r, He will
In the hol - low of his hand, in the hol - low of his hand, In the hol - low of his hand, in the hol - low of his hand;

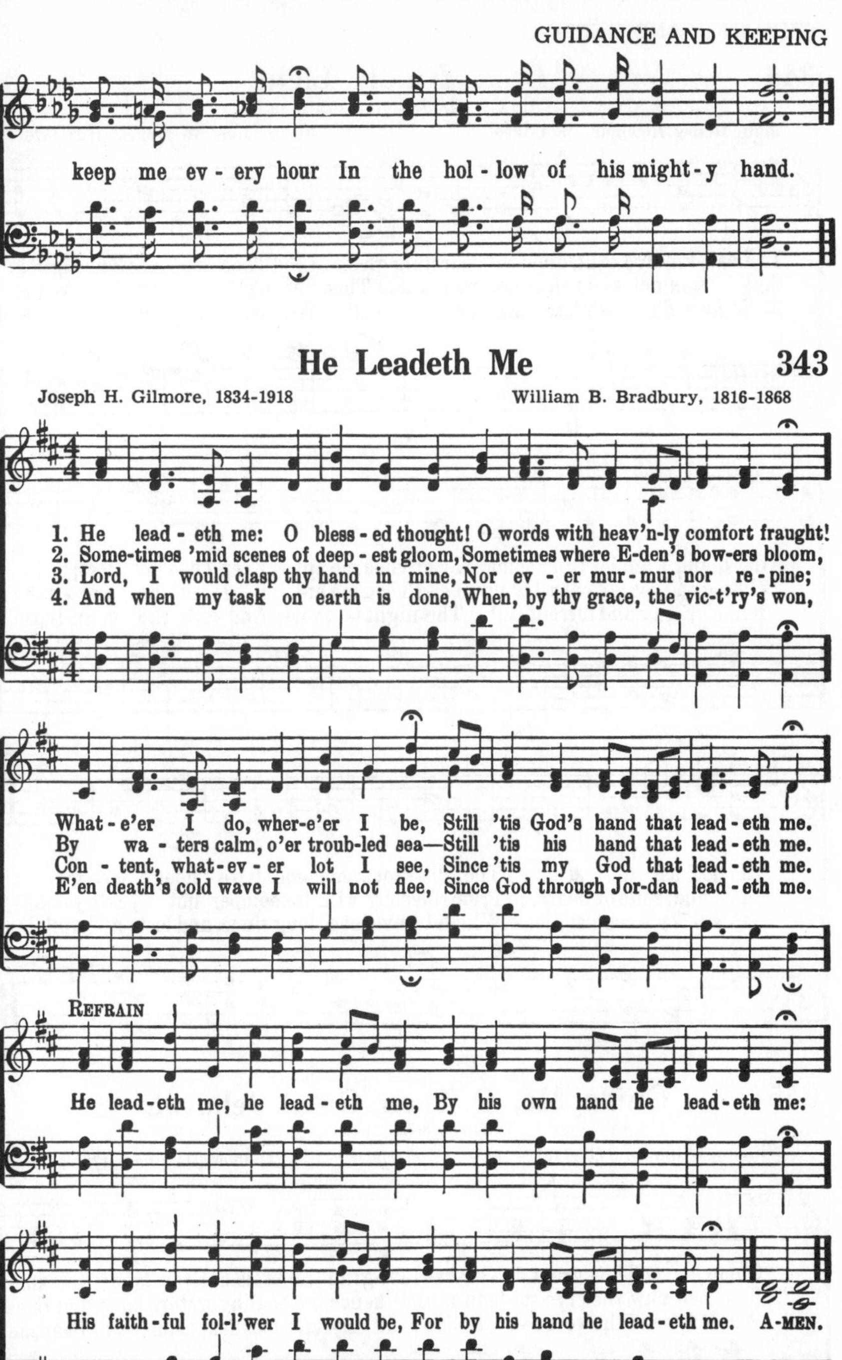
keep me ev - ery hour In the hol - low of his might - y hand.
He Leadeth Me 343
Joseph H. Gilmore, 1834-1918
William B. Bradbury, 1816-1868
1. He lead - eth me: O bless - ed thought! O words with heav'n-ly comfort fraught!
2. Some-times 'mid scenes of deep - est gloom, Sometimes where E-den's bow-ers bloom,
3. Lord, I would clasp thy hand in mine, Nor ev - er mur - mur nor re - pine;
4. And when my task on earth is done, When, by thy grace, the vic-t'ry's won,
What - e'er I do, wher-e'er I be, Still 'tis God's hand that lead - eth me.
By wa - ters calm, o'er troub-led sea—Still 'tis his hand that lead - eth me.
Con - tent, what-ev - er lot I see, Since 'tis my God that lead - eth me.
E'en death's cold wave I will not flee, Since God through Jor-dan lead - eth me.
Refrain
He lead-eth me, he lead - eth me, By his own hand he lead-eth me:
His faith-ful fol-l'wer I would be, For by his hand he lead-eth me. A-men.

344 Lead, Kindly Light

LUX BENIGNA. 10.4.10.4.10.10.

John Henry Newman, 1801-1890 John B. Dykes, 1823-1876

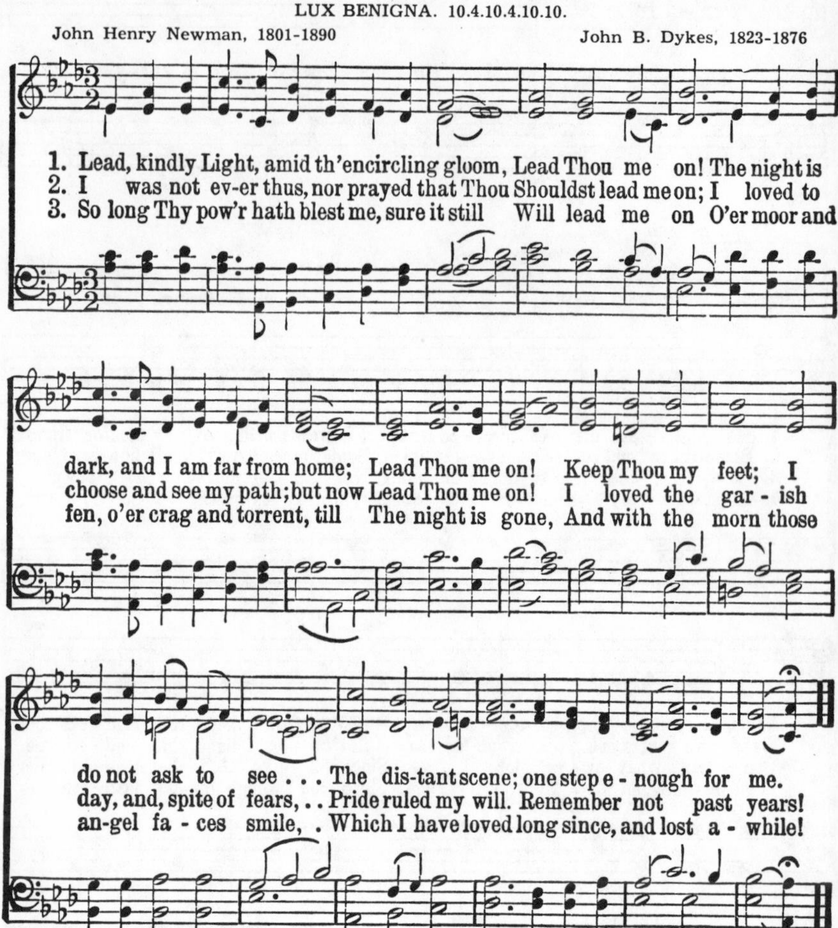
1. Lead, kindly Light, amid th'encircling gloom, Lead Thou me on! The night is
2. I was not ev-er thus, nor prayed that Thou Shouldst lead me on; I loved to
3. So long Thy pow'r hath blest me, sure it still Will lead me on O'er moor and
dark, and I am far from home; Lead Thou me on! Keep Thou my feet; I
choose and see my path; but now Lead Thou me on! I loved the gar - ish
fen, o'er crag and torrent, till The night is gone, And with the morn those
do not ask to see . . . The dis-tant scene; one step e - nough for me.
day, and, spite of fears, . . Pride ruled my will. Remember not past years!
an-gel fa - ces smile, . Which I have loved long since, and lost a - while!

345 Guide Me, O Thou Great Jehovah

ZION. 8.7.8.7.4.7.4.7.

William Williams, 1717-1791 Thomas Hastings, 1784-1872

1. Guide me, O Thou great Je - ho-vah, Pil-grim thro' this bar-ren land; I am
2. O - pen now the crys-tal foun-tain, Whence the healing waters flow; Let the
3. When I tread the verge of Jor-dan, Bid my anx-ious fears sub-side; Bear me

weak, but Thou art might-y, Hold me with Thy pow'rful hand; Bread of heav-en,
fi - ery, cloud-y pil - lar Lead me all my jour-ney thro'; Strong De-liv-'rer,
thro' the swell-ing cur-rent; Land me safe on Ca-naan's side; Songs of prais-es
Feed me till I want no more; Bread of heaven, Feed me till I want no more.
Be Thou still my strength and shield; Strong De-liv-'rer, Be Thou still my strength and shield.
I will ev - er give to Thee; Songs of prais-es I will ev - er give to Thee.
Come, Ye Disconsolate
346
CONSOLATION (WEBBE). 11.10.11.10.
Thomas Moore, 1779-1852
Alt. by Thomas Hastings, 1784-1872
Arr. from Samuel Webbe, 1740-1816
4
4
1. Come, ye dis - con - so - late, wher - e'er ye lan - guish; Come, at the
2. Joy of the des - o - late, light of the stray - ing, Hope of the
3. Here see the bread of life, see wa - ters flow - ing Forth from the
mer - cy - seat fer - vent - ly kneel; Here bring your wound - ed hearts,
pen - i - tent, fade - less and pure; Here speaks the Com - fort - er,
throne of God, pure from a - bove; Come to the feast of love;
here tell your an - guish; Earth has no sor - row that heav'n can-not heal.
ten - der - ly say - ing, "Earth has no sor - row that heav'n can-not cure."
come, ev - er know - ing Earth has no sor - row but heav'n can re - move.

347 Because He Loves Me

Charles W. Naylor, 1917 — Andrew L. Byers, 1918

1. When the storm winds rage and the rain falls fast, And the clouds hang low a-bove,
2. It was not that I was so good or great, For my heart was vile with sin;
3. If he loved me so when I grieved him sore That he sought me ten-der-ly,
4. I will trust his love, for it e'er will last, It is rich and warm and free;

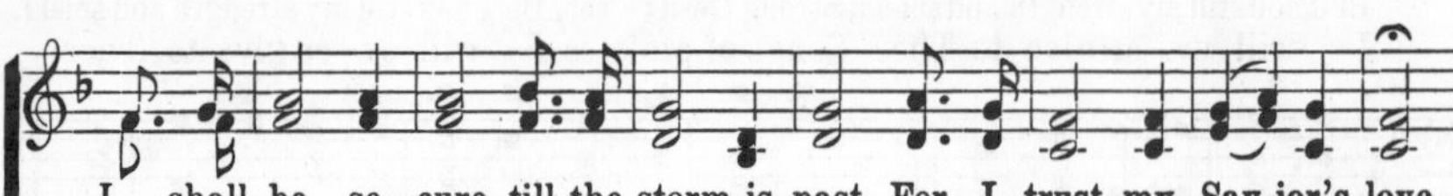

I shall be se-cure till the storm is past, For I trust my Sav-ior's love.
I had turned my back on the nar-row gate, Neither cared nor lived for him:
Till he won my heart and my sins he bore, So that I his child might be,
Thro' the years of life it will hold me fast, And my help and com-fort be.

And he knows the way and he holds my hand, And he will not let it go;
But I pleased my-self and I chose my way, For his grace I did not know;
Will he love me less since I love him, too, So my heart with fer-vor glows,
To my wait-ing heart all its treas-ures rare As a sparkling stream shall flow;

He will lead me home to that bet-ter land, Just because he loves me so.
But he sought me still thro' the night and day, Just because he loved me so.
And I haste each day all his will to do That my will-ing spir-it knows?
In the joy of God I shall ev-er share, Just because he loves me so. A-MEN.

In Heavenly Love Abiding

SEASONS. 7.6.7.6.D.

Anna L. Waring, 1820-1910

Felix B. Mendelssohn, 1809-1847

1. In heav'n-ly love a-bid-ing, No change my heart shall fear;
And safe in such con-fid-ing, For noth-ing chang-es here.
The storm may roar with-out me, My heart may low be laid;
But God is round a-bout me, And can I be dis-mayed?

2. Wher-ev-er he may guide me, No want shall turn me back;
My Shep-herd is be-side me, And noth-ing can I lack.
His wis-dom ev-er wak-eth, His sight is nev-er dim;
He knows the way he tak-eth, And I will walk with him.

3. Green pas-tures are be-fore me, Which yet I have not seen;
Bright skies will soon be o'er me, Where the dark clouds have been.
My hope I can-not meas-ure, My path to life is free;
My Sav-ior has my treas-ure, And he will walk with me.

A-MEN.

349 Come Closer to Me

Barney E. Warren, 1902 Barney E. Warren, 1902

1. When I get wea - ry with toils of the day, Off in the se - cret I
2. When all a - round in this cold, dark land, Noth-ing en - cour - ag - es
3. When in af - flic-tions I suf - fer long, Then to my heart comes this
4. When I am meet-ing with tri - als se - vere, When I am part - ing with

kneel and pray; There I can hear the Lord ten - der - ly say, "Come
me to stand, Je - sus says, reach-ing to me his hand, "Come
love - ly song: "Trust in my grace and you shall be strong; Come
loved ones dear, Look-ing to Je - sus, his voice I can hear: "Come

clos - er, my child, to me."

CHORUS

Clos - er, my child, to me,
Clos - er, my child, to me,
Clos - er, my child, to me, Come
clos - er, . . come clos - er. . .
Come clos-er, come clos-er,
rit.
Clos-er, my child, to me. A - MEN.

God's Way Is Best

350

Charles W. Naylor, 1904 — Clarence E. Hunter, 1906

1. God's way is best; if hu-man wis-dom A fair-er way may seem to show,
2. Had I the choosing of my path-way, In blind-ness I should go a-stray,
3. He lead-eth true; I will not ques-tion, Tho' thro' the val-ley I shall go,
4. God's way is best; heart, cease thy struggling To see and know and un-der-stand;
5. Thy way is best, so lead me on-ward, My all I give to thy con-trol;

'Tis on-ly that our earth-dimmed vision The truth can nev-er clear-ly know.
And wan-der far a-way in dark-ness, Nor reach that land of end-less day.
Tho' I should pass thro' clouds of tri-al And drink the cup of hu-man woe.
For-sake thy fears and doubts, but trusting, Sub-mit thy-self in-to his hand.
Thy lov-ing hand will tru-ly guide me, And safe to glo-ry bring my soul.

CHORUS

God's way is best, I will not mur-mur, Al-though the end I may not see;

Wher-e'er he leads I'll meekly fol-low–God's way is best, is best for me. A-MEN.

351 Keep Me, My Lord

Barney E. Warren, 1905 — Barney E. Warren, 1905

1. Keep me in touch with thee, My bless - ed Lord;
2. Lord, with thy gen - tle - ness I would be great;
3. Con - quer my ev - ery foe While here I stay;
4. O let thy watch - ful eye Be o - ver me;
Thine shall the glo - ry be, Mine the re - ward (the great re-ward);
Blest with thy ho - li - ness, Be this my state (my bless-ed state);
On to the end I'll go, Let me not stray (from thee a-way);
Hear thou my hum - ble cry, Com - ing to thee (com-ing to thee);
Cov - er my soul with grace, In that most ho - ly place;
To thee I all re - sign, O let thy will be mine;
Down in - to noth - ing - ness, Hid in thy right - eous - ness,
Guide thou my steps a - right, Be thou my song at night,
Till I shall see thy face Keep me, my Lord.
In thy great love di - vine Keep me, my Lord.
Firm in thy faith - ful - ness Keep me, my Lord.
My theme and heart's de - light; Keep me, my Lord. A - MEN.

He Will Care for Me

352

Charles W. Naylor, 1919 — Andrew L. Byers, 1919

1. I walk to-day in the Chris-tian way, Tho' dan-gers I may see;
2. No test I face, but suf-fi-cient grace Is read-y for my need;
3. He will not fail in the strong-est gale That storm-y winds can blow;
4. I trust in him, tho' dis-as-ters grim Be-fore me seem to be;
I will not fear, for the Lord is near, And he will care for me.
When sorrows rise to ob-scure my skies, He proves a friend in-deed.
And in his grace is a hid-ing place, Un-known to an-y foe.
He calms my fears and he dries my tears, And faith-ful is to me.
CHORUS
No mat-ter what hap-pens, he will care for me, He will care for
me, he will care for me; And his might-y hand will en-
a-ble me to stand, No mat-ter what hap-pens to me.
what hap-pens to me.

353 Leaning on the Everlasting Arms

Elisha A. Hoffman, 1839-1929 — Anthony J. Showalter, 1887

1. What a fel-low-ship, what a joy di-vine, Lean-ing on the ev-er-last-ing arms! What a bless-ed-ness, what a peace is mine,
2. O how sweet to walk in this pil-grim way, Lean-ing on the ev-er-last-ing arms! O how bright the path grows from day to day,
3. What have I to dread, what have I to fear, Lean-ing on the ev-er-last-ing arms? I have bless-ed peace with my Lord so near,
Lean-ing on the ev-er-last-ing arms!
CHORUS
Lean - - ing, Lean-ing on Je-sus, lean - ing, lean-ing on Je-sus, Safe and secure from all a-larms; Lean - ing, Lean-ing on Je-sus, lean - - ing, lean-ing on Je-sus, Lean-ing on the ev-er-last-ing arms. A-MEN.

He Hideth My Soul

354

Fanny J. Crosby, 1820-1915

William J. Kirkpatrick, 1838-1921

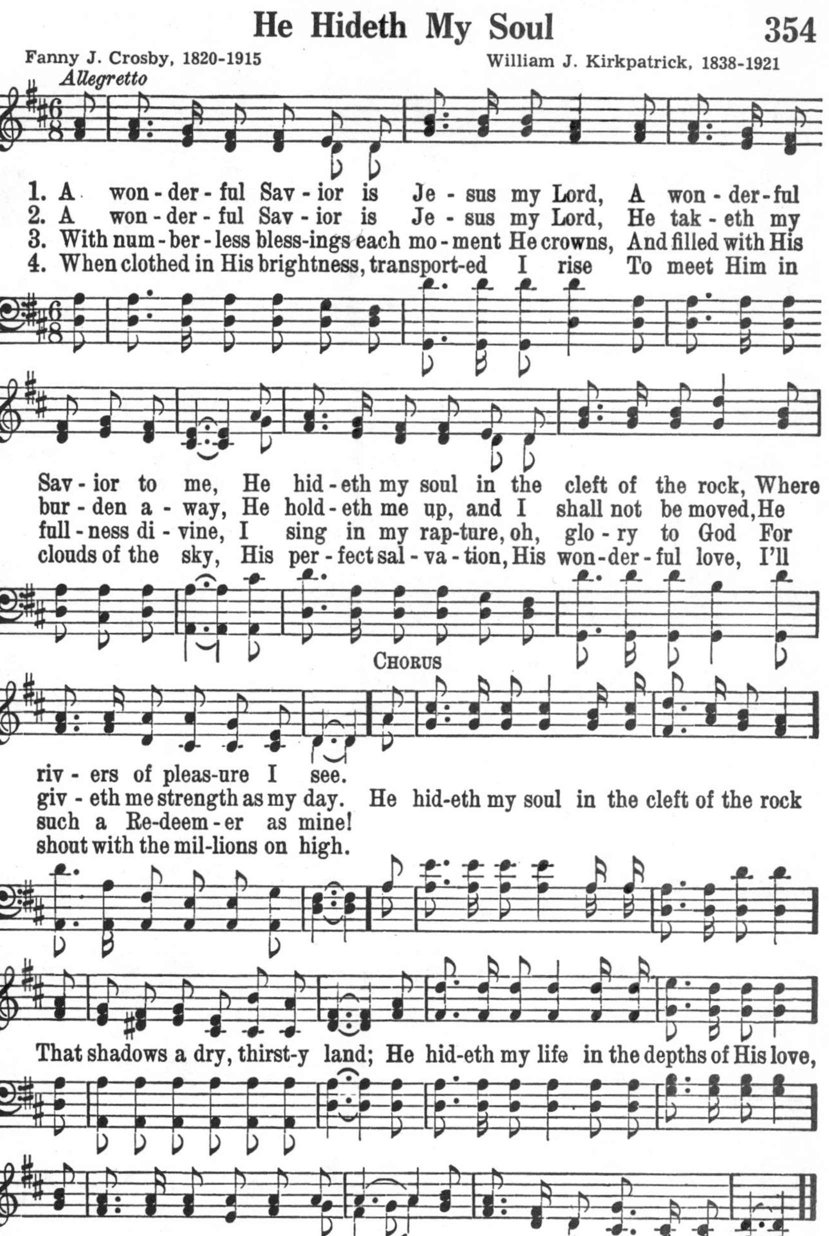
Allegretto
1. A won - der - ful Sav - ior is Je - sus my Lord, A won - der-ful Sav - ior to me, He hid - eth my soul in the cleft of the rock, Where riv - ers of pleas-ure I see.
2. A won - der - ful Sav - ior is Je - sus my Lord, He tak - eth my bur - den a - way, He hold - eth me up, and I shall not be moved, He giv - eth me strength as my day.
3. With num - ber - less bless-ings each mo - ment He crowns, And filled with His full - ness di - vine, I sing in my rap - ture, oh, glo - ry to God For such a Re-deem - er as mine!
4. When clothed in His brightness, transport-ed I rise To meet Him in clouds of the sky, His per - fect sal - va - tion, His won-der - ful love, I'll shout with the mil-lions on high.
Chorus
He hid-eth my soul in the cleft of the rock That shadows a dry, thirst-y land; He hid-eth my life in the depths of His love, And cov - ers me there with His hand, And cov - ers me there with His hand.

355 For Me All Is Well

Mrs. T. Wheeler | Andrew L. Byers, 1906

1. No sigh nor a tear since Je - sus is here, In his pres-ence se-
2. I sit at his feet and my joy is com-plete, He gives me this
3. O yield to him now and in low - li - ness bow, And drink from this
4. And when by and by he de-scends from on high He will take us to
cure - ly I dwell; I hear his sweet voice and it makes me re - joice,
mes - sage to tell: O lean on his arm, he will save from all harm
life - giv - ing well; The taste is so sweet and the joy so com - plete,
heav - en to dwell; We'll sing this glad song as we jour - ney a - long,
I know that for me all is well.
And fit you in heav - en to dwell.
Its pleas - ure we nev - er can tell.
"I know that for me all is well."
CHORUS
'Tis well with my soul since the
Lord made me whole, And his smiles all my sor-rows dis - pel; On his bos - om I
rest, in his love I am blest; I know that for me all is well. (all is well.)

Wonderful Peace 356

W. D. Cornell, alt. W. G. Cooper

1. Far a-way in the depths of my spir-it to-night Rolls a
2. What a treas-ure I have in this won-der-ful peace, Bur-ied
3. I am rest-ing to-night in this won-der-ful peace, Rest-ing
4. And me-thinks when I rise to that Cit-y of peace, Where the
5. Ah! soul, are you here with-out com-fort or rest, March-ing
mel-o-dy sweet-er than psalm; In ce-les-tial-like strains it un-
deep in the heart of my soul; So se-cure that no pow-er can
sweet-ly in Je-sus' con-trol; For I'm kept from all dan-ger by
Au-thor of peace I shall see, That one strain of the song which the
down the rough pathway of time? Make Je-sus your friend ere the
ceas-ing-ly falls O'er my soul like an in-fi-nite calm.
mine it a-way, While the years of e-ter-ni-ty roll.
night and by day, And His glo-ry is flood-ing my soul.
ran-somed will sing, In that heav-en-ly king-dom shall be:
shad-ows grow dark; Oh, ac-cept this sweet peace so sub-lime.
CHORUS
Peace! peace! won-der-ful peace, Com-ing down from the Fa-ther a-bove; Sweep
o-ver my spir-it for-ev-er, I pray, In fath-om-less bil-lows of love.

357 Jesus, Lover of My Soul

REFUGE. 7.7.7.7.D.

Charles Wesley, 1707-1788 | Joseph P. Holbrook, 1822-1888

1. Je - sus, Lov - er of my soul, Let me to thy bos - om fly,
2. Oth - er ref - uge have I none; Hangs my help - less soul on thee;
3. Thou, O Christ, art all I want; More than all in thee I find;
4. Plenteous grace with thee is found, Grace to cov - er all my sin;
While the near - er wa - ters roll, While the tem - pest still is high.
Leave, O leave me not a - lone, Still sup - port and com - fort me.
Raise the fall - en, cheer the faint, Heal the sick, and lead the blind.
Let the heal - ing streams a-bound; Make and keep me pure with - in.
Hide me, O my Sav - ior, hide, Till the storm of life is past;
All my trust on thee is stayed, All my help from thee I bring;
Just and ho - ly is thy name, Source of all true right-eous-ness;
Thou of life the foun - tain art, Free - ly let me take of thee;
Safe in - to the ha - ven guide, O re-ceive my soul at last.
Cov - er my de - fense-less head With the shad-ow of thy wing.
Thou art ev - er - more the same, Thou art full of truth and grace.
Spring thou up with-in my heart, Rise to all e - ter - ni - ty. A - MEN.

Jesus, Lover of My Soul 358

MARTYN. 7.7.7.7.D.

(Second tune—words on opposite page)

Charles Wesley, 1707-1788 — Simeon B. Marsh, 1798-1875

FINE.

1. { Je - sus, Lov - er of my soul, Let me to thy bos - om fly,
{ While the near - er wa - ters roll, While the tem - pest still is nigh.

D. C.—Safe in - to the ha - ven guide, O re - ceive my soul at last.

D. C.

Hide me, O my Sav - ior, hide, Till the storm of life is past; A - MEN.

Rock of Ages, Cleft for Me 359

TOPLADY. 7.7.7.7.7.7.

Augustus M. Toplady, 1740-1778, alt. — Thomas Hastings, 1784-1872

1. Rock of A - ges, cleft for me, Let me hide my - self in thee;
2. Could my tears for - ev - er flow, Could my zeal no lan - guor know,
3. While I draw this fleet - ing breath, When my eyes shall close in death,

Let the wa - ter and the blood, From thy wound - ed side which flowed,
These for sin could not a - tone; Thou must save, and thou a - lone;
When I rise to worlds un - known, And be - hold thee on thy throne,

Be of sin the dou - ble cure, Save from wrath and make me pure.
In my hand no price I bring, Sim - ply to thy cross I cling.
Rock of A - ges, cleft for me, Let me hide my - self in thee. A - MEN.

360 The Safe Retreat

Barney E. Warren, 1926 — Barney E. Warren, 1926

1. When the storm clouds rise and the sky is dark, When op-
2. When the light-nings flash and the thun-ders roll, And the
3. Soon the storms will pass and the sky will clear, And my
pressed with anx-ious care; I've a safe re-treat in the strong high tow'r,
storms in fu-ry beat; When they seem so sure to en-gulf my soul,
rest be calm and sweet; I will trust and wait with no anx-ious fear,
For no ill can harm me there.
Then I hide in the safe re-treat.
For I hide in the safe re-treat.
CHORUS
I will hide in the safe re-treat, . . . I will hide in the safe re - treat; . . When the storm clouds fly
I will hide, I will hide in the safe re-treat, I will hide, I will hide in the safe re-treat;
Till they pass me by I will hide in the safe re-treat. A-MEN.

In His Love Let Me Hide

361

Lucena C. Byrum, 1905 — Andrew L. Byers, 1907

1. Let me walk in the path which my Sav - ior hath trod, Let me fol - low so
2. Let my heart e'er be fixed on my treas-ures a - bove, Let the pleas-ures of
3. Do you ask why I love him the dear - est of all? Why so free - ly I
4. It is bless - ed to serve him and do his good will, For so pre-cious to
close by his side; For by trust - ing in him I am hap - py and free,
earth fade a - way; For there's noth-ing so love - ly as Je - sus to me,
yield un - to him? 'Tis be - cause he has loved me and died on the cross,
me is his love; Let my tal - ents and time all be giv - en to him,
In the fold of his love let me hide.
Let me ne'er from his love go a - stray.
My poor soul lost in sin to re - deem.
Till he calls me to meet him a - bove.
CHORUS
In his love let me hide, In his love let me hide (let me hide); For by trust-ing in
In the fold of his love let me hide, In the fold of his love let me hide;
him I am hap - py and free, In the fold of his love let me hide (let me hide).

362 Sweetly Resting

Mary D. James — W. Warren Bentley

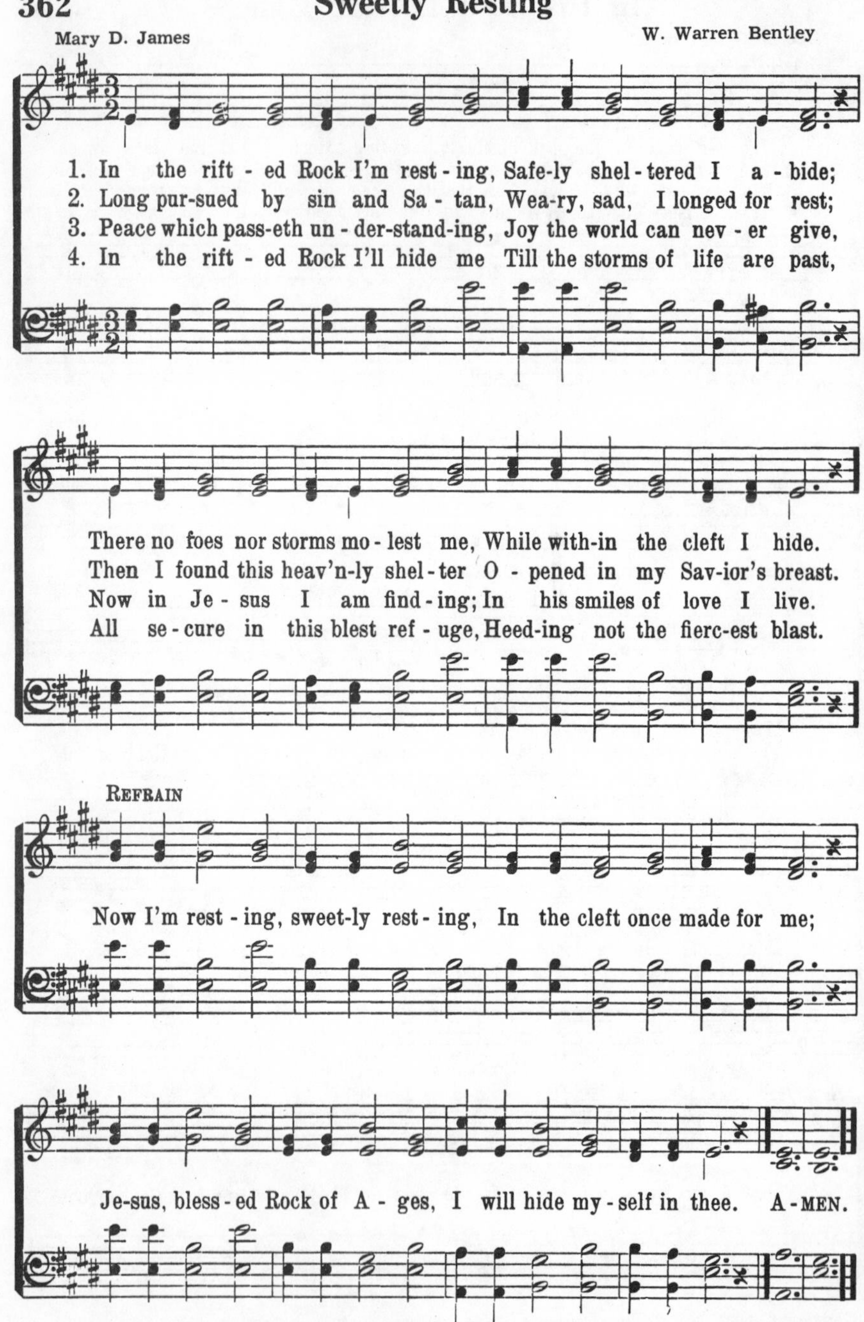
1. In the rift - ed Rock I'm rest - ing, Safe-ly shel - tered I a - bide;
2. Long pur-sued by sin and Sa - tan, Wea-ry, sad, I longed for rest;
3. Peace which pass-eth un - der-stand-ing, Joy the world can nev - er give,
4. In the rift - ed Rock I'll hide me Till the storms of life are past,
There no foes nor storms mo - lest me, While with-in the cleft I hide.
Then I found this heav'n-ly shel - ter O - pened in my Sav-ior's breast.
Now in Je - sus I am find - ing; In his smiles of love I live.
All se - cure in this blest ref - uge, Heed-ing not the fierc-est blast.
REFRAIN
Now I'm rest - ing, sweet-ly rest - ing, In the cleft once made for me;
Je-sus, bless - ed Rock of A - ges, I will hide my - self in thee. A - MEN.

My Home Is on the Rock 363

Johnson Oatman, Jr., 1856-1926 — Adam Geibel, 1855-1934

1. Praise God, I live in Beu-lah land, My house will all the storms withstand;
2. When come life's tri-als thick and fast, When clouds are o'er my pathway cast,
3. When troubles come that would ap-pall, When oth - er buildings round me fall,
4. And when my time has come to die, I'll have a man-sion in the sky;

It is not built on sink-ing sand, My home is on the rock.
Se-cure, I can with-stand the blast, My home is on the rock.
I rest in Christ my all in all, My home is on the rock.
But still I'll sing as a-ges fly, My home is on the rock.

CHORUS

My home is on the rock, The ev-er-last-ing rock;

I do not fear when storms are near, My home is on the rock. A-MEN.

364
Alone with God
Johnson Oatman, Jr., 1856-1926
William J. Kirkpatrick, 1838-1921
1. When storms of life are round me beat-ing, When rough the path that I have trod,
2. What tho' the clouds have gathered o'er me? What tho' I've passed beneath the rod?
3. 'Tis there I find new strength for du-ty, As o'er the sands of time I plod;
4. And when I see the mo-ment near-ing When I shall sleep beneath the sod,
With-in my clos-et door re-treat-ing, I love to be a-lone with God.
God's per-fect will there lies be-fore me, When I am thus a-lone with God.
I see the King in all his beau-ty, While resting there a-lone with God.
When time with me is dis-ap-pear-ing, I want to be a-lone with God.
CHORUS
A-lone with God, ... the world for-bid-den, A-lone with
A-lone with God,
God, ... O blest re-treat! A-lone with God, ... and
A-lone with God,
A-lone with God,
in him hid-den, To hold with him . . . . . com-mun-ion sweet. A-MEN.
To hold with him

Peace, Perfect Peace 365

PAX TECUM. 10.10.

Edward H. Bickersteth, 1825-1906

George T. Caldbeck, 1852-1912
Arr. by Charles J. Vincent, 1852-1934

1. Peace, per - fect peace, in this dark world of sin?
2. Peace, per - fect peace, by throng - ing du - ties pressed?
3. Peace, per - fect peace, with sor - rows surg - ing round?
4. Peace, per - fect peace, with loved ones far a - way?
5. Peace, per - fect peace, our fu - ture all un - known?

The blood of Je - sus whis - pers peace with - in.
To do the will of Je - sus, this is rest.
On Je - sus' bos - om naught but calm is found.
In Je - sus' keep - ing we are safe, and they.
Je - sus we know, and he is on the throne. A - MEN.

O for a Heart of Calm Repose 366

SPOHR. C.M.

Anonymous

Adapted from Louis Spohr, 1784-1859

1. O for a heart of calm re - pose A - mid the world's loud roar,
2. Come, Ho-ly Spir - it! still my heart With gen-tle-ness di - vine;
3. A - bove these scenes of storm and strife There spreads a re - gion fair;
4. Come, Ho-ly Spir - it! breath that peace, That vic-t'ry make me win;

A life that like a riv - er flows A-long a peace-ful shore!
In-dwell-ing peace Thou canst impart; O make that bless-ing mine!
Give me to live that high - er life, And breathe that heaven-ly air.
Then shall my soul her con-flict cease, And find a heaven with-in. A-MEN.

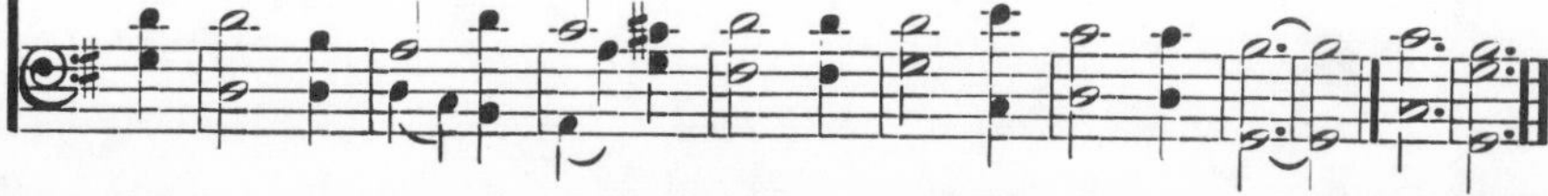

367 Hide Thou Me

Fanny J. Crosby, 1820-1915 — Robert Lowry, 1826-1899

1. In thy cleft, O Rock of A - ges, Hide thou me; When the fit - ful tem-pest
2. From the snare of sinful pleas-ure Hide thou me; Thou, my soul's e-ter - nal
3. In the lone-ly night of sor - row Hide thou me; Till in glo-ry dawns the

rag - es, Hide thou me; Where no mortal arm can sever From my heart thy love for-
treasure, Hide thou me; When the world its pow'r is wielding, And my heart is al-most
mor-row, Hide thou me; In the sight of Jordan's billow, Let thy bos - om be my

ev - er, Hide me, O thou Rock of A - ges, Safe in thee.
yielding, Hide me, O thou Rock of A - ges, Safe in thee.
pil - low; Hide me, O thou Rock of A - ges, Safe in thee. A - MEN.

368 Lord, I Hear of Showers of Blessing

Elizabeth Codner, 1824-1919 — William B. Bradbury, 1816-1868

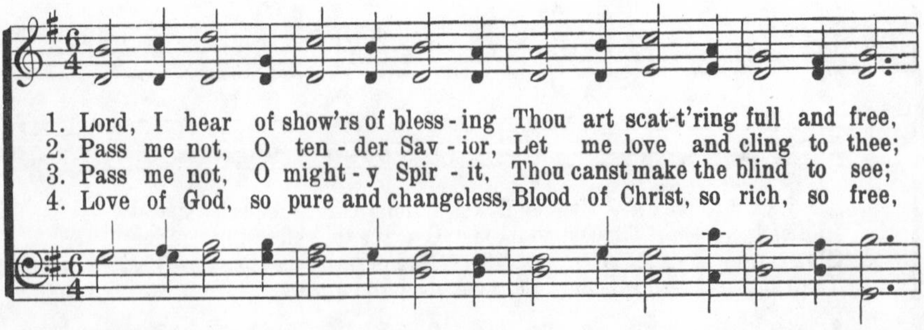

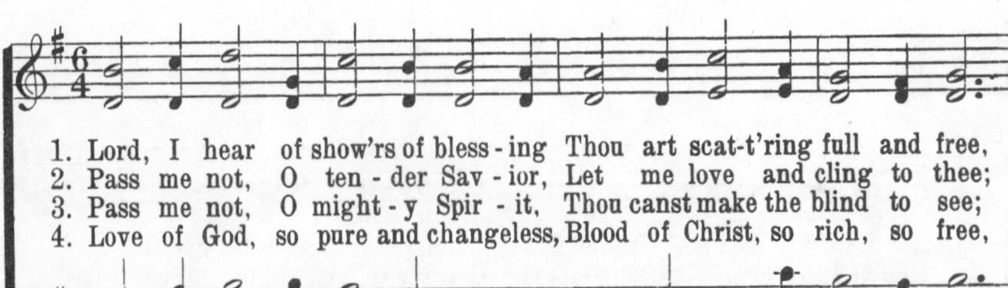
1. Lord, I hear of show'rs of bless - ing Thou art scat-t'ring full and free,
2. Pass me not, O ten - der Sav - ior, Let me love and cling to thee;
3. Pass me not, O might - y Spir - it, Thou canst make the blind to see;
4. Love of God, so pure and changeless, Blood of Christ, so rich, so free,

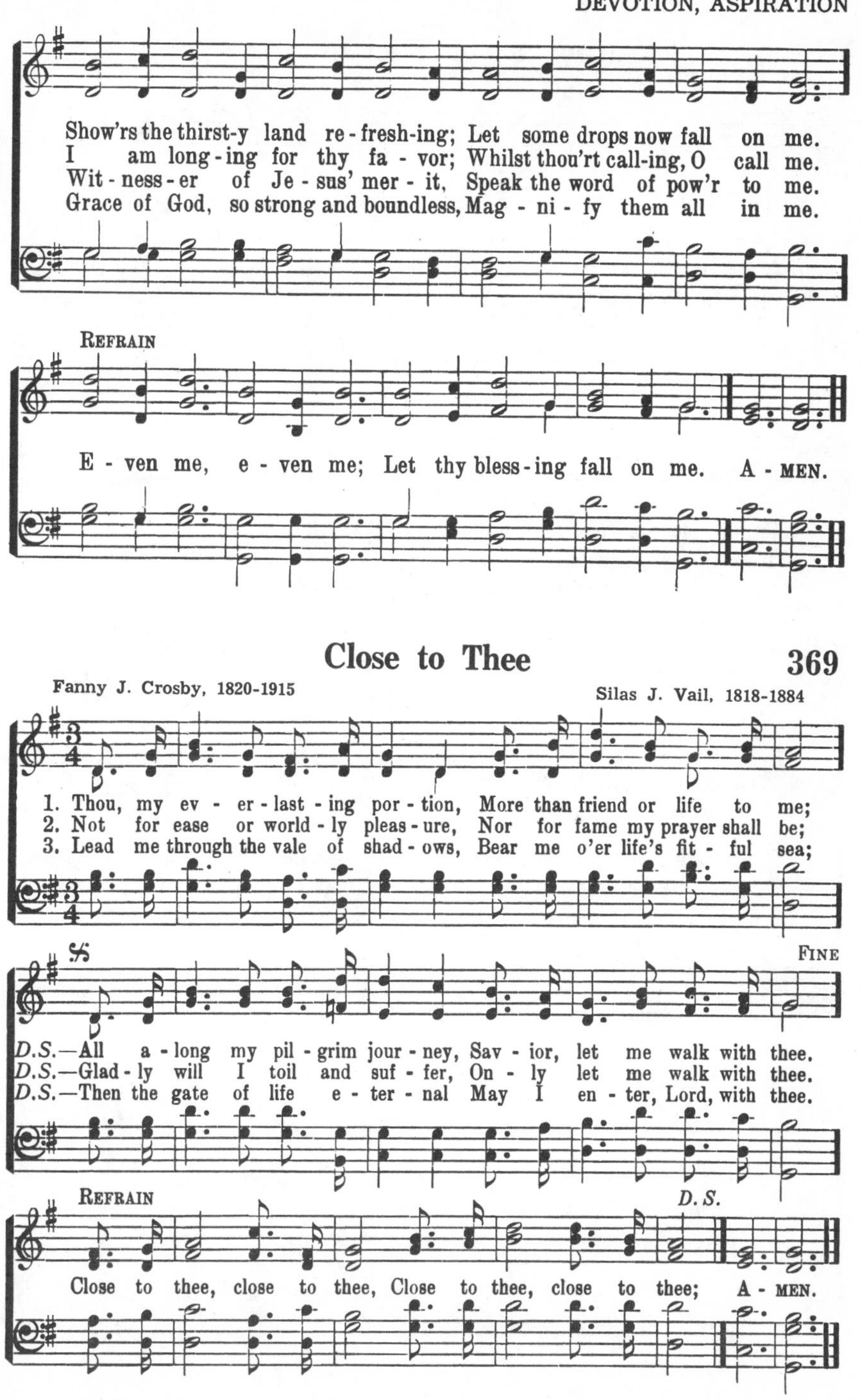
Show'rs the thirst-y land re-fresh-ing; Let some drops now fall on me.
I am long-ing for thy fa-vor; Whilst thou'rt call-ing, O call me.
Wit-ness-er of Je-sus' mer-it, Speak the word of pow'r to me.
Grace of God, so strong and boundless, Mag-ni-fy them all in me.
Refrain
E-ven me, e-ven me; Let thy bless-ing fall on me. A-men.
Close to Thee
369
Fanny J. Crosby, 1820-1915
Silas J. Vail, 1818-1884
1. Thou, my ev-er-last-ing por-tion, More than friend or life to me;
2. Not for ease or world-ly pleas-ure, Nor for fame my prayer shall be;
3. Lead me through the vale of shad-ows, Bear me o'er life's fit-ful sea;
Fine
D.S.—All a-long my pil-grim jour-ney, Sav-ior, let me walk with thee.
D.S.—Glad-ly will I toil and suf-fer, On-ly let me walk with thee.
D.S.—Then the gate of life e-ter-nal May I en-ter, Lord, with thee.
Refrain
D.S.
Close to thee, close to thee, Close to thee, close to thee; A-men.

370 Sitting at the Feet of Jesus

1. Sit - ting at the feet of Je - sus, O what words I hear him say!
2. Sit - ting at the feet of Je - sus, Where can mor-tal be more blest?
3. Bless me, O my Sav-ior, bless me, As I sit low at thy feet;

Hap - py place! so near, so pre - cious! May it find me there each day.
There I lay my sins and sor - rows, And when wea-ry find sweet rest.
O look down in love up - on me, Let me see thy face so sweet.

Sit - ting at the feet of Je - sus, I would look up - on the past;
Sit - ting at the feet of Je - sus, There I love to weep and pray;
Give me, Lord, the mind of Je - sus, Keep me ho - ly as he is;

For his love has been so gra - cious, It has won my heart at last.
While I from his full-ness gath-er Grace and comfort ev-ery day.
May I prove I've been with Je - sus, Who is all my right-eous-ness. A - MEN.

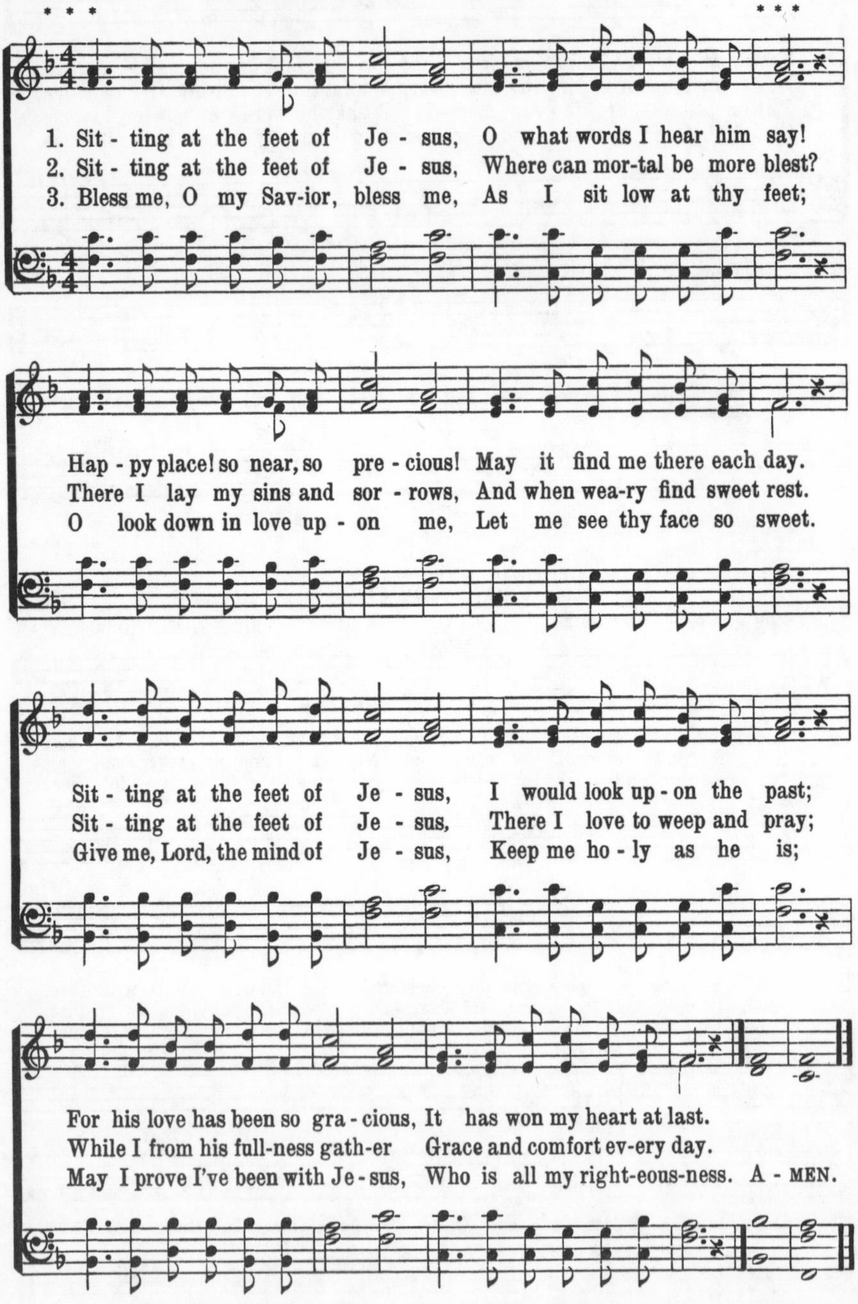

Near the Cross

371

Fanny J. Crosby, 1820-1915

William Howard Doane, 1832-1915

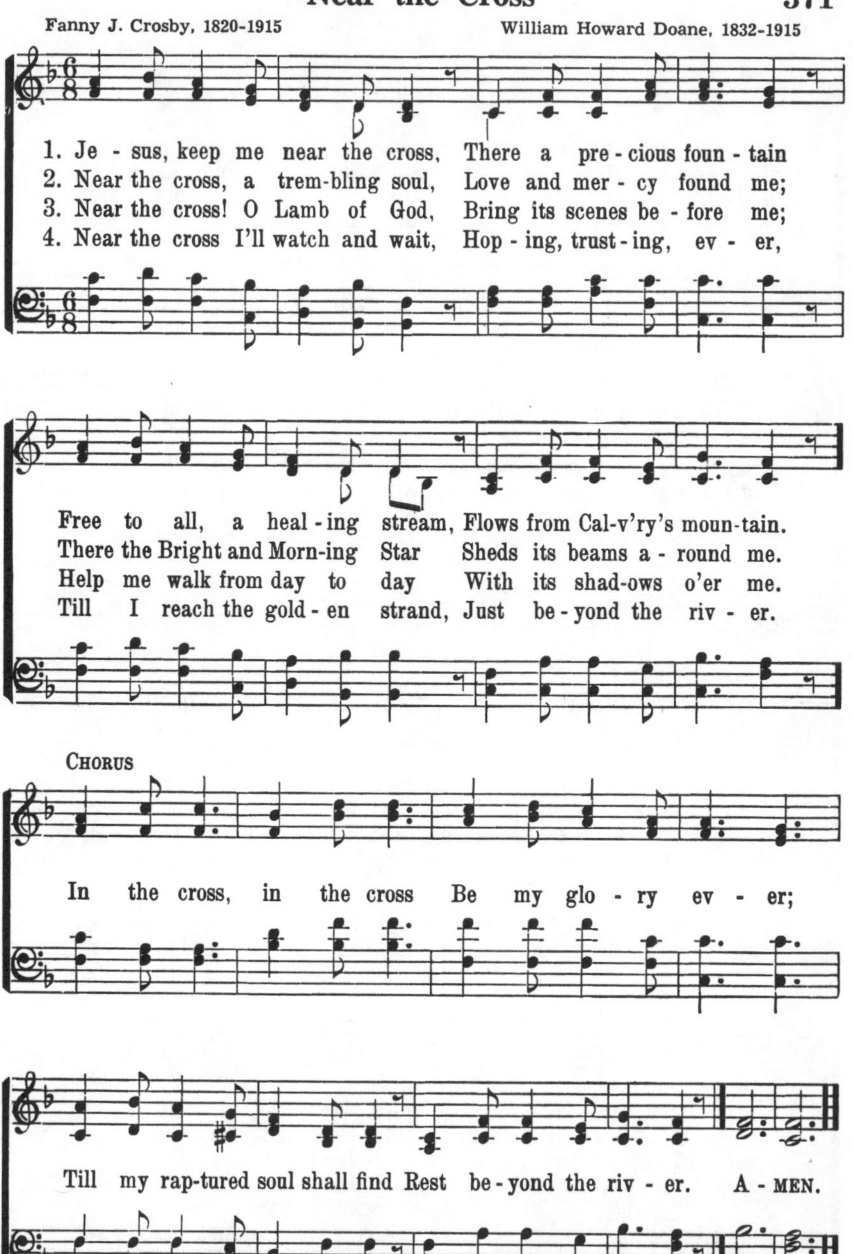
1. Je - sus, keep me near the cross, There a pre - cious foun - tain
2. Near the cross, a trem-bling soul, Love and mer - cy found me;
3. Near the cross! O Lamb of God, Bring its scenes be - fore me;
4. Near the cross I'll watch and wait, Hop - ing, trust - ing, ev - er,
Free to all, a heal - ing stream, Flows from Cal-v'ry's moun-tain.
There the Bright and Morn-ing Star Sheds its beams a - round me.
Help me walk from day to day With its shad-ows o'er me.
Till I reach the gold - en strand, Just be - yond the riv - er.
Chorus
In the cross, in the cross Be my glo - ry ev - er;
Till my rap-tured soul shall find Rest be - yond the riv - er. A - men.

372 Nearer, Still Nearer

Mrs. C. H. Morris, 1862-1929 Mrs. C. H. Morris, 1862-1929

1. Near - er, still near - er, close to thy heart, Draw me, my Sav - ior, so pre - cious thou art; Fold me, O fold me close to thy breast, Shel - ter me safe in that "ha - ven of rest," Shel - ter me safe in that "ha - ven of rest."
2. Near - er, still near - er, noth - ing I bring, Naught as an of - f'ring to Je - sus my King; On - ly my sin - ful, now con-trite heart, Grant me the cleans - ing thy blood doth im - part, Grant me the cleans-ing thy blood doth im - part.
3. Near - er, still near - er, Lord, to be thine, Sin, with its fol - lies, I glad - ly re - sign; All of its pleas - ures, pomp and its pride, Give me but Je - sus, my Lord cru - ci - fied, Give me but Je - sus, my Lord cru - ci - fied.
4. Near - er, still near - er, while life shall last, Till safe in glo - ry my an - chor is cast; Thro' end - less a - ges, ev - er to be, Near - er, my Sav - ior, still near - er to thee, Near - er, my Sav - ior, still near - er to thee. A - MEN.

I Need Thee Every Hour 373

Annie S. Hawks, 1835-1918 — Robert Lowry, 1826-1899

1. I need thee ev - ery hour, Most gra - cious Lord; No ten - der voice like thine Can peace af - ford.
2. I need thee ev - ery hour, Stay thou near by; Temp-ta-tions lose their pow'r When thou art nigh.
3. I need thee ev - ery hour, In joy or pain; Come quick-ly and a-bide, Or life is vain.
4. I need thee ev - ery hour, Most Ho - ly One; O make me thine in-deed, Thou bless - ed Son!

CHORUS

I need thee, O I need thee; Ev - ery hour I

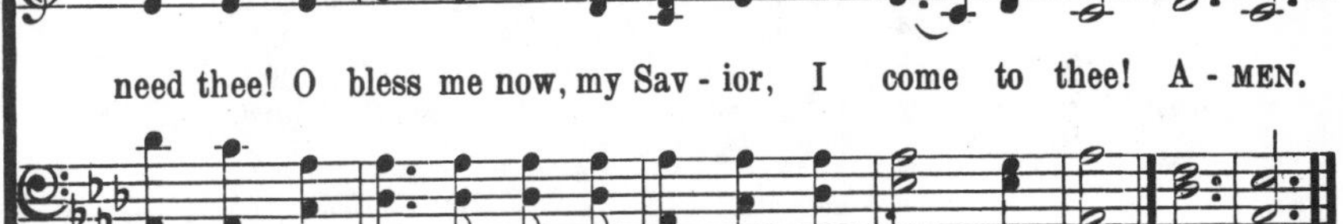
need thee! O bless me now, my Sav - ior, I come to thee! A - MEN.

O Gentle Savior 374

T. R. Birks — Arthur Sullivan, 1842-1900

1. O gentle Savior, from thy throne on high Look down in love and hear our humble cry.
2. Go where we go, a-bide where we abide, In life, in death, our comfort, strength, and guide.
3. O lead us dai-ly with thine eye of love, And bring us safely to our home a - bove. A - MEN.

375 My Jesus, I Love Thee

GORDON. 11.11.11.11.

William R. Featherstone, 1842-1878 — Adoniram J. Gordon, 1836-1895

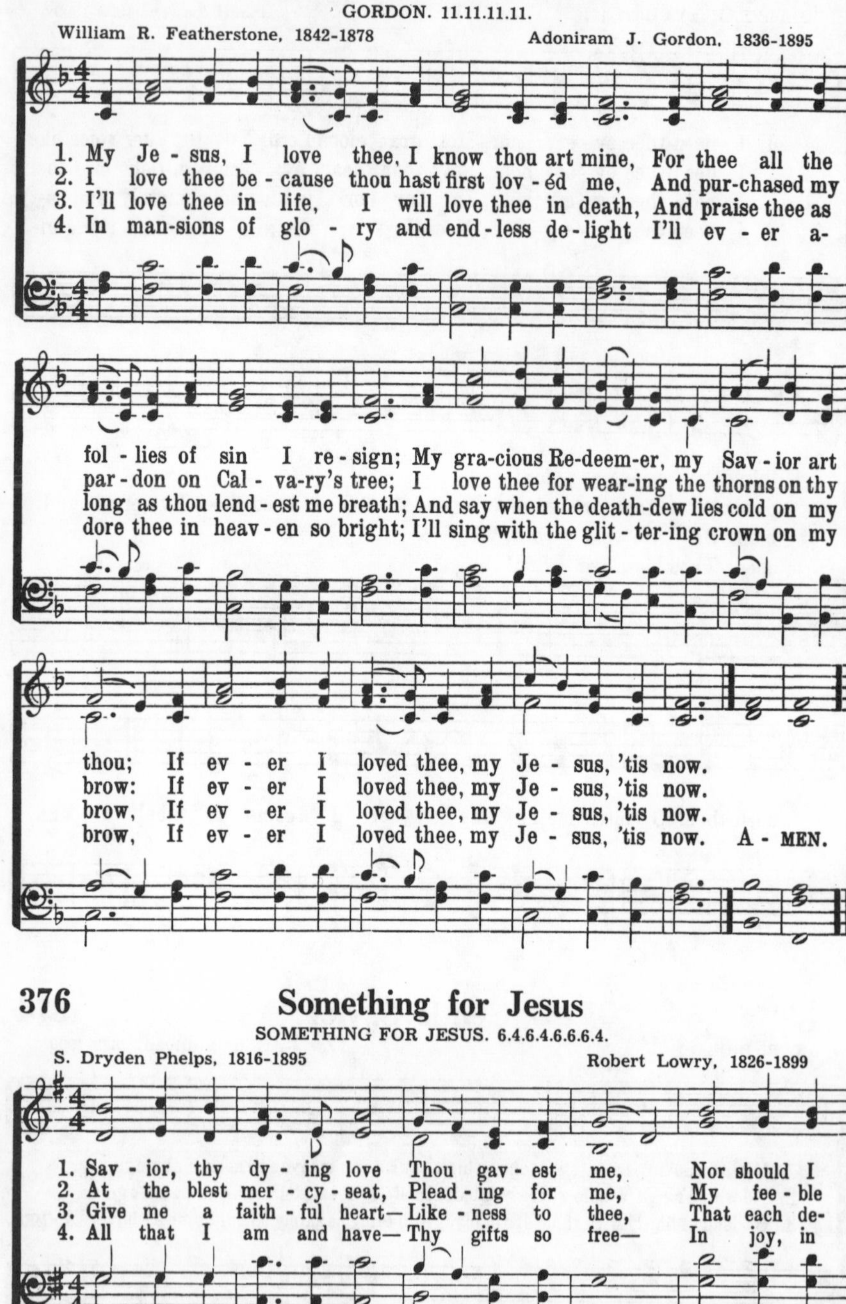
1. My Je - sus, I love thee, I know thou art mine, For thee all the fol - lies of sin I re - sign; My gra-cious Re-deem-er, my Sav - ior art thou; If ev - er I loved thee, my Je - sus, 'tis now.
2. I love thee be - cause thou hast first lov - éd me, And pur-chased my par - don on Cal - va-ry's tree; I love thee for wear-ing the thorns on thy brow: If ev - er I loved thee, my Je - sus, 'tis now.
3. I'll love thee in life, I will love thee in death, And praise thee as long as thou lend - est me breath; And say when the death-dew lies cold on my brow, If ev - er I loved thee, my Je - sus, 'tis now.
4. In man-sions of glo - ry and end - less de - light I'll ev - er a - dore thee in heav - en so bright; I'll sing with the glit - ter-ing crown on my brow, If ev - er I loved thee, my Je - sus, 'tis now. A - MEN.
376
Something for Jesus
SOMETHING FOR JESUS. 6.4.6.4.6.6.6.4.
S. Dryden Phelps, 1816-1895
Robert Lowry, 1826-1899
1. Sav - ior, thy dy - ing love Thou gav - est me, Nor should I
2. At the blest mer - cy - seat, Plead - ing for me, My fee - ble
3. Give me a faith - ful heart— Like - ness to thee, That each de-
4. All that I am and have— Thy gifts so free— In joy, in

aught with-hold, Dear Lord, from thee: In love my soul would bow, My heart ful-
faith looks up, Je - sus, to thee: Help me the cross to bear, Thy won-drous
part - ing day Hence-forth may see Some work of love be - gun, Some deed of
grief, thro' life, Dear Lord, for thee! And when thy face I see, My ran-somed
fill its vow, Some of-f'ring bring thee now, Some-thing for thee.
love de - clare, Some song to raise, or prayer, Some-thing for thee.
kind-ness done, Some wan-d'rer sought and won, Some-thing for thee.
soul shall be, Thro' all e - ter - ni - ty, Some-thing for thee. A - MEN.

Nearer, My God, to Thee 377

BETHANY. 6.4.6.4.6.6.6.4.

Sarah F. Adams, 1805-1848 Arr. by Lowell Mason, 1792-1872

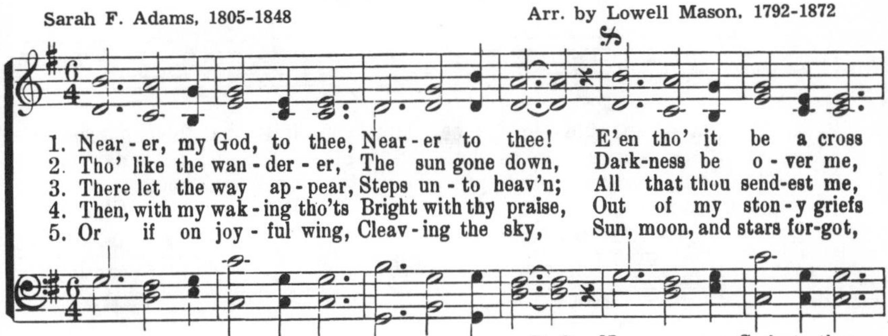

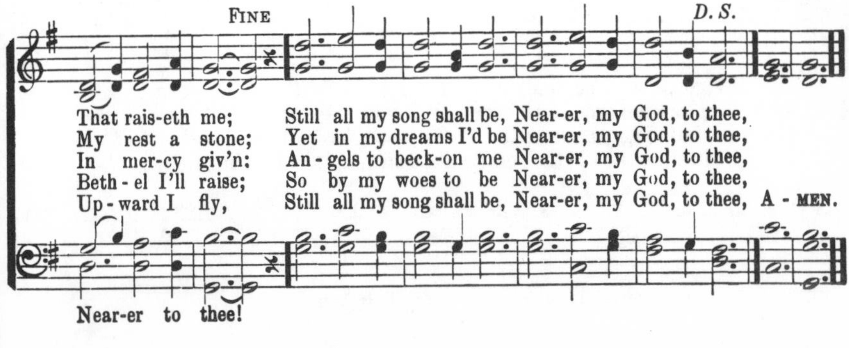

1. Near - er, my God, to thee, Near - er to thee! E'en tho' it be a cross That rais-eth me; Still all my song shall be, Near-er, my God, to thee, Near-er, my God, to thee, Near-er to thee!
2. Tho' like the wan - der - er, The sun gone down, Dark-ness be o - ver me, My rest a stone; Yet in my dreams I'd be Near-er, my God, to thee,
3. There let the way ap - pear, Steps un - to heav'n; All that thou send-est me, In mer-cy giv'n: An-gels to beck-on me Near-er, my God, to thee,
4. Then, with my wak - ing tho'ts Bright with thy praise, Out of my ston - y griefs Beth - el I'll raise; So by my woes to be Near-er, my God, to thee,
5. Or if on joy - ful wing, Cleav - ing the sky, Sun, moon, and stars for-got, Up - ward I fly, Still all my song shall be, Near-er, my God, to thee, A - MEN.

FINE

D. S.—Near - er, my God, to thee, Near-er to thee!

D. S.

378 Be Still

William Ebel, 1863-1918

P. J. Goerz, 1907
Har. by H. J. K. Goerz, 1907

1. O be still, thou soul of mine, Thou art not for - sak - en;
Tho' the pow'rs of sin may rage Thou shalt be un - shak - en.
He who gave his life for thee, Thus per - mits that thou shouldst be—
For thy good, as thou shalt see— Tempted for a sea - son.

2. Be cou - ra - geous, firm and true When life's bat - tle's wag - ing;
O be still, my soul, and rest When the tem - pest's rag - ing.
He who doth our sor - rows share In his love and ten - der care—
Tri - als more than thou canst bear—Will not let thee suf - fer.

3. Why shouldst thou so fear - ful be At the tempt - er's roar - ing?
Sim - ply trust in God a - lone, Sa - tan's wrath ig - nor - ing.
See God's ten - der-ness, and prove, With the saint - ed hosts a - bove,
His un - fail - ing, won-drous love, Ev - er for thee car - ing.

4. Yes, dear Lord, I will be still, I will trust thee ev - er;
I'll sub - mit to all thy will, Cling to thee for - ev - er.
Lord, thou know - est what is best, Con - fi - dent in this I'll rest
Till I dwell with all the blest And with thee in heav-en. A - MEN.

O Love That Wilt Not Let Me Go 379

ST. MARGARET. 8.8.8.8.6.

George Matheson, 1842-1906 | Albert L. Peace, 1844-1912

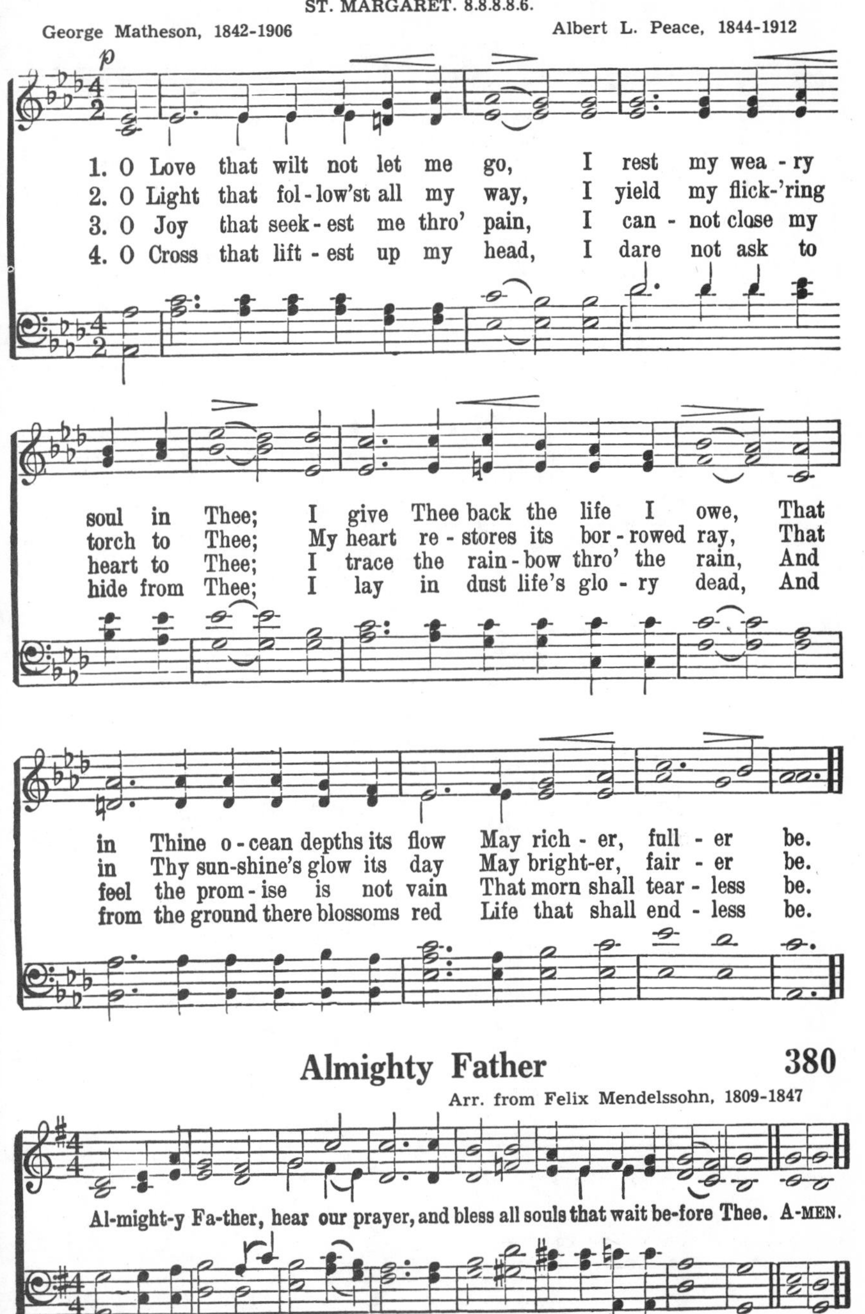
p
1. O Love that wilt not let me go, I rest my wea - ry soul in Thee; I give Thee back the life I owe, That in Thine o - cean depths its flow May rich - er, full - er be.
2. O Light that fol - low'st all my way, I yield my flick-'ring torch to Thee; My heart re - stores its bor - rowed ray, That in Thy sun-shine's glow its day May bright-er, fair - er be.
3. O Joy that seek - est me thro' pain, I can - not close my heart to Thee; I trace the rain - bow thro' the rain, And feel the prom - ise is not vain That morn shall tear - less be.
4. O Cross that lift - est up my head, I dare not ask to hide from Thee; I lay in dust life's glo - ry dead, And from the ground there blossoms red Life that shall end - less be.
Almighty Father 380
Arr. from Felix Mendelssohn, 1809-1847
Al-might-y Fa-ther, hear our prayer, and bless all souls that wait be-fore Thee. A-MEN.

381 The Old Rugged Cross

George Bennard, b. 1873 — George Bennard, b. 1873

1. On a hill far a-way stood an old rug-ged cross, The em-blem of suf-f'ring and shame; And I love that old cross where the dear-est and best For a world of lost sin-ners was slain.
2. Oh, that old rug-ged cross so de-spised by the world, Has a wondrous at-trac-tion for me; For the dear Lamb of God left His glo-ry a-bove, To bear it to dark Cal-va-ry.
3. In the old rug-ged cross, stained with blood so di-vine, A won-drous beau-ty I see; For 'twas on that old cross Je-sus suf-fered and died, To par-don and sanc-ti-fy me.
4. To the old rug-ged cross I will ev-er be true, Its shame and re-proach gladly bear; Then He'll call me some day to my home far a-way, Where His glo-ry for-ev-er I'll share.

CHORUS

So I'll cher-ish the old rug-ged cross, ... (the old rugged cross,) Till my tro-phies at last I lay down; I will cling to the old rug-ged cross, ... (cross, the old rug-ged cross,) And ex-change it some day for a crown.

Open My Eyes, That I May See 382

Clara H. Scott, 1841-1897 Clara H. Scott, 1841-1897

1. O - pen my eyes, that I may see Glimps-es of truth Thou hast for me;
2. O - pen my ears, that I may hear Voi - ces of truth Thou send-est clear;
3. O - pen my mouth, and let me bear Glad - ly the warm truth ev-'ry-where;
Place in my hands the won-der-ful key That shall un-clasp, and set me free.
And while the wave-notes fall on my ear, Ev - 'ry-thing false will dis - ap-pear.
O - pen my heart, and let me pre-pare Love with Thy chil-dren thus to share.
Si - lent - ly now I wait for Thee, Read-y, my God, Thy will to see;
Si - lent - ly now I wait for Thee, Read-y, my God, Thy will to see;
Si - lent - ly now I wait for Thee, Read-y, my God, Thy will to see;
O - pen my eyes, il - lu - mine me, Spir - it di - vine!
O - pen my ears, il - lu - mine me, Spir - it di - vine!
O - pen my heart, il - lu - mine me, Spir - it di - vine!

383 O Thou in Whose Presence

BELOVED (MEDITATION). 11.8.11.8.

Joseph Swain, 1761-1796 — Freeman Lewis, 1780-1859

1. O Thou in whose pres - ence my soul takes de - light, On
2. Where dost thou, dear Shep - herd, re - sort with thy sheep, To
3. He looks, and ten thou - sand of an - gels re - joice, And
4. Dear Shep - herd, I hear, and will fol - low thy call; I
whom in af - flic - tion I call, My com - fort by day, and my
feed them in pas - tures of love? Say, why in the val - ley of
myr - iads now wait for his word; He speaks, and e - ter - ni - ty,
know the sweet sound of thy voice; Pro - tect and de - fend me, for
song in the night, My hope, my sal - va - tion, my all!
death should I weep, Or a - lone in this wil - der - ness rove?
filled with his voice, Re - ech - oes the praise of the Lord.
thou art my all, And in thee I will ev - er re - joice. A - MEN.

384 Savior, Teach Me, Day by Day

SEYMOUR. 7.7.7.7.

Jane E. Leeson, 1807-1882 — Carl M. von Weber, 1786-1826

1. Sav - ior, teach me, day by day, Love's sweet les - son to o - bey:
2. With a child - like heart of love, At Thy bid - ding may I move,
3. Teach me all Thy steps to trace, Strong to fol - low in Thy grace,
4. Love in lov - ing finds em - ploy, In o - be - dience all her joy;

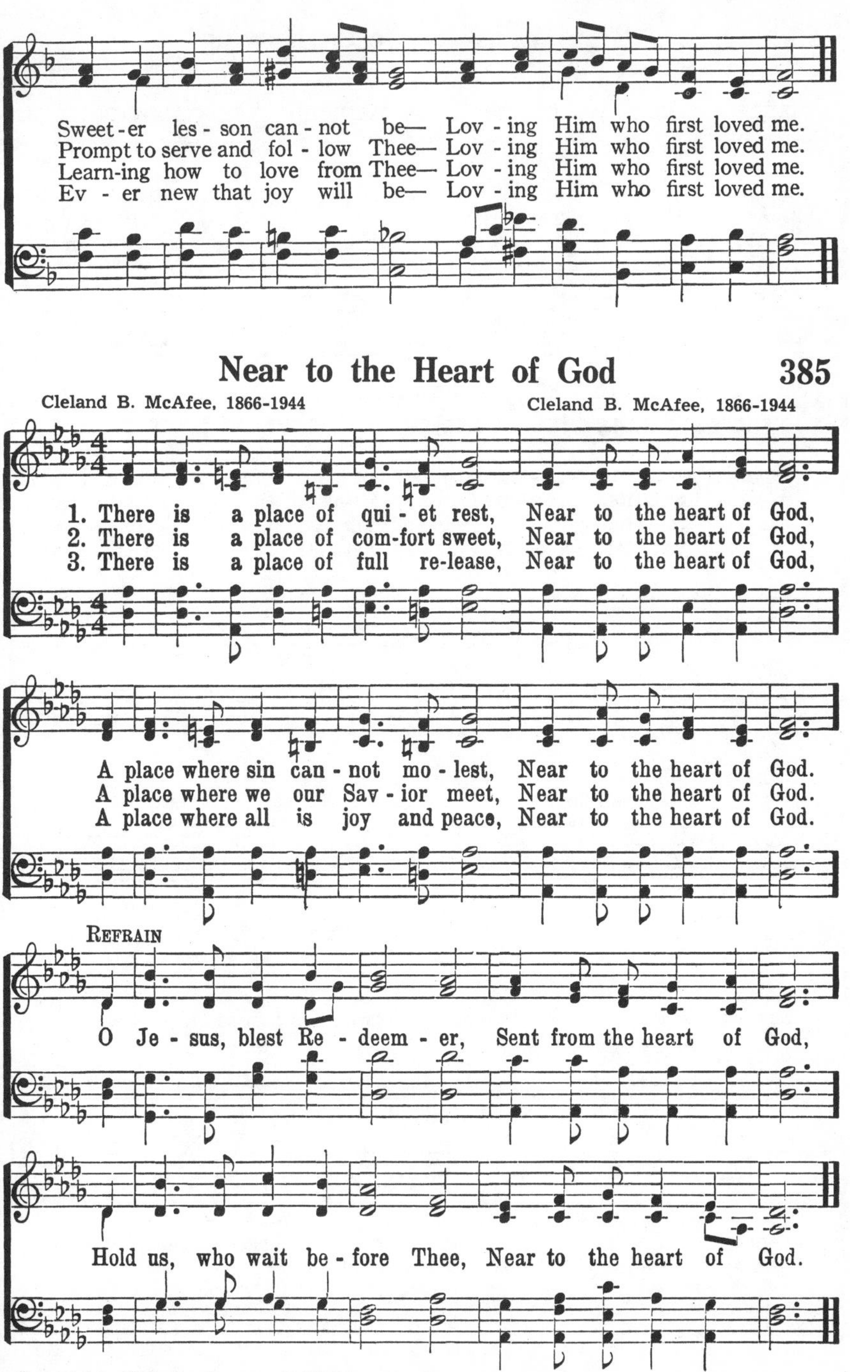
Sweet-er les-son can-not be— Lov-ing Him who first loved me.
Prompt to serve and fol-low Thee— Lov-ing Him who first loved me.
Learn-ing how to love from Thee— Lov-ing Him who first loved me.
Ev-er new that joy will be— Lov-ing Him who first loved me.
Near to the Heart of God
385
Cleland B. McAfee, 1866-1944
Cleland B. McAfee, 1866-1944
1. There is a place of qui-et rest, Near to the heart of God,
2. There is a place of com-fort sweet, Near to the heart of God,
3. There is a place of full re-lease, Near to the heart of God,
A place where sin can-not mo-lest, Near to the heart of God.
A place where we our Sav-ior meet, Near to the heart of God.
A place where all is joy and peace, Near to the heart of God.
Refrain
O Je-sus, blest Re-deem-er, Sent from the heart of God,
Hold us, who wait be-fore Thee, Near to the heart of God.

386 At the Cross of Jesus Bowing

D. Otis Teasley, 1905 — D. Otis Teasley, 1905

1. At the cross of Je - sus bow - ing, Here I find a safe re - treat
2. At the cross of Je - sus bow - ing, Here I count my bless-ings o'er;
3. At the cross of Je - sus bow - ing, Here I spend life's sweet-est hour;
4. At the cross of Je - sus bow - ing, Here I own his way is best;

From a world of care and troub-le, In his pres-ence calm and sweet.
Here I drink from life's pure foun-tain, Drink un - til I thirst no more.
Here I taste the joys of heav-en, Fill my heart with conqu'ring pow'r.
In the shel - ter of Mount Cal - v'ry, Let me in as - sur - ance rest.

CHORUS *p*

Sweet still - - - - ness of heav - - - - en a-
Still - ness di - vine, still - ness I feel,

round . . . . me I feel, ... While low . . . . . at the
'round me a heav - en - ly still - ness I feel, Low at the cross,

cross . . . of my Je - - - sus I kneel (I kneel). A - MEN.
low at the cross, low at the cross of my Je - sus I kneel.

My Jesus, as Thou Wilt

JEWETT. 6.6.6.6.D.

Benjamin Schmolck, 1672-1737
Tr. by Jane Borthwick, 1813-1897

Carl M. von Weber, 1786-1826
Arr. by Joseph P. Holbrook, 1822-1888

1. My Je - sus, as thou wilt! O may thy will be mine!
2. My Je - sus, as thou wilt! Tho' seen thro' man - y a tear,
3. My Je - sus, as thou wilt! All shall be well for me;

In - to thy hand of love I would my all re - sign:
Let not my star of hope Grow dim or dis - ap - pear:
Each chang-ing fu - ture scene I glad - ly trust with thee:

Thro' sor - row, or thro' joy, Con - duct me as thine own,
Since thou on earth hast wept, And sor - rowed oft a - lone,
Straight to my home a - bove I trav - el calm - ly on,

And help me still to say, My Lord, thy will be done!
If I must weep with thee, My Lord, thy will be done!
And sing in life or death, My Lord, thy will be done! A - MEN.

388 Savior, More than Life to Me

Fanny J. Crosby, 1820-1915 — William Howard Doane, 1832-1915

1. Sav - ior, more than life to me, I am clinging, clinging close to thee;
2. Thro' this changing world be-low, Lead me gen-tly, gen-tly as I go;
3. Let me love thee more and more, Till this fleet-ing, fleet-ing life is o'er;
Let thy pre-cious blood ap-plied, Keep me ev - er, ev - er near thy side.
Trust-ing thee, I can-not stray, I can nev - er, nev - er lose my way.
Till my soul is lost in love, In a bright-er, bright-er world a - bove.
CHORUS
Ev - ery day, ev - ery hour Let me feel thy cleansing pow'r;
Ev - ery day and hour, ev - ery day and hour
May thy ten - der love to me Bind me clos-er, clos-er, Lord, to thee. A - MEN.

389 Prayer of My Heart

K. Y. Plank, c. 1936 — K. Y. Plank, c. 1936

1. O for a clos - er walk with God, A life that bears no stain
2. O for a deep - er, rich - er life With treas-ures stored a - bove;
3. O for a faith that's root - ed deep In God's e - ter - nal word;

Of earth-ly pride or van-i-ties; A life that's not in vain!
A life that soars o'er car-nal strife And nes-tles in God's love!
A faith un-moved in time of trial, That's an-chored in my Lord!

Let Me See Jesus Only 390

W. Dale Oldham, c. 1936 W. Dale Oldham, c. 1936

1. Dead to ev-ery world-ly pleas-ure, Dead in-deed to sin am I;
2. Let me strive not for the rich-es Of this earth that soon de-cay;
3. Storms in fu-ry beat a-round me, Tem-pests oft my bark as-sail;
4. When I face death's chill-y riv-er, When up-on its brink I stand,
But a-live to Christ my Sav-ior, Dai-ly to him I'm draw-ing nigh.
From the world I've turned to Je-sus And his more a-bun-dant way.
But my Pi-lot's name is Je-sus, He will calm the wild-est gale.
I shall fear-less be if Je-sus Leads me gen-tly by the hand.
CHORUS
Let me see . . Je-sus on-ly, Je-sus on-ly, Je-sus on-ly,
Let me see
Let me see . . Je-sus on-ly, On-ly he can sat-is-fy.
Let me see

391
More like Christ
Charles W. Naylor. 1903
Barney E. Warren, 1907
1. More like Christ, my heart is pray-ing, More like Christ from day to day;
2. More like Christ in deeds of kind-ness, And in all the words I say;
3. More like Christ in bur - den-bear-ing, Help - ing all the sad and weak;
4. More like Christ in self - de - ni - al, Seek - ing not a life of ease;
All his grac - es rich dis - play - ing, While I tread my pil - grim way.
Yearn-ing for the souls in blind-ness, Who are go - ing far a - stray.
Tears and sor - rows glad - ly shar - ing, Oth - ers' pleas - ure would I seek.
Pa - tient in the depths of tri - al, That my Sav - ior I may please.
CHORUS
More like Christ ev - ery day, More like Christ, my heart doth say;
More like Christ, more like Christ ev - - ery day. A - MEN.
ev - ery pass - ing day.
Copyright, 1907, by Gospel Trumpet Co. in Truth in Song. B. E. Warren, owner.
392
More Love to Thee
Elizabeth P. Prentiss, 1818-1878
William Howard Doane, 1832-1915
1. More love to thee, O Christ, More love to thee! Hear thou the
2. Once earth - ly joy I craved, Sought peace and rest; Now thee a-
3. Let sor - row do its work, Send grief and pain; Sweet are thy
4. Then shall my lat - est breath Whis - per thy praise; This be the

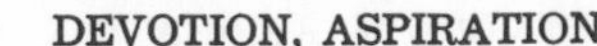

prayer I make On bend-ed knee; This is my ear-nest plea,
lone I seek, Give what is best: This all my prayer shall be,
mes-sen-gers, Sweet their re-frain, When they can sing with me,
part-ing cry My heart shall raise— This still its prayer shall be—
More love, O Christ, to thee, More love to thee, More love to thee! A-MEN.

More About Jesus

393

Eliza E. Hewitt, b. 1851 — John R. Sweney, 1837-1899

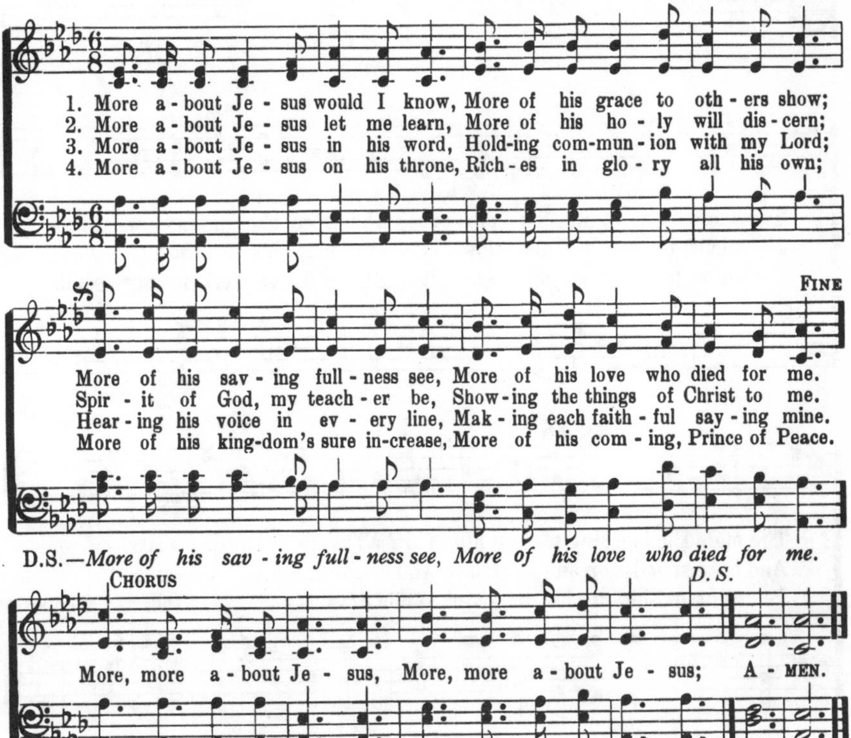

1. More a-bout Je-sus would I know, More of his grace to oth-ers show;
More of his sav-ing full-ness see, More of his love who died for me.

2. More a-bout Je-sus let me learn, More of his ho-ly will dis-cern;
Spir-it of God, my teach-er be, Show-ing the things of Christ to me.

3. More a-bout Je-sus in his word, Hold-ing com-mun-ion with my Lord;
Hear-ing his voice in ev-ery line, Mak-ing each faith-ful say-ing mine.

4. More a-bout Je-sus on his throne, Rich-es in glo-ry all his own;
More of his king-dom's sure in-crease, More of his com-ing, Prince of Peace.

FINE

D.S.—*More of his sav-ing full-ness see, More of his love who died for me.*

CHORUS

More, more a-bout Je-sus, More, more a-bout Je-sus; *D. S.* A-MEN.

394 The More I Learn About Jesus

Barney E. Warren, 1926 Barney E. Warren, 1926

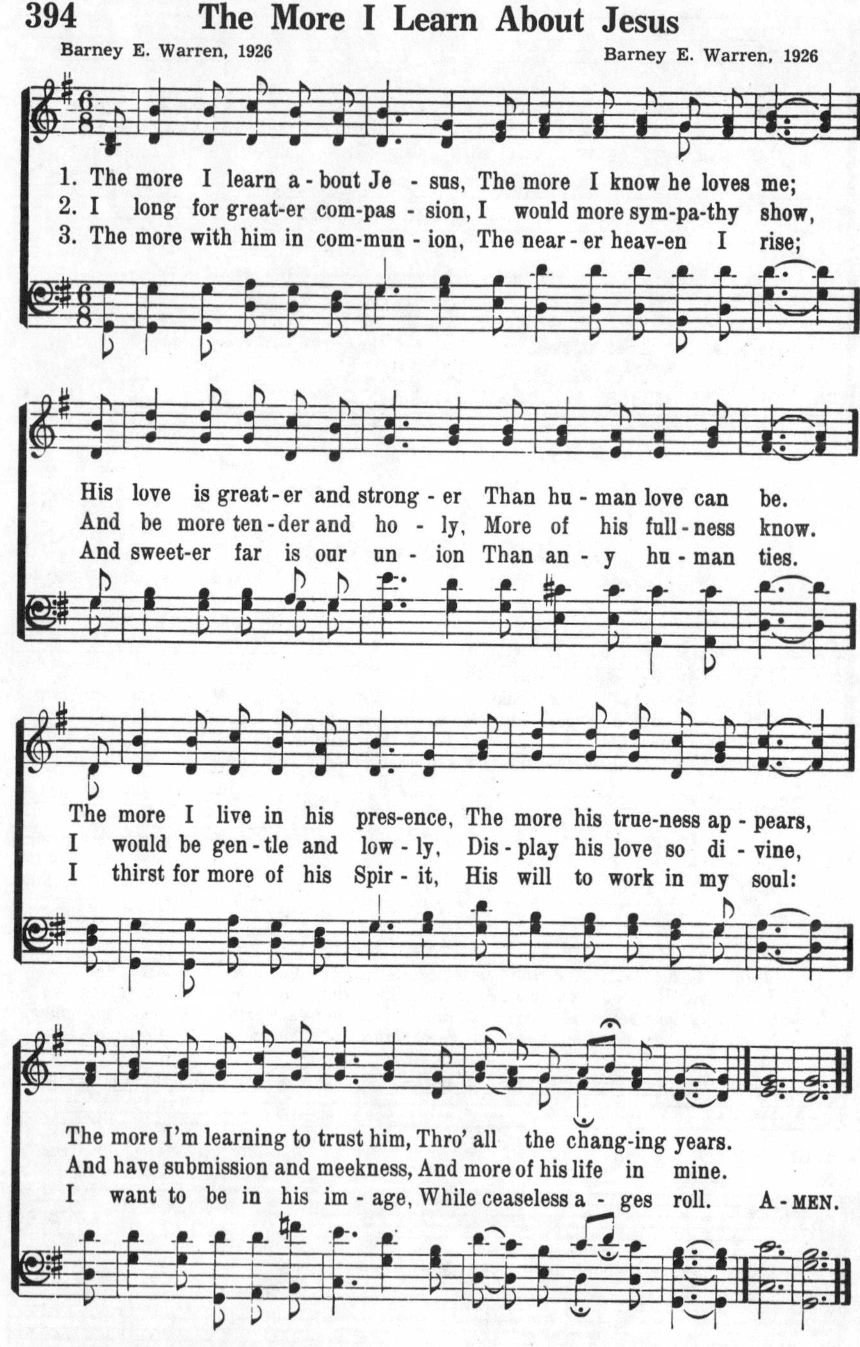
1. The more I learn a-bout Je - sus, The more I know he loves me;
2. I long for great-er com-pas - sion, I would more sym-pa-thy show,
3. The more with him in com-mun - ion, The near - er heav-en I rise;
His love is great-er and strong - er Than hu - man love can be.
And be more ten-der and ho - ly, More of his full-ness know.
And sweet-er far is our un - ion Than an - y hu - man ties.
The more I live in his pres-ence, The more his true-ness ap - pears,
I would be gen-tle and low - ly, Dis - play his love so di - vine,
I thirst for more of his Spir - it, His will to work in my soul:
The more I'm learning to trust him, Thro' all the chang-ing years.
And have submission and meekness, And more of his life in mine.
I want to be in his im - age, While ceaseless a - ges roll. A - MEN.

I Am Thine, O Lord 395

Fanny J. Crosby, 1820-1915 William Howard Doane, 1832-1915

1. I am thine, O Lord, I have heard thy voice, And it told thy love to me;
2. Con-se-crate me now to thy serv-ice, Lord, By the pow'r of grace di - vine;
3. O the pure de-light of a sin - gle hour That be-fore thy throne I spend;
4. There are depths of love that I can-not know Till I cross the nar - row sea;

But I long to rise in the arms of faith, And be clos - er drawn to thee.
Let my soul look up with a stead-fast hope, And my will be lost in thine.
When I kneel in prayer, and with thee, my God, I com-mune as friend with friend.
There are heights of joy that I may not reach Till I rest in peace with thee.

CHORUS

Draw me near - er, nearer, blessed Lord, To the cross where thou hast died;
near-er, near-er,

Draw me nearer, nearer, nearer, blessed Lord, To thy precious, bleeding side. A-MEN.

396 My Faith Looks Up to Thee

OLIVET. 6.6.4.6.6.6.4.
Ray Palmer, 1808-1887
Lowell Mason, 1792-1872
1. My faith looks up to thee, Thou Lamb of Cal-va-ry, Savior divine; Now hear me while I pray, Take all my guilt a-way, O let me from this day Be whol-ly thine.
2. May thy rich grace im-part Strength to my faint-ing heart, My zeal in-spire; As thou hast died for me, O may my love to thee Pure, warm, and changeless be, A liv-ing fire.
3. While life's dark maze I tread, And griefs a-round me spread, Be thou my guide; Bid dark-ness turn to day, Wipe sor-row's tears a-way, Nor let me ev-er stray From thee a-side.
4. When ends life's tran-sient dream, When death's cold. sul-len stream Shall o'er me roll; Blest Sav-ior, then in love, Fear and dis-trust re-move; O bear me safe a-bove, A ran-somed soul. A-MEN.
397 O for a Closer Walk with God
ST. AGNES. C.M.
William Cowper, 1731-1800
John B. Dykes, 1823-1876
1. O for a clos-er walk with God, A calm and heaven-ly frame,
2. Where is the bless-ed-ness I knew, When first I saw the Lord?
3. The dear-est i-dol I have known, What-e'er that i-dol be,
4. So shall my walk be close with God, Calm and se-rene my frame;

A light to shine up - on the road That leads me to the Lamb!
Where is the soul-re-fresh - ing view Of Je - sus and His word?
Help me to tear it from Thy throne, And wor-ship on - ly Thee.
So pur-er light shall mark the road That leads me to the Lamb. A-MEN.

Draw Me Close to Thee 398

Clara M. Brooks, 1911 W. H. Oldham. 1909

1. I would be near - er, my Sav - iour, Where I can hear thy voice
2. I would be kept in thy pres - ence, Free from the strife of tongues;
3. Keep me, O Lord, in thy shad - ow, When the dark tem - pests low'r;
4. Swift-ly the shad-ows are deep-'ning, Light of my life, be near;

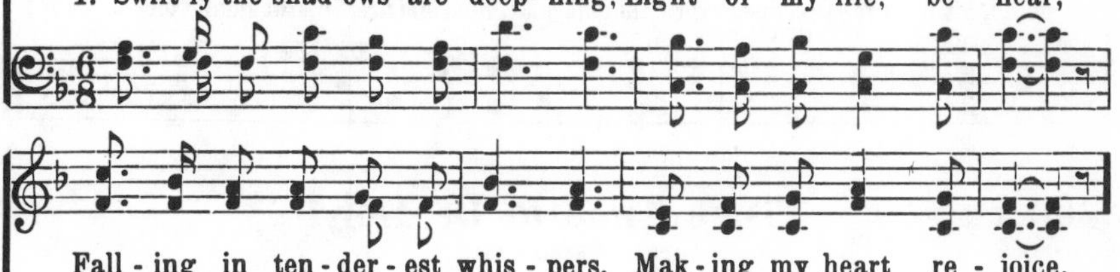

Fall - ing in ten - der - est whis - pers, Mak - ing my heart re - joice.
There shall the hum-ble a - dore thee, Rais - ing their grate - ful songs.
Safe - ly to rest on thy bos - om, Keep me for - ev - er - more.
Strengthen the trust I am keep - ing, Fill me with hope and cheer.

CHORUS

Draw me close to thee,...... Draw me close to thee;......
Sav - iour, draw me close to thee, Sav - iour, draw me close to thee;

Keep me, dear Sav-iour, so near thy side, Draw me close to thee. A-MEN.

399 Dear Lord and Father of Mankind

WHITTIER (REST). 8.6.8.8.6.

John G. Whittier, 1807-1892 — Frederick C. Maker, 1844-1927

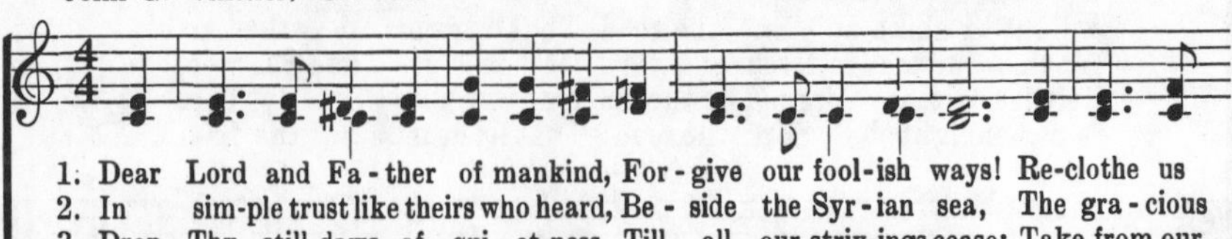

1. Dear Lord and Fa - ther of mankind, For - give our fool-ish ways! Re-clothe us
2. In sim-ple trust like theirs who heard, Be - side the Syr - ian sea, The gra - cious
3. Drop Thy still dews of qui - et-ness, Till all our striv-ings cease; Take from our
4. Breathe thro' the heats of our de - sire Thy cool-ness and Thy balm; Let sense be

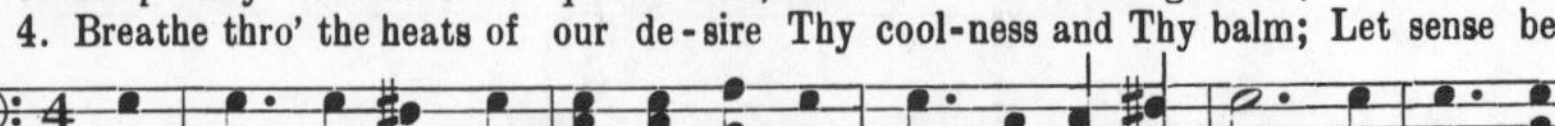

in our right-ful mind; In pur - er lives Thy serv-ice find, In deep - er rev-erence, praise.
call - ing of the Lord, Let us, like them, with-out a word, Rise up and fol - low Thee.
souls the strain and stress, And let our or-dered lives con-fess The beau-ty of Thy peace.
dumb, let flesh re - tire, Speak thro' the earth-quake, wind and fire, O still small voice of calm!

400 Take Time to Be Holy

HOLINESS. 6.5.6.5.D.

William D. Longstaff. 1822-1894 — George C. Stebbins, 1846-1945

1. Take time to be ho - ly, Speak oft with thy Lord; A - bide in Him
2. Take time to be ho - ly, The world rush-es on;.. Spend much time in
3. Take time to be ho - ly, Let Him be thy Guide, And run not be-
4. Take time to be ho - ly, Be calm in thy soul;. Each tho't and each
al - ways, And feed on His Word. Make friends of God's chil - dren;
se - cret With Je - sus a - lone; By look - ing to Je - sus,
fore Him, What - ev - er be - tide;.. In joy or in sor - row,
mo - tive Be - neath His con - trol;.. Thus led by His Spir - it

Help those who are weak; For-get-ting in noth-ing His bless-ing to seek.
Like Him thou shalt be;.. Thy friends in thy con-duct His likeness shall see..
Still fol-low thy Lord, And, look-ing to Je-sus, Still trust in His Word.
To foun-tains of love, Thou soon shalt be fit-ted For serv-ice a-bove.
What a Friend
401
CONVERSE. 8.7.8.7.D.
Joseph Scriven, 1820-1886
Charles C. Converse, 1832-1918
1. What a friend we have in Je-sus, All our sins and griefs to bear!
2. Have we tri-als and temp-ta-tions? Is there troub-le an-y-where?
3. Are we weak and heav-y-la-den, Cumbered with a load of care?--
What a priv-i-lege to car-ry Ev-ery-thing to God in prayer!
We should nev-er be dis-cour-aged, Take it to the Lord in prayer.
Pre-cious Sav-ior, still our ref-uge—Take it to the Lord in prayer.
O what peace we oft-en for-feit, O what need-less pain we bear,
Can we find a friend so faith-ful Who will all our sor-rows share?
Do thy friends de-spise, for-sake thee? Take it to the Lord in prayer;
All be-cause we do not car-ry Ev-ery-thing to God in prayer!
Je-sus knows our ev-ery weak-ness, Take it to the Lord in prayer.
In his arms he'll take and shield thee, Thou wilt find a sol-ace there. A-MEN.

402 Take the Name of Jesus with You

Lydia Baxter, 1809-1874 — William Howard Doane, 1832-1915

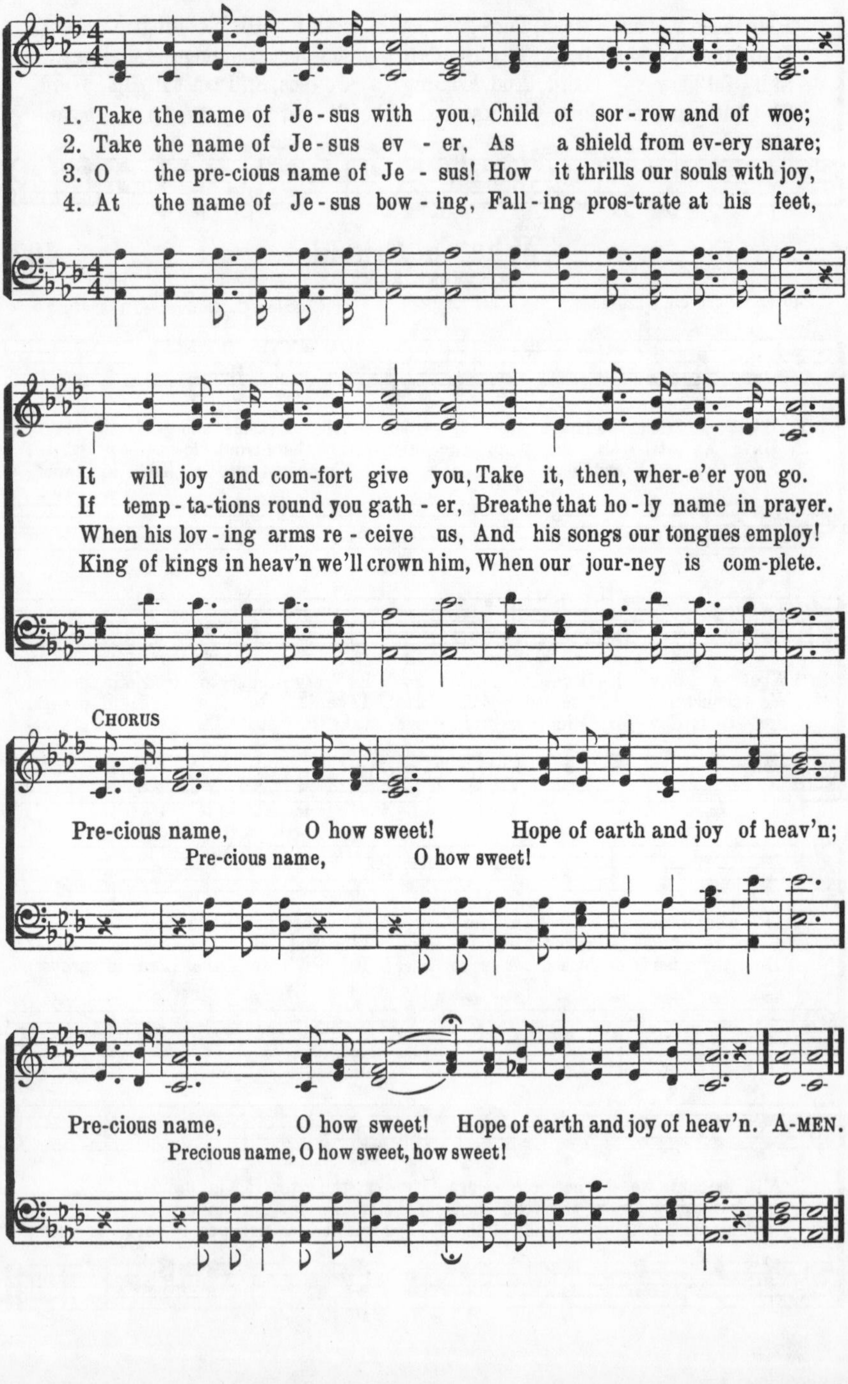

1. Take the name of Je-sus with you, Child of sor-row and of woe;
It will joy and com-fort give you, Take it, then, wher-e'er you go.

2. Take the name of Je-sus ev-er, As a shield from ev-ery snare;
If temp-ta-tions round you gath-er, Breathe that ho-ly name in prayer.

3. O the pre-cious name of Je-sus! How it thrills our souls with joy,
When his lov-ing arms re-ceive us, And his songs our tongues employ!

4. At the name of Je-sus bow-ing, Fall-ing pros-trate at his feet,
King of kings in heav'n we'll crown him, When our jour-ney is com-plete.

CHORUS

Pre-cious name, (Pre-cious name,) O how sweet! (O how sweet!) Hope of earth and joy of heav'n;
Pre-cious name, O how sweet! (Precious name, O how sweet, how sweet!) Hope of earth and joy of heav'n. A-MEN.

'Tis the Blessed Hour of Prayer 403

Fanny J. Crosby, 1820-1915 — William Howard Doane, 1832-1915

1. 'Tis the bless-ed hour of prayer, when our hearts low-ly bend, And we
2. 'Tis the bless-ed hour of prayer, when the Sav - ior draws near With a
3. 'Tis the bless-ed hour of prayer, when the tempt-ed and tried To the
4. At the bless-ed hour of prayer, trust-ing him, we be - lieve That the
gath - er to Je - sus, our Sav - ior and Friend; If we come to him in
ten - der com-pas - sion his chil - dren to hear; When he tells us we may
Sav - ior who loves them their sor - row con - fide; With a sym - pa-thiz - ing
bless-ing we're need-ing we'll sure - ly re - ceive; In the full - ness of this
faith, his pro - tec - tion to share, What a balm for the wea - ry!
cast at his feet ev - ery care, What a balm for the wea - ry!
heart he re - moves ev - ery care; What a balm for the wea - ry!
trust we shall lose ev - ery care; What a balm for the wea - ry!
CHORUS
O how sweet to be there! Bless-ed hour of prayer, bless-ed hour of
prayer, What a balm for the wea - ry! O how sweet to be there! A - MEN.

404 Hasten and Tell Him

Barney E. Warren, 1897 J. Henry Hall, 1897

1."Ask and it shall be giv - en you," broth - er, He is the Lord who
2. Has-ten and tell him, why do you tar - ry? O - pen your heart while
3. Has-ten and tell what tongue can-not ut - ter, Groaning and sigh - ing,
4. Has-ten and tell him ev - ery af - flic - tion, Tell him each pain and
car - eth for all; Come with your heart all bro - ken and bleed - ing;
Je - sus is near; Bring him the bur - dens you can-not car - ry,
load - ed with care; Bruis - ed and weak with doubt-ing, you fal - ter;
sor - row of heart; Here is the word: "All pow - er is giv - en;"
CHORUS
Come, he will hear and an-swer your call.
Tell him with cour-age, noth-ing to fear. Has-ten and tell him,
Tell him, he waits your bur-dens to bear.
'Lo! I am with you, nev - er to part.' Has - ten and tell him,
broth-er and sis - ter, Je - sus so ten - - der, lov - ing and
broth - er and sis - ter; Je - sus so ten - der, lov - ing, yes,
kind, ... Wait - ing to com - - - fort, bless and de-
lov - ing and kind, Wait - ing to com - fort, bless and de-

Sweet Hour of Prayer

405

SWEET HOUR. L.M.D.

William W. Walford (19th century) William B. Bradbury, 1816-1868

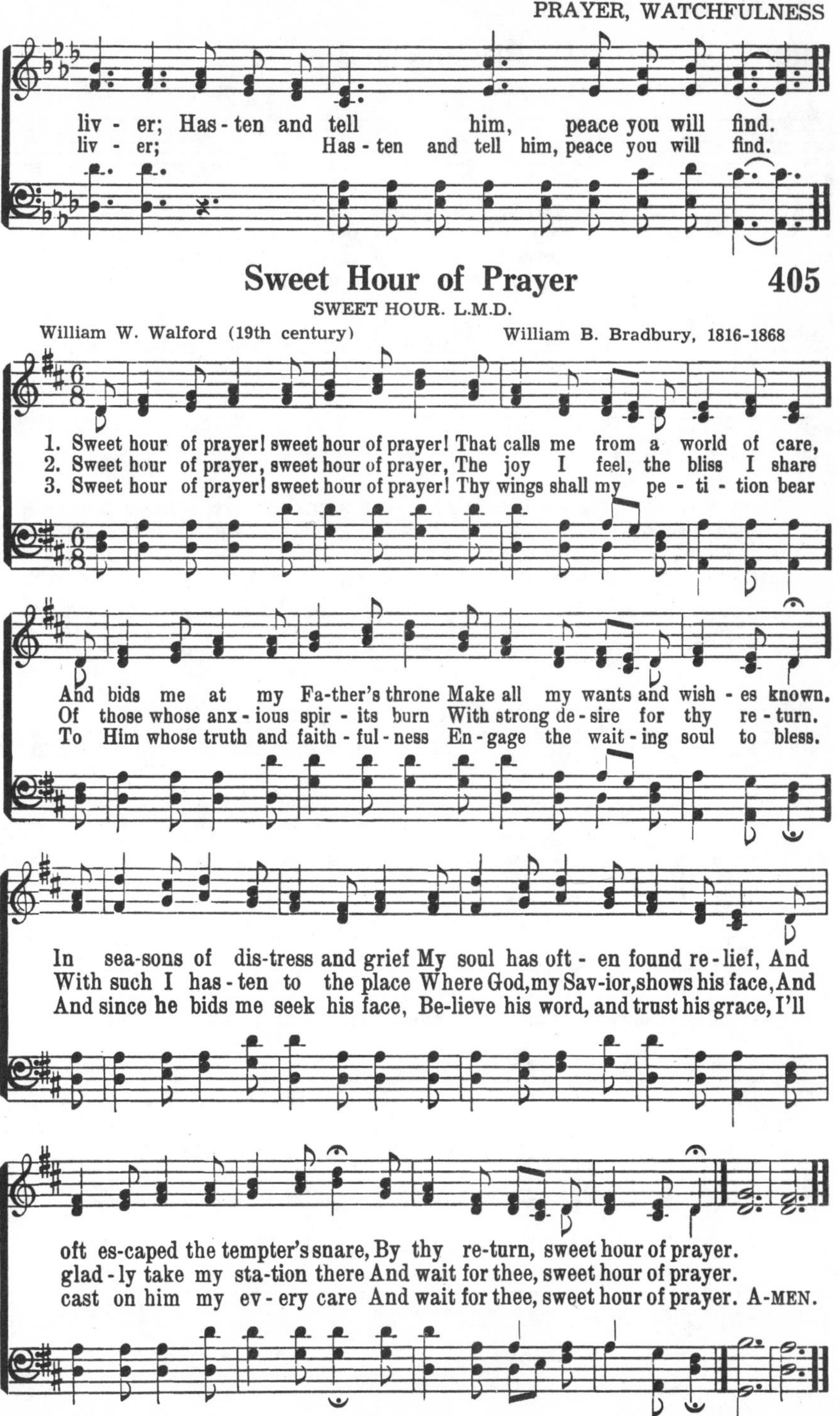
liv - er; Has - ten and tell him, peace you will find.
liv - er; Has - ten and tell him, peace you will find.
1. Sweet hour of prayer! sweet hour of prayer! That calls me from a world of care,
2. Sweet hour of prayer, sweet hour of prayer, The joy I feel, the bliss I share
3. Sweet hour of prayer! sweet hour of prayer! Thy wings shall my pe - ti - tion bear
And bids me at my Fa-ther's throne Make all my wants and wish - es known.
Of those whose anx - ious spir - its burn With strong de - sire for thy re - turn.
To Him whose truth and faith - ful - ness En - gage the wait - ing soul to bless.
In sea-sons of dis-tress and grief My soul has oft - en found re - lief, And
With such I has - ten to the place Where God, my Sav-ior, shows his face, And
And since he bids me seek his face, Be-lieve his word, and trust his grace, I'll
oft es-caped the tempter's snare, By thy re-turn, sweet hour of prayer.
glad - ly take my sta-tion there And wait for thee, sweet hour of prayer.
cast on him my ev - ery care And wait for thee, sweet hour of prayer. A-MEN.

406 A Blessing in Prayer

Eliza E. Hewitt, b. 1851 — William J. Kirkpatrick, 1838-1921

1. There is rest, sweet rest, at the Mas-ters's feet, There is fa - vor now at the
2. There is grace to help in our time of need, For our Friend a-bove is a
3. When our songs are glad with the joy of life, When our hearts are sad with its
4. There is per-fect peace tho' the wild waves roll; There are gifts of love for the

mer - cy - seat, For a-ton-ing blood has been sprinkled there; There is al-ways a
Friend in-deed, We may cast on him ev - ery grief and care; There is al-ways a
ills and strife, When the pow'rs of sin would the soul ensnare, There is al-ways a
seek-ing soul, Till we praise the Lord in his home so fair; There is al-ways a

bless-ing, a bless-ing in prayer.

CHORUS

There's a blessing in prayer, in be-liev-ing prayer;
When our Sav-ior's name to the throne we bear, Then a Fa-ther's love will re-
ceive us there; There is al - ways a bless-ing, a bless-ing in prayer. A - MEN.

Wonderful Power in Prayer 407

Eliza E. Hewitt, b. 1851 — Fred A. Fillmore, 1856-1925

1. No mat - ter how hard goes the bat - tle of life, God's chil-dren need nev - er de - spair; His con-quer-ing grace giveth peace 'mid the strife, There is won-der - ful pow'r in prayer.
2. We know that the ros - es not al - ways will bloom, The skies will not al - ways be fair; But go to the Fa - ther to bright-en the gloom, There is won-der - ful pow'r in prayer.
3. Per - haps you are seek-ing a soul far a - stray; That name to the mer - cy - seat bear; The Shepherd him-self will go with you to - day, There is won-der - ful pow'r in prayer.
4. Thro' all the swift chang-es that come to us here, Till white robes of glo - ry we wear, We'll look up to Je - sus for com-fort and cheer, There is won-der - ful pow'r in prayer.

CHORUS

Won - - der - ful pow'r, ...
Won-der - ful pow'r, won - der - ful pow'r,
A won - der - ful pow'r in prayer; For it mov - eth the Arm that mov - eth the worlds, There's a won - der - ful pow'r in prayer. A - MEN.

408 Consolation

Charles W. Naylor, 1918 — Andrew L. Byers, 1918

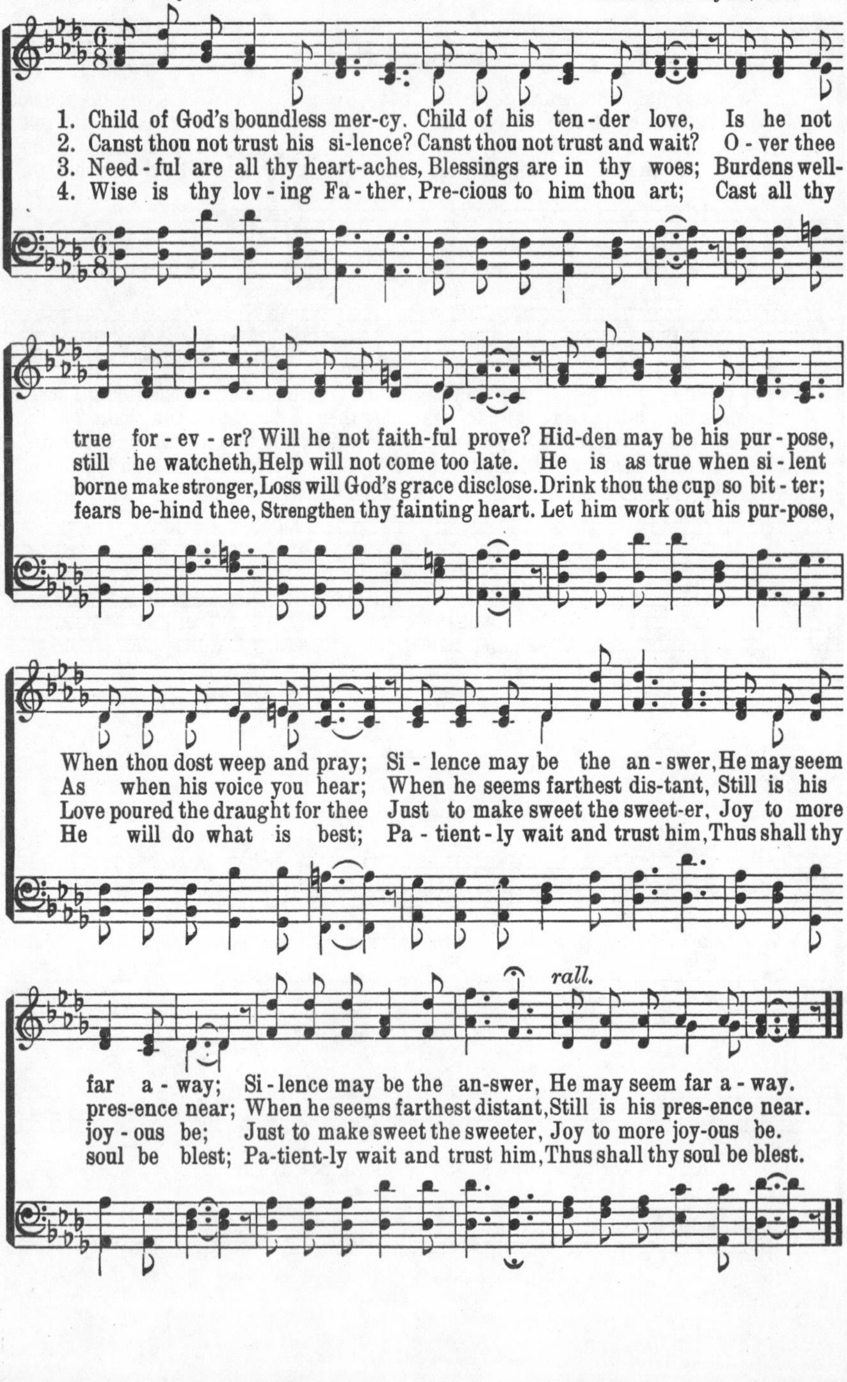

1. Child of God's boundless mer-cy. Child of his ten-der love, Is he not
2. Canst thou not trust his si-lence? Canst thou not trust and wait? O-ver thee
3. Need-ful are all thy heart-aches, Blessings are in thy woes; Burdens well-
4. Wise is thy lov-ing Fa-ther, Pre-cious to him thou art; Cast all thy

true for-ev-er? Will he not faith-ful prove? Hid-den may be his pur-pose,
still he watcheth, Help will not come too late. He is as true when si-lent
borne make stronger, Loss will God's grace disclose. Drink thou the cup so bit-ter;
fears be-hind thee, Strengthen thy fainting heart. Let him work out his pur-pose,

When thou dost weep and pray; Si-lence may be the an-swer, He may seem
As when his voice you hear; When he seems farthest dis-tant, Still is his
Love poured the draught for thee Just to make sweet the sweet-er, Joy to more
He will do what is best; Pa-tient-ly wait and trust him, Thus shall thy

far a-way; Si-lence may be the an-swer, He may seem far a-way.
pres-ence near; When he seems farthest distant, Still is his pres-ence near.
joy-ous be; Just to make sweet the sweeter, Joy to more joy-ous be.
soul be blest; Pa-tient-ly wait and trust him, Thus shall thy soul be blest.

rall.

Keep Praying, Toiling On 409

J. T. Latta — Ira B. Wilson, b. 1880

1. A - long life's rugged, thorn-y way, Keep praying, toil-ing on; There soon will
2. All fears and gloomy doubts discard, Keep praying, toil-ing on; Faith nev-er
3. If griefs seem more than you can bear, Keep praying, toil-ing on; For pray-ing
dawn a bright-er day, Keep pray-ing, toil - ing on. The tri - als you have
fails of its re-ward, Keep pray-ing, toil - ing on. Hold firm and stead-fast
light-ens ev - ery care, Keep pray-ing, toil - ing on. The Sav - ior has great
had are past; Bear patiently the ones thou hast; If oth-ers come, they will not last,
to the end; From duty do not swerve or bend; For help, on Him you can de-pend,
sym-pa - thy For struggling mortals such as we; And he will give us vic - to - ry—
Keep praying, toil-ing on.
CHORUS
Keep pray - ing, toil - ing, Pray-ing, toil-ing
Keep pray-ing, toil-ing, praying, toiling,
on; . . There soon will dawn a bright-er day, Keep pray-ing, toil-ing on.

410 Church of the Living God

D. Otis Teasley, 1876-1942 — Clarence E. Hunter, 1869-1945

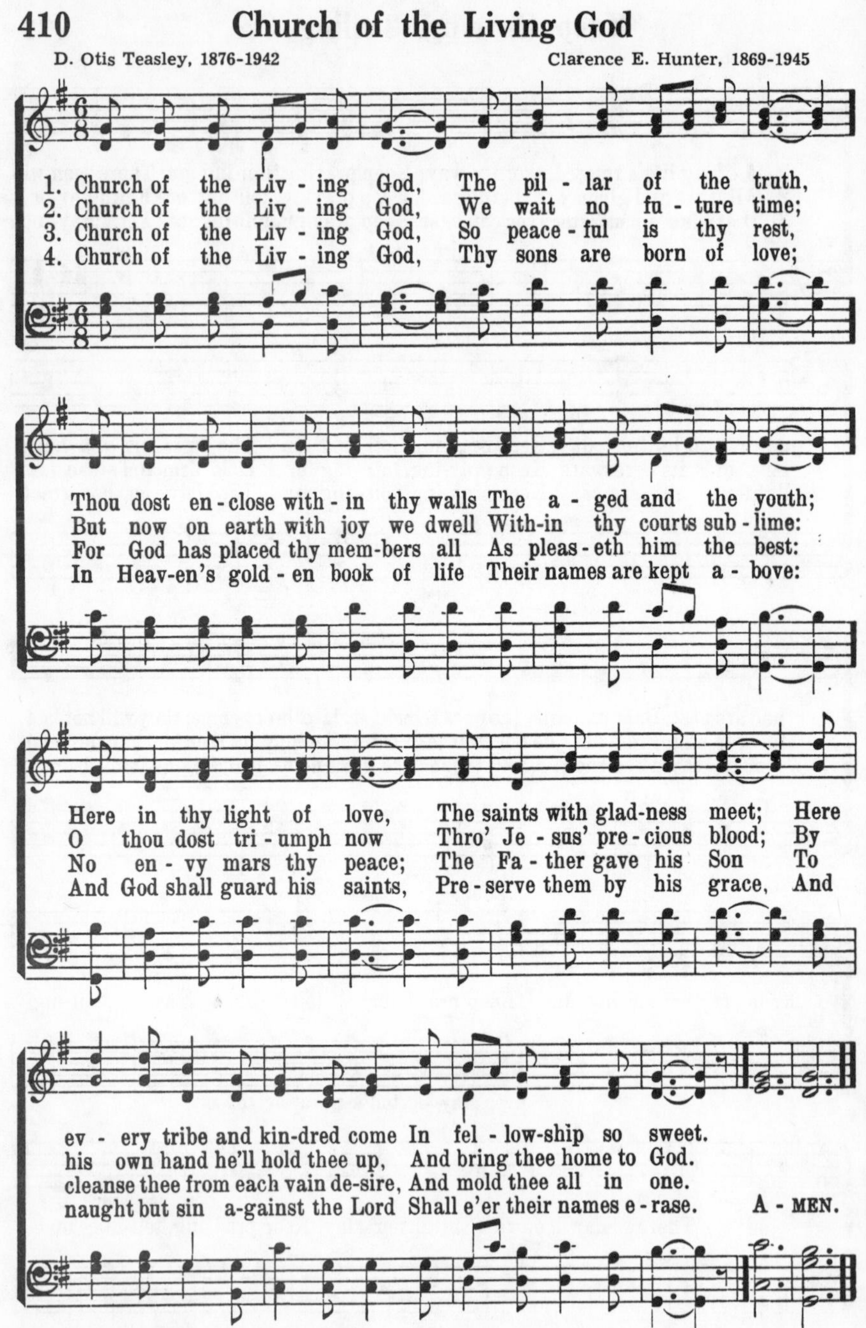
1. Church of the Liv - ing God, The pil - lar of the truth,
2. Church of the Liv - ing God, We wait no fu - ture time;
3. Church of the Liv - ing God, So peace - ful is thy rest,
4. Church of the Liv - ing God, Thy sons are born of love;
Thou dost en - close with - in thy walls The a - ged and the youth;
But now on earth with joy we dwell With-in thy courts sub - lime:
For God has placed thy mem - bers all As pleas - eth him the best:
In Heav - en's gold - en book of life Their names are kept a - bove:
Here in thy light of love, The saints with glad - ness meet; Here
O thou dost tri - umph now Thro' Je - sus' pre - cious blood; By
No en - vy mars thy peace; The Fa - ther gave his Son To
And God shall guard his saints, Pre - serve them by his grace, And
ev - ery tribe and kin - dred come In fel - low - ship so sweet.
his own hand he'll hold thee up, And bring thee home to God.
cleanse thee from each vain de - sire, And mold thee all in one.
naught but sin a - gainst the Lord Shall e'er their names e - rase.
A - MEN.

Church of God, Thou Spotless Virgin 411

Frances R. Havergal, 1836-1879
and Daniel S. Warner, 1842-1895

Harry E. Rogers, 1897

1. Church of God, thou spot-less vir-gin, Church of Christ for whom he died,
2. God him-self has set the mem-bers In his bod - y all com-plete,
3. Church of God, "be-lov-ed cit - y," Thou art of ce-les-tial mold;
4. God's own ho - li-ness with-in thee, His own beau - ty on thy brow;
5. Church of God, in heav-en writ-ten, Thine the ris - en life of Christ,
Thou hast known no hu-man found-er, Je - sus bought thee for his bride.
Or - gan-ized by Je-sus on - ly, O the un - ion pure and sweet!
Lo! from God and out of heav-en Came the cit - y of pure gold.
Glo - ri - fied in his own im - age, This thy won-drous por-tion now.
And the treas-ures to thee giv - en, Nev - er, nev - er can be priced.
Sanc - ti - fied by God the Fa-ther, Built by Je - sus Christ, the Son,
Church of God, the an-gels mar-vel At the mu-sic of thy song;
Stones of jas - per, clear as crys - tal Is the build-ing of thy wall;
In thee dwells the tri - une full-ness, Bless-ing all thy pil-grim days;
Far a - bove this world's con-fu - sion, Walk-ing close by Je - sus' side,
Repeat softly
Tem-pered by the Ho-ly Spir-it, Like the Ho - ly Three in One.
Earth and hell in ter-ror trem-ble, As thy ar - my moves a-long.
And the Lamb, thy light for-ev - er, Je - sus, Je - sus, all in all.
All a-round thee his sal-va-tion, And be-fore thee gates of praise.
Lean-ing on his lov-ing bos-om, Is the church, his chos-en bride. A - MEN.

412 Glorious Things of Thee Are Spoken

AUSTRIAN HYMN. 8.7.8.7.D.

John Newton, 1725-1807 Francis Joseph Haydn, 1732-1809

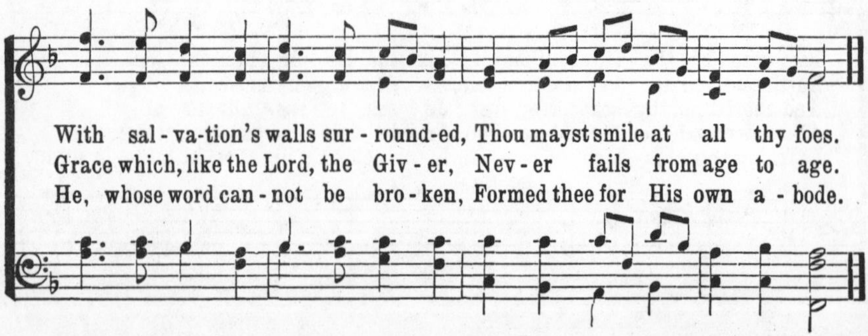

1. Glo-rious things of thee are spo - ken, Zi - on, cit - y of our God;
2. See, the streams of liv - ing wa - ters, Springing from e - ter - nal love,
3. Round each hab - i - ta - tion hov-ering, See the cloud and fire ap - pear

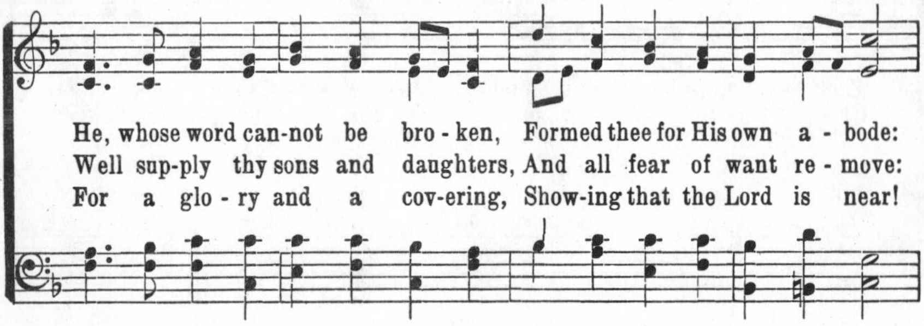

He, whose word can-not be bro - ken, Formed thee for His own a - bode:
Well sup-ply thy sons and daughters, And all fear of want re - move:
For a glo - ry and a cov-ering, Show-ing that the Lord is near!

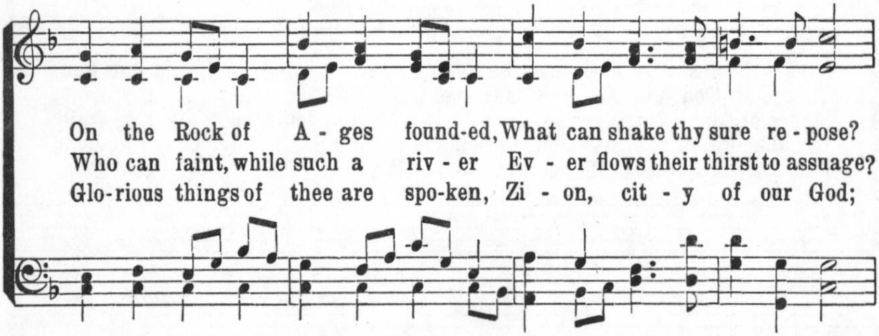

On the Rock of A - ges found-ed, What can shake thy sure re - pose?
Who can faint, while such a riv - er Ev - er flows their thirst to assuage?
Glo-rious things of thee are spo-ken, Zi - on, cit - y of our God;

With sal - va-tion's walls sur - round-ed, Thou mayst smile at all thy foes.
Grace which, like the Lord, the Giv - er, Nev - er fails from age to age.
He, whose word can - not be bro - ken, Formed thee for His own a - bode.

O Church of God

Charles W. Naylor, 1922 — Andrew L. Byers, 1923

1. The church of God one bod - y is, One Spir - it dwells with - in;
2. Di - vine - ly built, di - vine - ly ruled, To God she doth sub - mit;
3. God sets her mem-bers each in place, Ac - cord - ing to his will—
4. Sal - va - tion is her ho - ly walls, The cross her sign of pow'r;
5. In beau - ty stand, O Church of God, With right-eous-ness ar - rayed;

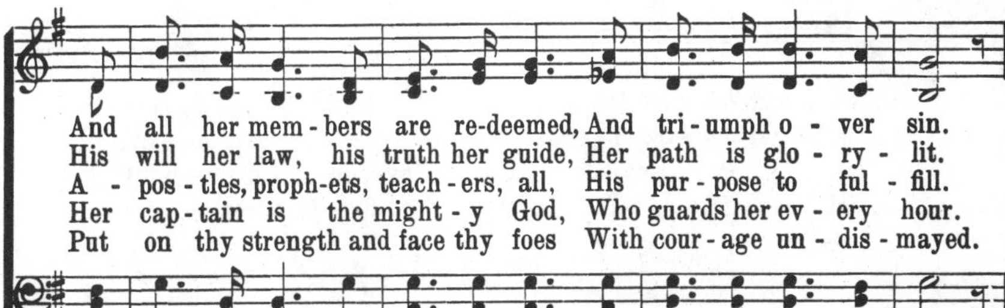

And all her mem - bers are re-deemed, And tri - umph o - ver sin.
His will her law, his truth her guide, Her path is glo - ry - lit.
A - pos - tles, proph-ets, teach - ers, all, His pur - pose to ful - fill.
Her cap - tain is the might - y God, Who guards her ev - ery hour.
Put on thy strength and face thy foes With cour - age un - dis - mayed.

CHORUS
O Church of God! I love thy courts, Thou moth-er of the free;

Thou bless-ed home of all the saved, I dwell con-tent in thee. A - MEN.

414 The Bond of Perfectness

Daniel S. Warner. 1893 — Barney E. Warren, 1893

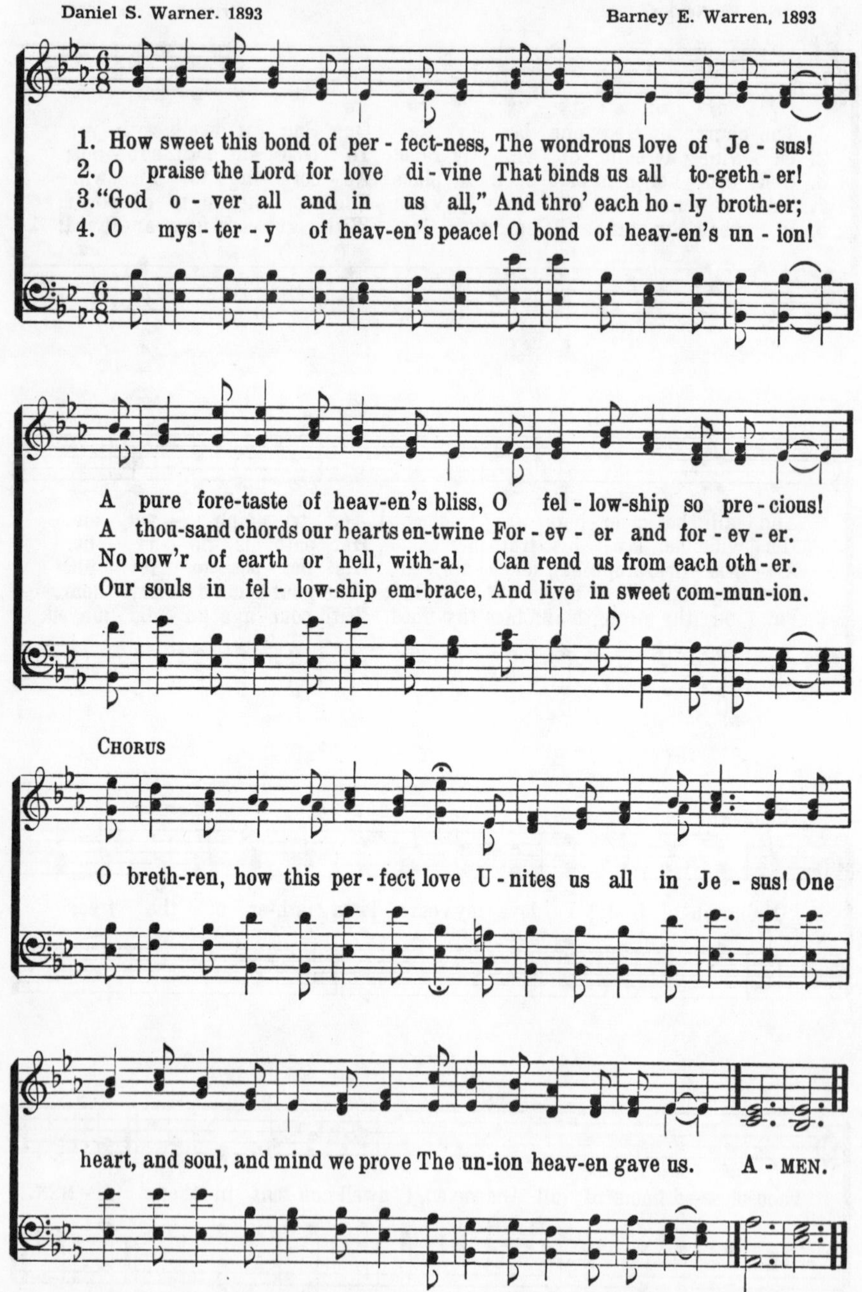
1. How sweet this bond of per - fect-ness, The wondrous love of Je - sus!
2. O praise the Lord for love di - vine That binds us all to-geth - er!
3."God o - ver all and in us all," And thro' each ho - ly broth-er;
4. O mys - ter - y of heav-en's peace! O bond of heav-en's un - ion!
A pure fore-taste of heav-en's bliss, O fel - low-ship so pre - cious!
A thou-sand chords our hearts en-twine For - ev - er and for - ev - er.
No pow'r of earth or hell, with-al, Can rend us from each oth - er.
Our souls in fel - low-ship em-brace, And live in sweet com-mun-ion.
CHORUS
O breth-ren, how this per - fect love U - nites us all in Je - sus! One heart, and soul, and mind we prove The un-ion heav-en gave us. A - MEN.

The Blameless Church

415

Barney E. Warren, 1907 — Amanda L. Speck, 1907

1. With-out spot and blame-less, O Sav-ior, What a glo-ri-ous church thou hast built! For this thou didst pa-tient-ly suf-fer, For this was thy blood free-ly spilt.
2. With-out spot and blame-less, so ho-ly, See the church in her beau-ty sub-lime; She lives on the bright hills of glo-ry, She reigns o-ver sin all the time.
3. With-out spot and blame-less he bought her, In the like-ness of heav-en a-bove; From depths that were sin-ful he sought her, And filled her with in-fi-nite love.
4. She's blame-less, with-out spot or wrin-kle, From the last stain of sin she is free; With blood from the cross he doth sprin-kle Her al-tars of cleans-ing for me.

CHORUS

With-out spot and blameless, my broth-er, She lives 'neath the all-cleans-ing blood; In heav-en and earth is no oth-er, Her build-er and mak-er is God. A-MEN.

416 I Love Thy Kingdom, Lord

ST. THOMAS. S.M.

Timothy Dwight, 1752-1817 — From *William's Psalmody,* 1770

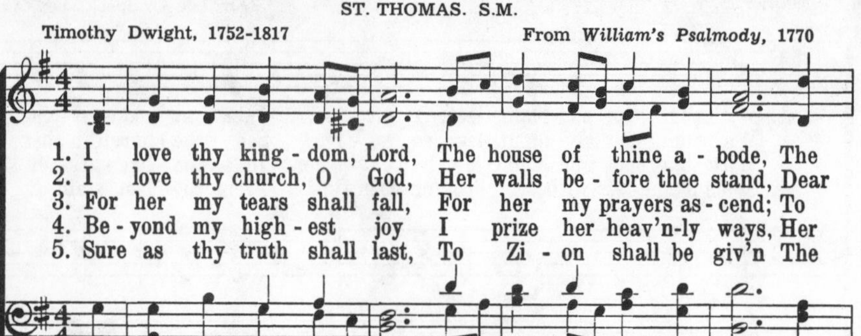
1. I love thy king - dom, Lord, The house of thine a - bode, The
2. I love thy church, O God, Her walls be - fore thee stand, Dear
3. For her my tears shall fall, For her my prayers as - cend; To
4. Be - yond my high - est joy I prize her heav'n-ly ways, Her
5. Sure as thy truth shall last, To Zi - on shall be giv'n The

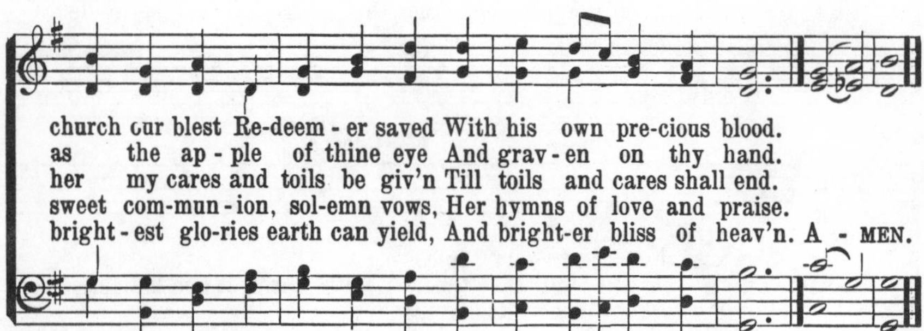
church our blest Re-deem - er saved With his own pre-cious blood.
as the ap - ple of thine eye And grav - en on thy hand.
her my cares and toils be giv'n Till toils and cares shall end.
sweet com-mun - ion, sol-emn vows, Her hymns of love and praise.
bright - est glo-ries earth can yield, And bright-er bliss of heav'n. A - MEN.

417 Zion Stands with Hills Surrounded

Thomas Kelly, 1769-1854 — William L. Viner, 1845

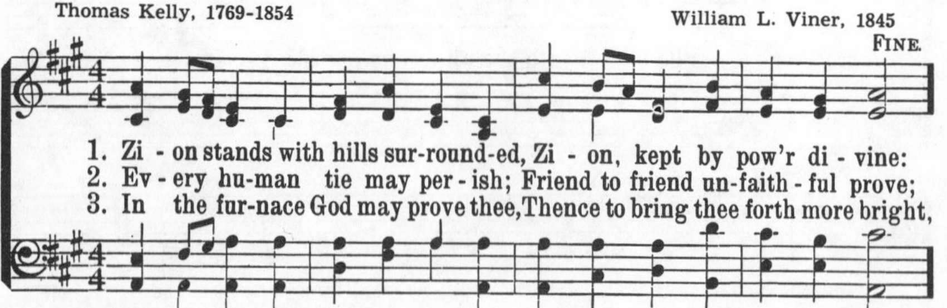
FINE.
1. Zi - on stands with hills sur-round-ed, Zi - on, kept by pow'r di - vine:
2. Ev - ery hu-man tie may per - ish; Friend to friend un-faith - ful prove;
3. In the fur-nace God may prove thee, Thence to bring thee forth more bright,

D.C.—Hap - py Zi - on, Hap - py Zi - on, What a fa - vored lot is thine!
D.C.—But no chang-es, But no chang-es Can at - tend Je - ho-vah's love.
D.C.—God is with thee, God is with thee, God, thine ev - er - last - ing light.

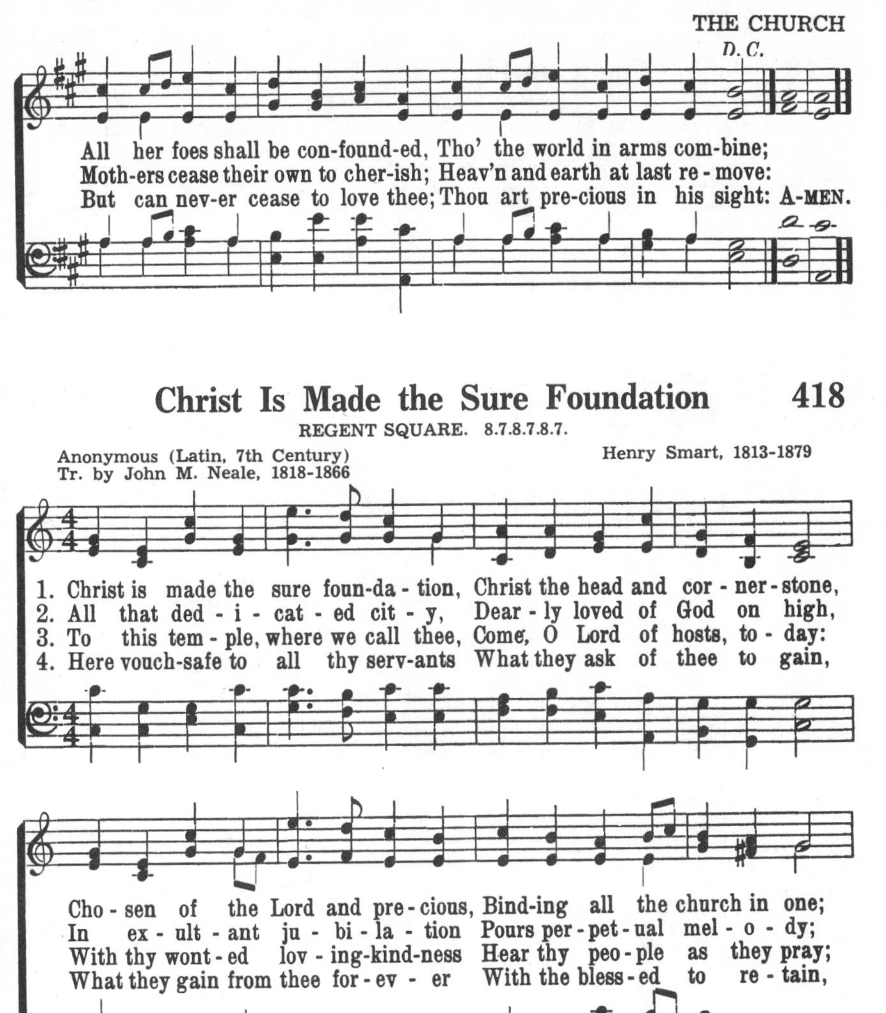
D. C.
All her foes shall be con-found-ed, Tho' the world in arms com-bine;
Moth-ers cease their own to cher-ish; Heav'n and earth at last re - move:
But can nev-er cease to love thee; Thou art pre-cious in his sight: A-MEN.

Christ Is Made the Sure Foundation 418

REGENT SQUARE. 8.7.8.7.8.7.

Anonymous (Latin, 7th Century)
Tr. by John M. Neale, 1818-1866

Henry Smart, 1813-1879

1. Christ is made the sure foun-da - tion, Christ the head and cor - ner - stone,
2. All that ded - i - cat - ed cit - y, Dear - ly loved of God on high,
3. To this tem - ple, where we call thee, Come, O Lord of hosts, to - day:
4. Here vouch-safe to all thy serv-ants What they ask of thee to gain,

Cho - sen of the Lord and pre - cious, Bind-ing all the church in one;
In ex - ult - ant ju - bi - la - tion Pours per - pet - ual mel - o - dy;
With thy wont - ed lov - ing-kind-ness Hear thy peo - ple as they pray;
What they gain from thee for - ev - er With the bless - ed to re - tain,

Ho - ly Zi - on's help for - ev - er, And her con - fi - dence a - lone.
God the One in Three a - dor - ing In glad hymns e - ter - nal - ly.
And thy full - est ben - e - dic - tion Shed with-in its walls al - way.
And here-aft - er in thy glo - ry Ev - er-more with thee to reign. A - MEN.

419 The Church's One Foundation

AURELIA. 7.6.7.6.D.

Samuel J. Stone, 1839-1900 — Samuel S. Wesley, 1810-1876

1. The Church-'s one foun - da - tion Is Je - sus Christ her Lord;
2. E - lect from ev - 'ry na - tion, Yet one o'er all the earth,
3. 'Mid toil and trib - u - la - tion, And tu - mult of her war,
4. Yet she on earth hath un - ion With God the Three in One,

She is His new cre - a - tion By wa - ter and the word:
Her char - ter of sal - va - tion, One Lord, one faith, one birth;
She waits the con - sum - ma - tion Of peace for - ev - er - more;
And mys - tic sweet com - mun - ion With those whose rest is won:

From Heav'n He came and sought her To be His ho - ly bride; With
One ho - ly name she bless - es, Par-takes one ho - ly food, And
Till, with the vi - sion glo - rious, Her long - ing eyes are blest, And
O hap - py ones and ho - ly! Lord, give us grace that we, Like

His own blood He bought her, And for her life He died.
to one hope she press - es, With ev - 'ry grace en - dued.
the great church vic - to - rious Shall be the church at rest.
them, the meek and low - ly, On high may dwell with Thee. A-MEN.

The Church Has One Foundation 420

Vss. 1, 2, and part of 3 by Samuel J. Stone, 1839-1900
Remainder by Charles W. Naylor, 1907
Andrew L. Byers, 1907

1. The church has one foun - da - tion, 'Tis Je - sus Christ her Lord;
2. E - lect from ev - ery na - tion, Yet one o'er all the earth,
3. Long with a scorn - ful won - der Men saw her sore op - pressed,
4. The eve-ning sun is shin - ing, The cloud - y day is past;
5. Back to the one foun - da - tion, From sects and creeds made free,

She is his new cre - a - tion Thro' wa - ter by the word.
Her char - ter of sal - va - tion—One Lord, one faith, one birth.
By schisms rent a - sun - der, By her - e - sies dis - tressed.
The time of their re - pin - ing Is at an end at last.
Come saints of ev - ery na - tion To bless - ed u - ni - ty.

From heav'n he came and sought her To be his ho - ly bride;
One ho - ly name she bless-es, Par-takes one ho - ly food;
Yet saints their watch were keeping To hail a bright - er day,
The voice of God is call - ing To u - ni - ty a - gain;
Once more the an - cient glo - ry Shines as in days of old,

1. From heav'n he came and sought her To be his ho - ly bride; . .

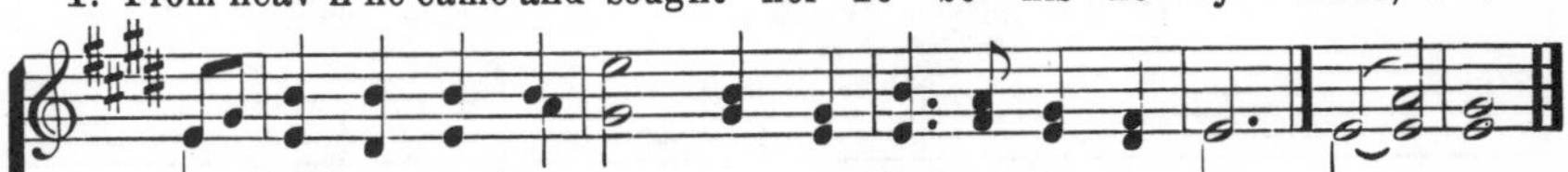

With his own blood he bought her, And for her life he died.
And to one hope she press - es, With ev-ery grace en-dued.
When God should stop their weeping, Take their reproach a-way.
Di - vis - ion walls are fall - ing, With all the creeds of men.
And tells the won-drous sto - ry—One God, one faith, one fold. A - MEN.

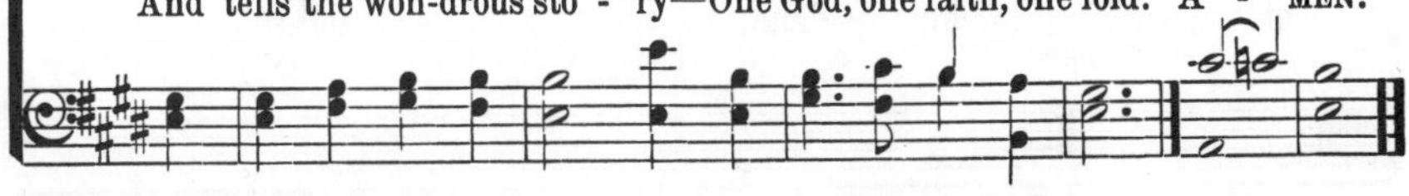

421 The Reformation Glory

Charles W. Naylor, 1922 — Andrew L. Byers, 1922

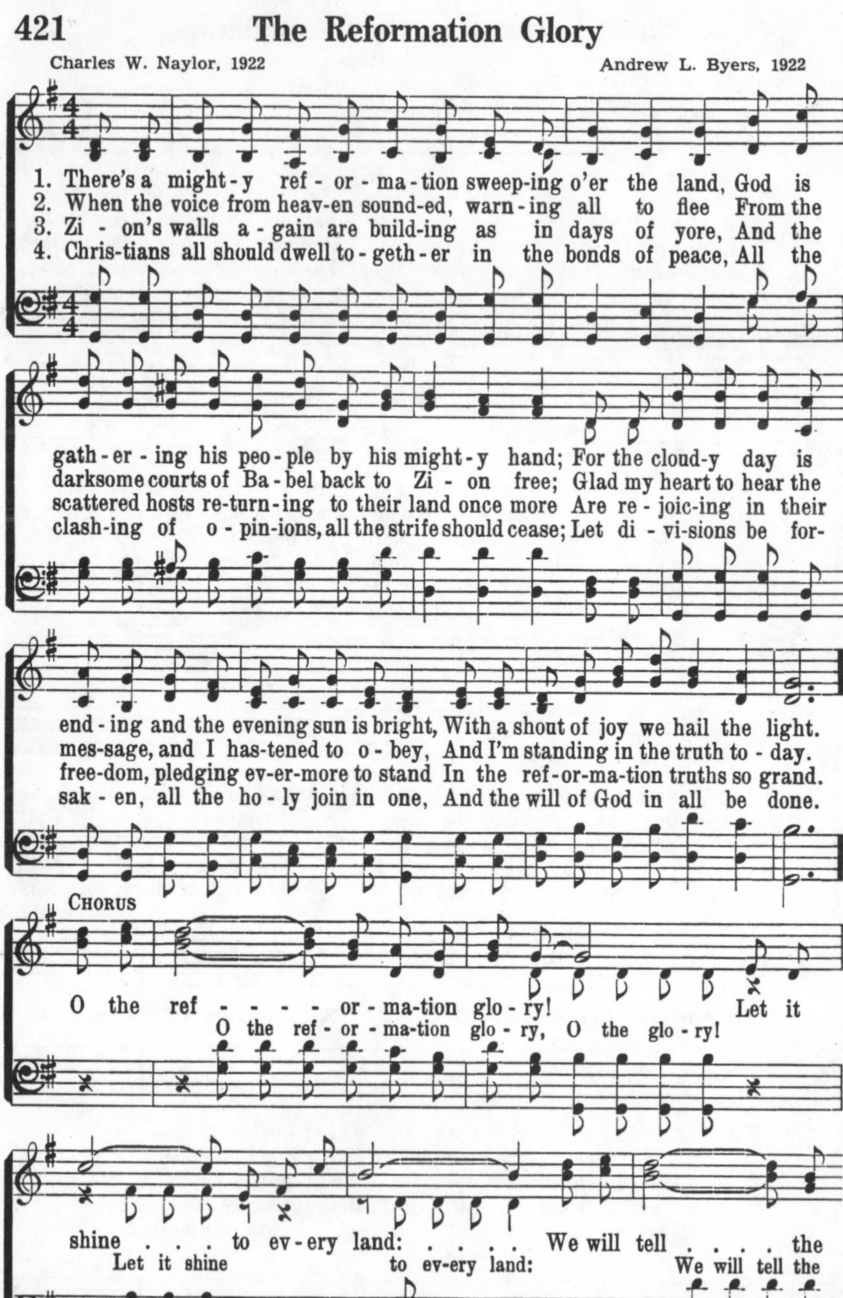
1. There's a might-y ref-or-ma-tion sweep-ing o'er the land, God is gath-er-ing his peo-ple by his might-y hand; For the cloud-y day is end-ing and the evening sun is bright, With a shout of joy we hail the light.
2. When the voice from heav-en sound-ed, warn-ing all to flee From the darksome courts of Ba-bel back to Zi-on free; Glad my heart to hear the mes-sage, and I has-tened to o-bey, And I'm standing in the truth to-day.
3. Zi-on's walls a-gain are build-ing as in days of yore, And the scattered hosts re-turn-ing to their land once more Are re-joic-ing in their free-dom, pledging ev-er-more to stand In the ref-or-ma-tion truths so grand.
4. Chris-tians all should dwell to-geth-er in the bonds of peace, All the clash-ing of o-pin-ions, all the strife should cease; Let di-vi-sions be for-sak-en, all the ho-ly join in one, And the will of God in all be done.
CHORUS
O the ref - - - - or-ma-tion glo-ry! Let it
O the ref-or-ma-tion glo-ry, O the glo-ry!
shine . . to ev-ery land: . . . . We will tell . . . . the
Let it shine to ev-ery land: We will tell the

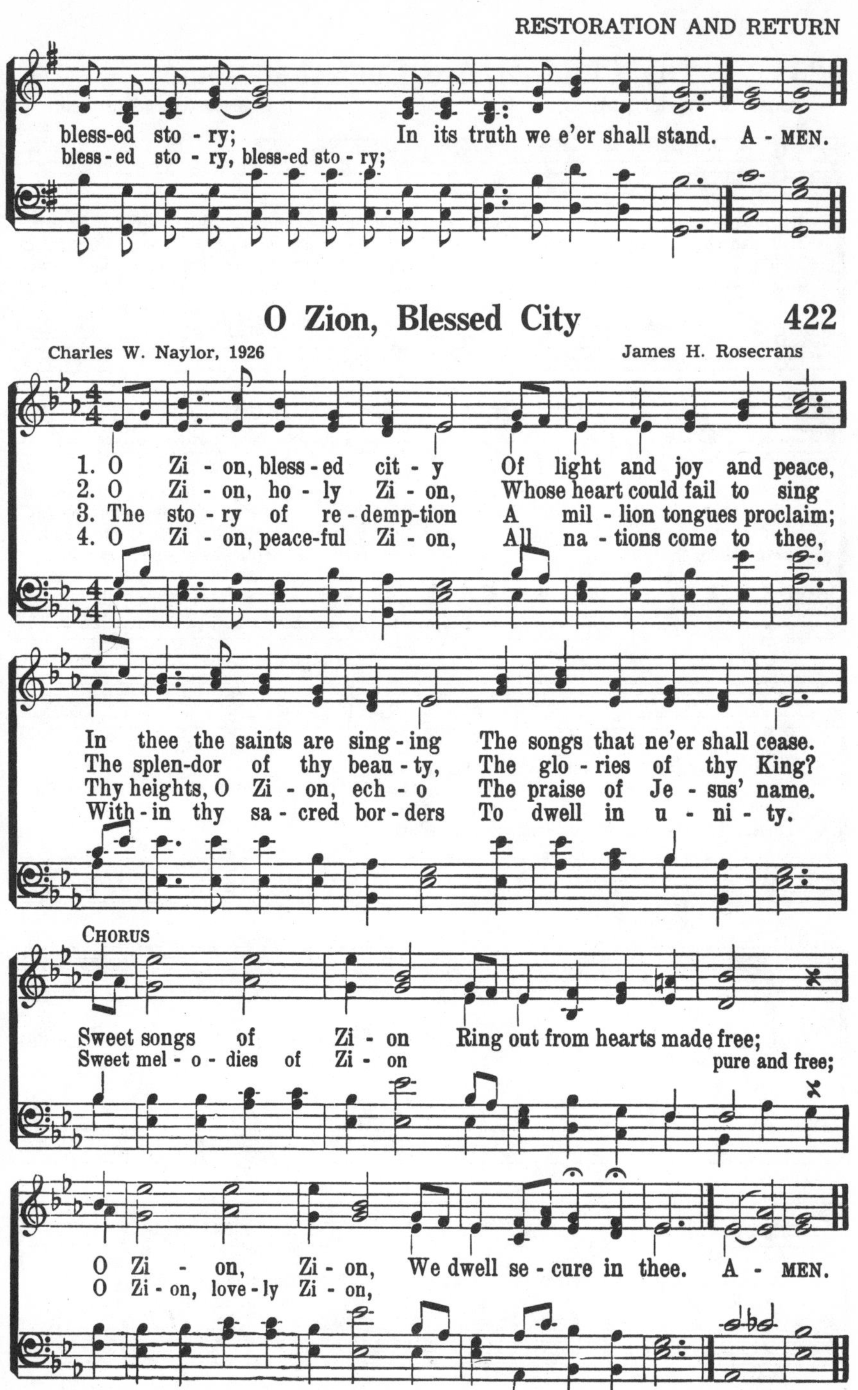
bless-ed sto - ry; In its truth we e'er shall stand. A - MEN.
bless - ed sto - ry, bless-ed sto - ry;
O Zion, Blessed City 422
Charles W. Naylor, 1926
James H. Rosecrans
1. O Zi - on, bless - ed cit - y Of light and joy and peace,
2. O Zi - on, ho - ly Zi - on, Whose heart could fail to sing
3. The sto - ry of re - demp-tion A mil - lion tongues proclaim;
4. O Zi - on, peace-ful Zi - on, All na - tions come to thee,
In thee the saints are sing - ing The songs that ne'er shall cease.
The splen-dor of thy beau - ty, The glo - ries of thy King?
Thy heights, O Zi - on, ech - o The praise of Je - sus' name.
With - in thy sa - cred bor - ders To dwell in u - ni - ty.
CHORUS
Sweet songs of Zi - on Ring out from hearts made free;
Sweet mel - o - dies of Zi - on pure and free;
O Zi - on, Zi - on, We dwell se - cure in thee. A - MEN.
O Zi - on, love - ly Zi - on,

423 Thy Children Are Gathering Home

Charles W. Naylor, 1907 Charles W. Naylor, 1907

1. Long scat - tered thy chil - dren, O Zi - on, have been, But now they are gath - er - ing home: The Spir - it is call - ing, they glad - ly o - bey, With songs of re - joic - ing they come.
2. False shep - herds di - vid - ed and scat - tered the flock, And hire - lings ruled o'er them for gain, But back to their fold on mount Zi - on's fair height They come to for - ev - er re - main.
3. To u - ni - ty, glo - ri - ous, rich and com - plete, One faith and one bod - y, one Lord, One way and one Spir - it, one hope and one God, They come at the call of his word.
4. Sec - ta - ri - an walls shall no lon - ger di - vide, False teach - ers shall lead them no more; True pas - tors shall feed them on heav - en - ly food, Their sor - rows and sigh - ings are o'er.
CHORUS
Thy chil - dren are gath - er - ing home,........ With joy they are gath - er - ing home;........ From all the di - vi - sions in which they were scattered, Thy chil - dren are gath - er - ing home. A - MEN.
gath - er - ing home,
gath - er - ing home;

'Twas Sung by the Poets 424

Daniel S. Warner, 1842-1895 B. F. Bear

1. 'Twas sung by the po - ets, fore - seen in the Spir - it, A
2. We stand in the glo - ry that Je - sus has giv - en, The
3. Now filled with the Spir - it and clad in the ar - mor Of
4. The proph-et's keen vi - sion, trans - pierc - ing the a - ges, Be-
5. The fig - tree is bud - ding, the eve - ning is shin - ing, We
time of re - fresh - ing is near; When creeds and di - vi - sions would
moon, as the day - spring doth shine; The light of the sun is now
light and om - nip - o - tent truth, We'll tes - ti - fy ev - er, and
held us to Zi - on re - turn; We'll sing of our free - dom, though
wel - come the won - der - ful light! We look for the Sav - ior, for
fall to de - mer - it, And saints in sweet un - ion ap - pear.
e - qual to sev - en, So bright is the glo - ry di - vine.
Je - sus we'll hon - or, And stand from sin Ba - bel a - loof.
Bab - y - lon rag - es, We'll shout as her cit - y doth burn.
time is de - clin - ing, E - ter - ni - ty's loom - ing in sight!
CHORUS
O glo - ry to Je - sus! we hail the bright day, And high on our ban - ner sal-
va - tion dis-play: The mists of con - fu - sion are pass - ing a - way. A - MEN.

425 Back to the Blessed Old Bible

D. Otis Teasley, 1901 — D. Otis Teasley, 1901

1. Back to the bless-ed old Bi-ble, Back to the cit-y of God, Back to the one-ness of heav-en, Back where the faith-ful have trod. Back from the land of con-fu-sion, Free from the bond-age of creeds; Back to the light of the morn-ing, Je-sus our Cap-tain leads.
2. Back to the bless-ed old Bi-ble, Saints of Je-ho-vah, re-joice; Je-sus is call-ing his peo-ple Back to the land of their choice. Oft-en our fa-thers had sought it While they in Ba-bel a-bode, Now we have found the fair cit-y, Church of the liv-ing God.
3. Back to the bless-ed old Bi-ble, Leav-ing con-fu-sion and strife; Flee-ing from Ba-bel to Zi-on Back to the joy of our life. O-ver the moun-tains we wan-dered, Look-ing in vain for the right, Now in the eve-ning we've found it, Truth of the gos-pel light.
4. Back to the bless-ed old Bi-ble, Back at the Mas-ter's call, Back to the words of our Sav-ior, Lov-ing, o-bey-ing them all. Nev-er in sects to be scat-tered, Nev-er a-gain to do wrong: U-ni-ty, ho-li-ness, heav-en, Ev-er shall be our song.
CHORUS
Back to the bless-ed old Bi-ble, Back to the light of its word:

Be on our ban - ners for - ev - er, "Ho - li - ness un - to the Lord."

The Church Triumphant 426

Daniel S. Warner, 1893 | Barney E. Warren, 1893

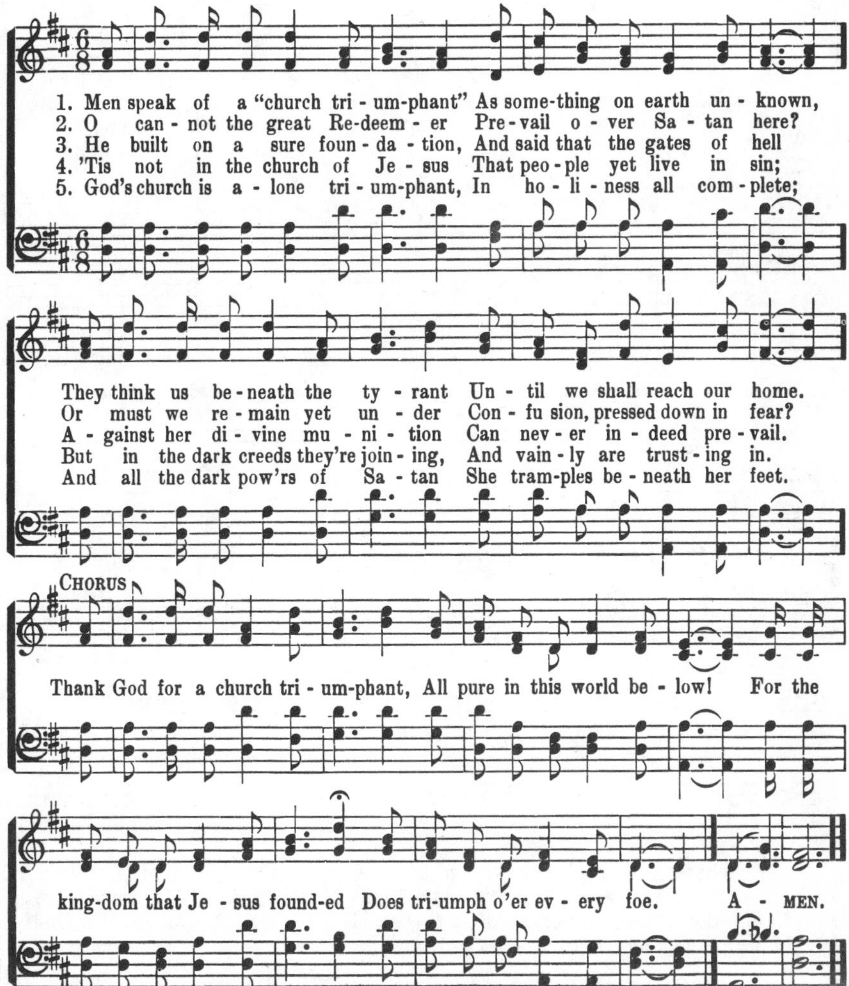

1. Men speak of a "church tri - um-phant" As some-thing on earth un - known,
2. O can - not the great Re-deem - er Pre - vail o - ver Sa - tan here?
3. He built on a sure foun - da - tion, And said that the gates of hell
4. 'Tis not in the church of Je - sus That peo - ple yet live in sin;
5. God's church is a - lone tri - um-phant, In ho - li - ness all com - plete;

They think us be-neath the ty - rant Un - til we shall reach our home.
Or must we re - main yet un - der Con - fu sion, pressed down in fear?
A - gainst her di - vine mu - ni - tion Can nev - er in - deed pre - vail.
But in the dark creeds they're join - ing, And vain - ly are trust - ing in.
And all the dark pow'rs of Sa - tan She tram-ples be - neath her feet.

CHORUS

Thank God for a church tri - um-phant, All pure in this world be - low! For the king-dom that Je - sus found-ed Does tri-umph o'er ev - ery foe. A - MEN.

427 Brighter Days Are Sweetly Dawning
Daniel S. Warner, 1885
H. R. Jeffrey, 1885
1. Bright-er days are sweet-ly dawn-ing, O the glo - ry looms in sight!
2. Lo! the ran-somed are re-turn-ing, Robed in shin-ing crys-tal white,
3. Free from Ba - bel, in the Spir - it, Free to wor - ship God a - right,
4. Hal - le - lu - jah! saints are sing-ing Vic - t'ry in Je - ho-vah's might;
For the cloud - y day is wan-ing, And the eve-ning shall be light.
Leap-ing, shout-ing home to Zi - on, Hap - py in the eve-ning light.
Joy and glad-ness we're re - ceiv-ing, O how sweet this eve-ning light!
Glo - ry! glo - ry! keep it ring-ing, We are saved in eve-ning light!
CHORUS
O what gold - en glo - ry stream-ing! Pur - er light is com - ing fast;
Now in Christ we've found a freedom Which e - ter - nal - ly shall last. A - MEN.
428 O Where Are Kings and Empires Now?
ST. ANNE. C.M.
A. Cleveland Coxe, 1818-1896
Probably by William Croft, 1678-1727
1. O where are kings and em - pires now, Of old that went and came?
2. We mark her good - ly bat - tle-ments And her foun - da - tions strong;
3. For not like king-doms of the world Thy ho - ly Church, O God!
4. Un - sha - ken as e - ter - nal hills, Im - mov - a - ble she stands,

But, Lord, Thy Church is pray - ing yet, A thou-sand years the same.
We hear with - in the sol - emn voice Of her un - end-ing song.
Tho' earth-quake shocks are threatening her, And tem-pests are a-broad;
A moun-tain that shall fill the earth, A house not made with hands. A - MEN.
Beautiful, Peaceful Zion
429
Daniel S. Warner, 1893
Barney E. Warren, 1893
1. Beau - ti - ful, peace-ful Zi - on, We've heard of thy won - ders of old;
2. Out of the shad-ows hang - ing Dark o - ver the val - ley of fear,
3. Beau - ti - ful, ho - ly Zi - on, O moun-tain of glo - ry di - vine,
4. Wel - come the joy - ful ti - dings Of Zi - on, the moun-tain of love;
And out of the a - ges ris - ing, The cit - y of light we be - hold.
We mount up to Zi - on's glo - ry, As crys - tal e - ter - nal - ly clear.
We come to thy peace-ful sum - mit, Where heav-en - ly songs ev - er chime.
'Tis free-dom from Ba - bel bond - age, And com - ing, that free-dom we prove.
CHORUS
Com - - - ing, com - - - ing, Zi - on, we come to thee;
Com-ing to thee, com - ing to thee,
Com - - ing, com - - ing, Com-ing with joy to thee. A - MEN.
Com-ing to thee, com - ing to thee,

430 The Church's Jubilee

Charles W. Naylor, 1923
Andrew L. Byers, 1923
1. The light of e - ven - tide now shines the dark - ness to dis - pel,
2. The Bi - ble is our rule of faith and Christ a - lone is Lord,
3. The day of sects and creeds for us for - ev - er - more is past,
4. O bless - ed truth that broke our bonds! in it we now re - joice,
The glo - ries of fair Zi - on's state ten thou - sand voic - es tell;
All we are e - qual in his sight when we o - bey his word;
Our broth - er - hood are all the saints up - on the world so vast;
While in the ho - ly church of God we hear our Sav - ior's voice;
For out of Ba - bel God doth call his scat - tered saints in one,
No earth - ly mas - ter do we know, to man - rule will not bow,
We reach our hands in fel - low - ship to ev - ery blood-washed one,
And glad - ly to his bless - ed will sub - mis - sive we shall be,
To - geth - er all one church com - pose, the bod - y of his Son.
But to each oth - er and to God e - ter - nal true - ness vow.
While love en - twines a - bout each heart in which God's will is done.
And from the yokes of Ba - bel's lords from hence-forth we are free.
CHORUS
O Church of God, the day of ju - bi - lee ....
O bless - ed Church of God, the day of ju - bi - lee

Has dawned so bright and glo - ri - ous for thee:.......
Has dawned so fair and bright and glo - - ri - - ous for thee:
Re - joice, be...... glad! thy Shep - herd has be - gun........
Re - joice, and e'er be glad! thy Shep - herd has be - gun
His long di - vid - ed flock a - gain to gath - er in - to one. A - MEN.
Blest Feast of Love Divine
431
DENNIS. S.M.
Edward Denny, 1796-1889
From Hans G. Nageli, 1773-1836
Arr. by Lowell Mason, 1792-1872
1. Blest feast of love di - vine! 'Tis grace that makes us free To
2. That blood which flowed for sin, In sym - bol here we see, And
3. O if this glimpse of love Be so di - vine - ly sweet, What
feed up - on this bread and wine, In mem-'ry, Lord, of thee.
feel the bless - ed pledge with-in That we are loved by thee.
will it be, O Lord, a - bove, Thy gladd'ning smile to meet? A - MEN.

432 We Meet, As in That Upper Room

MORECAMBE. 10.10.10.10.

George W. Briggs, b. 1875 — Frederick C. Atkinson, 1841-1897

1. We meet, as in that upper room they met;
Thou at the table, blessing, yet dost stand:
"This is my body:" so Thou givest yet:
Faith still receives the cup as from Thy hand.
2. One body we, one body who partake,
One church united in communion blest;
One name we bear, one bread of life we break
With all Thy saints on earth and saints at rest.
3. One with each other, Lord, for one in Thee,
Who art our Saviour and our living Head;
Then open Thou our eyes, that we may see;
Be known to us in breaking of the bread. A-MEN.

433 A Parting Hymn We Sing

BOYLSTON. S.M.

Aaron R. Wolfe, 1831-1902 — Lowell Mason, 1792-1872

1. A parting hymn we sing Around thy table, Lord,
2. Here have we seen thy face, And felt thy presence here,
3. The purchase of thy blood—By sin no longer led—
4. In self-forgetful love Be our communion shown,

A - gain our grate - ful trib - ute bring, Our sol - emn vows re - cord.
So may the sav - or of thy grace In word and life ap - pear.
The path our dear Re - deem-er trod May we re - joic - ing tread.
Un - til we join the church a - bove, And know as we are known.
Here at Thy Table, Lord
434
BREAD OF LIFE. 6.4.6.4.D.
May P. Hoyt, alt.
William F. Sherwin, 1826-1888
1. As to thy ban-quet hall We en - ter in, We know thy grace and pow'r Now save from sin: Here at thy ta - ble, Lord, This sa - cred hour, O let us feel thee near In lov - ing pow'r.
2. Sit at the feast, dear Lord, Break thou the bread; Fill thou the cup that brings Life to the dead: That we may have the peace Found but in thee, And dwell, di-vine-ly kept, In lib - er - ty.
3. So shall our life of faith Be full, be sweet; And we shall find our strength For each day meet: Fed by thy liv - ing bread, All hun - ger past, We shall be sat - is - fied With thee at last.
4. Come then, O ho - ly Christ, Feed us, we pray; Touch with thy pierc - ed hand Each com - mon day; Mak - ing this earth - ly life Full of thy grace, Till in the home of heav'n We find our place. A-MEN.

435 Buried with Jesus

Daniel S. Warner, 1887
Barney E. Warren, 1887
1. Down in - to the flow - ing riv - er, Lo, the Lamb of
2. Here I fol - low the ex - am - ple Of the ho - - ly
3. Here I wit - ness a con - fes - sion As I merge from
4. O how sweet to fol - low Je - sus By this fig - - ure
God we see; There he speaks in clear ex - am - ple,
Son of God, Who has washed me in the foun - tain
hu - man sight In the tomb of yield - ing wa - ter,
thus to show That we're cleansed in life's pure riv - er,
"Take the cross and fol - low me."
Of his sin - a - ton - ing blood.
That the blood has made me white.
E - ven whit - er than the snow!
p CHORUS With expression
Gen - tly bur - ied with my
m
f
Sav - ior, Let me sink be - neath the wave; Cru - ci - fied to
earth for - ev - er, Hence a - lone to God I live. A - MEN.

Here, Savior, We Would Come 436

TRENTHAM. S.M.

Anonymous
From Alexander Campbell's *Christian Hymn Book*

Robert Jackson, 1842-1914

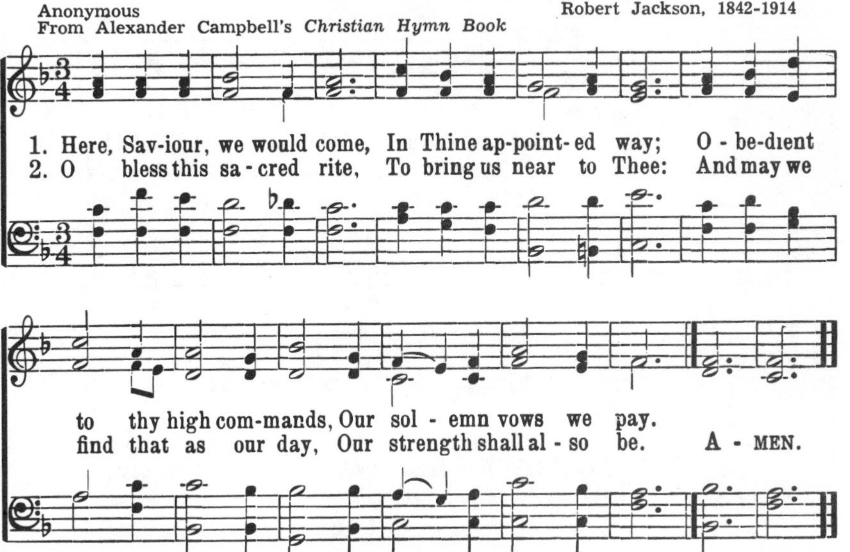
1. Here, Sav-iour, we would come, In Thine ap-point-ed way; O - be-dient to thy high com-mands, Our sol - emn vows we pay.
2. O bless this sa - cred rite, To bring us near to Thee: And may we find that as our day, Our strength shall al - so be. A - MEN.

Where Cross the Crowded Ways of Life 437

GERMANY. L.M.

Frank Mason North, 1850-1935

William Gardiner's Sacred Melodies, 1815

1. Where cross the crowd-ed ways of life, Where sound the cries of race and clan, A-
2. In haunts of wretch-ed - ness and need, On shad-owed thresholds dark with fears, From
3. The cup of wa - ter giv'n for thee Still holds the fresh-ness of thy grace; Yet
4. O Mas - ter, from the moun-tain-side, Make haste to heal these hearts of pain; A-
5. Till sons of men shall learn thy love And fol-low where thy feet have trod; Till

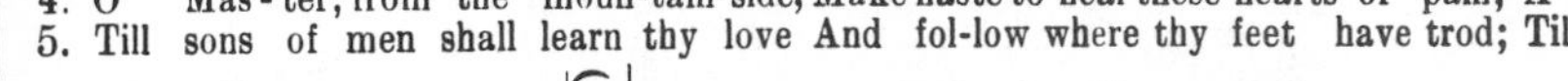

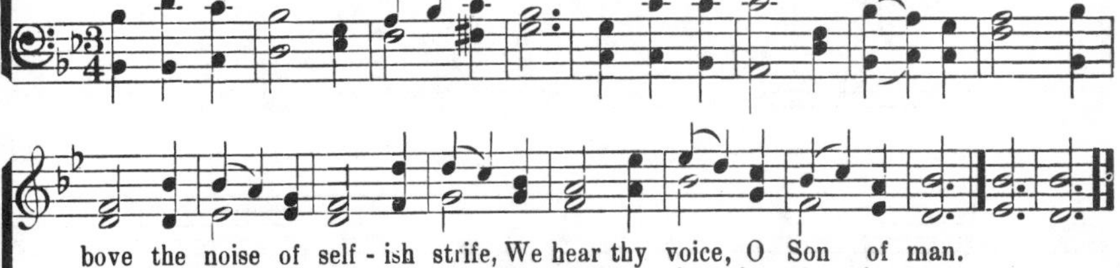

bove the noise of self - ish strife, We hear thy voice, O Son of man.
paths where hide the lures of greed, We catch the vi - sion of thy tears.
long these mul - ti-tudes to see The sweet com-pas-sion of thy face.
mong these rest-less throngs a - bide, O tread the cit - y's streets a - gain;
glo - rious from thy heav'n a - bove Shall come the cit - y of our God. A - MEN.

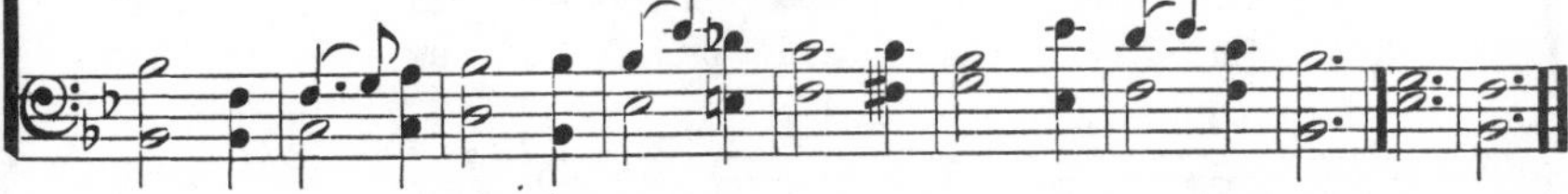

438 God of Our Fathers

NATIONAL HYMN. 10.10.10.10.

Daniel C. Roberts, 1841-1907 George W. Warren, 1828-1902

Trumpets, before each verse.
1. God of our fa - thers, whose al - might - y hand
Leads forth in beau - ty all the star - ry band
Of shin - ing worlds in splen - dor thro' the skies,
Our grate - ful songs be - fore Thy throne a - rise.
2. Thy love di - vine hath led us in the past,
In this free land by Thee our lot is cast;
Be Thou our rul - er, guard - ian, guide and stay,
Thy word our law, Thy paths our cho - sen way.
3. From war's a - larms, from dead - ly pes - ti - lence,
Be Thy strong arm our ev - er strong de - fense;
Thy true re - lig - ion in our hearts in - crease,
Thy boun - teous good - ness nour - ish us in peace.
4. Re - fresh Thy peo - ple on their toil - some way,
Lead us from night to nev - er - end - ing day;
Fill all our lives with love and grace di - vine,
And glo - ry, laud, and praise be ev - er Thine.

In Christ There Is No East or West 439

ST. PETER. C.M.

John Oxenham, 1852-1941 | Alexander R. Reinagle, 1799-1877

1. In Christ there is no East or West, In Him no South or North;
2. In Him shall true hearts ev - 'ry - where Their high com-mun - ion find;
3. Join hands then, brothers of the faith, What-e'er your race may be:
4. In Christ now meet both East and West, In Him meet South and North;

But one great fel - low-ship of Love Throughout the whole wide earth.
His serv - ice is the gold - en cord Close-bind-ing all man - kind.
Who serves my Fa - ther as a son Is sure - ly kin to Me.
All Christ - ly souls are one in Him Throughout the whole wide earth.

Words from *Bees in Amber*. Used by permission of the American Tract Society, owner of the copyright.

Blest Be the Tie That Binds 440

DENNIS. S.M.

John Fawcett, 1740-1817 | From Hans G. Nageli, 1773-1836
Arr. by Lowell Mason, 1792-1872

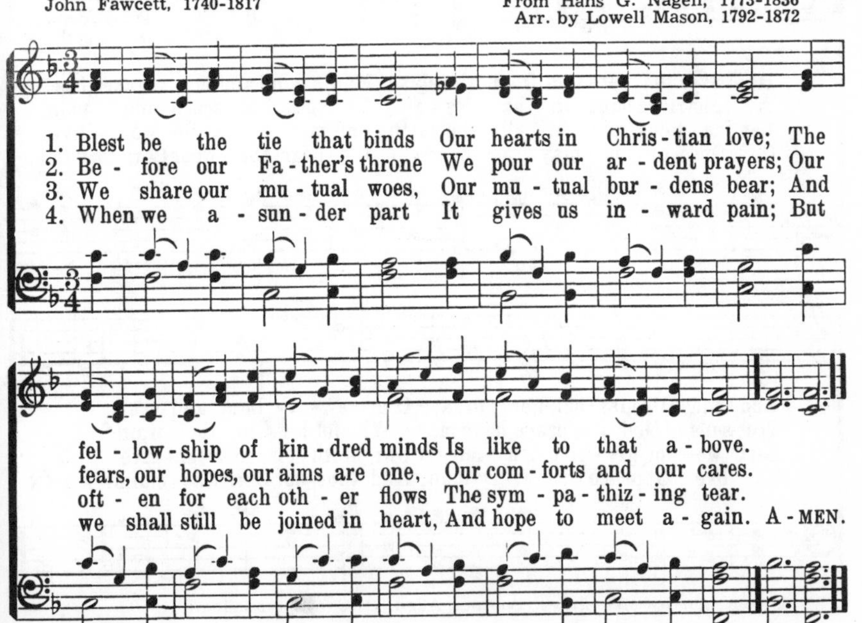
1. Blest be the tie that binds Our hearts in Chris - tian love; The
2. Be - fore our Fa - ther's throne We pour our ar - dent prayers; Our
3. We share our mu - tual woes, Our mu - tual bur - dens bear; And
4. When we a - sun - der part It gives us in - ward pain; But
fel - low - ship of kin - dred minds Is like to that a - bove.
fears, our hopes, our aims are one, Our com - forts and our cares.
oft - en for each oth - er flows The sym - pa - thiz - ing tear.
we shall still be joined in heart, And hope to meet a - gain. A - MEN.

441 The Son of God Goes Forth for Peace

ALL SAINTS, NEW. C.M.D.

Ernest Bourner Allen | Henry S. Cutler, 1824-1902

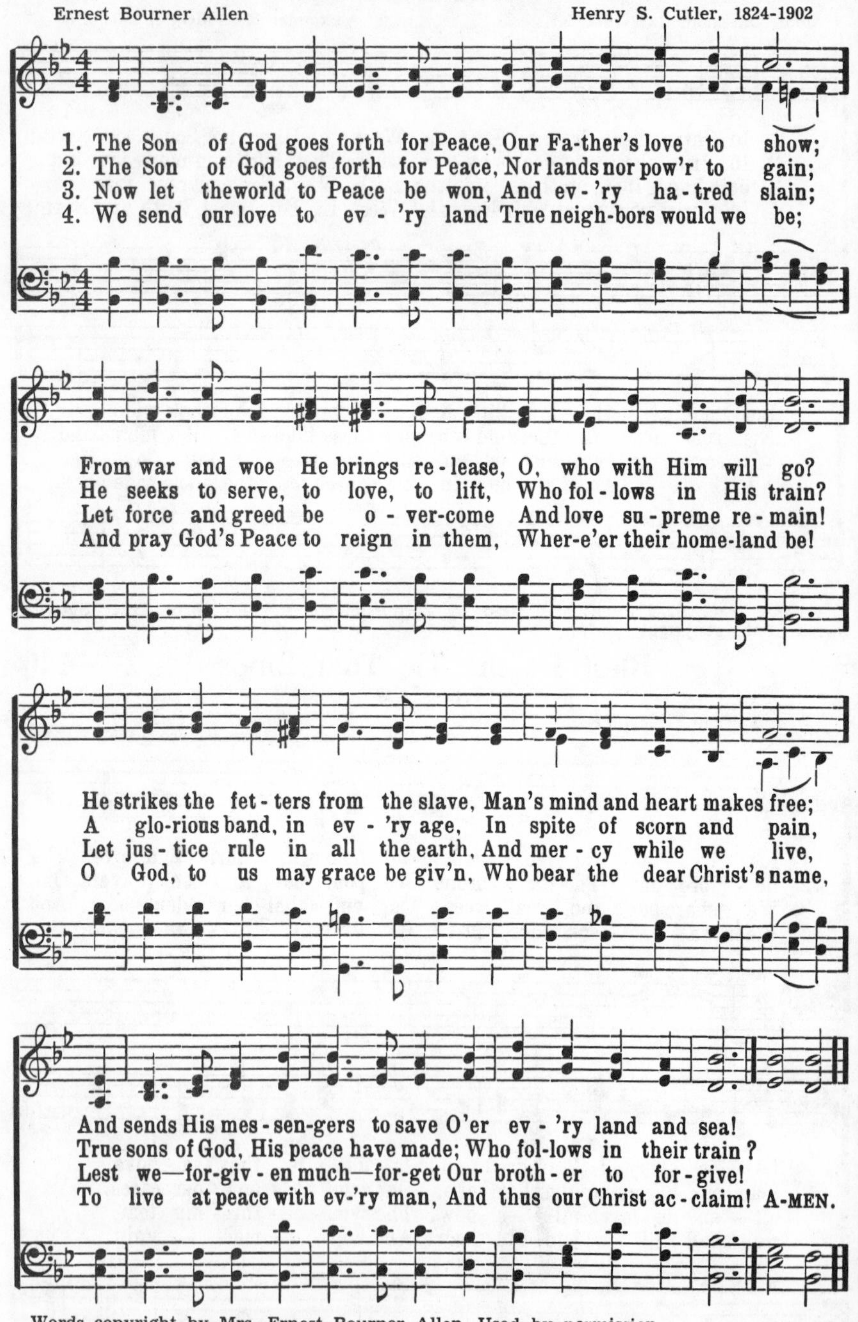
1. The Son of God goes forth for Peace, Our Fa-ther's love to show;
2. The Son of God goes forth for Peace, Nor lands nor pow'r to gain;
3. Now let the world to Peace be won, And ev-'ry ha-tred slain;
4. We send our love to ev-'ry land True neigh-bors would we be;
From war and woe He brings re-lease, O, who with Him will go?
He seeks to serve, to love, to lift, Who fol-lows in His train?
Let force and greed be o-ver-come And love su-preme re-main!
And pray God's Peace to reign in them, Wher-e'er their home-land be!
He strikes the fet-ters from the slave, Man's mind and heart makes free;
A glo-rious band, in ev-'ry age, In spite of scorn and pain,
Let jus-tice rule in all the earth, And mer-cy while we live,
O God, to us may grace be giv'n, Who bear the dear Christ's name,
And sends His mes-sen-gers to save O'er ev-'ry land and sea!
True sons of God, His peace have made; Who fol-lows in their train?
Lest we—for-giv-en much—for-get Our broth-er to for-give!
To live at peace with ev-'ry man, And thus our Christ ac-claim! A-MEN.

We've a Story to Tell to the Nations 442

Colin Sterne, 1862-1928 Adapted from H. Ernest Nichol, 1862-1928

1. We've a sto - ry to tell to the na - tions That shall
2. We've a song to be sung to the na - tions That shall
3. We've a mes - sage to give to the na - tions, That the
4. We've a Sav - ior to show to the na - tions Who the
turn their hearts to the right, A sto - ry of truth and mer - cy,
lift their hearts to the Lord, A song that shall con - quer e - vil
Lord who reign - eth a - bove Hath sent us His Son to save us,
path of sor - row hath trod, That all of the world's great peo - ples
A sto - ry of peace and light, A sto - ry of peace and light.
And shat - ter the spear and sword, And shat - ter the spear and sword.
And show us that God is love, And show us that God is love.
Might come to the truth of God, Might come to the truth of God.
Chorus
For the darkness shall turn to dawn-ing, And the dawning to noonday bright,
rall.
And Christ's great kingdom shall come to earth, The kingdom of love and light.

443 O Zion, Haste

TIDINGS. 11.10.11.10. with Refrain

Mary A. Thompson, 1834-1923 James Walch, 1837-1901

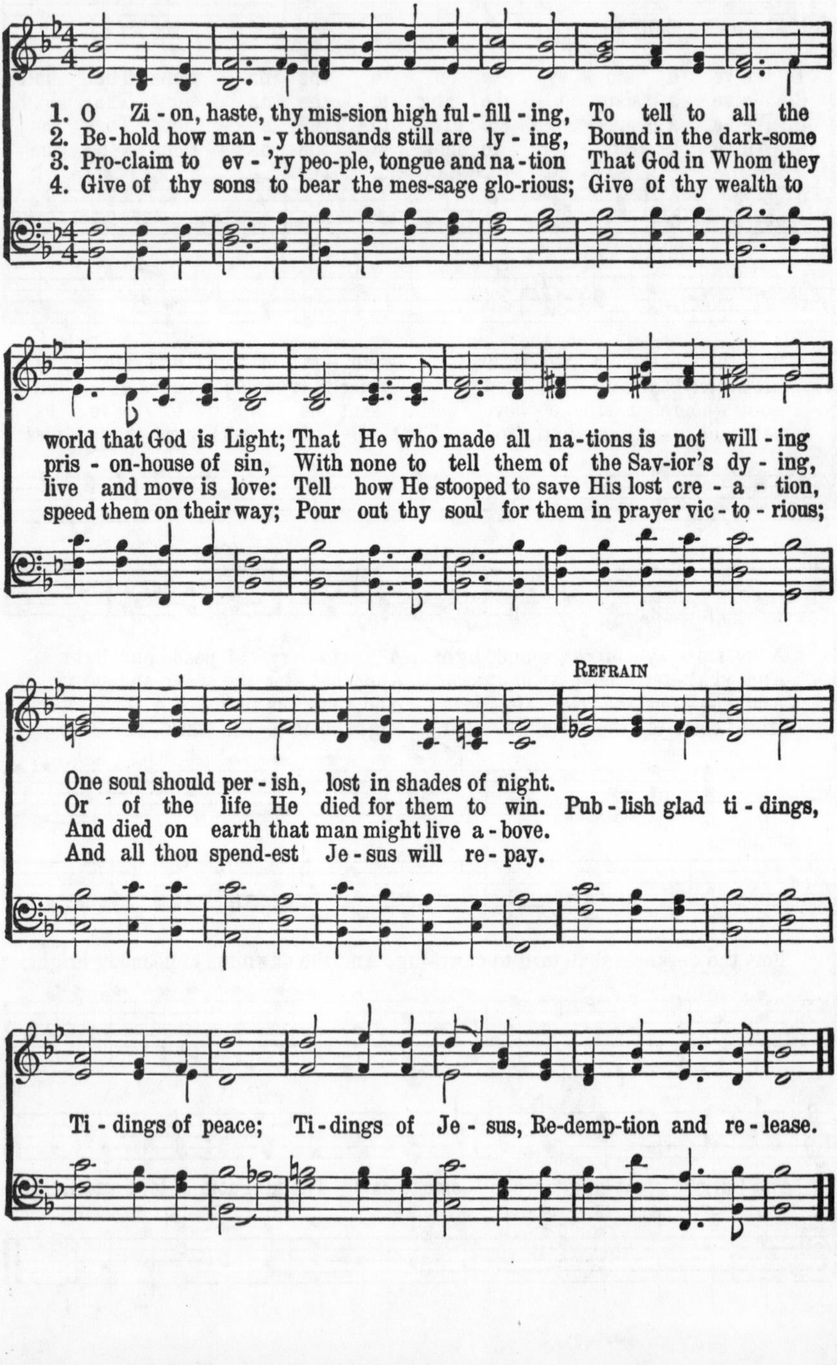

1. O Zi - on, haste, thy mis-sion high ful - fill - ing, To tell to all the
2. Be - hold how man - y thousands still are ly - ing, Bound in the dark-some
3. Pro - claim to ev - 'ry peo - ple, tongue and na - tion That God in Whom they
4. Give of thy sons to bear the mes-sage glo-rious; Give of thy wealth to

world that God is Light; That He who made all na - tions is not will - ing
pris - on-house of sin, With none to tell them of the Sav-ior's dy - ing,
live and move is love: Tell how He stooped to save His lost cre - a - tion,
speed them on their way; Pour out thy soul for them in prayer vic - to - rious;

One soul should per - ish, lost in shades of night.
Or of the life He died for them to win.
And died on earth that man might live a - bove.
And all thou spend-est Je - sus will re - pay.

REFRAIN

Pub - lish glad ti - dings,

Ti - dings of peace; Ti - dings of Je - sus, Re-demp-tion and re - lease.

Rescue the Perishing 444

Fanny J. Crosby, 1820-1915 William Howard Doane, 1832-1915

1. Res - cue the per-ish-ing, Care for the dy - ing, Snatch them in pit - y from
2. Tho' they are slighting Him, Still He is wait-ing, Wait-ing the pen - i - tent
3. Down in the hu-man heart, Crushed by the tempter, Feel-ings lie bur - ied that
4. Res - cue the per-ish-ing, Du - ty de-mands it; Strength for thy la-bor the

sin and the grave; Weep o'er the er - ring one, Lift up the fall - en,
child to re - ceive; Plead with them ear-nest-ly, Plead with them gen-tly,
grace can re - store; Touched by a lov - ing heart, Wak-ened by kind-ness,
Lord will pro - vide; Back to the nar-row way Pa - tient - ly win them;

CHORUS

Tell them of Je - sus the migh - ty to save.
He will for - give if they on - ly be-lieve. Res-cue the per - ish-ing,
Chords that are bro - ken will vi - brate once more.
Tell the poor wan-d'rer a Sav - ior has died.

Care for the dy - ing; Je - sus is mer - ci - ful, Je - sus will save.

445 Send the Light

Charles H. Gabriel, 1856-1932 — Charles H. Gabriel, 1856-1932

1. There's a call comes ring - ing o'er the rest - less wave, "Send the light! .... send the light!"
2. We have heard the Mac - e - do - nian call to - day, "Send the light! .... send the light!"
3. Let us pray that grace may ev - ery-where a-bound; Send the light! .... send the light!
4. Let us not grow wea - ry in the work of love, Send the light! .... send the light!
Send the light!
send the light!
There are souls to res - cue, there are souls to save,
And a gold - en of - f'ring at the cross we lay,
And a Christ-like spir - it ev - ery-where be found,
Let us gath - er jew - els for a crown a - bove,
Send the light! ...... send the light! ....
Send the light! send the light!
Refrain
Send the light, ... the bless - ed gos - pel light; Let it shine .... from shore to shore! ....
Send the light, the bless - ed gos - pel light; Let it shine from shore to shore!
1
2
shine .... for - ev - er - more. ....
Let it shine for - ev - er-more.

The Touch of His Tender Hand 446

Clara M. Brooks, c. 1918 — Andrew L. Byers, 1918

1. Far a - way in a land that is dark - er than night, With nev - er a star in the sky, In the isles of the sea for a Sav - ior they wait— For the touch of his hand they sigh.

2. Un - loved and un-cher - ished they sink in - to woe For com - fort your hands could be - stow; O Sav - ior, thy heart must be break - ing with grief, Still call - ing for reap - ers to go.

3. The Day - star is shed - ding his beau - ti - ful rays That each may be warmed and be blest; Yet mil - lions now per - ish from cold win-ter's blast, And die with - out com - fort or rest.

4. The Hand that bro't life to the lone wid-ow's son, And heal - ing in dear Gal - i - lee— For its life - giv - ing touch they are call - ing a - far, They are call - ing to you and to me.

Chorus

For the touch of his hand, (For the touch of his ten - der hand,) For the touch of his hand, (For the touch of his ten - der hand,) They wait in the isles of the roll - ing sea For the touch of his ten - der hand.

447 Hear Them Calling

William G. Schell, 1893

Barney E. Warren, 1893

1. On the bor-ders of e-ter-ni-ty the world is stand-ing now,
2. We're re-joic-ing for our free-dom in the glo-rious gos-pel light.
3. "Go ye, there-fore," said the Mas-ter; do you hear the great command?
In a mo-ment all the wick-ed will be lost in end-less woe;
Yet the mil-lions have not seen it, still they roam in deep-est night;
Bear the mes-sage of sal-va-tion to the lost in ev-ery land:
O they need the gos-pel mes-sage that they may sal-va-tion know,
Hear, O hear from ev-ery na-tion cries of sor-row and dis-tress,
O re-view your con-se-cra-tion, look up-on the har-vest field;
Who will has-ten now to tell them? broth-er, sis-ter, will you go?
Time is sure-ly, swift-ly end-ing, haste their dy-ing souls to bless.
Go and la-bor till the eve-ning—there shall be a gold-en yield.
CHORUS
Hear them call - - - ing for the gos - - - pel, Come and
Call-ing, hear them call-ing, call-ing for the gos-pel,

1
2
help us to be saved; . . . to be saved. . . .
Help us, come and help us, help us to be saved; come and help us to be saved.

From Greenland's Icy Mountains 448

MISSIONARY HYMN. 7.6.7.6.D.

Reginald Heber, 1783-1826 Lowell Mason, 1792-1872

1. From Greenland's i-cy mountains, From In-dia's cor-al strand; Where Afric's sun-ny
2. What tho' the spi - cy breez - es Blow soft o'er Ceylon's isle; Tho' ev-ery pros-pect
3. Shall we, whose souls are lighted With wisdom from on high, Shall we to men be-
4. Waft, waft, ye winds, his sto - ry, And you, ye wa-ters, roll, Till like a sea of

foun-tains Roll down their golden sand; From many an an-cient riv - er, From many a
pleas - es, And on - ly man is vile: In vain with lav - ish kind-ness The gifts of
night - ed The lamp of life de - ny? Sal - va - tion! O sal - va-tion! The joy - ful
glo - ry It spreads from pole to pole; Till o'er our ransomed na-ture The Lamb for

palm - y plain, They call us to de - liv - er Their land from error's chain.
God are strown; The hea-then in his blind-ness Bows down to wood and stone.
sound proclaim, Till earth's re-mot-est na-tion Has learned Messiah's name.
sin - ners slain, Re-deem-er, King, Cre-a - tor, In bliss re - turns a - gain. A - MEN.

449 Christ for the World We Sing

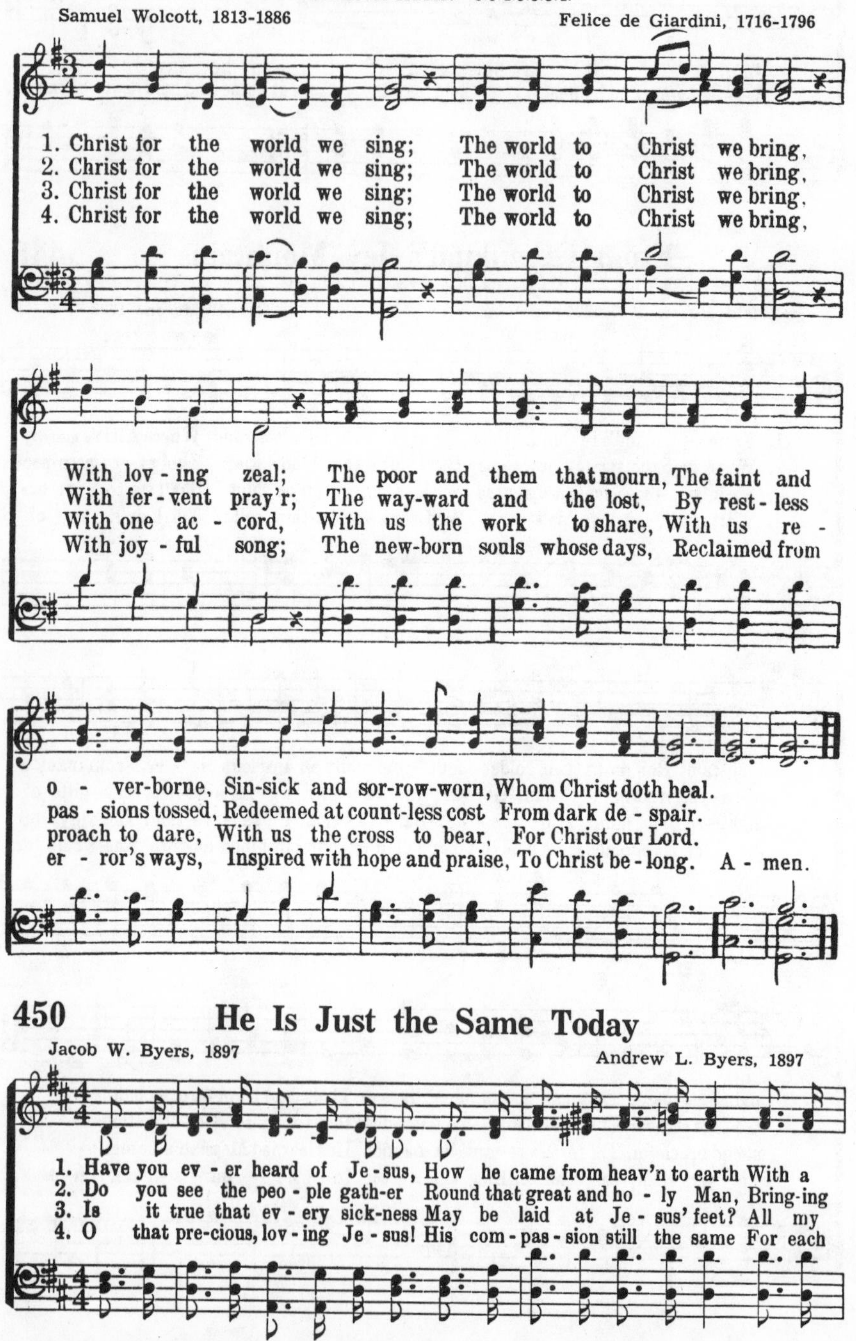
ITALIAN HYMN. 6.6.4.6.6.6.4.
Samuel Wolcott, 1813-1886
Felice de Giardini, 1716-1796
1. Christ for the world we sing; The world to Christ we bring, With lov-ing zeal; The poor and them that mourn, The faint and o-ver-borne, Sin-sick and sor-row-worn, Whom Christ doth heal.
2. Christ for the world we sing; The world to Christ we bring, With fer-vent pray'r; The way-ward and the lost, By rest-less pas-sions tossed, Redeemed at count-less cost From dark de-spair.
3. Christ for the world we sing; The world to Christ we bring, With one ac-cord, With us the work to share, With us re-proach to dare, With us the cross to bear, For Christ our Lord.
4. Christ for the world we sing; The world to Christ we bring, With joy-ful song; The new-born souls whose days, Reclaimed from er-ror's ways, Inspired with hope and praise, To Christ be-long. A-men.
450
He Is Just the Same Today
Jacob W. Byers, 1897
Andrew L. Byers, 1897
1. Have you ev-er heard of Je-sus, How he came from heav'n to earth With a
2. Do you see the peo-ple gath-er Round that great and ho-ly Man, Bring-ing
3. Is it true that ev-ery sick-ness May be laid at Je-sus' feet? All my
4. O that pre-cious, lov-ing Je-sus! His com-pas-sion still the same For each

name of might-y vir-tue, Tho' by ver - y hum-ble birth? When the world was held in
all the sick and suff'ring, Com-ing to him all who can? See him look with great com-
troub-le, care, and sor-row, And I rest in joy com-plete? Yes, my broth-er, ev - ery
sin - ful, suf-f'ring mor-tal Who seeks ref-uge in his name. Heed the pres - ent in - vi-
bond-age Un - der Sa-tan's dis-mal sway, Je - sus healed their dread dis-eas-es—He is
pas - sion As they faint - ed by the way! How he called them gen-tly to him! He is
sad-ness, If by faith to him you pray, He'll re-move with ten - der mer-cy, For he's
ta - tion, O you need not stay a - way! Come, re-ceive his heal - ing fa - vor, For he's
CHORUS
just the same to-day. He is just.......... the same to-day, He is
He is just the same to-day, just the same to-day, He is
just............ the same to-day (the same to-day); Yes, he healed in Gal - li - lee,
just the same to-day, just the same to-day;
Set the suf-f'ring captives free, And he's just...... the same to-day (the same to-day).
And he's just the same, he is just the same to-day.
And he's just the same, the same to - day.............

451 Healing in His Wings

Mary J. Nichols, 1913 — Andrew L. Byers, 1923

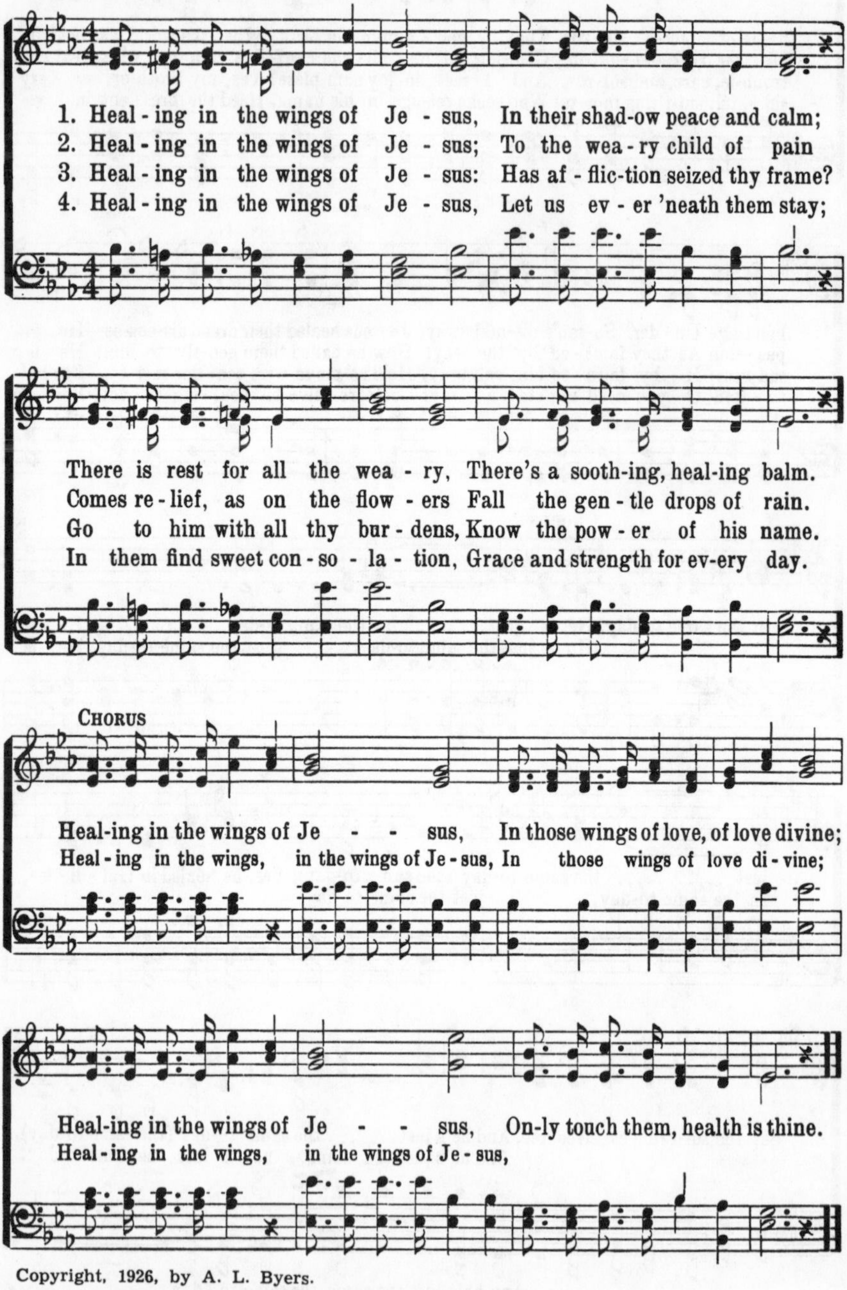

1. Heal - ing in the wings of Je - sus, In their shad-ow peace and calm;
There is rest for all the wea - ry, There's a sooth-ing, heal-ing balm.

2. Heal - ing in the wings of Je - sus; To the wea - ry child of pain
Comes re - lief, as on the flow - ers Fall the gen - tle drops of rain.

3. Heal - ing in the wings of Je - sus: Has af - flic-tion seized thy frame?
Go to him with all thy bur - dens, Know the pow - er of his name.

4. Heal - ing in the wings of Je - sus, Let us ev - er 'neath them stay;
In them find sweet con - so - la - tion, Grace and strength for ev-ery day.

Chorus

Heal-ing in the wings of Je - - sus, In those wings of love, of love divine;
Heal - ing in the wings, in the wings of Je - sus, In those wings of love di - vine;
Heal-ing in the wings of Je - - sus, On-ly touch them, health is thine.
Heal - ing in the wings, in the wings of Je - sus,

O Lord, Thou Healest Me!

452

Daniel S. Warner, 1887 — Barney E. Warren, 1887

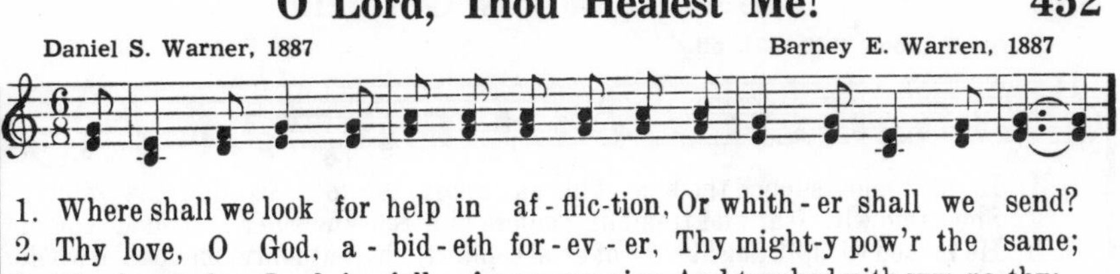

1. Where shall we look for help in af - flic-tion, Or whith - er shall we send?
2. Thy love, O God, a - bid - eth for - ev - er, Thy might-y pow'r the same;
3. Thy heart, dear Lord, is full of com-pas-sion And touched with sym-pa-thy;
4. O Christ, thou art my per-fect Phy - si-cian, Thro' faith I now am whole;

"The prayer of faith will save," it is writ-ten, 'Tis truth till time shall end.
And all thy Word de-clares thou art will - ing To heal the sick and lame.
Why then should I con - tin - ue to suf - fer? I know thou heal - est me.
Thy heal-ing touch per - vad-eth my bod - y And thrills with joy my soul.

CHORUS

I touch the word of his prom - ise, As firm as heav-en's throne;

And trust - ing him this ver - y mo-ment, I know the work is done.

453 The Hem of His Garment

George F. Root, 1820-1895, alt. — George F. Root, 1820-1895

1. In faith she touched the hem of his gar-ment As to his side she stole,
2. She came with fear and trembling before him, She knew her Lord had come;
3. He turned with, "Daughter, be of good comfort, Thy faith hath made thee whole;"

A - mid the crowd that gathered a-round him, And straightway she was whole.
She felt that from him vir-tue had healed her, The might-y deed was done.
And peace which passeth all un-der-stand-ing With gladness filled her soul.

CHORUS

I've touched the hem of his gar - ment, And now I, too, am free;

His heal - ing pow'r; this ver - y hour, Gives life and health to me.

454 Happy the Home When God Is There

ST. AGNES. C.M.

Henry Ware, the Younger, 1794-1843 — John B. Dykes, 1823-1876

1. Hap - py the home when God is there, And love fills ev - ery breast;
2. Hap - py the home where Je - sus' Name Is sweet to ev - ery ear;
3. Hap - py the home where prayer is heard, And praise is wont to rise;
4. Lord, let us in our homes a - gree This bless-ed peace to gain;

When one their wish, and one their prayer, And one their heaven-ly rest.
Where chil-dren ear - ly lisp His fame, And par-ents hold Him dear.
Where par-ents love the sa - cred Word And all its wis-dom prize.
U - nite our hearts in love to Thee, And love to all will reign. A-MEN.
O Happy Home
455
ALVERSTOKE. 11.10.11.10.
Carl J. P. Spitta, 1801-1859
Adapted from a tr. by Sarah B. Findlater, 1823-1907
Joseph Barnby, 1838-1896
1. O hap - py home, where Thou art loved the dear - est,
2. O hap - py home, where each one serves Thee, low - ly,
3. O hap - py home, where Thou art not for - got - ten
4. Un - til at last, when earth's day's work is end - ed
Thou lov - ing Friend, and Sav - iour of our race,
What - ev - er his ap - point - ed work may be,
When joy is o - ver - flow - ing, full, and free;
All meet Thee in the bless - ed home a - bove,
And where a - mong the guests there nev - er com - eth
Till ev - ery com - mon task seems great and ho - ly,
O hap - py home, where ev - ery wound - ed spir - it
From whence Thou cam - est, where Thou hast as - scend - ed,
One who can hold such high and hon - ored place!
When it is done, O Lord, as un - to Thee!
Is brought, Phy - si - cian, Com - fort - er, to Thee—
Thy ev - er - last - ing home of peace and love! A - MEN.

456 O Perfect Love

O PERFECT LOVE. 11.10.11.10.

Dorothy B. Gurney, 1858-1932 — Arr. from Joseph Barnby, 1838-1896

1. O per - fect Love, all hu - man thought tran-scend - ing,
2. O per - fect Life, be Thou their full as - sur - ance
3. Grant them the joy which bright-ens earth - ly sor - row;
Low - ly we kneel in prayer be - fore Thy throne,
Of ten - der char - i - ty and stead - fast faith,
Grant them the peace which calms all earth - ly strife,
That theirs may be the love which knows no end - ing,
Of pa - tient hope and qui - et, brave en - dur - ance,
And to life's day the glo - rious un-known mor - row
Whom Thou for ev - er - more dost join in one.
With child - like trust that fears nor pain nor death.
That dawns up - on e - ter - nal love and life.
A-MEN.

Lord of Life and King of Glory 457

SICILIAN MARINERS' HYMN. 8.7.8.7.8.7.

Christian Burke, b. 1859

Arr. from a Sicilian melody

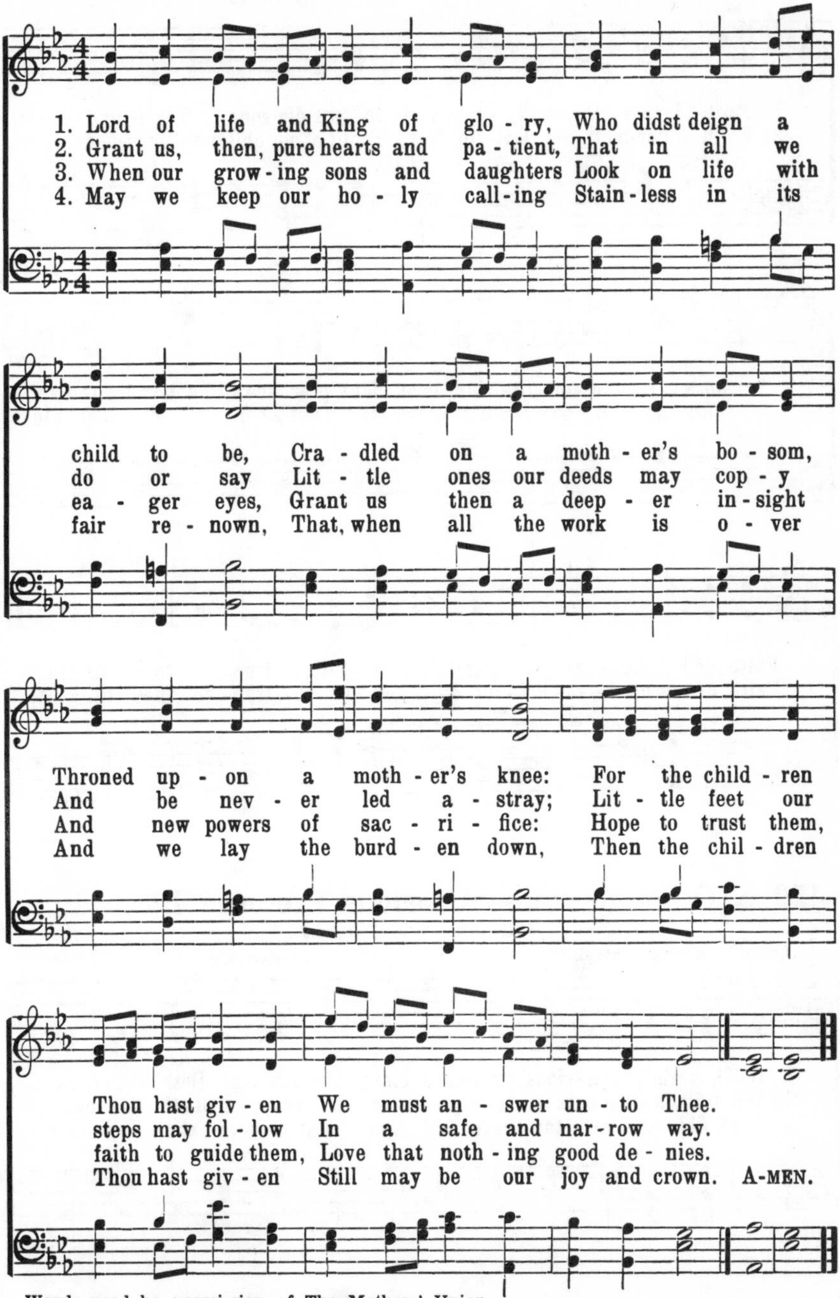

1. Lord of life and King of glo - ry, Who didst deign a child to be, Cra - dled on a moth - er's bo - som, Throned up - on a moth - er's knee: For the child - ren Thou hast giv - en We must an - swer un - to Thee.

2. Grant us, then, pure hearts and pa - tient, That in all we do or say Lit - tle ones our deeds may cop - y And be nev - er led a - stray; Lit - tle feet our steps may fol - low In a safe and nar - row way.

3. When our grow - ing sons and daughters Look on life with ea - ger eyes, Grant us then a deep - er in - sight And new powers of sac - ri - fice: Hope to trust them, faith to guide them, Love that noth - ing good de - nies.

4. May we keep our ho - ly call - ing Stain - less in its fair re - nown, That, when all the work is o - ver And we lay the burd - en down, Then the chil - dren Thou hast giv - en Still may be our joy and crown. A-MEN.

458 Faith of Our Mothers

ST. CATHERINE. 8.8.8.8.8.8.

A. B. Patton

Henry F. Hemy, 1818-1888
alt. by James G. Walton, 1821-1905

1. Faith of our moth-ers, liv - ing still In cra-dle song and bed-time prayer;
2. Faith of our moth-ers, lov - ing faith, Fount of our childhood's trust and grace,

In nurs-ery lore and fire-side love, Thy presence still per-vades the air:
Oh, may thy con - se - cra-tion prove Source of a fin - er, no - bler race:

Faith of our moth-ers, liv - ing faith, We will be true to thee till death.
Faith of our moth-ers, lov - ing faith, We will be true to thee till death.

459 O Thou Whose Gracious Presence Blest

WHITTIER (REST). 8.6.8.8.6.

Louis F. Benson, 1855-1930

Frederick C. Maker, 1844-1927

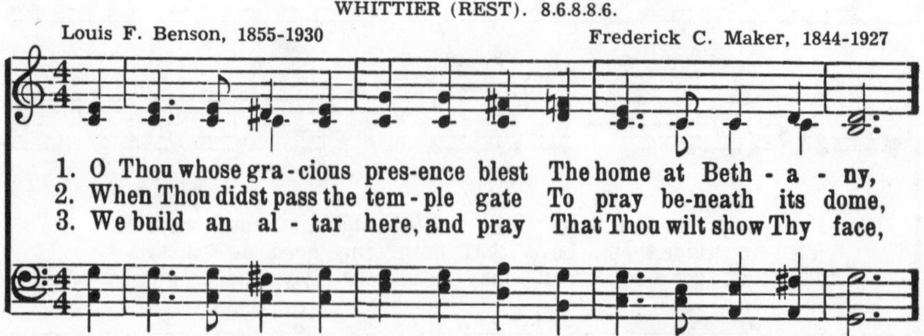
1. O Thou whose gra-cious pres-ence blest The home at Beth - a - ny,
2. When Thou didst pass the tem - ple gate To pray be-neath its dome,
3. We build an al - tar here, and pray That Thou wilt show Thy face,

This shel - ter from the world's un - rest, This home made read - y for its guest, We ded - i - cate to Thee.
It was Thy Fa - ther's house, more great Be - cause by love made con - se - crate; It was Thine on - ly home.
Dear Lord, if Thou wilt come to stay, This home we con - se- crate to - day Will be a ho - ly place. A-MEN.
Words used by permission of Mrs. Robert F. Jeffreys.
Praise Him, Praise Him
460
Anonymous
Anonymous
1. Praise him, praise him, all ye lit - tle chil-dren, God is love, God is love;
2. Love him, love him, all ye lit - tle chil-dren, God is love, God is love;
3. Thank him, thank him, all ye lit - tle chil-dren, God is love, God is love;
4. Serve him, serve him, all ye lit - tle chil-dren, God is love, God is love;
Praise him, praise him, all ye lit-tle children, God is love, God is love.
Love him, love him, all ye lit-tle children, God is love, God is love.
Thank him, thank him, all ye lit-tle children, God is love, God is love.
Serve him, serve him, all ye lit-tle children, God is love, God is love. A-MEN.

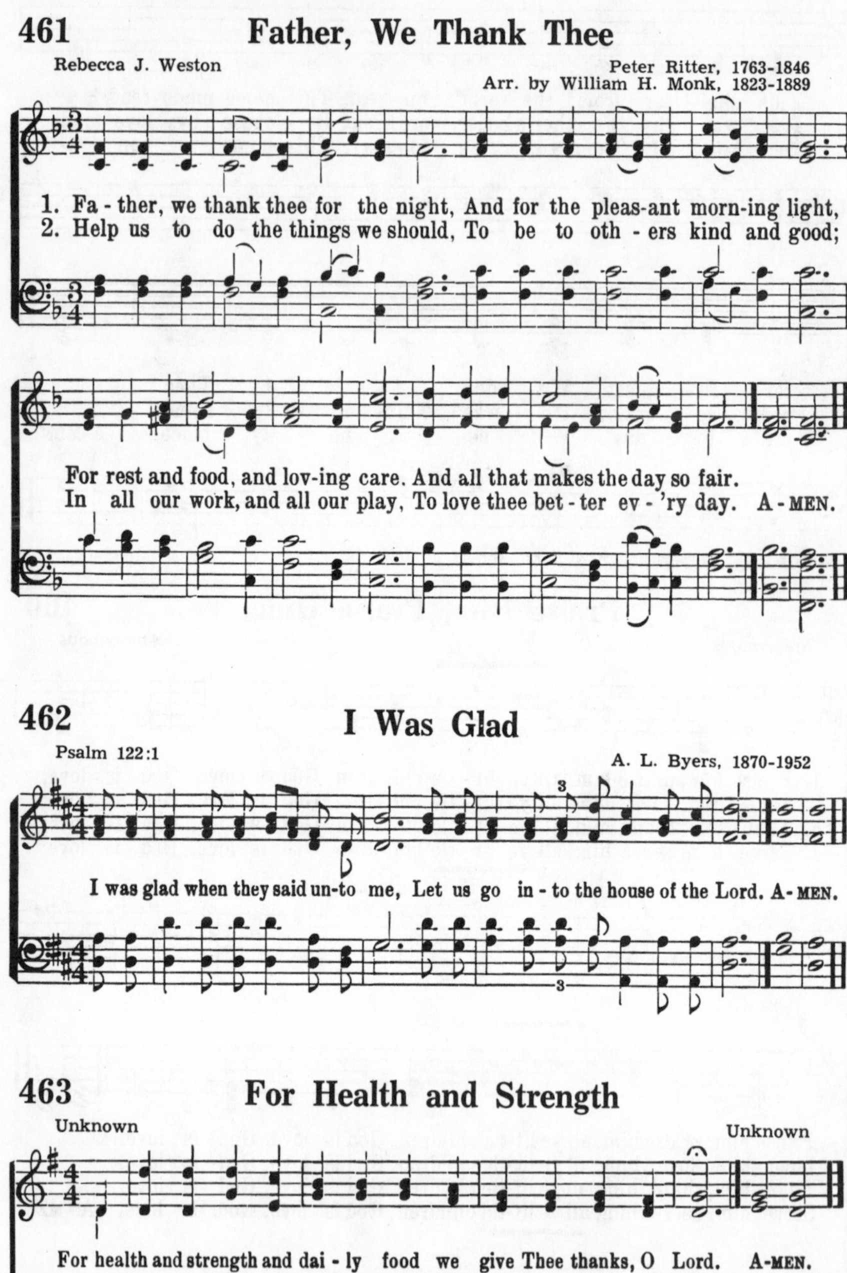
461 Father, We Thank Thee
Rebecca J. Weston
Peter Ritter, 1763-1846
Arr. by William H. Monk, 1823-1889
1. Fa - ther, we thank thee for the night, And for the pleas-ant morn-ing light,
2. Help us to do the things we should, To be to oth - ers kind and good;
For rest and food, and lov-ing care. And all that makes the day so fair.
In all our work, and all our play, To love thee bet - ter ev - 'ry day. A - MEN.
462 I Was Glad
Psalm 122:1
A. L. Byers, 1870-1952
I was glad when they said un-to me, Let us go in - to the house of the Lord. A - MEN.
463 For Health and Strength
Unknown
Unknown
For health and strength and dai - ly food we give Thee thanks, O Lord. A-MEN.

A Thankful Song 464

Mary Rumsey

Alsatian

To God, who gives our dai - ly bread, A thank - ful song we'll raise,
And pray that He, who sends us food, May fill our hearts with praise.

Thanks for Bread 465

Traditional

Traditional

1. Morn - ing has come, the ta - ble spread.
2. Noon - time has come, the ta - ble spread.
3. Eve - ning has come, the ta - ble spread.

Thanks be to God who gives us bread. A - MEN.

466 O That Will Be Glory

Charles H. Gabriel, 1856-1932 Charles H. Gabriel, 1856-1932

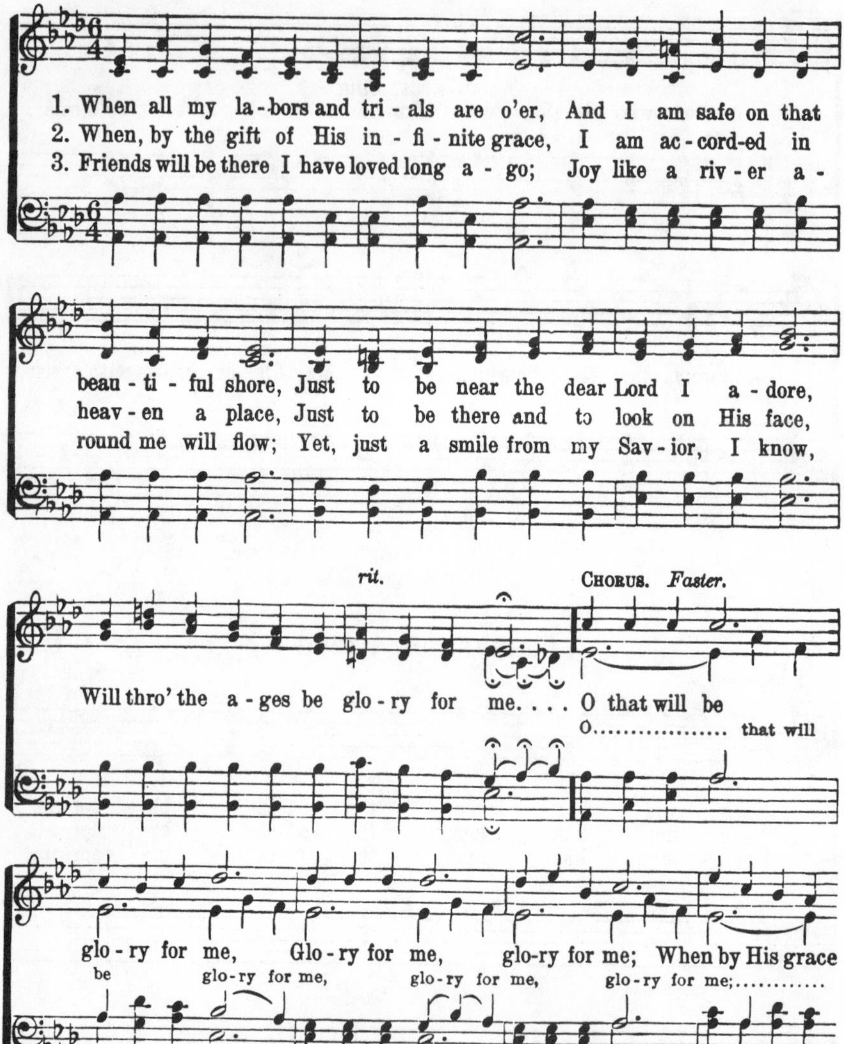

1. When all my la-bors and tri-als are o'er, And I am safe on that beau-ti-ful shore, Just to be near the dear Lord I a-dore, Will thro' the a-ges be glo-ry for me. . . .
2. When, by the gift of His in-fi-nite grace, I am ac-cord-ed in heav-en a place, Just to be there and to look on His face,
3. Friends will be there I have loved long a-go; Joy like a riv-er a-round me will flow; Yet, just a smile from my Sav-ior, I know,

rit.

CHORUS. *Faster.*

O that will be glo-ry for me, Glo-ry for me, glo-ry for me; When by His grace I shall look on His face, That will be glo-ry, be glo-ry for me.

O.................. that will be glo-ry for me, glo-ry for me, glo-ry for me;............

rit.

When We All Get to Heaven 467

Eliza E. Hewitt, b. 1851

Mrs. J. G. Wilson

1. Sing the won-drous love of Je - sus, Sing his mer - cy and his grace;
2. While we walk the pil - grim pathway, Clouds will o - ver-spread the sky;
3. Let us then be true and faith - ful, Trust-ing, serv - ing ev - ery day;
4. On - ward to the prize be - fore us! Soon his beau-ty we'll be - hold;
In the man-sions, bright and bless-ed, He'll pre-pare for us a place.
But when trav-'ling days are o - ver, Not a shad-ow, not a sigh.
Just one glimpse of him in glo - ry Will the toils of life re - pay.
Soon the pearl - y gates will o - pen, We shall tread the streets of gold.
for us a place.
CHORUS
When we all get to heav - en, What a day of re-
When we all
What a
joic - ing that will be! When we all see
day of re - joic - ing that will be! When we all
Je - sus, We'll sing and shout the vic - to - ry. . . . . . .
shout, and shout the vic - to - ry.

468 When My King Shall Call for Me

Lizzie DeArmond, 1924 | Andrew L. Byers, 1924

1. With a hap-py song I will haste a-long, In his serv-ice faith-ful be;
2. In the val-ley deep, on the mountain steep, Tho' his face I can-not see,
3. He will hold me fast to the ver-y last, For a tow'r of strength is he;
4. In a cheer-y way let me toil each day, Help-ing oth-ers lov-ing-ly,

All the things that fret I shall soon for-get, When my King shall call for me.
With a pur-pose true all his will I'll do Till my King shall call for me.
So I'll sing his praise thro' the long, long days, When my King shall call for me.
With my work well done at the set of sun, When my King shall call for me.

CHORUS

May he find me in my place When my King shall call for me; . . .
May he find me in my place When my King shall call for me;

With a loy-al heart do-ing well my part When my King shall call for me.

When We Get Home

Luella Byers Henry, 1890

C. Z. Lindley, 1890

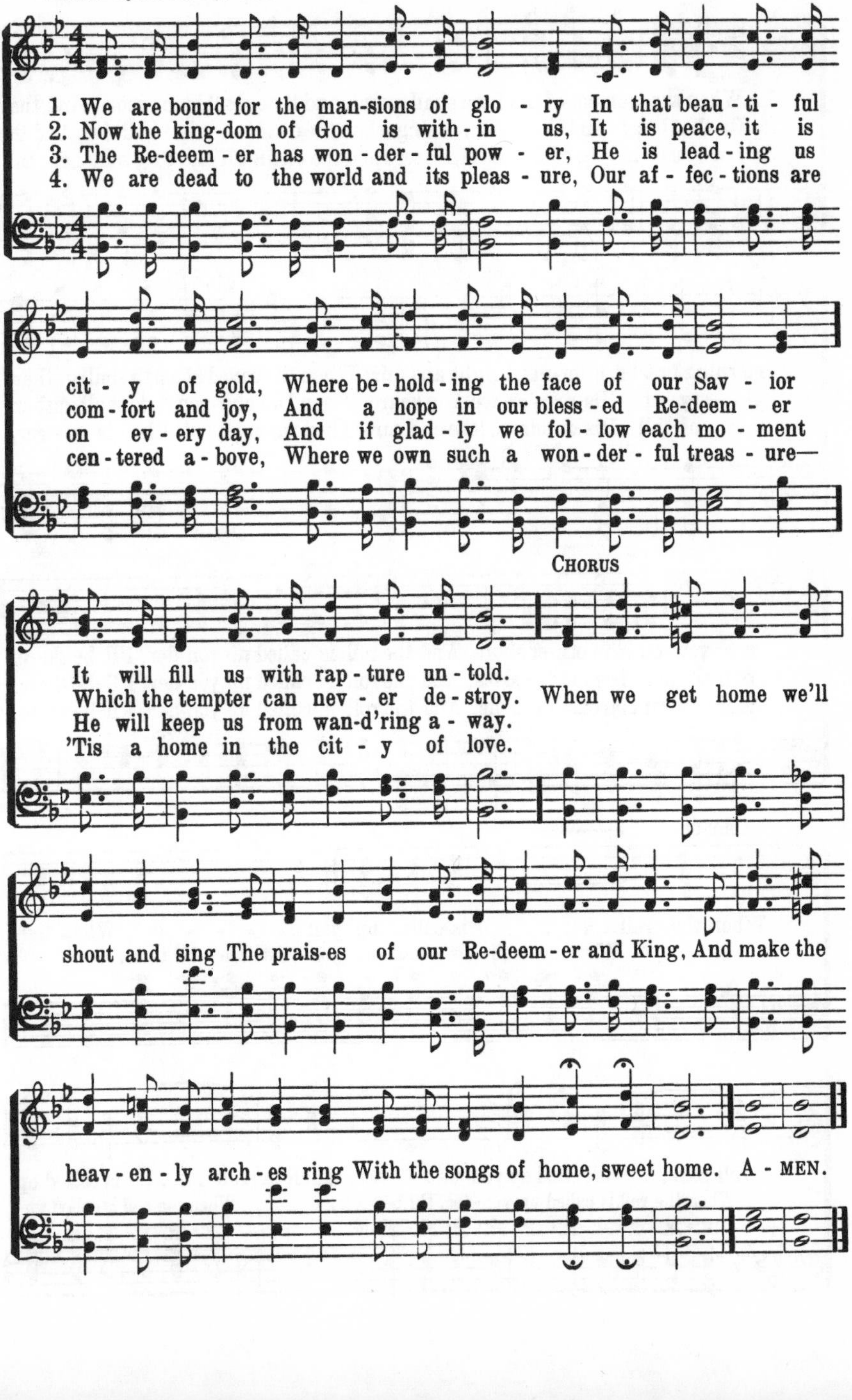

1. We are bound for the man-sions of glo - ry In that beau - ti - ful
2. Now the king-dom of God is with - in us, It is peace, it is
3. The Re-deem - er has won - der - ful pow - er, He is lead - ing us
4. We are dead to the world and its pleas - ure, Our af - fec - tions are

cit - y of gold, Where be - hold - ing the face of our Sav - ior
com - fort and joy, And a hope in our bless - ed Re-deem - er
on ev - ery day, And if glad - ly we fol - low each mo - ment
cen - tered a - bove, Where we own such a won - der - ful treas - ure—

It will fill us with rap - ture un - told.
Which the tempter can nev - er de - stroy.
He will keep us from wan-d'ring a - way.
'Tis a home in the cit - y of love.

CHORUS

When we get home we'll shout and sing The prais-es of our Re-deem - er and King, And make the heav - en - ly arch - es ring With the songs of home, sweet home. A - MEN.

470 When the Roll Is Called Up Yonder
J. M. Black, b. 1859
J. M. Black, b. 1859
1. When the trumpet of the Lord shall sound, and time shall be no more, And the morning breaks, e-ter-nal, bright and fair; When the saved of earth shall gather o - ver on the oth-er shore, And the roll is called up yon-der, I'll be there.
2. On that bright and cloudless morning when the dead in Christ shall rise, And the glo - ry of His res - ur-rec-tion share; When His cho-sen ones shall gather to their home beyond the skies, And the roll is called up yon-der, I'll be there.
3. Let us la - bor for the Mas - ter from the dawn till set - ting sun, Let us talk of all His wondrous love and care; Then when all of life is o - ver, and our work on earth is done, And the roll is called up yon-der, I'll be there.
CHORUS.
When the roll . . . . . . is called up yon - - - - der, When the roll . . . . is called up yon - - der, When the roll . . . . is called up
When the roll is called up yon - der, I'll be there, When the roll is called up yon-der, I'll be there, When the roll is called up

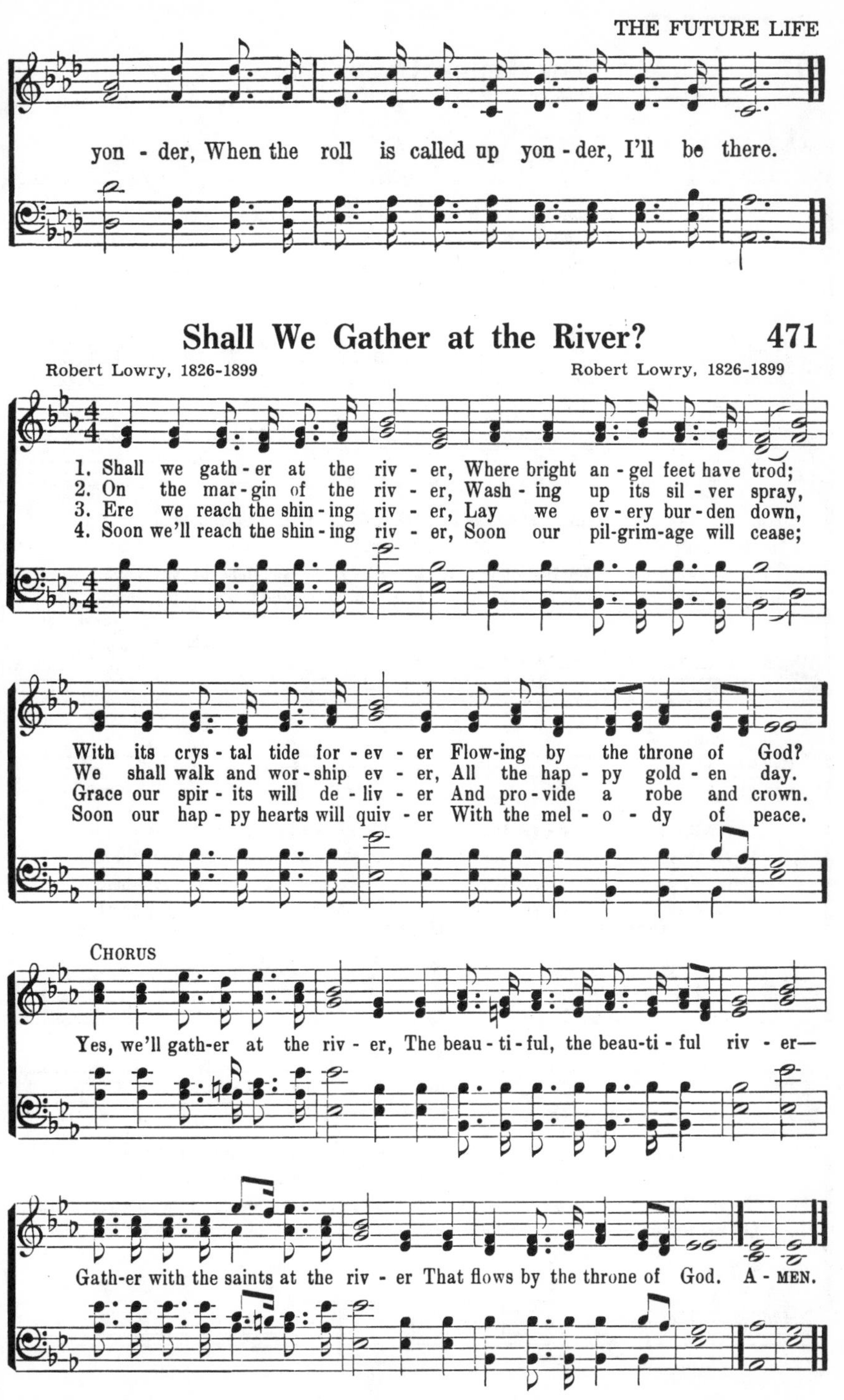
yon - der, When the roll is called up yon - der, I'll be there.
Shall We Gather at the River? 471
Robert Lowry, 1826-1899
Robert Lowry, 1826-1899
1. Shall we gath - er at the riv - er, Where bright an - gel feet have trod;
2. On the mar - gin of the riv - er, Wash - ing up its sil - ver spray,
3. Ere we reach the shin - ing riv - er, Lay we ev - ery bur - den down,
4. Soon we'll reach the shin - ing riv - er, Soon our pil - grim - age will cease;
With its crys - tal tide for - ev - er Flow - ing by the throne of God?
We shall walk and wor - ship ev - er, All the hap - py gold - en day.
Grace our spir - its will de - liv - er And pro - vide a robe and crown.
Soon our hap - py hearts will quiv - er With the mel - o - dy of peace.
CHORUS
Yes, we'll gath - er at the riv - er, The beau - ti - ful, the beau - ti - ful riv - er—
Gath - er with the saints at the riv - er That flows by the throne of God. A - MEN.

472 The Home Over There

D. W. C. Huntington, b. 1830 — Tullius C. O'Kane, 1830-1912

1. O think of the home o - ver there, By the side of the riv - er of light,
2. O think of the friends o - ver there, Who be-fore us the jour-ney have trod,
3. My Sav - ior is now o - ver there, There my kindred and friends are at rest;
4. I'll soon be at home o - ver there, For the end of my jour-ney I see;

o-ver there,

Where the saints, all im-mor-tal and fair, Are robed in their garments of white.
Of the songs that they breathe on the air, In their home in the pal - ace of God.
Then a-way from my sor-row and care, Let me fly to the land of the blest.
Man - y dear to my heart o - ver there Are watch-ing and wait-ing for me.

o-ver there.

CHORUS

O-ver there, o - ver there, O think of the home o - ver there!
O-ver there, o - ver there, O think of the friends o - ver there!
O-ver there, o - ver there, My Sav - ior is now o - ver there,
O-ver there, o - ver there, I'll soon be at home o - ver there,

O-ver there, o-ver there, o-ver there,

O - ver there, o - ver there, o-ver there, O think of the home o - ver there!
O - ver there, o - ver there, o-ver there, O think of the friends o - ver there!
O - ver there, o - ver there, o-ver there, My Sav - ior is now o - ver there.
O - ver there, o - ver there, o-ver there, I'll soon be at home o - ver there.

O - ver there,

Hope of the Righteous

473

Luella Byers Henry, 1888

John S. Byers, 1888

1. Be - yond this world of toil and care, Be - yond this vale of gloom,
2. O what a bless - ed hope is this, An an - chor to the soul!
3. To en - ter heav'n we must be pure And ho - ly in his sight,
4. We'll pray for God to keep our feet Up - on the Cor - ner - stone;
There is a land, a hap - py land, A place we call our home.
And if we do our Sav - ior's will We'll safe - ly reach the goal.
And ev - ery day we tru - ly must Be walk - ing in the light.
We'll give our hearts and lives to him, For we are not our own.
CHORUS
O yes, we'll trust him while we live! We'll trust him when we die!
rit.
And then when all our work is done We'll reign with him on high. A - MEN.

474 I Have a Home

Barney E. Warren, 1897 Barney E. Warren, 1897

1. I have a home . . . . pre - pared for me, ...
2. I have a home . . . . in heav'n a - bove, ...
3. I have a home . . . . for - ev - er free . . . . . .
4. I have a home, ... how sweet to know . . . . . .
1. I have a home pre - pared for me,
A man - sion bright . . . . a - cross the sea; . . . . . .
Where all is pure . . . . . . and per - fect love; . . . . . .
From toil and care . . . . . . and mis - er - y; . . . . . .
'Tis well se - cured . . . . . from ev - ery foe! . . . . .
A man - sion bright a - cross the sea, a - cross the sea;
And when I pass . . . . . . to yon bright shore . . . .
A home where sin . . . . . . can nev - er be, ...
Where storm-y seas . . . . . can nev - er roll, ...
Where peace and joy . . . . . . do reign su - preme, ...
And when I pass to yon bright shore
I'll dwell with Christ . . . . for - ev - er-more (for - ev - er-more).
Where all is per - - - - - - fect pu - ri - ty (yes, pu - ri - ty).
Where bliss e - ter - - - - - - nal crowns the soul(yes, crowns the soul).
Where love shall be . . . . . . my on - ly theme(my on - ly theme).
I'll dwell with Christ for - ev - er - more (for - ev - er-more).

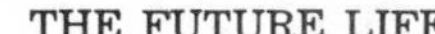

CHORUS

I'll live for him, till life shall end,

I'll live for him........... till life shall end,........... Then on my

Then on my pin-ions I will as-cend To that bright home

pin - - - ions I'll as - cend........ To that bright home....... where all is

p rit.

for - ev - er fair, And take my crown, beau-ti-ful crown to wear.

fair,..........And take my star - - - - ry crown to wear..............

I'm Going Home 475

William Hunter, 1811-1877

William Miller, 1801-1878
Arr. by Hubert P. Main, 1839-1926

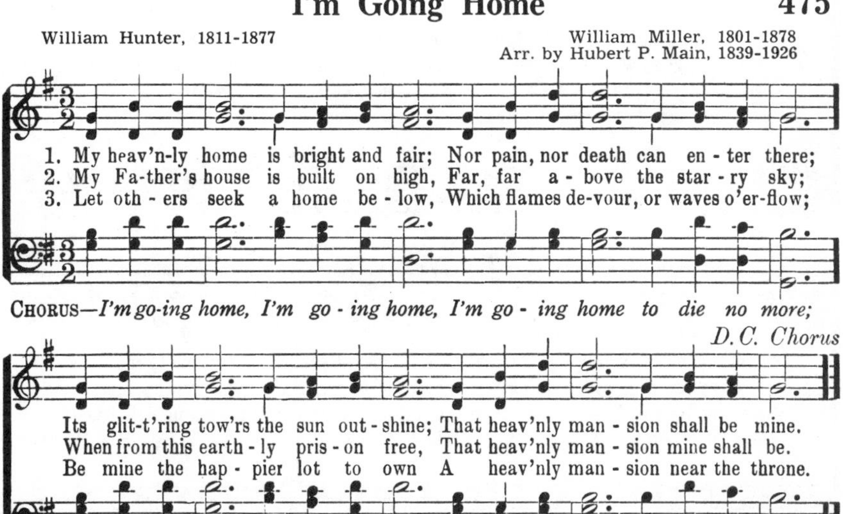
1. My heav'n-ly home is bright and fair; Nor pain, nor death can en - ter there;
2. My Fa-ther's house is built on high, Far, far a - bove the star - ry sky;
3. Let oth - ers seek a home be - low, Which flames de-vour, or waves o'er-flow;
CHORUS—*I'm go-ing home, I'm go - ing home, I'm go - ing home to die no more;*
D.C. Chorus
Its glit-t'ring tow'rs the sun out - shine; That heav'nly man - sion shall be mine.
When from this earth - ly pris - on free, That heav'nly man - sion mine shall be.
Be mine the hap - pier lot to own A heav'nly man - sion near the throne.
To die no more, to die no more, I'm go - ing home to die no more.

476 Home of the Soul

Ellen H. Gates, 1865 — Philip Phillips, 1834-1875

1. I will sing you a song of that beau - ti - ful land, The far a - way
2. O that home of the soul, in my vi - sions and dreams, Its bright jas - per
3. That un-change-a - ble home is for you and for me, Where Je - sus of
4. O how sweet it will be in that beau - ti - ful land, So free from all
home of the soul, Where no storms ev-er beat on the glit - ter - ing strand While the
walls I can see, Till I fan - cy but thin - ly the vail in - ter - venes Be-
Naz - a-reth stands; The King of all king-doms for - ev - er is he, And he
sor - row and pain, With songs on our lips and with harps in our hands To
years of e - ter - ni - ty roll, While the years of e - ter - ni - ty roll; Where no
tween the fair cit - y and me, Be - tween the fair cit - y and me; Till I
hold - eth our crowns in his hands, And he hold - eth our crowns in his hands; The
meet one an - oth - er a - gain, To meet one an - oth - er a - gain; With
storms ev - er beat on the glittering strand While the years of e - ter - ni - ty roll.
fan - cy but thin - ly the vail in-ter-venes Be - tween the fair cit - y and me.
King of all kingdoms for-ev - er is he, And he holdeth our crowns in his hands.
songs on our lips and with harps in our hands To meet one an-oth - er a - gain. A - MEN.

Shall We Meet Beyond the River? 477

Horace L. Hastings, 1858

Elihu S. Rice, 1866

1. Shall we meet be-yond the riv-er, Where the surg-es cease to roll, Where in all the bright for-ev-er Sor-row ne'er shall press the soul?
2. Shall we meet in that blest har-bor When our storm-y voyage is o'er? Shall we meet and cast the an-chor By the fair, ce-les-tial shore?
3. Shall we meet in yon-der cit-y, Where the tow'rs of crys-tal shine. Where the walls are all of jas-per, Built by work-man-ship di-vine?
4. Shall we meet with Christ our Sav-ior, When he comes to claim his own? Shall we know his bless-ed fa-vor, And sit down up-on his throne?

CHORUS

Shall we meet, shall we meet, Shall we meet be-yond the riv-er? Shall we meet be-yond the riv-er, Where the surg-es cease to roll? A-MEN.

*We shall meet, we shall meet, We shall meet be-yond the riv-er; Yes, we'll meet be-yond the riv-er, Where the surg-es cease to roll.

*After last stanza

478 The Sweet By and By

Sanford F. Bennett, 1836-1898 Joseph P. Webster, 1819-1875

1. There's a land that is fair-er than day, And by faith we can see it a-far; For the Fa-ther waits o-ver the way, To pre-pare us a dwell-ing-place there.
2. We shall sing on that beau-ti-ful shore The me-lo-di-ous songs of the blest, And our spir-its shall sor-row no more, Not a sigh for the bless-ing of rest.
3. To our boun-ti-ful Fa-ther a-bove, We will of-fer the trib-ute of praise, For the glo-ri-ous gift of his love, And the bless-ings that hal-low our days.
REFRAIN
In the sweet by and by,
In the sweet by and by,
We shall meet on that beau-ti-ful shore;
by and by;
In the sweet
In the sweet
by and by,
by and by,
We shall meet on that beau-ti-ful shore. A-MEN.

Safe in the Arms of Jesus 479

Fanny J. Crosby, 1820-1915 William Howard Doane, 1832-1915

1. Safe in the arms of Je - sus, Safe on his gen - tle breast,
2. Safe in the arms of Je - sus, Safe from cor - rod - ing care,
3. Je - sus, my heart's dear ref - uge, Je - sus has died for me;
CHORUS—*Safe in the arms of Je - sus, Safe on his gen - tle breast,*
FINE
There by his love o'er - shad - ed Sweet - ly my soul shall rest.
Safe from the world's temp-ta - tions, Sin can - not harm me there.
Firm on the Rock of A - ges Ev - er my trust shall be.
There by his love o'er - shad - ed Sweet - ly my soul shall rest.
Hark! 'tis the voice of an - gels Borne in a song to me
Free from the blight of sor - row, Free from my doubts and fears;
Here let me wait with pa - tience, Wait till the night is o'er,
D. C. Chorus
O - ver the fields of glo - ry, O - ver the jas - per sea.
On - ly a few more tri - als, On - ly a few more tears!
Wait till I see the morn - ing Break on the gold - en shore.

480 Beautiful

Barney E. Warren, 1897 — Barney E. Warren, 1897

1. Beau - ti - ful robes so white, Beau-ti - ful land of light, Beau-ti - ful
2. Beau - ti - ful thought to me, We shall for - ev - er be Thine in e-
3. Beau - ti - ful things on high, O - ver in yon - der sky, Soon I shall
home so bright, Where there shall come no night; Beau - ti - ful crown I'll wear,
ter - ni - ty, When from this world we're free; Free from its toil and care,
leave this shore, Counting my treas-ures o'er; Where we shall nev - er die,
Shining with stars o'er there, Yonder in mansions fair, Gather us there. . .
Heav-en - ly joys to share, Let me cross o-ver there; This is my prayer. . .
Car - ry me by and by, Nev-er to sor-row more, Heav-en-ly store. . .
Chorus
Beau - ti - ful robes, ... Beau-ti - ful land,
Beau - ti - ful robes of white, Beau - ti - ful land of light,
Beau-ti - ful home, ... Beau-ti - ful band; . . .
Beau - ti - ful home so bright, Beau - ti - ful band of might;

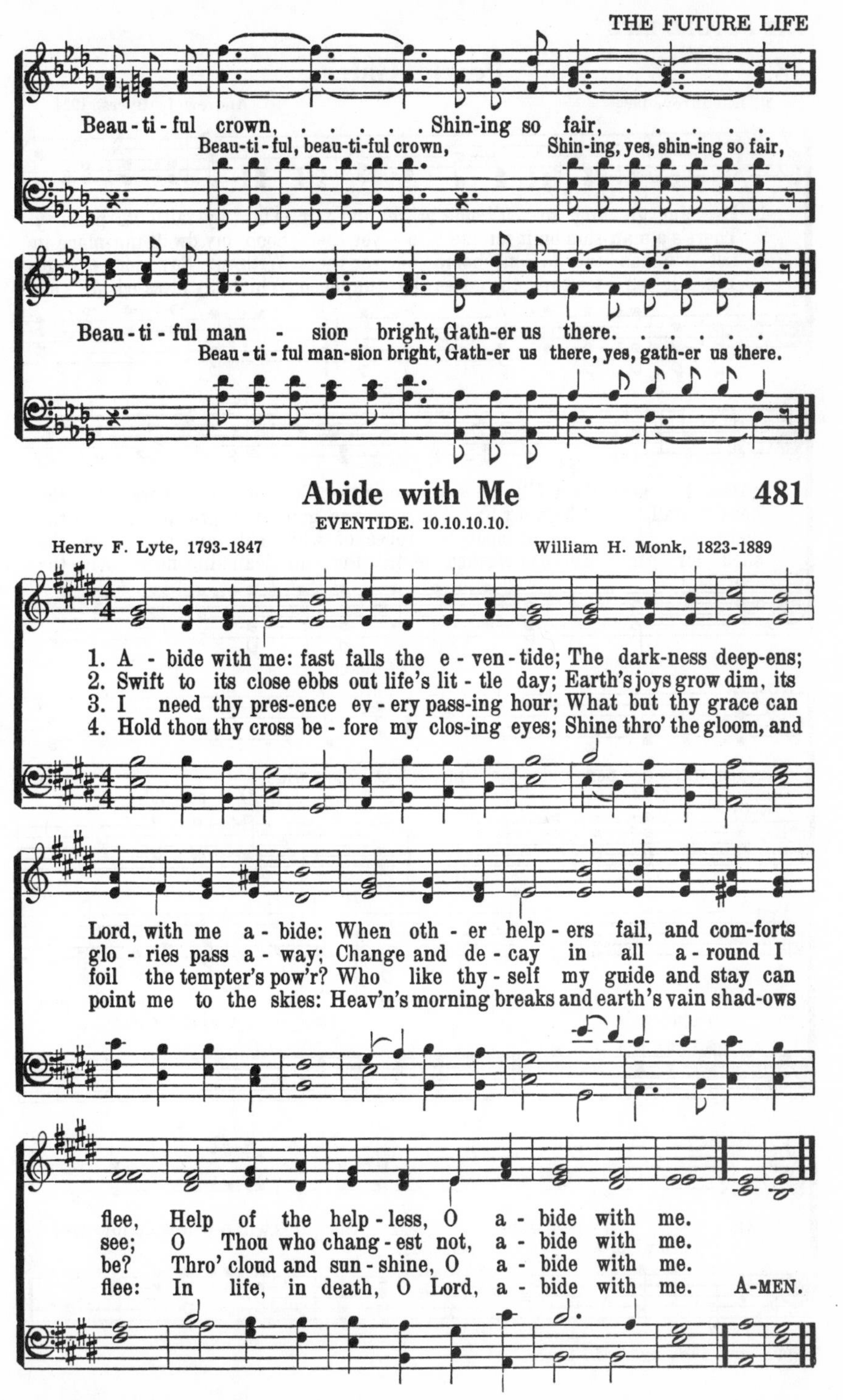
Beau-ti-ful crown, ... Shin-ing so fair, ...
Beau-ti-ful, beau-ti-ful crown, Shin-ing, yes, shin-ing so fair,
Beau-ti-ful man - sion bright, Gath-er us there. . . . . .
Beau-ti-ful man-sion bright, Gath-er us there, yes, gath-er us there.
Abide with Me
481
EVENTIDE. 10.10.10.10.
Henry F. Lyte, 1793-1847
William H. Monk, 1823-1889
1. A - bide with me: fast falls the e - ven - tide; The dark-ness deep-ens;
2. Swift to its close ebbs out life's lit - tle day; Earth's joys grow dim, its
3. I need thy pres-ence ev - ery pass-ing hour; What but thy grace can
4. Hold thou thy cross be - fore my clos-ing eyes; Shine thro' the gloom, and
Lord, with me a - bide: When oth - er help - ers fail, and com-forts
glo - ries pass a - way; Change and de - cay in all a - round I
foil the tempter's pow'r? Who like thy - self my guide and stay can
point me to the skies: Heav'n's morning breaks and earth's vain shad-ows
flee, Help of the help - less, O a - bide with me.
see; O Thou who chang - est not, a - bide with me.
be? Thro' cloud and sun - shine, O a - bide with me.
flee: In life, in death, O Lord, a - bide with me. A-MEN.

482 Pearly Gates

H. R. Jeffrey, 1885 — Andrew L. Byers, 1924

1. I am go - ing to a home bright and fair, And by faith its pearl - y
2. There's a man-sion built for me o - ver there, Soon my dwell-ing-place in
3. Let me has - ten to my home o - ver there, With my Sav - ior ev - er-
4. Yes, I'll en - ter thro' the gates by the blood Which my bless-ed Je - sus
gates I see: Soon I'll be a - mong the blest o - ver there, For the
heav'n shall be, Which my Sav - ior now has gone to pre - pare, And the
more to be; Then in spot - less robes of white I'll ap - pear, For the
shed for me: He has washed me in the all-cleans-ing flood, And the
gates will o - pen wide for me.
CHORUS
O - pen wide, o - pen
O - pen wide,
wide; O the gates will o - pen wide for me: O - pen
o - pen wide; yes, o - pen wide for me:
wide, o - pen wide; Yes, the gates will o-pen wide for me.
O - pen wide, o - pen wide;

Adoration

483

Clara M. Brooks, 1911 D. Otis Teasley, 1911

1. I have found the joy of God In his sa-cred blest a-bode, O the com-fort of the peace that fills my soul! And a day his courts with-in Far ex-ceed-eth all in sin, In his se-cret pres-ence I'm a-bid-ing.
2. Of my life the foun-tain spring Now my all to thee I bring, Thou, O Lord, art all my heart's su-preme de-light! Whom have I in heav'n but thee? None on earth so dear to me, Thou a-lone art al-to-geth-er love-ly.
3. How the heav'n-ly cho-rus rings, While my heart in rap-ture sings Sweet-est an-thems of my Sav-ior's joy-ful praise! He's the fair-est of the fair, Noth-ing can with him com-pare, He's to me the chief a-mong ten thou-sand.
4. Take the world, for Christ is mine, In his king-dom I would shine, Let me la-bor all my days and years for him: Per-fect love and bliss a-bound, In his pres-ence I have found Life is joy su-preme and full of glo-ry.
FINE
CHORUS
D. S.—He for me is wait-ing at the por-tals.
I shall see him, I shall see him, I shall see him in his beau-ty o-ver there; In his like-ness I'll be-hold him, A-MEN.
I shall see him, I shall see him, o-ver there; In his like-ness I'll be-hold him,
D. S.

484 Will You Go with Us to Heaven?

Daniel S. Warner, 1893 — Barney E. Warren, 1893

1. We are go - ing home to heav - en's gold - en cit - y, We have tast - ed of its pre - cious fruit of love; Then, dear sin - ner, if you'd be for - ev - er hap - py, Jour - ney with us to that bliss - ful world a - bove.
2. Come to - day and seek sal - va - tion and be read - y, Not a mo - ment lon - ger should your soul de - lay; God is call - ing, and his wondrous love and mer - cy Will re - ceive you in that home of end - less day.
3. We are go - ing through to glo - ry by the Bi - ble, See the way-mark, 'Be ye ho - ly through the blood;' In the name of Je - sus will you meek - ly trav - el With the pil - grims to that beau - ti - ful a - bode?
4. Choose this day if you will go to that fair cit - y: Will you share a blest e - ter - ni - ty of love? Je - sus calls you, all the ransomed wait to greet you, And the an - gels sing to wel - come you a - bove.
CHORUS
Will you go Will you go? to that cit - - - - y? will you go with us? Je - sus will re - ceive you there;........ Je - sus will re - ceive you there; Will you go? Will you go? Will you go with us? O

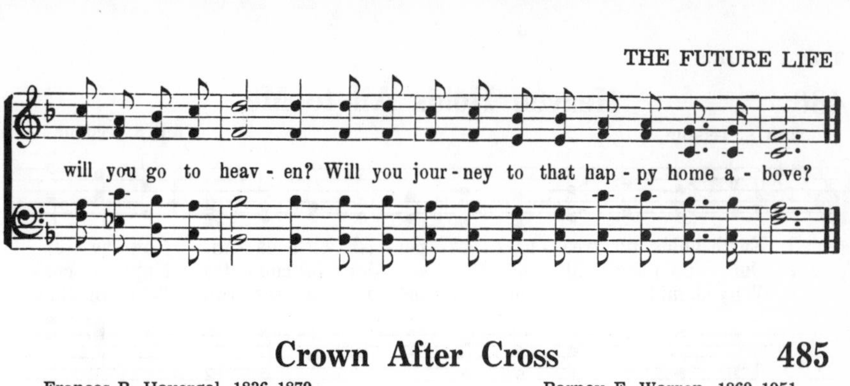
will you go to heav - en? Will you jour - ney to that hap - py home a - bove?

Crown After Cross 485

Frances R. Havergal, 1836-1879 Barney E. Warren, 1869-1951

1. Light aft - er dark - ness, Gain aft - er loss, Strength aft - er weak - ness,
2. Sheaves aft-er sow - ing, Sun aft - er rain, Sight aft - er mys - ter - y,
3. Near aft - er dis - tant, Gleam aft-er gloom, Love aft - er lone - li - ness,

Crown aft - er cross; Sweet aft - er bit - ter, Hope aft - er fears,
Peace aft - er pain; Joy aft - er sor - row, Calm aft - er blast,
Life aft - er tomb; Aft - er long ag - o - ny Rap - ture of bliss,

Home aft - er wan - der - ing, Praise aft - er tears.
Rest aft - er wea - ri-ness, Sweet rest at last.
Right was the path - way Lead - ing to this.

CHORUS

Now comes the weep - ing,

Then the glad reap - ing; Now comes the la - bor hard, Then the re - ward. A - MEN.

rit.

486 Heaven Holds All to Me

Tillit S. Teddlie | Tillit S. Teddlie

1. Earth holds no treas-ures but per-ish with us-ing, How-ev-er pre-cious they be; Yet there's a coun-try to which I am go-ing, Heav-en holds all to me.
2. Out on the hills of that won-der-ful coun-try, Hap-py, con-tent-ed and free, Loved ones are wait-ing and watch-ing my com-ing, Heav-en holds all to me.
3. Why should I long for the world and its sor-rows, When in that home o'er the sea Mil-lions are sing-ing the won-der-ful sto-ry? Heav-en holds all to me.

CHORUS

Heav-en holds all to me, . . . (to me,) Bright-er its glo-ry will be; Joy with-out meas-ure will be my treas-ure, Heav-en holds all to me.

The Unclouded Day

487

J. K. Alwood — J. K. Alwood

1. O they tell me of a home far be - yond the skies, O they
2. O they tell me of a home where my friends have gone, O they
3. O they tell me of a King in his beau - ty there, And they
4. O they tell me that he smiles on his chil - dren there, And his
tell me of a home far a - way; O they tell me of a home
tell me of that land far a - way, Where the tree of life
tell me that mine eyes shall be - hold Where he sits on the throne
smile drives their sor - rows all a - way; And they tell me that no tears
D. S.—O they tell me of a home
FINE
where no storm-clouds rise, O they tell me of an un - cloud - ed day.
in e - ter - nal bloom Sheds its fragrance thro' the un - cloud - ed day.
that is whit - er than snow, In the cit - y that is made of gold.
ev - er come a - gain In that love - ly land of un - cloud - ed day.
where no storm - clouds rise, O they tell me of an un - cloud - ed day.
CHORUS
D. S.
O the land of cloud-less day, O the land of an un-cloud-ed day; A-MEN.

488 Heavenly Welcome

Jennie Mast

Jennie Mast
Har. by Rhoda K. Byrum, 1906

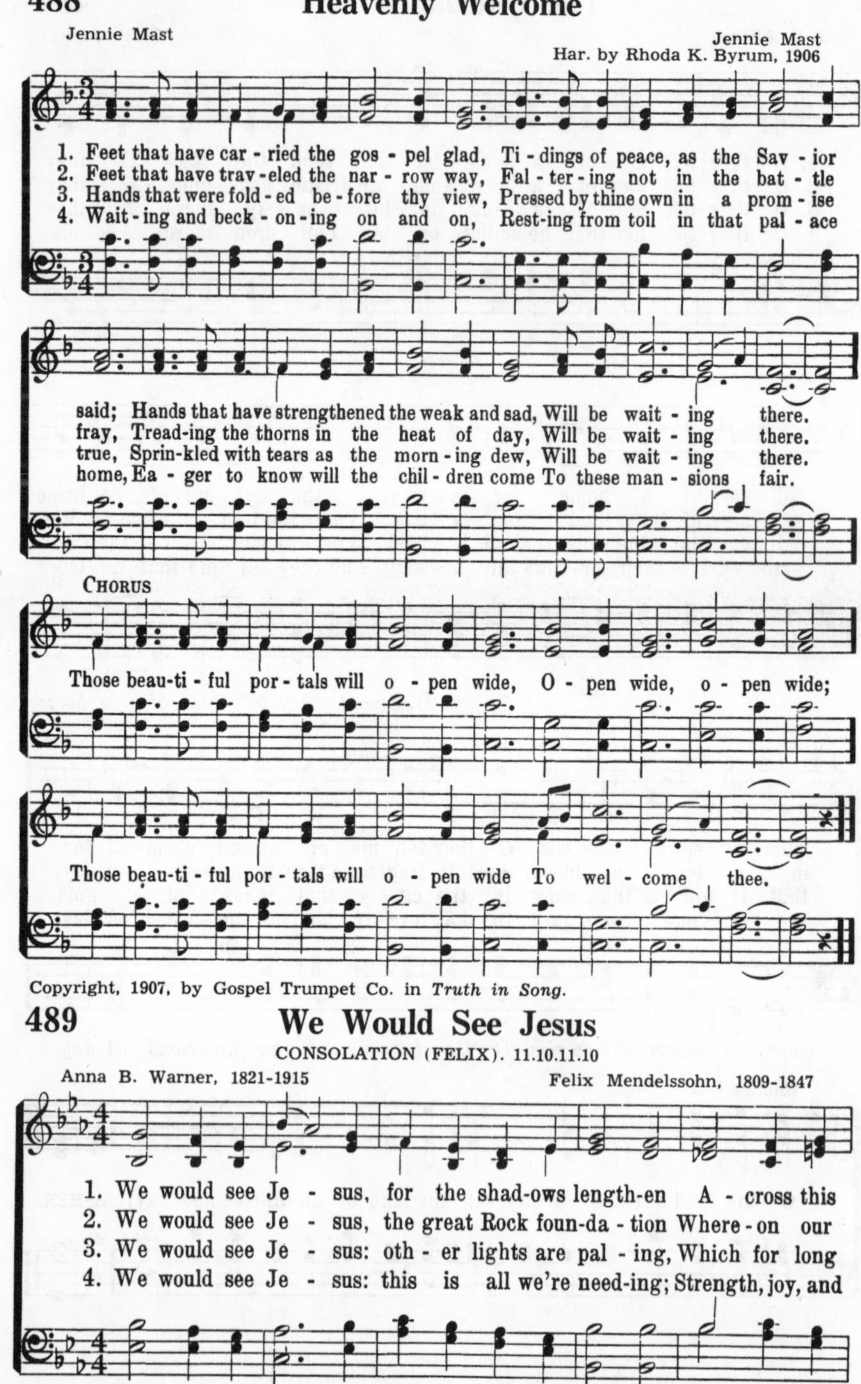
1. Feet that have car - ried the gos - pel glad, Ti - dings of peace, as the Sav - ior said; Hands that have strengthened the weak and sad, Will be wait - ing there.
2. Feet that have trav - eled the nar - row way, Fal - ter - ing not in the bat - tle fray, Tread - ing the thorns in the heat of day, Will be wait - ing there.
3. Hands that were fold - ed be - fore thy view, Pressed by thine own in a prom - ise true, Sprin - kled with tears as the morn - ing dew, Will be wait - ing there.
4. Wait - ing and beck - on - ing on and on, Rest - ing from toil in that pal - ace home, Ea - ger to know will the chil - dren come To these man - sions fair.
CHORUS
Those beau - ti - ful por - tals will o - pen wide, O - pen wide, o - pen wide;
Those beau - ti - ful por - tals will o - pen wide To wel - come thee.
1. We would see Je - sus, for the shad - ows length - en A - cross this
2. We would see Je - sus, the great Rock foun - da - tion Where - on our
3. We would see Je - sus: oth - er lights are pal - ing, Which for long
4. We would see Je - sus: this is all we're need - ing; Strength, joy, and

489 We Would See Jesus

CONSOLATION (FELIX). 11.10.11.10

Anna B. Warner, 1821-1915

Felix Mendelssohn, 1809-1847

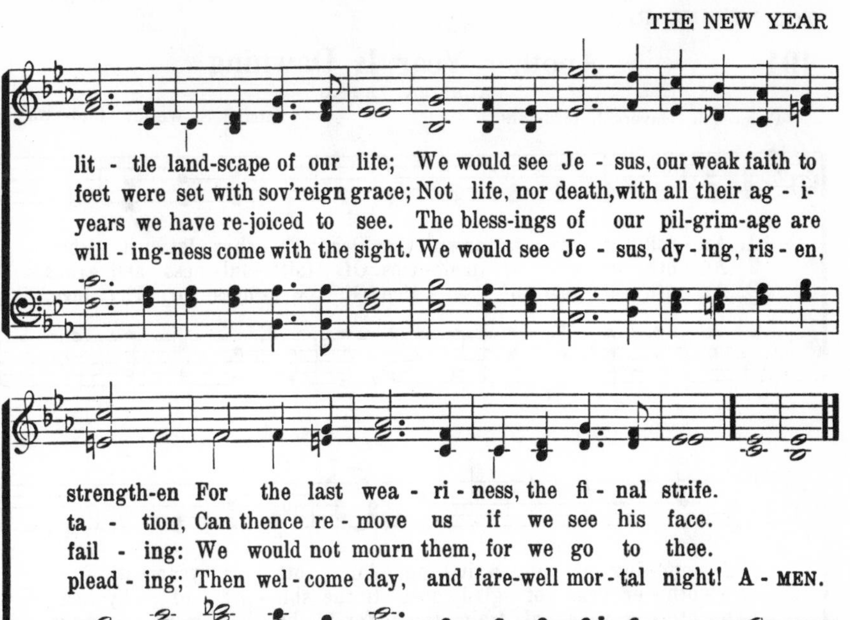
lit - tle land-scape of our life; We would see Je - sus, our weak faith to
feet were set with sov'reign grace; Not life, nor death, with all their ag - i-
years we have re-joiced to see. The bless-ings of our pil-grim-age are
will - ing-ness come with the sight. We would see Je - sus, dy - ing, ris - en,
strength-en For the last wea - ri - ness, the fi - nal strife.
ta - tion, Can thence re - move us if we see his face.
fail - ing: We would not mourn them, for we go to thee.
plead - ing; Then wel - come day, and fare-well mor - tal night! A - MEN.

Great God, We Sing That Mighty Hand 490

FEDERAL STREET. L.M.

Philip Doddridge, 1702-1751 — Henry K. Oliver, 1800-1885

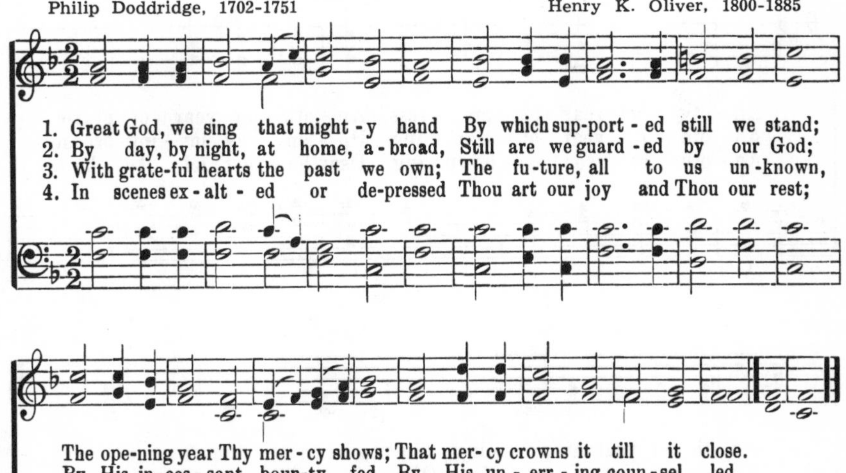
1. Great God, we sing that might - y hand By which sup-port - ed still we stand;
2. By day, by night, at home, a - broad, Still are we guard - ed by our God;
3. With grate-ful hearts the past we own; The fu - ture, all to us un - known,
4. In scenes ex - alt - ed or de-pressed Thou art our joy and Thou our rest;

The ope-ning year Thy mer - cy shows; That mer - cy crowns it till it close.
By His in - ces - sant boun - ty fed, By His un - err - ing coun - sel led.
We to Thy guard-ian care com - mit, And, peace-ful, leave be-fore thy feet.
Thy good-ness all our hopes shall raise, A - dored thro' all our chang-ing days. A-MEN.

491 Another Year Is Dawning

AURELIA. 7.6.7.6.D.

Frances R. Havergal, 1836-1879 — Samuel S. Wesley, 1810-1876

1. Another year is dawning, Dear Father, let it be
In working or in waiting Another year with Thee;
Another year of progress, Another year of praise,
Another year of proving Thy presence all the days;

2. Another year of mercies, Of faithfulness and grace,
Another year of gladness In the shining of Thy face,
Another year of leaning Upon Thy loving breast,
Another year of trusting, Of quiet, happy rest;

3. Another year of service, Of witness for Thy love,
Another year of training For holier work above.
Another year is dawning, Dear Father, let it be
On earth, or else in heaven, Another year for Thee. A-MEN.

Standing at the Portal 492

ST. ALBAN. 6.5.6.5.D. with Refrain

Frances R. Havergal, 1836-1879

Franz Joseph Haydn, 1732-1809
Arr. by John B. Dykes, 1823-1876

1. Stand-ing at the por-tal Of the ope-ning year, Words of com-fort meet us, Hush-ing ev-'ry fear; Spo-ken thro' the si-lence By our Fa-ther's voice, Ten-der, strong, and faith-ful, Mak-ing us re-joice.

2. "I, the Lord, am with thee, Be thou not a-fraid; I will help and strengthen, Be thou not dis-mayed; Yea, I will up-hold thee With my own right hand; Thou art called and chos-en In my sight to stand."

3. For the year be-fore us, Oh, what rich sup-plies! For the poor and need-y Liv-ing streams shall rise; For the sad and sin-ful Shall His grace a-bound; For the faint and fee-ble Per-fect strength be found.

4. He will nev-er fail us, He will not for-sake; His e-ter-nal cov'-nant He will nev-er break. Rest-ing on his prom-ise, What have we to fear? God is all-suf-fi-cient For the com-ing year.

REFRAIN

On-ward, then, and fear not, Chil-dren of the day; For His word shall nev-er, Nev-er pass a-way. A-MEN.

493 Come, Ye Thankful People, Come

ST. GEORGE'S, WINDSOR. 7.7.7.7.D.

Henry Alford, 1810-1871

George J. Elvey, 1816-1893

1. Come, ye thank - ful peo - ple, come, Raise the song of har - vest - home:
2. All the world is God's own field, Fruit un - to His praise to yield;
3. For the Lord our God shall come, And shall take His har - vest home;
4. E - ven so, Lord, quick - ly come To Thy fi - nal har - vest - home;

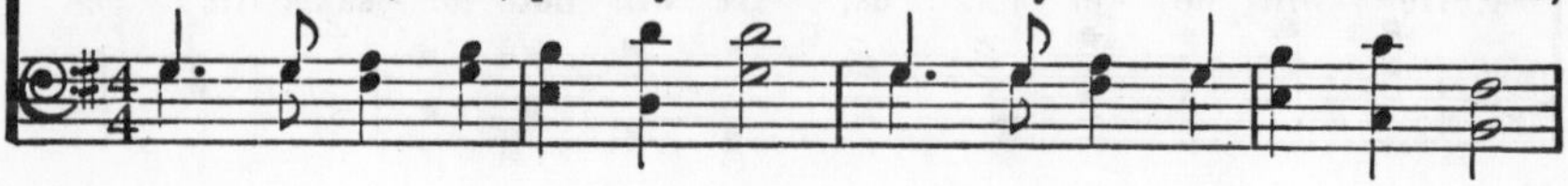

All is safe - ly gath - ered in, Ere the win - ter storms be - gin;
Wheat and tares to - geth - er sown, Un - to joy or sor - row grown;
From His field shall in that day All of - fens - es purge a - way;
Gath - er Thou Thy peo - ple in, Free from sor - row, free from sin;

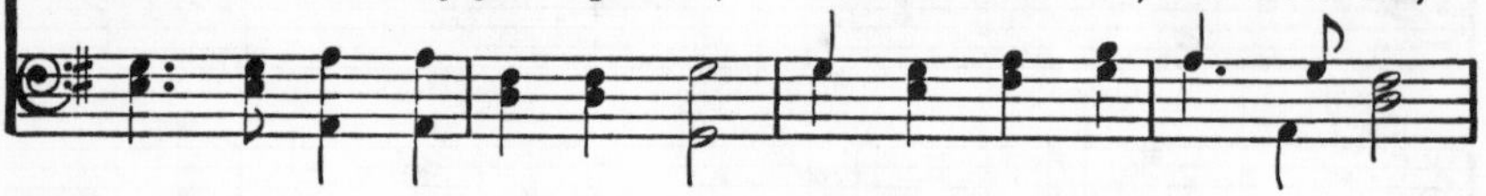

God, our Ma - ker, doth pro - vide For our wants to be sup - plied:
First the blade, and then the ear, Then the full corn shall ap - pear:
Give His an - gels charge at last In the fire the tares to cast;
There, for - ev - er pu - ri - fied, In Thy pres-ence to a - bide.

Come to God's own tem - ple, come, Raise the song of har - vest-home.
Lord of har - vest, grant that we Wholesome grain and pure may be.
But the fruit - ful ears to store In His gar - ner ev - er - more.
Come, with all Thine an - gels, come, Raise the glo-rious har - vest-home.

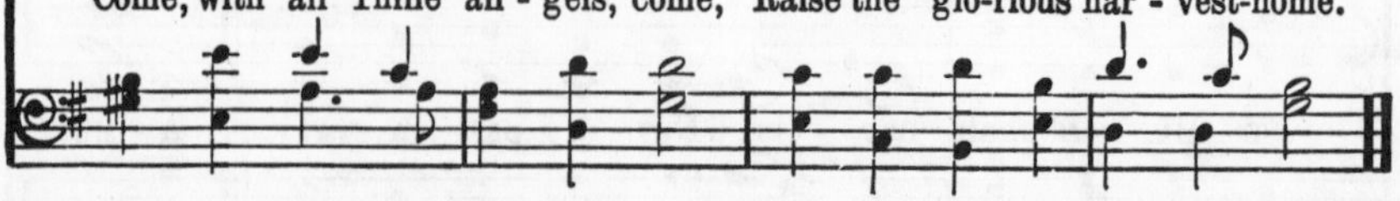

We Plow the Fields, and Scatter 494

WIR PFLUGEN. 7.6.7.6.D. with Refrain

Matthias Claudius, 1740-1815
Tr. by Jane M. Campbell, 1817-1878

Johann A. P. Schulz, 1747-1800

1. We plough the fields, and scat-ter The good seed on the land, But it is fed and wa - tered By God's al-might - y hand; He sends the snow in win - ter, The warmth to swell the grain, The breez - es and the sun-shine, And soft re-fresh-ing rain.
2. He on - ly is the Mak - er Of all things near and far; He paints the way-side flow - er, He lights the eve-ning star; The winds and waves o-bey Him, By Him the birds are fed; Much more to us, His chil - dren, He gives our dai - ly bread.
3. We thank Thee, then, O Fa - ther, For all things bright and good; The seed-time and the har - vest, Our life, our health, our food; No gifts have we to of - fer For all Thy love im - parts, But that which Thou de - sir - est, Our hum-ble, thank-ful hearts.
REFRAIN
All good gifts a-round us Are sent from heav'n a-bove; Then thank the Lord, O thank the Lord For all His love. A-MEN.

495 Our Glad Thanksgiving

Clara M. Brooks, 1919 — Andrew L. Byers, 1919

1. To thee, O Lord Je - ho - vah, We hymn our grate-ful praise
2. Blest to - kens of thy mer - cy To sin - ful hosts ap - pear,
3. For hope of joys e - ter - nal, For par - don thro' the blood,
4. Ye saints, go tell of Je - sus Till earth tri - um-phant rings,
For all thy lov - ing - kind - ness. The wis - dom of thy ways.
And with thy match-less good - ness Thou crown-est all the year.
And for thy Ho - ly Spir - it, We thank thee. O our God.
Till ev - ery crea - ture bow - ing, Shall praise the King of kings!
CHORUS
Thou dost note the sparrow's fall, Thou dost hear us when we call; O ac-
cept our glad thanksgiving For thy ten-der mer-cies all!
Hearts that know thy name a-dore thee;
Na - tions fain would bow be-fore thee—
Crown thee King of kings! Proclaim thee Lord of all!
A-MEN.

For All the Blessings of the Year 496

OLDBRIDGE. 8.8.8.4.

Albert H. Hutchinson | Robert N. Quaile, b. 1867

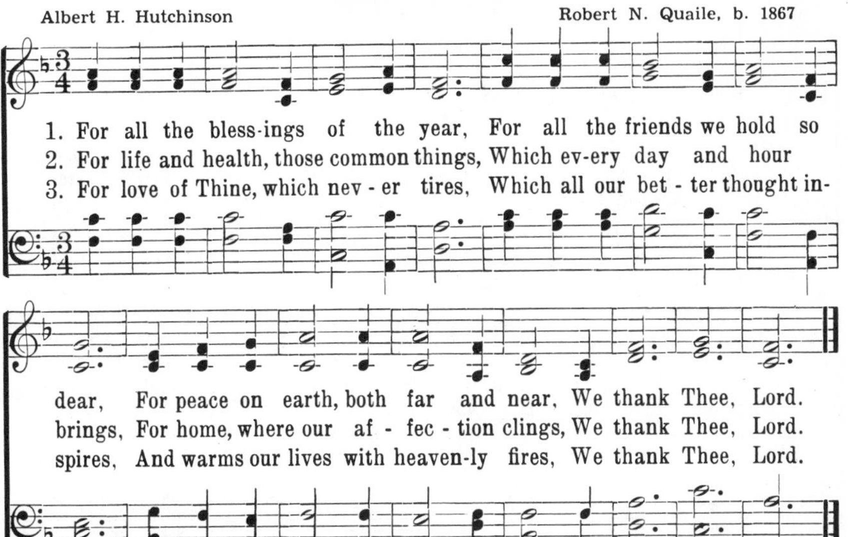
1. For all the bless-ings of the year, For all the friends we hold so dear, For peace on earth, both far and near, We thank Thee, Lord.
2. For life and health, those common things, Which ev-ery day and hour brings, For home, where our af - fec - tion clings, We thank Thee, Lord.
3. For love of Thine, which nev - er tires, Which all our bet - ter thought in-spires, And warms our lives with heaven-ly fires, We thank Thee, Lord.

O Lord of Heaven and Earth and Sea 497

WHO GIVEST ALL. L.M.

Christopher Wordsworth, 1807-1885 | Louis LeSaint

Alto prominent for four measures

1. O Lord of heav'n and earth and sea, To thee all praise and glo - ry be;
2. The gold-en sun-shine, ver - nal air, Sweet flow'rs and fruit, thy love declare;
3. For peaceful homes and healthful days, For all the blessings earth dis-plays,
4. We lose what on our-selves we spend; We have as treas-ures with-out end

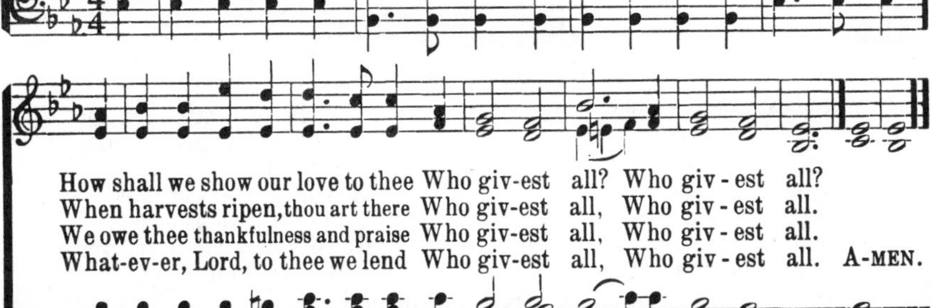
How shall we show our love to thee Who giv-est all? Who giv - est all?
When harvests ripen, thou art there Who giv-est all, Who giv - est all.
We owe thee thankfulness and praise Who giv-est all, Who giv - est all.
What-ev-er, Lord, to thee we lend Who giv-est all, Who giv - est all. A-MEN.

498 My Country, 'Tis of Thee

AMERICA. 6.6.4.6.6.6.4.

Samuel F. Smith. 1808-1895 — Henry Carey, c. 1690-1743

1. My coun - try, 'tis of thee, Sweet land of lib - er - ty,
2. My na - tive coun - try, thee, Land of the no - ble free,
3. Let mu - sic swell the breeze, And ring from all the trees
4. Our fa - thers' God, to thee, Au - thor of lib - er - ty,
Of thee I sing; Land where my fa - thers died, Land of the
Thy name I love; I love thy rocks and rills, Thy woods and
Sweet free-dom's song; Let mor - tal tongues a - wake; Let all that
To thee we sing; Long may our land be bright With free-dom's
pil-grims' pride, From ev - 'ry moun-tain side Let free-dom ring!
tem - pled hills; My heart with rap-ture thrills, Like that a - bove.
breathe partake; Let rocks their si-lence break, The sound pro-long.
ho - ly light; Pro - tect us by thy might, Great God, our King. A-MEN.

499 God Save the King

(Tune above)

1 God save our gracious King,
Long live our noble King,
God save the King:
Send him victorious,
Happy and glorious,
Long to reign over us,
God save the King.

2 Thy choicest gifts in store
On him be pleased to pour;
Long may he reign.
May he defend our laws,
And ever give us cause
To sing with heart and voice,
God save the King.

* 3. Our loved Dominion bless
With peace and happiness
From shore to shore:
And let our Empire be
United, loyal, free,
True to herself and thee
Forevermore. AMEN.

* This stanza was written for Canada

America, the Beautiful 500

MATERNA. C.M.D.

Katharine Lee Bates, 1859-1929 Samuel A. Ward, 1847-1903

1. O beau - ti - ful for spa-cious skies, For am - ber waves of grain,
2. O beau - ti - ful for pil - grim feet, Whose stern, im-pas-sioned stress
3. O beau - ti - ful for he - roes proved In lib - er - at - ing strife,
4. O beau - ti - ful for pa - triot dream That sees be - yond the years
For pur - ple moun-tain maj - es - ties A - bove the fruit - ed plain!
A thor-ough-fare for free - dom beat A - cross the wil - der - ness!
Who more than self their coun - try loved, And mer - cy more than life!
Thine al - a - bas - ter cit - ies gleam, Undimmed by hu - man tears!
A - mer - i - ca! A - mer - i - ca! God shed His grace on thee,
A - mer - i - ca! A - mer - i - ca! God mend thine ev - 'ry flaw,
A - mer - i - ca! A - mer - i - ca! May God thy gold re - fine,
A - mer - i - ca! A - mer - i - ca! God shed His grace on thee,
And crown thy good with broth - er-hood From sea to shin - ing sea!
Con - firm thy soul in self - con-trol, Thy lib - er - ty in law!
Till all suc-cess be no - ble-ness, And ev - 'ry gain di - vine!
And crown thy good with broth - er-hood From sea to shin - ing sea!

501 Praise God, from Whom All Blessings Flow

OLD HUNDREDTH. L.M.

Thomas Ken, 1637-1711 — Melody from "Genevan Psalter," 1551

Praise God, from whom all bless-ings flow; Praise Him, all crea-tures here be-low;
Praise Him a-bove, ye heav'n-ly host; Praise Fa-ther, Son, and Ho-ly Ghost.
502
Gloria Patri
Anonymous, second century
Charles Meineke, 1782-1850
Glo-ry be to the Fa-ther, and to the Son, and to the Ho-ly Ghost; As it
was in the be-gin-ning, is now, and ev-er shall be, world without end. A-men, A-men.
503
Let the Words of My Mouth
Psalm 19:14
Adolph Baumbach, 1830-1880
Let the words of my mouth and the med-i-ta-tions of my heart be ac-

cept-a-ble in thy sight, O Lord, my strength and my Re-deem-er. A - MEN.
O Worship the Lord
504
John Porter
O wor - ship the Lord in the beau - ty of
ho - li - ness, Serve Him with glad - ness, all the earth.
Bless Thou the Gifts
505
CANONBURY. L.M.
Samuel Longfellow, 1819-1892
Robert Schumann, 1810-1856
Bless Thou the gifts our hands have bro't; Bless Thou the work our hearts have planned;
Ours is the faith, the will, the tho't; The rest, O God, is in Thy hand. A - MEN.

506 Hear Our Prayer, O Lord
George Whelpton, 1847-1930
pp
Hear our prayer, O Lord, Hear our prayer, O Lord,
In - cline Thine ear to us, And grant us Thy peace. A-MEN.
507 The Lord Bless Thee, and Keep Thee
Numbers 6:24-26
Lucy Rider Meyer, 1849-1922
The Lord bless thee and keep thee! The Lord make His face shine upon thee, and be
gra-cious un - to thee, And be gra-cious un - to thee: The Lord lift up His
coun-te-nance, His countenance up-on thee, And give thee peace. . . . . ,. . .
And give thee peace.

WORSHIP AIDS

Responsive and Unison Readings from the Scriptures

Topical Index to Readings

READINGS

CHRISTIAN LIFE AND SERVICE

Blessedness of the Godly 81, 84
Christian Discipline 1, 46, 48, 52
Christian Love 21, 25, 50, 74, 76, 83
Christian Unity 19
Christian Warfare 53
Church, The 19, 20
Confession and Penitence 63
Confidence in God 59, 72, 80, 82
Courage 1, 49
Evangelism 45
Faith 37, 49
Fellowship 24
Forgiveness 57
Friendship 23
Guidance 12
Healing 28
Holiness and Righteousness 61, 69, 71
Hope 26
Immortality 54, 55
Judgment, The 61
Kingdom of God 31
Longing for God 65
Lord's Day, The 18
Missions 42, 43, 45, 78
Obedience 35, 50
Peace 7, 22, 39
Praise and Adoration 56, 68, 75
Prayer 39, 44, 63, 77, 78
Salvation 17, 64, 67
Service and Social Justice 40, 43, 58
Stewardship 41, 82
Thanksgiving 9, 56, 75
Unity 19
Victory 54, 64, 73
Wisdom 27, 51
Worship 18, 29, 39

GOD THE FATHER

God in Nature 68
God Our Sufficiency 22, 26, 34, 59, 72, 80

READINGS

God's Greatness and Glory 36, 68, 70, 80
God's Promises 33
God's Sovereignty 8
Word of God, The 12, 32

GOD THE SON

Advent 10, 11, 79
Baptism 60
Healer 28
Incarnation 62
Lord and Redeemer 2, 62, 66
Resurrection 4, 5
Temptation 47
Triumphant Entry 3

GOD THE HOLY SPIRIT

Coming of the Spirit 6
Spirit-Filled Life 30, 69

HOME AND FAMILY

A Father's Honor 16
A Worthy Woman 15
Worth of a Child 13

SPECIAL DAYS

Armistice Day 78
Bible Sunday 12, 32
Children's Day 13
Christmas 10, 11, 79
Easter 4, 5
Father's Day 16
Good Friday 2
Independence Day 8
Memorial Day 7
Mother's Day 15
New Year's Day 1
Palm Sunday 3
Pentecost 6
Temperance Sunday 48
Thanksgiving Day 9, 56, 75
Youth Week 14, 38

Responsive Readings

1 An Exhortation to Courage

Now after the death of Moses the servant of the Lord it came to pass, that the Lord spake unto Joshua the son of Nun, Moses' minister, saying,

Moses my servant is dead; now therefore arise, go over this Jordan, thou, and all this people, unto the land which I do give them. . . .

Every place that the sole of your foot shall tread upon, that have I given unto you, as I said unto Moses.

There shall not any man be able to stand before thee all the days of thy life:

As I was with Moses, so will I be with thee: I will not fail thee, nor forsake thee.

Only be thou strong and very courageous, that thou mayest observe to do according to all the law, which Moses my servant commanded thee:

Turn not from it to the right hand or to the left, that thou mayest prosper whithersoever thou goest.

This book of the law shall not depart out of thy mouth; but thou shalt meditate therein day and night, that thou mayest observe to do according to all that is written therein:

For then thou shalt make thy way prosperous, and then thou shalt have good success.

Have not I commanded thee? Be strong and of a good courage; be not afraid, neither be thou dismayed: for the Lord thy God is with thee whithersoever thou goest.

Joshua 1:1-3, 5, 7-9

2 Christ Our Redeemer

Who hath believed our report? and to whom is the arm of the Lord revealed?

For he shall grow up before him as a tender plant, and as a root out of a dry ground: he hath no form nor comeliness; and when we shall see him, there is no beauty that we should desire him.

He is despised and rejected of men; a man of sorrows, and acquainted with grief: and we hid as it were our faces from him; he was despised, and we esteemed him not.

Surely he hath borne our griefs, and carried our sorrows; yet we did esteem him stricken, smitten of God, and afflicted.

But he was wounded for our transgressions, he was bruised for our iniquities: the chastisement of our peace was upon him; and with his stripes we are healed.

All we like sheep have gone astray; we have turned everyone to his own way; and the Lord hath laid on him the iniquity of us all.

He was oppressed, and he was afflicted, yet he opened not his mouth: he is brought as a lamb to the slaughter, and as a sheep before her shearers is dumb, so he openeth not his mouth.

Therefore will I divide him a portion with the great, and he shall divide the spoil with the strong; because he hath poured out his soul unto death: and he was numbered with the transgressors; and he bare the sin of many, and made intercession for the transgressors.

Isaiah 53:1-7, 12

3 Hosanna in the Highest!

And when they came nigh to Jerusalem, unto Bethphage and Bethany, at the mount of Olives, he sendeth forth two of his disciples.

And saith unto them, Go your way into the village over against you: and as soon as ye be entered into it, ye shall find a colt tied, whereon never man sat; loose him, and bring him.

And if any man say unto you, Why do ye this? say ye that the Lord hath need of him; and straightway he will send him hither.

And they went their way, and found the colt tied by the door without in a place where two ways met; and they loose him.

And certain of them that stood there said unto them, What do ye, loosing the colt?

And they said unto them even as Jesus had commanded: and they let them go.

And they brought the colt to Jesus, and cast their garments on him; and he sat upon him.

And many spread their garments in the way: and others cut down branches off the trees, and strewed them in the way.

And they that went before, and they that followed, cried, saying, Hosanna; Blessed is he that cometh in the name of the Lord:

Blessed be the kingdom of our father David, that cometh in the name of the Lord: Hosanna in the highest.

Mark 11:1-10

4 Our Risen Lord

In the end of the sabbath, as it began to dawn toward the first day of the week, came Mary Magdalene and the other Mary to see the sepulcher.

And, behold, there was a great earthquake: for the angel of the Lord descended from heaven, and came and rolled back the stone from the door, and sat upon it.

His countenance was like lightning, and his raiment white as snow:

And for fear of him the keepers did shake, and become as dead men.

And the angel answered and said unto the women, Fear not ye: for I know that ye seek Jesus, which was crucified.

He is not here: for he is risen, as he said. Come, see the place where the Lord lay.

And go quickly, and tell his disciples that he is risen from the dead; and, behold, he goeth before you into Galilee; there shall ye see him: lo, I have told you.

And they departed quickly from the sepulcher with fear and great joy; and did run to bring his disciples word.

And as they went to tell his disciples, behold, Jesus met them, saying, All hail. And they came and held him by the feet, and worshiped him.

Then said Jesus unto them, Be not afraid: go tell my brethren that they go into Galilee, and there shall they see me.

Matthew 28:1-10

5 The Resurrection of the Lord

Now upon the first day of the week, very early in the morning, they came unto the sepulcher, bringing the spices which they had prepared, and certain others with them.

And they found the stone rolled away from the sepulcher.

And they entered in, and found not the body of the Lord Jesus.

And it came to pass, as they were much perplexed thereabout, behold, two men stood by them in shining garments:

And as they were afraid, and bowed down their faces to the earth, they said unto them, Why seek ye the living among the dead?

He is not here, but is risen: remember how he spake unto you when he was yet in Galilee.

And they remembered his words,

And returned from the sepulcher, and told all these things unto the eleven, and to all the rest.

And their words seemed to them as idle tales, and they believed them not.

Then arose Peter, and ran unto the sepulcher; and stooping down, he beheld the linen clothes laid by themselves, and departed, wondering in himself at that which was come to pass.

Luke 24:1-6, 8-9, 11-12

6 The Coming of the Holy Spirit

And when the day of Pentecost was fully come, they were all with one accord in one place.

And they were all filled with the Holy Ghost, and began to speak with other tongues, as the Spirit gave them utterance.

Now when this was noised abroad, the multitude came together, and were confounded, because that every man heard them speak in his own language.

And they were all amazed, and were in doubt, saying one to another, What meaneth this?

But Peter, standing up with the eleven, lifted up his voice, and said unto them, Ye men of Judea, and all ye that dwell at Jerusalem, be this known unto you, and hearken to my words:

For these are not drunken, as ye suppose, seeing it is but the third hour of the day.

But this is that which was spoken by the prophet Joel:

And it shall come to pass in the last days, saith God, I will pour out of my Spirit upon all flesh: and your sons and your daughters shall prophesy, and your young men shall see visions, and your old men shall dream dreams:

And on my servants and on my handmaidens I will pour out in those days of my Spirit; and they shall prophesy:

And it shall come to pass, that whosoever shall call on the name of the Lord shall be saved.

Acts 2:1, 4, 6, 12, 14-18, 21

7 A Message of Peace

The wilderness and the solitary place shall be glad for them; and the desert shall rejoice, and blossom as the rose.

And the parched ground shall become a pool, and the thirsty land springs of water: in the habitation of dragons, where each lay, shall be grass with reeds and rushes.

And an highway shall be there, and a way, and it shall be called The way of holiness; the unclean shall not pass over it; but it shall be for those: the wayfaring men, though fools, shall not err therein.

And the ransomed of the Lord shall return, and come to Zion with songs and everlasting joy upon their heads: they shall obtain joy and gladness, and sorrow and sighing shall flee away.

The wolf also shall dwell with the lamb, and the leopard shall lie down with the kid; and the calf and the young lion and the fatling together; and a little child shall lead them.

They shall not hurt nor destroy in all my holy mountain: for the earth shall be full of the knowledge of the Lord, as the waters cover the sea.

And he shall judge among the nations, and shall rebuke many people: and they shall beat their swords into plowshares, and their spears into pruning hooks: nation shall not lift up sword against nation, neither shall they learn war any more.

O house of Jacob, come ye, and let us walk in the light of the Lord.

Isaiah 35:1, 7-8, 10; 11:6, 9; 2:4-5

8 God Our Sovereign

The Lord reigneth, he is clothed with majesty; the Lord is clothed with strength, wherewith he hath girded himself: the world also is stablished, that it cannot be moved.

Thy throne is established of old: thou art from everlasting.

The floods have lifted up, O Lord, the floods have lifted up their voice; the floods lift up their waves.

The Lord on high is mightier than the noise of many waters, yea, than the mighty waves of the sea.

Thy testimonies are very sure: holiness becometh thine house, O Lord, forever.

Rid me, and deliver me from the hand of strange children, whose mouth speaketh vanity, and their right hand is a right hand of falsehood:

That our sons may be as plants grown up in their youth; that our daughters may be as corner stones, polished after the similitude of a palace:

That our garners may be full, affording all manner of store: that our sheep may bring forth thousands and ten thousands in our streets:

That our oxen may be strong to labor; that there be no breaking in, nor going out; that there be no complaining in our streets.

Happy is that people, that is in such a case: yea, happy is that people, whose God is the Lord.

Psalms 93; 144:11-15

9 Thanksgiving to Our God

O give thanks unto the Lord; call upon his name: make known his deeds among the people.

Sing unto him, sing psalms unto him: talk ye of all his wondrous works.

Glory ye in his holy name: let the heart of them rejoice that seek the Lord.

Seek the Lord, and his strength: seek his face evermore.

Remember his marvelous works that he hath done; his wonders, and the judgments of his mouth.

He is the Lord our God: his judgments are in all the earth.

O come, let us sing unto the Lord: let us make a joyful noise to the rock of our salvation.

Let us come before his presence with thanksgiving, and make a joyful noise unto him with psalms.

For the Lord is a great God, and a great King above all gods.

Let the people praise thee, O God; let all the people praise thee.

O let the nations be glad and sing for joy: for thou shalt judge the people righteously, and govern the nations upon earth.

Let the people praise thee, O God; let all the people praise thee.

Then shall the earth yield her increase; and God, even our own God, shall bless us.

God shall bless us; and all the ends of the earth shall fear him.

Psalms 105:1-5, 7; 95:1-3; 67:3-7

10 The Coming of the Wise Men

Now when Jesus was born in Bethlehem of Judea in the days of Herod the king, behold, there came wise men from the east to Jerusalem,

Saying, Where is he that is born King of the Jews? for we have seen his star in the east, and are come to worship him.

When Herod the king had heard these things he was troubled, and all Jerusalem with him.

And when he had gathered all the chief priests and scribes of the people together, he demanded of them where Christ should be born.

And they said unto him, In Bethlehem of Judea: for thus it is written by the prophet,

And thou Bethlehem, in the land of Juda, art not the least among the princes of Juda: for out of thee shall come a Governor, that shall rule my people Israel.

Then Herod, when he had privily called the wise men, inquired of them diligently what time the star appeared.

And he sent them to Bethlehem, and said, Go and search diligently for the young child; and when ye have found him, bring me word again, that I may come and worship him also.

When they had heard the king they departed; and lo, the star, which they saw in the east, went before them, till it came and stood over where the young child was.

When they saw the star, they rejoiced with exceeding great joy.

Matthew 2:1-10

11 Jesus Is Born

And she brought forth her firstborn son, and wrapped him in swaddling clothes, and laid him in a manger; because there was no room for them in the inn.

And there were in the same country shepherds abiding in the field, keeping watch over their flock by night.

And, lo, the angel of the Lord came upon them, and the glory of the Lord shone round about them: and they were sore afraid.

And the angel said unto them, Fear not: for, behold, I bring you good tidings of great joy, which shall be to all people.

For unto you is born this day in the city of David a Savior, which is Christ the Lord.

And this shall be a sign unto you; ye shall find the babe wrapped in swaddling clothes, lying in a manger.

And suddenly there was with the angel a multitude of the heavenly host praising God, and saying,

Glory to God in the highest, and on earth peace, good will toward men.

And it came to pass, as the angels were gone away from them into heaven, the shepherds said one to another, Let us now go even unto Bethlehem, and see this thing which is come to pass, which the Lord hath made known unto us.

And they came with haste, and found Mary, and Joseph, and the babe lying in a manger.

Luke 2:7-16

12 God's Word Our Guide

All scripture is given by inspiration of God, and is profitable for doctrine, for reproof, for correction, for instruction in righteousness:

That the man of God may be perfect, thoroughly furnished unto all good works.

And now, brethren, I commend you to God, and to the word of his grace, which is able to build you up, and to give you an inheritance among all them which are sanctified.

Search the scriptures; for in them ye think ye have eternal life: and they are they which testify of me.

Princes have persecuted me without a cause: but my heart standeth in awe of thy word.

I rejoice at thy word, as one that findeth great spoil.

I hate and abhor lying: but thy law do I love.

Seven times a day do I praise thee because of thy righteous judgments.

Great peace have they which love thy law: and nothing shall offend them.

Lord, I have hoped in thy salvation, and done thy commandments.

My soul hath kept thy testimonies; and I love them exceedingly.

I have kept thy precepts and thy testimonies; for all my ways are before thee.

II Timothy 3:16-17; Acts 20:32; John 5:39; Psalm 119:161-168

13 The Worth of a Child

At the same time came the disciples unto Jesus, saying, Who is the greatest in the kingdom of heaven?

And Jesus called a little child unto him, and set him in the midst of them,

And said, Verily I say unto you, Except ye be converted, and become as little children, ye shall not enter into the kingdom of heaven.

Whosoever therefore shall humble himself as this little child, the same is greatest in the kingdom of heaven.

And whoso shall receive one such little child in my name receiveth me.

But whoso shall offend one of these little ones which believe in me, it were better for him that a millstone were hanged about his neck, and that he were drowned in the depth of the sea.

Woe unto the world because of offenses! for it must needs be that offenses come; but woe to that man by whom the offense cometh!

Take heed that ye despise not one of these little ones; for I say unto you, That in heaven their angels do always behold the face of my Father which is in heaven.

For the Son of man is come to save that which was lost.

Even so it is not the will of your Father which is in heaven, that one of these little ones should perish.

Matthew 18:1-7, 10-11, 14

14 Remember Thy Creator

Remember now thy Creator in the days of thy youth, while the evil days come not, nor the years draw nigh, when thou shalt say, I have no pleasure in them;

While the sun, or the light, or the moon, or the stars, be not darkened, nor the clouds return after the rain.

Rejoice, O young man, in the days of thy youth; and let thy heart cheer thee in the days of thy youth, and walk in the ways of thine heart, and in the sight of thine eyes: but know thou, that for all these things God will bring thee into judgment.

Therefore remove sorrow from thy heart, and put away evil from thy flesh: for childhood and youth are vanity.

Wherewithal shall a young man cleanse his way? by taking heed thereto according to thy word.

With my whole heart have I sought thee: O let me not wander from thy commandments.

Thy word have I hid in mine heart, that I might not sin against thee.

Blessed art thou, O Lord: teach me thy statutes.

With my lips have I declared all the judgments of thy mouth.

I have rejoiced in the way of thy testimonies, as much as in all riches.

I will meditate in thy precepts, and have respect unto thy ways.

I will delight myself in thy statutes: I will not forget thy word.

Ecclesiastes 12:1-2; 11:9-10; Psalm 119:1-16

15 A Worthy Woman

A worthy woman who can find? For her price is far above rubies.

The heart of her husband trusteth in her, and he shall have no lack of gain.

She doeth him good and not evil all the days of her life.

She stretcheth out her hand to the poor; yea, she reacheth forth her hands to the needy.

She is not afraid of the snow for her household; for all her household are clothed with scarlet.

Strength and dignity are her clothing; and she laugheth at the time to come.

She openeth her mouth with wisdom; and the law of kindness is on her tongue.

She looketh well to the ways of her household, and eateth not the bread of idleness.

Her children rise up and call her blessed; her husband also, and he praiseth her, saying:

Many daughters have done worthily, but thou excellest them all.

Grace is deceitful, and beauty is vain; but a woman that feareth Jehovah, she shall be praised.

Give her of the fruit of her hands; and let her works praise her in the gates.

Proverbs 31:10-12, 20-21, 25-31 (A.R.V.)

16 A Father's Honor

Hear, O Israel: The Lord our God is one Lord:

And thou shalt love the Lord thy God with all thine heart, and with all thy soul, and with all thy might.

And these words, which I command thee this day, shall be in thine heart:

And thou shalt teach them diligently unto thy children, and shalt talk of them when thou sittest in thine house, and when thou walkest by the way, and when thou liest down, and when thou risest up.

And thou shalt bind them for a sign upon thine hand, and they shall be as frontlets between thine eyes.

And thou shalt write them upon the posts of thine house, and on thy gates.

My son, hear the instruction of thy father, and forsake not the law of thy mother:

For they shall be an ornament of grace unto thy head, and chains about thy neck.

Children, obey your parents in the Lord: for this is right.

Honor thy father and mother; which is the first commandment with promise;

That it may be well with thee, and thou mayest live long on the earth.

And, ye fathers, provoke not your children to wrath: but bring them up in the nurture and admonition of the Lord.

Deuteronomy 6:4-9; Proverbs 1:8-9; Ephesians 6:1-4

17 The Way of Life

Blessed is the man that walketh not in the counsel of the ungodly, nor standeth in the way of sinners, nor sitteth in the seat of the scornful.

But his delight is in the law of the Lord; and in his law doth he meditate day and night.

Seek ye the Lord while he may be found, call ye upon him while he is near:

Let the wicked forsake his way, and the unrighteous man his thoughts: and let him return unto the Lord, and he will have mercy upon him; and to our God, for he will abundantly pardon.

She shall bring forth a son, and thou shalt call his name Jesus: for he shall save his people from their sins.

For God so loved the world, that he gave his only begotten Son, that whosoever believeth in him should not perish, but have everlasting life.

If we say that we have fellowship with him, and walk in darkness, we lie, and do not the truth:

But if we walk in the light, as he is in the light, we have fellowship one with another, and the blood of Jesus Christ his Son cleanseth us from all sin.

If we confess our sins, he is faithful and just to forgive us our sins, and to cleanse us from all unrighteousness.

Psalm 1:1-2; Isaiah 55:6-7; Matthew 1:21; John 3:16; I John 1:6-7, 9

18 The Lord's Day

This is the day which the Lord hath made; we will rejoice and be glad in it.

Blessed is he that cometh in the name of the Lord; we have blessed you out of the house of the Lord. God is the Lord which hath showed us light.

O give thanks unto the Lord; for he is good: for his mercy endureth forever.

Now upon the first day of the week, very early in the morning, they came unto the sepulcher, bringing the spices which they had prepared . . .

And they found the stone rolled away from the sepulcher. And they entered in, and found not the body of the Lord Jesus.

And as they were afraid, and bowed down their faces to the earth, they said unto them, Why seek ye the living among the dead? He is not here, but is risen.

And upon the first day of the week, when the disciples came together to break bread, Paul preached unto them.

I was in the Spirit on the Lord's day, and heard behind me a great voice, as of a trumpet, saying, I am Alpha and Omega, the first and the last: and, What thou seest, write in a book, and send it unto the seven churches.

And when I saw him, I fell at his feet as dead. And he laid his right hand upon me, saying unto me, Fear not . . . I am he that liveth, and was dead; and, behold, I am alive for evermore. Amen.

Psalm 118:24, 26-27, 29; Luke 24:1-3, 5-6; Acts 20:7a; Revelation 1:10-11; 17-18

19 One in Christ

Behold, how good and how pleasant it is for brethren to dwell together in unity!

As the body is one, and hath many members, and all the members of that one body, being many, are one body: so also is Christ.

For by one Spirit are we all baptized into one body, whether we be Jews or Gentiles, whether we be bond or free; and have been made all to drink into one Spirit.

Now hath God set the members every one of them in the body, as it has pleased him.

With all lowliness and meekness, with long-suffering, forbearing one another in love; endeavoring to keep the unity of the Spirit in the bond of peace.

There is one body, and one Spirit, even as ye are called in one hope of your calling; one Lord, one faith, one baptism,

One God and Father of all, who is above all, and through all, and in you all.

And for their sakes I sanctify myself, that they also might be sanctified through the truth.

Neither pray I for these alone, but for them also which shall believe on me through their word;

That they all may be one; as thou, Father, art in me, and I in thee, that they also may be one in us: that the world may believe that thou hast sent me.

Psalm 133:1; I Corinthians 12:12-13, 18; Ephesians 4:2-6; John 17:19-21

20 God's Church

Thou art an holy people unto the Lord thy God, and the Lord hath chosen thee to be a peculiar people unto himself, above all the nations that are upon the earth.

And of Zion it shall be said, This and that man was born in her: and the highest himself shall establish her.

The Lord shall count, when he writeth up the people, that this man was born in her.

Jesus saith unto them, But whom say ye that I am? And Simon Peter answered and said, Thou art the Christ, the Son of the living God.

And Jesus answered and said unto him, Blessed art thou, Simon Barjona: for flesh and blood hath not revealed it unto thee, but my Father which is in heaven.

And I say also unto thee, That thou art Peter, and upon this rock I will build my church; and the gates of hell shall not prevail against it.

Take heed therefore unto yourselves, and to all the flock, over the which the Holy Ghost hath made you overseers, to feed the church of God, which he hath purchased with his own blood.

And I John saw the holy city, new Jerusalem, coming down from God out of heaven, prepared as a bride adorned for her husband.

And I heard a great voice out of heaven saying, Behold, the tabernacle of God is with men, and he will dwell with them, and they shall be his people.

Deuteronomy 14:2; Psalm 87:5-6; Matthew 16:15-18; Acts 20:28; Revelation 21:2-3

21 Brotherly Love

There is neither Jew nor Greek, there is neither bond nor free, there is neither male nor female: for ye are all one in Christ Jesus.

He that saith he is in the light, and hateth his brother, is in darkness even until now.

He that loveth his brother abideth in the light, and there is none occasion of stumbling in him.

But he that hateth his brother is in darkness, and walketh in darkness, and knoweth not whither he goeth, because that darkness hath blinded his eyes.

God that made the world and all things therein, seeing that he is Lord of heaven and earth, dwelleth not in temples made with hands;

Neither is worshiped with men's hands, as though he needed anything, seeing he giveth to all life, and breath, and all things;

And hath made of one blood all nations of men for to dwell on the face of the earth. . . .

For in him we live, and move, and have our being; as certain also of your own poets have said, For we are also his offspring.

If a man say, I love God, and hateth his brother, he is a liar;

For he that loveth not his brother whom he hath seen, how can he love God whom he hath not seen?

And this commandment have we from him, That he who loveth God love his brother also.

Galatians 3:28; I John 2:9-11; Acts 17:24-26, 28: I John 4:20-21

22 God the Source of Peace

He maketh wars to cease unto the end of the earth; he breaketh the bow, and cutteth the spear in sunder; he burneth the chariot in the fire.

And he shall judge among many people, and rebuke strong nations afar off; and they shall beat their swords into plowshares, and their spears into pruning hooks: nation shall not lift up a sword against nation, neither shall they learn war any more.

But they shall sit every man under his vine and under his fig tree; and none shall make them afraid: for the mouth of the Lord of hosts hath spoken it.

For all people will walk every one in the name of his god, and we will walk in the name of the Lord our God forever and ever.

Ye have heard that it hath been said, An eye for an eye, and a tooth for a tooth:

But I say unto you, That ye resist not evil: but whosoever shall smite thee on thy right cheek, turn to him the other also.

Ye have heard that it hath been said, Thou shalt love thy neighbor, and hate thine enemy.

But I say unto you, Love your enemies, and pray for them that persecute you . . . that ye may be sons of your Father who is in heaven.

Blessed are the peacemakers: for they shall be called the children of God.

Psalm 46:9; Micah 4:3-5; Matthew 5:38-39, 43-44, 9

23 The Demands of Friendship

Ruth said, Entreat me not to leave thee, or to return from following after thee: for whither thou goest, I will go; and where thou lodgest, I will lodge: thy people shall be my people, and thy God my God.

A friend loveth at all times, and a brother is born for adversity.

A man that hath friends must show himself friendly: and there is a friend that sticketh closer than a brother.

And, behold, two of them went that same day to a village called Emmaus . . . and they talked together of all these things which had happened.

And it came to pass, that, while they communed together and reasoned, Jesus himself drew near, and went with them.

And they said one to another, Did not our heart burn within us, while he talked with us by the way?

These things have I spoken unto you, that my joy might remain in you, and that your joy might be full.

Greater love hath no man than this, that a man lay down his life for his friends.

Ye are my friends, if ye do whatsoever I command you.

Henceforth I call you not servants; for the servant knoweth not what his lord doeth: but I have called you friends; for all things that I have heard of my Father I have made known unto you.

Ruth 1:16; Proverbs 17:17; 18:24; Luke 24:13-15, 32; John 15:11, 13-15

24 Fellowship in God

The Lord is righteous in all his ways, and holy in all his works.

The Lord is nigh unto all them that call upon him, to all that call upon him in truth.

I say unto you, That if two of you shall agree on earth as touching any thing that they shall ask, it shall be done for them of my Father which is in heaven.

For where two or three are gathered together in my name, there am I in the midst of them.

That which we have seen and heard declare we unto you, that ye also may have fellowship with us: and truly our fellowship is with the Father, and with his Son Jesus Christ.

And these things write we unto you, that your joy may be full.

This then is the message which we have heard of him, and declare unto you, that God is light, and in him is no darkness at all.

If we say that we have fellowship with him, and walk in darkness, we lie, and do not the truth:

But if we walk in the light, as he is in the light, we have fellowship one with another, and the blood of Jesus Christ his Son cleanseth us from all sin.

And they, continuing daily with one accord in the temple, and breaking bread from house to house, did eat their meat with gladness and singleness of heart, praising God, and having favor with all the people.

Psalm 145:17-18; Matthew 18:19-20; I John 1:3-7; Acts 2:46-47a

25 Exhortation to Love

The Lord hath appeared of old unto me, saying, Yea, I have loved thee with an everlasting love: therefore with loving-kindness have I drawn thee.

Covet earnestly the best gifts: and yet show I unto you a more excellent way.

Though I speak with the tongues of men and of angels, and have not love, I am become as sounding brass, or a tinkling cymbal.

Beloved, let us love one another: for love is of God; and every one that loveth is born of God, and knoweth God.

He that loveth not knoweth not God; for God is love.

In this was manifested the love of God toward us, because that God sent his only begotten Son into the world, that we might live through him.

Herein is love, not that we loved God, but that he loved us, and sent his Son to be the propitiation for our sins.

Beloved, if God so loved us, we ought also to love one another.

A new commandment I give unto you, That ye love one another; as I have loved you, that ye also love one another.

By this shall all men know that ye are my disciples, if ye have love one to another.

Greater love hath no man than this, that a man lay down his life for his friends.

Jeremiah 31:3; I Corinthians 12:31; 13:1; I John 4:7-11; John 13:34-35; 15:13

26 God Our Hope

As the hart panteth after the water brooks, so panteth my soul after thee, O God. My soul thirsteth for God, for the living God.

Why art thou cast down, O my soul? and why art thou disquieted within me? hope in God: for I shall yet praise him who is the health of my countenance, and my God.

Let not your heart be troubled: ye believe in God, believe also in me.

In my Father's house are many mansions: if it were not so, I would have told you. I go to prepare a place for you.

And if I go and prepare a place for you, I will come again, and receive you unto myself; that where I am, there ye may be also.

Therefore being justified by faith, we have peace with God through our Lord Jesus Christ:

By whom also we have access by faith into this grace wherein we stand, and rejoice in hope of the glory of God.

And not only so, but we glory in tribulations also: knowing that tribulation worketh patience; and patience, experience; and experience, hope:

And hope maketh not ashamed; because the love of God is shed abroad in our hearts by the Holy Ghost which is given unto us.

Now the God of hope fill you with all joy and peace in believing, that ye may abound in hope, through the power of the Holy Ghost.

Psalms 42:1-2a; 43:5; John 14:1-3; Romans 5:1-5; 15:13

27 Source of Wisdom

My son, if thou wilt receive my words, and hide my commandments with thee; so that thou incline thine ear unto wisdom, and apply thine heart to understanding;

Yea, if thou criest after knowledge, and liftest up thy voice for understanding; if thou seekest her as silver, and searchest for her as for hid treasures;

Then shalt thou understand the fear of the Lord, and find the knowledge of God. For the Lord giveth wisdom: out of his mouth cometh knowledge and understanding.

Trust in the Lord with all thine heart; and lean not unto thine own understanding.

In all thy ways acknowledge him, and he shall direct thy paths.

And it came to pass, that after three days they found him in the temple, sitting in the midst of the doctors, both hearing them and asking them questions.

And all that heard him were astonished at his understanding and answers.

And he said unto them, How is it that ye sought me? wist ye not that I must be about my Father's business?

If any man will do his will, he shall know of the doctrine.

Study to show thyself approved unto God, a workman that needeth not to be ashamed, rightly dividing the word of truth.

Proverbs 2:1-6; 3:5-6; Luke 2:46-47, 49; John 7:17; II Timothy 2:15

28 Christ Our Healer

Surely he hath borne our griefs, and carried our sorrows: yet we did esteem him stricken, smitten of God, and afflicted.

For he was wounded for our transgressions, he was bruised for our iniquities: the chastisement of our peace was upon him; and with his stripes we are healed.

And Jesus went about all Galilee, teaching in their synagogues, and preaching the gospel of the kingdom, and healing all manner of sickness and all manner of disease among the people.

And great multitudes came unto him, having with them those that were lame, blind, dumb, maimed, and many others, and cast them down at Jesus' feet; and he healed them:

Insomuch that the multitude wondered, when they saw the dumb to speak, the maimed to be whole, the lame to walk, and the blind to see: and they glorified the God of Israel.

Is any among you afflicted? let him pray. Is any merry? let him sing psalms.

Is any sick among you? let him call for the elders of the church; and let them pray over him, anointing him with oil in the name of the Lord:

And the prayer of faith shall save the sick, and the Lord shall raise him up; and if he have committed sins, they shall be forgiven him.

Confess your faults one to another, and pray one for another, that ye may be healed. The effectual fervent prayer of a righteous man availeth much.

Isaiah 53:4-5; Matthew 4:23; 15:30-31; James 5:13-16

29 True Worship

Behold, I stand at the door, and knock: if any man hear my voice, and open the door, I will come in to him, and will sup with him, and he with me.

The earth is the Lord's and the fullness thereof; the world, and they that dwell therein.

For he hath founded it upon the seas, and established it upon the floods.

Who shall ascend into the hill of the Lord? or who shall stand in his holy place?

He that hath clean hands, and a pure heart; who hath not lifted up his soul unto vanity, nor sworn deceitfully.

He shall receive the blessing from the Lord, and righteousness from the God of his salvation.

Lift up your heads, O ye gates; even lift them up, ye everlasting doors; and the King of glory shall come in. The hour cometh and now is, when the true worshipers shall worship the Father in spirit and in truth: for the Father seeketh such to worship him.

God is a Spirit; and they that worship him must worship him in spirit and in truth.

Ask, and it shall be given you; seek, and ye shall find; knock, and it shall be opened unto you:

For every one that asketh receiveth; and he that seeketh findeth; and to him that knocketh it shall be opened.

Revelation 3:20; Psalm 24:1-5, 9; John 4:23-24; Matthew 7:7-8

30 The Spirit-Filled Life

And it shall come to pass afterward, that I will pour out my spirit upon all flesh; and your sons and your daughters shall prophesy, your old men shall dream dreams, your young men shall see visions.

If ye then, being evil, know how to give good gifts to your children: how much more shall your heavenly Father give the Holy Spirit to them that ask him?

And, behold, I send the promise of my Father upon you: but tarry ye in the city of Jerusalem, until ye be endued with power from on high.

And when the day of Pentecost was fully come, they were all with one accord in one place.

And suddenly there came a sound from heaven as of a rushing mighty wind, and it filled all the house where they were sitting.

And there appeared unto them cloven tongues, like as of fire, and it sat upon each of them.

And they were all filled with the Holy Ghost, and began to speak with other tongues, as the Spirit gave them utterance.

If ye be led of the Spirit, ye are not under the law. . . . But the fruit of the Spirit is love, joy, peace, long-suffering, gentleness, goodness, faith, meekness, temperance: against such there is no law.

And they that are Christ's have crucified the flesh with the affections and lusts. If we live in the Spirit, let us also walk in the Spirit.

Joel 2:28; Luke 11:13; 24:49; Acts 2:1-4; Galatians 5:18, 22-25

31 The Nature of the Kingdom

Jesus came into Galilee, preaching the gospel of the kingdom of God, and saying, The time is fulfilled, and the kingdom of God is at hand: repent ye, and believe the gospel.

God, who at sundry times and in divers manners spake in time past unto the fathers by the prophets,

Hath in these last days spoken unto us by his Son, whom he hath appointed heir of all things, by whom also he made the worlds.

Unto the Son he saith, Thy throne, O God, is forever and ever: a scepter of righteousness is the scepter of thy kingdom.

Thou hast loved righteousness, and hated iniquity; therefore God, even thy God, hath anointed thee with the oil of gladness above thy fellows.

Jesus answered, My kingdom is not of this world; if my kingdom were of this world, then would my servants fight, that I should not be delivered to the Jews: but now is my kingdom not from hence.

Pilate therefore said unto him, Art thou a king then? Jesus answered, Thou sayest that I am a king. To this end was I born, and for this cause came I into the world, that I should bear witness unto the truth.

The kingdom of God is not meat and drink; but righteousness, and peace, and joy in the Holy Spirit.

Let us therefore follow after the things which make for peace, and things wherewith one may edify another.

Mark 1:14-15; Hebrews 1:1-2, 8-9; John 18:36-37; Romans 14:17, 19

32 God's Word

All scripture is given by inspiration of God, and is profitable for doctrine, for reproof, for correction, for instruction in righteousness.

That the man of God may be perfect, thoroughly furnished unto all good works.

Study to show thyself approved unto God, a workman that needeth not to be ashamed, rightly dividing the word of truth.

For the word of God is quick, and powerful, and sharper than any two-edged sword, piercing even to the dividing asunder of soul and spirit, and of the joints and marrow, and is a discerner of the thoughts and intents of the heart.

O how love I thy law! It is my meditation all the day.

How sweet are thy words unto my taste! yea, sweeter than honey to my mouth!

Through thy precepts I get understanding: therefore I hate every false way.

Thy word is a lamp unto my feet, and a light unto my path.

I have sworn, and I will perform it, that I will keep thy righteous judgments.

Thy testimonies are wonderful: therefore doth my soul keep them.

The entrance of thy words giveth light; it giveth understanding unto the simple.

II Timothy 3:16-17; 2:15; Hebrews 4:12; Psalm 119:97, 103-106, 129-130

33 Great and Precious Promises

The Lord is not slack concerning his promise, as some men count slackness; but is long-suffering to usward, not willing that any should perish, but that all should come to repentance.

Grace and peace be multiplied unto you through the knowledge of God, and of Jesus our Lord,

According as his divine power hath given unto us all things that pertain unto life and godliness, through the knowledge of him that hath called us to glory and virtue:

Whereby are given unto us exceeding great and precious promises: that by these ye might be partakers of the divine nature, having escaped the corruption that is in the world through lust.

Believe me that I am in the Father, and the Father in me: or else believe me for the very work's sake.

Verily, verily, I say unto you, He that believeth on me, the works that I do shall he do also;

And greater works than these shall he do; because I go unto my Father.

And whatsoever ye shall ask in my name, that will I do, that the Father may be glorified in the Son.

And we know that all things work together for good to them that love God, to them who are the called according to his purpose.

What shall we then say to these things? If God be for us, who can be against us?

II Peter 3:9; 1:2-4; John 14:11-13; Romans 8:28, 31

34 God's Care and Protection

He that dwelleth in the secret place of the most High shall abide under the shadow of the Almighty.

I will say of the Lord, He is my refuge and my fortress: my God; in him will I trust.

Surely he shall deliver thee from the snare of the fowler, and from the noisome pestilence.

He shall cover thee with his feathers, and under his wings shalt thou trust: his truth shall be thy shield and buckler.

Thou shalt not be afraid for the terror by night; nor for the arrow that flieth by day;

Nor for the pestilence that walketh in darkness; nor for the destruction that wasteth at noonday.

A thousand shall fall at thy side, and ten thousand at thy right hand; but it shall not come nigh thee.

Therefore I say unto you, Take no thought for your life, what ye shall eat, or what ye shall drink; nor yet for your body, what ye shall put on.

Is not the life more than meat, and the body than raiment?

Behold the fowls of the air: for they sow not, neither do they reap, nor gather into barns; yet your heavenly Father feedeth them.

Are ye not much better than they?

Take therefore no thought for the morrow: for the morrow shall take thought for the things of itself. Sufficient unto the day is the evil thereof.

Psalm 91:1-7; Matthew 6:25-26, 34

35 Keeping God's Commandments

Hear, O Israel: The Lord our God is one Lord:

And thou shalt love the Lord thy God with all thine heart, and with all thy soul, and with all thy might.

And these words, which I command thee this day, shall be in thine heart:

And thou shalt teach them diligently unto thy children, and shalt talk of them when thou sittest in thine house, and when thou walkest by the way, and when thou liest down, and when thou risest up.

And thou shalt bind them for a sign upon thine hand, and they shall be as frontlets before thine eyes.

My son, forget not my law; but let thine heart keep my commandments:

For length of days, and long life, and peace, shall they add to thee.

Let not mercy and truth forsake thee: bind them about thy neck; write them upon the table of thine heart:

So shalt thou find favor and good understanding in the sight of God and man.

Trust in the Lord with all thine heart; and lean not unto thine own understanding.

In all thy ways acknowledge him, and he shall direct thy paths.

Deuteronomy 6:4-8; Proverbs 3:1-6

36 God's Greatness and Glory

The heavens declare the glory of God, and the firmament showeth his handiwork.

Day unto day uttereth speech, and night unto night showeth knowledge.

There is no speech nor language, where their voice is not heard.

Their line is gone out through all the earth, and their words to the end of the world.

In them hath he set a tabernacle for the sun, which is as a bridegroom coming out of his chamber, and rejoiceth as a strong man to run a race.

His going forth is from the end of the heaven, and his circuit unto the ends of it: and there is nothing hid from the heat thereof.

The law of the Lord is perfect, converting the soul:

The testimony of the Lord is sure, making wise the simple:

The statutes of the Lord are right, rejoicing the heart:

The commandment of the Lord is pure, enlightening the eyes. The fear of the Lord is clean, enduring forever:

The judgments of the Lord are true and righteous altogether.

Unison:

Let the words of my mouth, and the meditation of my heart, be acceptable in thy sight, O Lord, my strength and my redeemer.

Psalm 19:1-9, 14

37 The Assurance of Faith

The Lord is my light and my salvation; whom shall I fear? the Lord is the strength of my life; of whom shall I be afraid?

When the wicked, even mine enemies and my foes, came upon me to eat up my flesh, they stumbled and fell.

Though an host should encamp against me, my heart shall not fear: though war should rise against me, in this will I be confident.

Now faith is the substance of things hoped for, the evidence of things not seen.

For by it the elders obtained a good report.

Through faith we understand that the worlds were framed by the word of God, so that things which are seen were not made of things which do appear.

By faith Enoch was translated that he should not see death; and was not found, because God had translated him: for before his translation he had this testimony, that he pleased God.

But without faith it is impossible to please him: for he that cometh to God must believe that he is, and that he is a rewarder of them that diligently seek him.

By faith Abraham, when he was called to go out into a place which he should after receive for an inheritance, obeyed; and he went out, not knowing whither he went.

Wait on the Lord: be of good courage, and he shall strengthen thine heart: wait, I say, on the Lord.

Psalm 27:1-3; Hebrews 11:1-3, 5-6, 8; Psalm 27:14

38 The Call to Youth

Let no man despise thy youth; but be thou an example of the believers, in word, in conversation, in charity, in spirit, in faith, in purity.

Till I come, give attendance to reading, to exhortation, to doctrine.

Neglect not the gift that is in thee, which was given thee by prophecy, with the laying on of the hands of the presbytery.

Meditate upon these things; give thyself wholly to them; that thy profiting may appear to all.

Take heed unto thyself, and unto the doctrine; continue in them: for in doing this thou shalt both save thyself, and them that hear thee.

Rebuke not an elder, but entreat him as a father; and the younger men as brethren.

Remember now thy Creator in the days of thy youth, while the evil days come not, nor the years draw nigh, when thou shalt say, I have no pleasure in them;

While the sun, or the light, or the moon, or the stars, be not darkened, nor the clouds return after the rain:

Vanity of vanities, saith the preacher; all is vanity.

Let us hear the conclusion of the whole matter: Fear God, and keep his commandments: for this is the whole duty of man.

For God shall bring every work into judgment, with every secret thing, whether it be good, or whether it be evil.

I Timothy 4:12-16; 5:1; Ecclesiastes 12:1-2, 8, 13-14

39 The House of Prayer and Peace

And Jesus went into the temple of God, and cast out all them that sold and bought in the temple, and overthrew the tables of the moneychangers, and the seats of them that sold doves,

And said unto them, It is written, My house shall be called the house of prayer; but ye have made it a den of thieves.

I was glad when they said unto me, Let us go into the house of the Lord. Our feet shall stand within thy gates, O Jerusalem.

Jerusalem is builded as a city that is compact together: whither the tribes go up, the tribes of the Lord, unto the testimony of Israel, to give thanks unto the name of the Lord.

Pray for the peace of Jerusalem: they shall prosper that love thee. Peace be within thy walls, and prosperity within thy palaces.

For my brethren and companions' sakes, I will now say, Peace be within thee. Because of the house of the Lord our God I will seek thy good.

One thing have I desired of the Lord, that will I seek after; that I may dwell in the house of the Lord all the days of my life, to behold the beauty of the Lord, and to inquire in his temple.

For in the time of trouble he shall hide me in his pavilion: in the secret of his tabernacle shall he hide me; he shall set me up upon a rock.

Matthew 21:12-13; Psalms 122:1-4, 6-9; 27:4-5

40 Serving One Another

I beseech you therefore, brethren, by the mercies of God, that ye present your bodies a living sacrifice, holy, acceptable unto God, which is your reasonable service.

And be not conformed to this world: but be ye transformed by the renewing of your mind, that ye may prove what is that good, and acceptable, and perfect, will of God.

For as we have many members in one body, and all members have not the same office:

So we, being many, are one body in Christ, and every one members one of another.

Let love be without dissimulation. Abhor that which is evil; cleave to that which is good.

Be kindly affectioned one to another with brotherly love; in honor preferring one another;

Not slothful in business; fervent in spirit; serving the Lord;

Rejoicing in hope; patient in tribulation; continuing instant in prayer;

Distributing to the necessity of saints; given to hospitality.

Bless them which persecute you: bless, and curse not.

Therefore if thine enemy hunger, feed him; if he thirst, give him drink: for in so doing thou shalt heap coals of fire on his head.

Be not overcome of evil, but overcome evil with good.

Romans 12:1-2, 4-5, 9-14, 20-21

41 Good Stewards of God's Grace

Lay up for yourselves treasures in heaven, where neither moth nor rust doth corrupt, and where thieves do not break through nor steal:

For where your treasure is, there will your heart be also.

This I say, He which soweth sparingly shall reap also sparingly; and he which soweth bountifully shall reap also bountifully.

Every man according as he purposeth in his heart, so let him give . . . for God loveth a cheerful giver.

And God is able to make all grace abound toward you; that ye, always having all sufficiency in all things, may abound to every good work.

And above all things have fervent charity among yourselves: for charity shall cover the multitude of sins.

Use hospitality one to another without grudging.

As every man hath received the gift, even so minister the same one to another, as good stewards of the manifold grace of God.

Honor the Lord with thy substance, and with the first fruits of all thine increase:

So shall thy barns be filled with plenty, and thy presses shall burst out with new wine.

He hath showed thee, O man, what is good; and what doth the Lord require of thee, but to do justly, and to love mercy, and to walk humbly with thy God?

Matthew 6:20-21; II Corinthians 9:6-8; I Peter 4:8-10; Proverbs 3:9-10; Micah 6:8

42 The Gospel for All People

O sing unto the Lord a new song: sing unto the Lord, all the earth.

Sing unto the Lord, bless his name; show forth his salvation from day to day.

Declare his glory among the heathen, his wonders among all people.

For the Lord is great, and greatly to be praised: he is to be feared above all gods.

And Jesus came and spake unto them, saying, All power is given unto me in heaven and in earth.

Go ye therefore, and teach all nations, baptizing them in the name of the Father, and of the Son, and of the Holy Ghost:

Teaching them to observe all things whatsoever I have commanded you: and, lo, I am with you alway, even unto the end of the world.

Now after that John was put in prison, Jesus came into Galilee, preaching the gospel of the kingdom of God,

And saying, The time is fulfilled, and the kingdom of God is at hand: repent ye, and believe the gospel.

Now as he walked by the sea of Galilee, he saw Simon and Andrew his brother casting a net into the sea: for they were fishers.

And Jesus said unto them, Come ye after me, and I will make you to become fishers of men.

And straightway they forsook their nets, and followed him.

Psalm 96:1-4; Matthew 28:18-20; Mark 1:14-18

43 The Urgency of the Gospel

And he came to Nazareth, where he had been brought up: and as his custom was, he went into the synagogue on the sabbath day, and stood up for to read.

And there was delivered unto him the book of the prophet Esaias. And when he had opened the book, he found the place where it was written,

The Spirit of the Lord is upon me, because he hath anointed me to preach the gospel to the poor; he hath sent me to heal the broken-hearted,

To preach deliverance to the captives, and recovering of sight to the blind, to set at liberty them that are bruised, to preach the acceptable year of the Lord.

Say not ye, There are yet four months, and then cometh the harvest? behold I say unto you, Lift up your eyes, and look on the fields; for they are white already to harvest.

And he that reapeth receiveth wages, and gathereth fruit unto life eternal: that both he that soweth and he that reapeth may rejoice together.

And herein is that saying true, One soweth, and another reapeth.

I sent you to reap that whereon ye bestowed no labor: other men labored, and ye are entered into their labors.

And let us not be weary in well-doing: for in due season we shall reap, if we faint not.

Luke 4:16-19; John 4:35-38; Galatians 6:9

44 The Manner of Prayer

Take heed that ye do not your alms before men, to be seen of them: otherwise ye have no reward of your Father which is in heaven.

Therefore when thou doest thine alms, do not sound a trumpet before thee, as the hypocrites do in the synagogues and in the streets, that they may have glory of men. Verily I say unto you, They have their reward.

But when thou doest alms, let not thy left hand know what thy right hand doeth.

That thine alms may be in secret and thy Father which seeth in secret himself shall reward thee openly.

And when thou prayest, thou shalt not be as the hypocrites are; for they love to pray standing in the synagogues and in the corners of the streets, that they may be seen of men. Verily I say unto you, They have their reward.

But thou, when thou prayest, enter into thy closet, and when thou hast shut thy door, pray to thy Father which is in secret, and thy Father which seeth in secret shall reward thee openly.

But when ye pray, use not vain repetitions, as the heathen do; for they think that they shall be heard for their much speaking.

Be not ye therefore like unto them: for your Father knoweth what things ye have need of, before ye ask him.

Matthew 6:1-8

45 The Water of Life

Jesus cometh to a city of Samaria, which is called Sychar. . . .

Now Jacob's well was there. Jesus therefore, being wearied with his journey, sat thus on the well. . . .

There cometh a woman of Samaria to draw water: Jesus saith unto her, Give me to drink.

Then saith the woman of Samaria unto him, How is it that thou, being a Jew, asketh drink of me, which am a woman of Samaria? for the Jews have no dealings with the Samaritans.

Jesus answered and said unto her, If thou knewest the gift of God, and who it is that saith to thee, Give me to drink; thou wouldest have asked of him, and he would have given thee living water. . . . Whosoever drinketh of this water shall thirst again:

But whosoever drinketh of the water that I shall give him shall never thirst; but the water that I shall give him shall be in him a well of water springing up into everlasting life.

The woman saith unto him, Sir, give me this water, that I thirst not, neither come hither to draw. . . .

Jesus saith, . . . Say not ye, There are yet four months and then cometh the harvest? Behold, I say unto you, Lift up your eyes, and look on the fields; for they are white already to harvest.

John 4:5-7, 9-10, 14-15, 35

46 Christian Self-Denial

Jesus began to show unto his disciples how that he must go unto Jerusalem, and suffer many things of the elders and chief priests and scribes, and be killed, and be raised again the third day.

Then Peter took him, and began to rebuke him, saying, Be it far from thee, Lord: this shall not be unto thee.

But he turned, and said unto Peter, Get thee behind me, Satan: thou art an offense unto me: for thou savorest not the things that be of God, but those that be of men.

Then said Jesus unto his disciples, If any man will come after me, let him deny himself, and take up his cross, and follow me.

For whosoever will save his life shall lose it: and whosoever will lose his life for my sake shall find it.

For what is a man profited, if he shall gain the whole world, and lose his own soul? or what shall a man give in exchange for his soul?

For the Son of man shall come in the glory of his Father with his angels; and then he shall reward every man according to his works.

Verily I say unto you, There be some standing here, which shall not taste of death, till they see the Son of man coming in his kingdom.

Matthew 16:21-28

47 The Temptation of Jesus

Then was Jesus led up of the spirit into the wilderness to be tempted of the devil.

And when he had fasted forty days and forty nights, he was afterward an hungered.

And when the tempter came to him, he said, If thou be the Son of God, command that these stones be made bread.

But he answered and said, It is written, Man shall not live by bread alone, but by every word that proceedeth out of the mouth of God.

Then the devil taketh him up into the holy city, and setteth him on a pinnacle of the temple.

And saith unto him, If thou be the Son of God, cast thyself down; for it is written, He shall give his angels charge concerning thee; and in their hands they shall bear thee up, lest at any time thou dash thy foot against a stone.

Jesus said unto him, It is written again, Thou shalt not tempt the Lord thy God.

Again, the devil taketh him up into an exceeding high mountain and showeth him all the kingdoms of the world, and the glory of them;

And saith unto him, All these things will I give thee, if thou wilt fall down and worship me.

Then saith Jesus unto him, Get thee hence, Satan: for it is written, Thou shalt worship the Lord thy God and him only shalt thou serve.

Then the devil leaveth him, and, behold, angels came and ministered unto him.

Matthew 4:1-11

48 An Exhortation to Self-Control

Therefore, my brethren dearly beloved and longed for, my joy and crown, so stand fast in the Lord.

Rejoice in the Lord alway; and again I say, Rejoice.

Let your moderation be known unto all men. The Lord is at hand.

Be careful for nothing; but in everything by prayer and supplication with thanksgiving let your requests be made known unto God.

And the peace of God, which passeth all understanding shall keep your hearts and minds through Christ Jesus.

Finally, brethren, whatsoever things are true, whatsoever things are honest, whatsoever things are just, whatsoever things are pure, whatsoever things are lovely, whatsoever things are of good report; if there be any virtue, and if there be any praise, think on these things.

Those things, which ye have both learned, and received, and heard, and seen in me, do: and the God of peace shall be with you.

I know both how to be abased, and I know how to abound: everywhere . . . I am instructed both to be full and to be hungry, both to abound and to suffer need.

I can do all things through Christ which strengtheneth me.

Philippians 4:1, 4-9, 12-13

49 The Courage of Faith

The Lord is my light and my salvation; whom shall I fear? The Lord is the strength of my life; of whom shall I be afraid?

When the wicked, even mine enemies and my foes, came upon me to eat up my flesh, they stumbled and fell.

Though an host should encamp against me, my heart shall not fear: though war should rise against me, in this will I be confident.

One thing have I desired of the Lord, that will I seek after; that I may dwell in the house of the Lord all the days of my life, to behold the beauty of the Lord, and to inquire in his temple.

For in the time of trouble he shall hide me in his pavilion: in the secret of his tabernacle shall he hide me; he shall set me up upon a rock.

And now shall mine head be lifted up above mine enemies round about me: therefore will I offer in his tabernacle sacrifices of joy; I will sing, yea, I will sing praises unto the Lord.

Teach me thy way, O Lord, and lead me in a plain path, because of mine enemies.

I had fainted, unless I had believed to see the goodness of the Lord in the land of the living.

Wait on the Lord: be of good courage, and he shall strengthen thine heart: wait, I say, on the Lord.

Psalm 27:1-6, 11, 13-14

50 The Obedience of Love

If ye love me, keep my commandments.

He that hath my commandments, and keepeth them, he it is that loveth me: and he that loveth me shall be loved of my Father, and I will love him and will manifest myself to him.

If a man love me, he will keep my words: and my Father will love him, and we will come unto him, and make our abode with him.

He that loveth me not keepeth not my sayings: and the word which ye hear is not mine, but the Father's which sent me.

If ye keep my commandments, ye shall abide in my love; even as I have kept my Father's commandments, and abide in his love.

These things have I spoken unto you, that my joy might remain in you, and that your joy might be full.

This is my commandment, That ye love one another, as I have loved you.

Greater love hath no man than this, that a man lay down his life for his friends.

Ye are my friends, if ye do whatsoever I command you.

John 14:15, 21, 23-24; 15:10-14

51 The Value of True Wisdom

Happy is the man that findeth wisdom and the man that getteth understanding.

For the merchandise of it is better than the merchandise of silver, and the gain thereof than fine gold.

She is more precious than rubies: and all the things thou canst desire are not to be compared unto her.

Length of days is in her right hand; and in her left hand riches and honor.

Her ways are ways of pleasantness, and all her paths are peace.

She is a tree of life to them that lay hold upon her: and happy is every one that retaineth her.

The Lord by wisdom hath founded the earth; by understanding hath he established the heavens.

By his knowledge the depths are broken up, and the clouds drop down the dew.

My son, let not them depart from thine eyes: keep sound wisdom and discretion:

So shall they be life unto thy soul, and grace to thy neck.

Then shalt thou walk in thy way safely, and thy foot shall not stumble.

For the Lord shall be thy confidence and shall keep thy foot from being taken.

Proverbs 3:13-23, 26

52 The Cost of Discipleship

And there went great multitudes with him: and he turned, and said unto them,

If any man come to me, and hate not his father, and mother, and wife, and children, and brethren, and sisters, yea, and his own life also, he cannot be my disciple.

And whosoever doth not bear his cross, and come after me, cannot be my disciple.

For which of you, intending to build a tower, sitteth not down first, and counteth the cost, whether he have sufficient to finish it?

Lest haply, after he hath laid the foundation, and is not able to finish it, all that behold it begin to mock him,

Saying, This man began to build, and was not able to finish.

Or what king, going to make war against another king, sitteth not down first, and consulteth whether he be able with ten thousand to meet him that cometh against him with twenty thousand?

Or else, while the other is yet a great way off, he sendeth an ambassage and desireth conditions of peace.

So likewise, whosoever he be of you that forsaketh not all that he hath, he cannot be my disciple.

Luke 14:25-33

53 The Christian Warfare

Finally, my brethren, be strong in the Lord, and in the power of his might.

Put on the whole armor of God, that ye may be able to stand against the wiles of the devil.

For we wrestle not against flesh and blood, but against principalities, against powers, against the rulers of darkness of this world, against spiritual wickedness in high places.

Wherefore take unto you the whole armor of God, that ye may be able to withstand in the evil day, and having done all, to stand.

Stand therefore, having your loins girt about with truth, and having on the breastplate of righteousness;

And your feet shod with the preparation of the gospel of peace;

Above all taking the shield of faith, wherewith ye shall be able to quench all the fiery darts of the wicked.

And take the helmet of salvation, and the sword of the Spirit, which is the word of God:

Praying always with all prayer and supplication in the Spirit, and watching thereunto with all perseverance and supplication for all saints.

Ephesians 6:10-18

54 Victory over Death

Behold, I show you a mystery; We shall not all sleep, but we shall all be changed,

In a moment, in the twinkling of an eye, at the last trump: for the trumpet shall sound, and the dead shall be raised incorruptible, and we shall be changed.

For this corruptible must put on incorruption, and this mortal must put on immortality.

So when this corruptible shall have put on incorruption, and this mortal shall have put on immortality, then shall be brought to pass the saying that is written, Death is swallowed up in victory.

O death, where is thy sting? O grave, where is thy victory?

The sting of death is sin; and the strength of sin is the law.

But thanks be to God, which giveth us the victory through our Lord Jesus Christ.

Therefore, my beloved brethren, be ye steadfast, unmovable, always abounding in the work of the Lord, forasmuch as ye know that your labor is not in vain in the Lord.

I Corinthians 15:51-58

55 Eternal Life in Christ

Let not your heart be troubled: ye believe in God, believe also in me.

In my Father's house are many mansions; if it were not so, I would have told you. I go to prepare a place for you.

And if I go and prepare a place for you, I will come again, and receive you unto myself; that where I am, there ye may be also. And whither I go ye know, and the way ye know.

Thomas saith unto him, Lord, we know not whither thou goest; and how can we know the way?

Jesus saith unto him, I am the way, the truth, and the life: no man cometh unto the Father, but by me.

If ye had known me, ye should have known my Father also: and from henceforth ye know him, and have seen him.

Philip saith unto him, Lord, show us the Father, and it sufficeth us.

Jesus saith unto him, Have I been so long time with you, and yet hast thou not known me, Philip? he that hath seen me hath seen the Father; and how sayest thou then, Show us the Father?

Believest thou not that I am in the Father, and the Father in me? the words that I speak unto you I speak not of myself: but the Father that dwelleth in me, he doeth the works.

John 14:1-10

56 An Exhortation to Praise

Praise ye the Lord. Sing unto the Lord a new song, and his praise in the congregation of saints.

Let Israel rejoice in him that made him: let the children of Zion be joyful in their King.

For the Lord taketh pleasure in his people: he will beautify the meek with salvation.

Let the saints be joyful in glory, let them sing aloud upon their beds.

Let the high praises of God be in their mouth, and a two-edged sword in their hand.

Praise ye the Lord. Praise God in his sanctuary: praise him in the firmament of his power.

Praise him for his mighty acts: praise him according to his excellent greatness.

Praise him with the sound of the trumpet: praise him with the psaltery and harp.

Praise him with the timbrel and dance: praise him with stringed instruments and organs.

Praise him upon the loud cymbals: praise him upon the high sounding cymbals.

Let every thing that hath breath praise the Lord. Praise ye the Lord.

Psalms 149:1-2, 4-6; 150

57 The Obligation of Forgiveness

Ye have heard that it was said by them of old time, Thou shalt not kill; and whosoever shall kill shall be in danger of the judgment.

But I say unto you, That whosoever is angry with his brother without a cause shall be in danger of the judgment: and whosoever shall say to his brother, Raca, shall be in danger of the council, but whosoever shall say, Thou fool, shall be in danger of hell fire.

Therefore if thou bring thy gift to the altar, and there rememberest that thy brother hath ought against thee;

Leave there thy gift before the altar, and go thy way; first be reconciled to thy brother, and then come and offer thy gift.

Ye have heard that it hath been said, Thou shalt love thy neighbor and hate thine enemy.

But I say unto you, Love your enemies, bless them that curse you, do good to them that hate you, and pray for them which despitefully use you and persecute you;

That ye may be the children of your Father which is in heaven; for he maketh his sun to rise on the evil and on the good, and sendeth rain on the just and on the unjust.

For if ye love them which love you, what reward have ye? Do not even the publicans the same?

Be ye therefore perfect, even as your Father which is in heaven is perfect.

Matthew 5:21-24, 43-46, 48

58 God's Care for the Oppressed

Praise ye the Lord. Praise the Lord, O my soul.

While I live will I praise the Lord: I will sing praises unto my God while I have any being.

Put not your trust in princes, nor in the son of man, in whom there is no help.

His breath goeth forth, he returneth to his earth; in that very day his thoughts perish.

Happy is he that hath the God of Jacob for his help, whose hope is in the Lord his God:

Which made heaven, and earth, the sea, and all that therein is: which keepeth truth forever.

Which executeth judgment for the oppressed: which giveth food to the hungry. The Lord looseth the prisoners:

The Lord openeth the eyes of the blind: the Lord raiseth them that are bowed down: the Lord loveth the righteous:

The Lord preserveth the strangers; he relieveth the fatherless and widow: but the way of the wicked he turneth upside down.

The Lord shall reign forever, even thy God, O Zion, unto all generations. Praise ye the Lord.

Jesus said, The Spirit of the Lord is upon me, because he hath anointed me to preach the gospel to the poor; he hath sent me to heal the brokenhearted, to preach deliverance to the captives, and recovering of sight to the blind, to set at liberty them that are bruised, to preach the acceptable year of the Lord.

Psalm 146; Luke 4:18-19

59 God Our Refuge

God is our refuge and strength, a very present help in trouble.

Therefore will not we fear, though the earth be removed, and though the mountains be carried into the midst of the sea;

Though the waters thereof roar and be troubled, though the mountains shake with the swelling thereof.

There is a river, the streams whereof shall make glad the city of God, the holy place of the tabernacles of the most High.

God is in the midst of her; she shall not be moved; God shall help her, and that right early.

The heathen raged, the kingdoms were moved: he uttered his voice, the earth melted.

The Lord of hosts is with us; the God of Jacob is our refuge.

Come, behold the works of the Lord, what desolations he hath made in the earth.

He maketh wars to cease unto the end of the earth; he breaketh the bow, and cutteth the spear in sunder; he burneth the chariot in the fire.

Be still, and know that I am God: I will be exalted among the heathen, I will be exalted in the earth.

The Lord of hosts is with us; the God of Jacob is our refuge.

Psalm 46

60 The Baptism of Jesus

In those days came John the Baptist, preaching in the wilderness of Judea,

And saying, Repent ye: for the kingdom of heaven is at hand.

For this is he that was spoken of by the prophet Esaias, saying, The voice of one crying in the wilderness, Prepare ye the way of the Lord, make his paths straight.

I indeed baptize you with water unto repentance: but he that cometh after me is mightier than I, whose shoes I am not worthy to bear; he shall baptize you with the Holy Ghost, and with fire:

Whose fan is in his hand, and he will thoroughly purge his floor, and gather his wheat into the garner; but he will burn up the chaff with unquenchable fire.

Then cometh Jesus from Galilee to Jordan unto John, to be baptized of him.

But John forbade him, saying, I have need to be baptized of thee, and comest thou to me?

And Jesus answering said unto him, Suffer it to be so now: for thus it becometh us to fulfill all righteousness. Then he suffered him.

And Jesus, when he was baptized, went up straightway out of the water: and, lo, the heavens were opened unto him, and he saw the Spirit of God descending . . . upon him:

And lo a voice from heaven, saying, This is my beloved Son, in whom I am well pleased.

Matthew 3:1-3, 11-17

61 A Test of Righteousness

When the Son of man shall come in his glory, and all the holy angels with him, then shall he sit upon the throne of his glory:

And before him shall be gathered all nations: and he shall separate them one from another, as a shepherd divideth his sheep from the goats:

And he shall set the sheep on his right hand, but the goats on the left.

Then shall the King say unto them on his right hand, Come, ye blessed of my Father, inherit the kingdom prepared for you from the foundation of the world:

Then shall he say also unto them on the left hand, Depart from me, ye cursed, into everlasting fire, prepared for the devil and his angels:

For I was an hungered, and ye gave me no meat: I was thirsty, and ye gave me no drink:

I was a stranger, and ye took me not in: naked, and ye clothed me not: sick, and in prison, and ye visited me not.

Then shall they also answer him, saying, Lord, when saw we thee an hungered, or athirst, or a stranger, or naked, or sick, or in prison, and did not minister unto thee?

Then shall he answer them, saying, Verily, I say unto you, Inasmuch as ye did it not to one of the least of these, ye did it not to me.

And these shall go away into everlasting punishment: but the righteous into life eternal.

Matthew 25:31-34, 41-46

62 The Word Made Flesh

In the beginning was the Word, and the Word was with God, and the Word was God.

The same was in the beginning with God.

All things were made by him; and without him was not anything made that was made.

In him was life; and the life was the light of men.

And the light shineth in darkness; and the darkness comprehended it not.

That was the true Light, which lighteth every man that cometh into the world.

He was in the world, and the world was made by him, and the world knew him not.

He came unto his own, and his own received him not.

But as many as received him, to them gave he power to become the sons of God, even to them that believe on his name:

Which were born, not of blood, nor of the will of the flesh, nor of the will of man, but of God.

And the Word was made flesh, and dwelt among us, (and we beheld his glory, the glory as of the only begotten of the Father,) full of grace and truth.

John 1:1-5, 9-14

63 A Prayer of Penitence

Have mercy upon me, O God, according to thy loving-kindness: according unto the multitude of thy tender mercies, blot out my transgressions.

Wash me thoroughly from mine iniquity, and cleanse me from my sin.

For I acknowledge my transgressions: and my sin is ever before me.

Against thee, thee only, have I sinned, and done this evil in thy sight. . . .

Behold, I was shapen in iniquity; and in sin did my mother conceive me.

Purge me with hyssop, and I shall be clean; wash me, and I shall be whiter than snow.

Make me to hear joy and gladness; that the bones which thou hast broken may rejoice.

Hide thy face from my sins, and blot out all mine iniquities.

Create in me a clean heart, O God; and renew a right spirit within me.

Cast me not away from thy presence; and take not thy holy spirit from me.

Restore unto me the joy of thy salvation; and uphold me with thy free spirit.

Then will I teach transgressors thy ways; and sinners shall be converted unto thee.

Deliver me from blood guiltiness, O God, thou God of my salvation: and my tongue shall sing aloud of thy righteousness.

O Lord, open thou my lips; and my mouth shall show forth thy praise.

Psalm 51:1-5, 7-15

64 Victory over Sin

What shall we say then? Shall we continue in sin, that grace may abound?

God forbid. How shall we, that are dead to sin, live any longer therein?

Know ye not, that so many of us as were baptized into Jesus Christ were baptized unto his death?

Therefore we are buried with him by baptism into death: that like as Christ was raised up from the dead by the glory of the Father, even so we also should walk in newness of life.

For if we have been planted together in the likeness of his death, we shall be also in the likeness of his resurrection:

Knowing this, that our old man is crucified with him, that the body of sin might be destroyed, that henceforth we should not serve sin. For he that is dead is freed from sin.

Now if we be dead with Christ we believe that we shall also live with him:

Knowing that Christ being raised from the dead dieth no more; death hath no more dominion over him.

For in that he died, he died unto sin once: but in that he liveth, he liveth unto God.

Likewise reckon ye also yourselves to be dead indeed unto sin, but alive unto God through Jesus Christ our Lord.

Let not sin therefore reign in your mortal body. . . . Sin shall not have dominion over you.

Romans 6:1-12, 14

65 The Soul's Thirst for God

As the hart panteth after the water brooks, so panteth my soul after thee, O God.

My soul thirsteth for God, for the living God; when shall I come and appear before God?

My tears have been my meat day and night, while they continually say unto me, Where is thy God?

When I remember these things, I pour out my soul in me: for I had gone with the multitude, I went with them to the house of God, with the voice of joy and praise, with a multitude that kept holyday.

Why art thou cast down, O my soul? And why art thou disquieted in me? Hope thou in God: for I shall yet praise him for the help of his countenance.

O my God, my soul is cast down within me; therefore will I remember thee from the land of Jordan, and of the Hermonites, from the hill Mizar.

Deep calleth unto deep at the noise of thy waterspouts: all thy waves and billows are gone over me.

Yet the Lord will command his loving-kindness in the daytime, and in the night his song shall be with me, and my prayer unto the God of my life.

Why art thou cast down, O my soul? And why art thou disquieted within me? Hope thou in God; for I shall yet praise him, who is the health of my countenance, and my God.

Psalm 42:1-8, 11

66 Christ's Sufferings Foretold

He is despised and rejected of men; a man of sorrows, and acquainted with grief: and we hid as it were our faces from him; he was despised, and we esteemed him not.

Surely he hath borne our griefs, and carried our sorrows: yet we did esteem him stricken, smitten of God, and afflicted.

But he was wounded for our transgressions, he was bruised for our iniquities: the chastisement of our peace was upon him; and with his stripes we are healed.

All we like sheep have gone astray; we have turned every one to his own way; and the Lord hath laid on him the iniquity of us all.

He was oppressed, and he was afflicted, yet he opened not his mouth: he is brought as a lamb to the slaughter, and as a sheep before her shearers is dumb, so he openeth not his mouth.

And he made his grave with the wicked, and with the rich in his death; because he had done no violence, neither was any deceit in his mouth.

He hath poured out his soul unto death; and he was numbered with the transgressors; and he bare the sin of many, and made intercession for the transgressors.

Isaiah 53:3-7, 9, 12

67 The New Birth

There was a man of the Pharisees, named Nicodemus, a ruler of the Jews:

The same came to Jesus by night, and said unto him, Rabbi, we know that thou art a teacher come from God: for no man can do these miracles that thou doest, except God be with him.

Jesus answered and said unto him, Verily, verily, I say unto thee, Except a man be born again, he cannot see the kingdom of God.

Nicodemus saith unto him, How can a man be born when he is old? can he enter a second time into his mother's womb, and be born?

Jesus answered, Verily, verily I say unto thee, Except a man be born of water and of the Spirit, he cannot enter into the kingdom of God.

That which is born of the flesh is flesh; and that which is born of the Spirit is spirit. Marvel not that I said unto thee, Ye must be born again.

The wind bloweth where it listeth, and thou hearest the sound thereof, but canst not tell whence it cometh, and whither it goeth: so is every one that is born of the Spirit.

Verily, verily, I say unto thee, We speak that we do know, and testify that we have seen.

As Moses lifted up the serpent in the wilderness, even so must the Son of man be lifted up: that whosoever believeth in him should not perish but have everlasting life.

John 3:1-8, 11, 14-15

68 Praise for God's Creation

O Lord, our Lord, how excellent is thy name in all the earth! who hast set thy glory above the heavens.

Out of the mouth of babes and sucklings hast thou ordained strength because of thine enemies, that thou mightest still the enemy and the avenger.

When I consider thy heavens, the work of thy fingers, the moon and the stars, which thou hast ordained;

What is man, that thou art mindful of him, and the son of man, that thou visitest him?

For thou hast made him a little lower than the angels, and hast crowned him with glory and honor.

Thou madest him to have dominion over the works of thy hands; thou hast put all things under his feet:

All sheep and oxen, yea, and the beasts of the field;

The fowl of the air, and the fish of the sea, and whatsoever passeth through the paths of the seas.

O Lord our Lord, how excellent is thy name in all the earth!

I will praise thee, O Lord, with my whole heart; I will show forth all thy marvelous works.

I will be glad and rejoice in thee: I will sing praise to thy name, O thou most High.

Psalms 8; 9:1-2

69 The Fruits of the Spirit

Walk in the Spirit, and ye shall not fulfill the lust of the flesh.

For the flesh lusteth against the Spirit, and the Spirit against the flesh: and these are contrary the one to the other: so that ye cannot do the things that ye would.

But if ye be led of the Spirit, ye are not under the law.

Now the works of the flesh are manifest, which are these: Adultery, fornication, uncleanness, lasciviousness, idolatry, witchcraft, hatred, variance, emulations, wrath, strife, seditions, heresies, envyings, murders, drunkenness, revelings, and such like:

Of the which I tell you before, as I have also told you in time past, that they which do such things shall not inherit the kingdom of God.

But the fruit of the Spirit is love, joy, peace, long-suffering, gentleness, goodness, faith, meekness, temperance: against such there is no law.

And they that are Christ's have crucified the flesh with the affections and lusts.

If we live in the Spirit, let us also walk in the Spirit.

Galatians 5:16-25

70 The King of Glory

The earth is the Lord's, and the fullness thereof; the world, and they that dwell therein.

For he hath founded it upon the seas, and established it upon the floods.

Who shall ascend into the hill of the Lord? or who shall stand in his holy place?

He that hath clean hands, and a pure heart; who hath not lifted up his soul unto vanity, nor sworn deceitfully.

He shall receive the blessing from the Lord, and righteousness from the God of his salvation.

This is the generation of them that seek him, that seek thy face, O Jacob.

Lift up your heads, O ye gates; and be ye lift up, ye everlasting doors; and the King of glory shall come in.

Who is this King of glory? The Lord strong and mighty, the Lord mighty in battle.

Lift up your heads, O ye gates; even lift them up, ye everlasting doors; and the King of glory shall come in.

Who is this King of glory? The Lord of hosts, he is the King of glory.

Psalm 24

Unison Readings

71 Exhortation to Holiness

I beseech you, therefore, brethren, by the mercies of God, that ye present your bodies a living sacrifice, holy, acceptable unto God, which is your reasonable service. And be not conformed to this world: but be ye transformed by the renewing of your mind, that ye may prove what is that good, and acceptable, and perfect, will of God.

For I say, through the grace given unto me, to every man that is among you, not to think of himself more highly than he ought to think; but to think soberly, according as God hath dealt to every man the measure of faith. For as we have many members in one body, and all members have not the same office: so we, being many, are one body in Christ, and every one members one of another. Having then gifts differing according to the grace that is given to us, whether prophecy, let us prophesy according to the proportion of faith; or ministry, let us wait on our ministering: or he that teacheth, on teaching; or he that exhorteth, on exhortation: he that giveth, let him do it with simplicity; he that ruleth, with diligence; he that showeth mercy, with cheerfulness.

Let love be genuine. Abhor that which is evil; cleave to that which is good. Be kindly affectioned one to another with brotherly love; in honor preferring one another; not slothful in business; fervent in spirit; serving the Lord; rejoicing in hope; patient in tribulation; continuing instant in prayer; distributing to the necessity of saints; given to hospitality.

Bless them which persecute you: bless, and curse not. Rejoice with them that do rejoice, and weep with them that weep.

Be of the same mind one toward another. Mind not high things, but condescend to men of low estate. Be not wise in your own conceits. Recompense to no man evil for evil. Provide things honest in the sight of all men.

If it be possible, as much as lieth in you, live peaceably with all men. Dearly beloved, avenge not yourselves, but rather give place unto wrath: for it is written, Vengeance is mine; I will repay, saith the Lord. Therefore if thine enemy hunger, feed him; if he thirst, give him drink: for in so doing thou shalt heap coals of fire on his head.

Be not overcome of evil, but overcome evil with good.

Romans 12

72 The Lord Our Shepherd

The Lord is my shepherd; I shall not want. He maketh me to lie down in green pastures: he leadeth me beside the still waters. He restoreth my soul: he leadeth me in the paths of righteousness for his name's sake.

Yea, though I walk through the valley of the shadow of death, I will fear no evil: for thou art with me; thy rod and thy staff they comfort me. Thou preparest a table before me in the presence of mine enemies: thou anointest my head with oil; my cup runneth over.

Surely goodness and mercy shall follow me all the days of my life: and I will dwell in the house of the Lord forever.

Psalm 23

73 More than Conquerors

We are saved by hope: but hope that is seen is not hope: for what a man seeth, why doth he yet hope for? But if we hope for that we see not, then do we with patience wait for it.

We know that all things work together for good to them that love God, to them who are the called according to his purpose.

If God be for us, who can be against us? He that spared not his own Son, but delivered him up for us all, how shall he not with him also freely give us all things?

Who shall separate us from the love of Christ? shall tribulation, or distress, or persecution, or famine, or nakedness, or peril, or sword?

Nay, in all these things we are more than conquerors through him that loved us. For I am persuaded that neither death, nor life, nor angels, nor principalities, nor powers, nor things present, nor things to come, nor height, nor depth, nor any other creature, shall be able to separate us from the love of God, which is in Christ Jesus our Lord.

Romans 8:24-25, 28, 31b, 32, 35, 37-39

74 Love, the Supreme Gift

Though I speak with the tongues of men and of angels, and have not love, I am become as sounding brass, or a tinkling cymbal. And though I have the gift of prophecy, and understand all mysteries, and all knowledge; and though I have all faith, so that I could remove mountains, and have not love, I am nothing. And though I bestow all my goods to feed the poor, and though I give my body to be burned, and have not love, it profiteth me nothing.

Love suffereth long, and is kind; love envieth not; love vaunteth not itself, is not puffed up, doth not behave itself unseemly, seeketh not her own, is not easily provoked, thinketh no evil; rejoiceth not in iniquity, but rejoiceth in the truth; beareth all things, believeth all things, hopeth all things, endureth all things.

Love never faileth: but whether there be prophecies, they shall fail; whether there be tongues, they shall cease; whether there be knowledge, it shall vanish away. For we know in part, and we prophesy in part. But when that which is perfect is come, then that which is in part shall be done away. When I was a child, I spake as a child, I understood as a child, I thought as a child; but when I became a man, I put away childish things. For now we see through a glass, darkly; but then face to face: now I know in part; but then shall I know even as also I am known.

And now abideth faith, hope, love, these three; but the greatest of these is love. Follow after love.

I Corinthians 13:1—14:1a

75 A Call to Praise

Make a joyful noise unto the Lord, all ye lands. Serve the Lord with gladness: come before his presence with singing.

Know ye that the Lord he is God: it is he that hath made us, and not we ourselves; we are his people, and the sheep of his pasture.

Enter into his gates with thanksgiving, and into his courts with praise: be thankful unto him, and bless his name. For the Lord is good, his mercy is everlasting; and his truth endureth to all generations.

Psalm 100

76 The Bonds of Love

I am the true vine, and my Father is the husbandman. Every branch in me . . . that beareth fruit, he purgeth it, that it may bring forth more fruit.

Now ye are clean through the word which I have spoken unto you. Abide in me, and I in you. As the branch cannot bear fruit of itself, except it abide in the vine; no more can ye, except ye abide in me.

I am the vine, ye are the branches. He that abideth in me, and I in him, the same bringeth forth much fruit: for without me ye can do nothing. If a man abide not in me, he is cast forth as a branch, and is withered; and men gather them, and cast them into the fire, and they are burned. If ye abide in me, and my words abide in you, ye shall ask what ye will, and it shall be done unto you.

Herein is my Father glorified, that ye bear much fruit; so shall ye be my disciples. As the Father hath loved me, so have I loved you: continue ye in my love.

If ye keep my commandments, ye shall abide in my love; even as I have kept my Father's commandments, and abide in his love. These things have I spoken unto you, that my joy might remain in you, and that your joy might be full.

This is my commandment, That ye love one another, as I have loved you. Greater love hath no man than this, that a man lay down his life for his friends. Ye are my friends, if ye do whatsoever I command you.

Henceforth I call you not servants; for the servant knoweth not what his lord doeth: but I have called you friends; for all things that I have heard of my Father I have made known unto you.

John 15:1-15

77 The Lord's Prayer

And it came to pass, that as he was praying in a certain place, when he ceased, one of his disciples said unto him, Lord, teach us to pray. . . .

And he said unto them, When ye pray, say,

Our Father which art in heaven, Hallowed be thy name. Thy kingdom come. Thy will be done, as in heaven, so in earth. Give us day by day our daily bread. And forgive us our sins; for we also forgive every one that is indebted to us. And lead us not into temptation; but deliver us from evil.

And I say unto you, Ask, and it shall be given you; seek, and ye shall find; knock, and it shall be opened unto you. For every one that asketh receiveth; and he that seeketh findeth; and to him that knocketh it shall be opened.

Luke 11:1-4, 9-10

78 A Prayer for All Nations

God be merciful unto us, and bless us; and cause his face to shine upon us; that thy way may be known upon earth, thy saving health among all nations. Let the people praise thee, O God; let all the people praise thee.

O let the nations be glad and sing for joy: for thou shalt judge the people righteously, and govern the nations upon earth.

Let the people praise thee, O God; let all the people praise thee. Then shall the earth yield her increase; and God, even our own God, shall bless us. God shall bless us; and all the ends of the earth shall fear him.

Psalm 67

79 The Angels' Song

And there were in the same country shepherds abiding in the field, keeping watch over their flock by night. And, lo, the angel of the Lord came upon them, and the glory of the Lord shone round about them: and they were sore afraid.

And the angel said unto them, Fear not: for, behold, I bring you good tidings of great joy, which shall be to all people. For unto you is born this day, in the city of David, a Savior, which is Christ the Lord. And this shall be a sign unto you; Ye shall find the babe wrapped in swaddling clothes, lying in a manger.

And suddenly there was with the angel a multitude of the heavenly host, praising God, and saying,

Glory to God in the highest, and on earth peace, good will toward men.

Luke 2:8-14

80 The Everlasting God

Lord, thou hast been our dwelling place in all generations. Before the mountains were brought forth, or ever thou hadst formed the earth and the world, even from everlasting to everlasting, thou art God.

Thou turnest man to destruction; and sayest, Return, ye children of men. For a thousand years in thy sight are but as yesterday when it is past, and as a watch in the night. Thou carriest them away as with a flood; they are as a sleep: in the morning they are like grass which groweth up. In the morning it flourisheth, and groweth up; in the evening it is cut down, and withereth.

The days of our years are threescore years and ten; and if by reason of strength they be fourscore years, yet is their strength labor and sorrow: for it is soon cut off, and we fly away.

So teach us to number our days, that we may apply our hearts unto wisdom. . . . O satisfy us early with thy mercy; that we may rejoice and be glad all our days.

Psalm 90:1-6, 10, 12, 14

81 The Beatitudes

Seeing the multitudes, he went up into a mountain, and when he was set, his disciples came unto him: and he opened his mouth, and taught them, saying,

Blessed are the poor in spirit: for theirs is the kingdom of heaven.

Blessed are they that mourn: for they shall be comforted.

Blessed are the meek: for they shall inherit the earth.

Blessed are they which do hunger and thirst after righteousness: for they shall be filled.

Blessed are the merciful: for they shall obtain mercy.

Blessed are the pure in heart: for they shall see God.

Blessed are the peacemakers: for they shall be called the children of God.

Blessed are they which are persecuted for righteousness' sake: for theirs is the kingdom of heaven.

Blessed are ye, when men shall revile you, and persecute you, and shall say all manner of evil against you falsely, for my sake. Rejoice, and be exceeding glad: for great is your reward in heaven: for so persecuted they the prophets which were before you.

Matthew 5:1-12

82 The True Treasure

Lay not up for yourselves treasures upon earth, where moth and rust . . . corrupt, and where thieves break through and steal: but lay up for yourselves treasures in heaven, where neither moth nor rust . . . corrupt, and where thieves do not break through nor steal: for where your treasure is, there will your heart be also.

No man can serve two masters: for either he will hate the one, and love the other; or else he will hold to the one, and despise the other. Ye cannot serve God and mammon.

Therefore I say unto you, Take no thought for your life, what ye shall eat, or what ye shall drink; nor yet for your body, what ye shall put on. Is not the life more than meat, and the body than raiment? Your heavenly Father knoweth that ye have need of all these things. But seek ye first the kingdom of God, and his righteousness; and all these things shall be added unto you.

Matthew 6:19-21, 24-25, 32b-33

83 Love Made Perfect

Beloved, let us love one another: for love is of God; and every one that loveth is born of God, and knoweth God. He that loveth not, knoweth not God; for God is love. In this was manifested the love of God toward us, because that God sent his only begotten Son into the world, that we might live through him. Herein is love, not that we loved God, but that he loved us, and sent his Son to be the propitiation for our sins. Beloved, if God so loved us, we ought also to love one another.

No man hath seen God at any time. If we love one another, God dwelleth in us, and his love is perfected in us. . . . Herein is our love made perfect, that we may have boldness in the day of judgment; because as he is, so are we in this world.

There is no fear in love; but perfect love casteth out fear; because fear hath torment. He that feareth is not made perfect in love. We love him because he first loved us.

If a man say, I love God, and hateth his brother, he is a liar: for he that loveth not his brother whom he hath seen, how can he love God whom he hath not seen? And this commandment have we from him, That he who loveth God love his brother also.

I John 4:7-12, 17-21

84 Happiness of the Godly

Blessed is the man that walketh not in the counsel of the ungodly, nor standeth in the way of sinners, nor sitteth in the seat of the scornful. But his delight is in the law of the Lord; and in his law doth he meditate day and night. And he shall be like a tree planted by the rivers of water, that bringeth forth his fruit in his season; his leaf also shall not wither; and whatsoever he doeth shall prosper.

The ungodly are not so: but are like the chaff which the wind driveth away. Therefore the ungodly shall not stand in the judgment, nor sinners in the congregation of the righteous.

For the Lord knoweth the way of the righteous; but the way of the ungodly shall perish.

Psalm 1

Indexes

Alphabetical Index of Tunes 490
Metrical Index of Tunes 491
Songs Particularly Suitable for Choir Presentation 492
Songs Particularly Suitable for Use with Children 493
Topical Index 494
Index of Titles and First Lines 503

Alphabetical Index of Tunes

	HYMN
Adeste Fideles	37, 323
All Saints, New	441
Alverstoke	455
Amazing Grace	270
America	498
Angel's Story	205
Antioch	38
Ariel	84
Arlington	222
Aurelia	419, 491
Austrian Hymn	412
Azmon	92
Beacon Hill	191
Beecher	98
Beloved (Meditation)	383
Bethany	377
Bliss	179
Boylston	201, 433
Bradbury	122
Bradford	73
Bread of Life	110, 434
Brocklesbury	60
Canonbury	160, 505
Carol	39
Chautauqua	23
Christmas	52
Christmas Song	44
Cleansing Fountain	116
Consolation (Felix)	489
Consolation (Webbe)	346
Converse	401
Coronation	86
Crusader's Hymn	79
Cushman	56
Dennis	31, 431, 440
Diadem	87
Diademata	74, 230
Dix	7, 47
Dominus Regit Me	29
Duke Street	80
Easter Hymn	68
Ebeling (Bonn)	51
Ein' Feste Burg	25
Ellers	16
Ellesdie	194
Eucharist	63
Evangel	108
Eventide	481
Faithful Guide	94
Federal Street	166, 490
Gabriel	107
Galilee	186
Germany	188, 437
Gift of Life	53
Gordon	375
Greenland	24
Hamburg	62
Hankey	297
Hendon	159
Holiness	400
Hursley	20
Hymn to Joy	2
Italian Hymn	1, 11, 449
Jewett	387
Kings of Orient	50
Kremser	5
Laban	15, 223
Lancashire	76, 227
Laudes Domini	19
Lord's Day	12
Lux Benigna	344
Lyons	6
Maitland	200
Man of Sorrows	65
Margaret	55
Martyn	358
Martyrdom (Avon)	66
Maryton	210
Materna	58, 239, 500
Mendebras	10
Mendelssohn	41
Mercy	96
Merrial	21
Missionary Hymn	448
Morecambe	99, 432
Muller	49
National Hymn	438
Nettleton	13
Nicaea	3
O Perfect Love	456
Old Hundredth	501
Oldbridge	496
Olive's Brow	64
Olivet	396
Pax Tecum	365
Peek	190
Pilot	338
Rathbun	67
Refuge	357
Regent Square	48, 418
Reverena	8
St. Agnes	35, 93, 397, 454
St. Alban	492
St. Anne	34, 428
St. Catherine	196, 458
St. Christopher	61
St. Edmund	169
St. George's, Windsor	493
St. Gertrude	224
St. Louis	40
St. Margaret	379
St. Peter	439
St. Theodulph	90
St. Thomas	187, 416
Schumann	173
Seasons	348
Serenity	72
Seymour	384
Sicilian Mariners' Hymn	14, 457
Something for Jesus	376
Spohr	366
Stille Nacht	46
Stories of Jesus	54
Sweet Hour	405
Sweet Story	59
Tell Me the Story	57
Terra Beata	30
The First Noel	42
Tidings	443
Toplady	359
Trentham	178, 436
Waltham	45
Webb	184, 192
Wellesley	32
Whittier (Rest)	399, 459
Who Givest All	497
Wir Pflugen	494
Woodworth	152
Work Song	182
Worship the Lord	4
Zion	345

Metrical Index of Tunes

S.M. — HYMN

Boylston 201, 433
Dennis 31, 431, 440
Laban 15, 223
St. Thomas 187, 416
Schumann 173
Trentham 178, 436

S.M.D.

Diademata 74, 230
Terra Beata 30

C.M.

Amazing Grace 270
Antioch 38
Arlington 222
Azmon 92
Bradford 73
Christmas 52
Coronation 86
Diadem 87
Maitland 200
Martyrdom (Avon) 66
St. Agnes 35, 93, 397, 454
St. Anne 34, 428
St. Peter 439
Serenity 72
Spohr 366

C.M.D.

All Saints, New 441
Carol 39
Cleansing Fountain 116
Gabriel 107
Materna 58, 239, 500

L.M.

Canonbury 160, 505
Duke Street 80
Eucharist 63
Federal Street 166, 490
Germany 188, 437
Hamburg 62
Hursley 20
Maryton 210
Old Hundredth 501
Olive's Brow 64
Waltham 45
Who Givest All 497
Woodworth 152

L.M.D.

Sweet Hour 405

5.6.8.5.8.

Crusader's Hymn 79

6.4.6.4.D.

Bread of Life 110, 434

6.4.6.4.6.6.6.4.

Bethany 377
St. Edmund 169
Something for Jesus 376

6.5.6.5.

Merrial 21

6.5.6.5.D.

Holiness 400

6.5.6.5.D. with Refrain

St. Alban 492
St. Gertrude 224

6.6.4.6.6.6.4.

America 498
Italian Hymn 1, 11, 449
Olivet 396

6.6.6.6.D.

Jewett 387

6.6.6.6.6.6. — HYMN

Bliss 179
Laudes Domini 19

6.6.6.6.12.12.

Christmas Song 44

7.6.7.6. with Refrain

Lord's Day 12

7.6.7.6.D.

Angel's Story 205
Aurelia 419, 491
Greenland 24
Lancashire 76, 227
Mendebras 10
Missionary Hymn 448
St. Theodulph 90
Seasons 348
Webb 184, 192
Work Song 182

7.6.7.6.D. with Refrain

Evangel 108
Hankey 297
Wir Pflugen 494

7.6.8.6.8.6.8.6.

St. Christopher 61

7.7.7.7.

Mercy 96
Seymour 384

7.7.7.7. with Alleluias

Easter Hymn 68

7.7.7.7.D.

Faithful Guide 94
Martyn 358
Refuge 357
St. George's, Windsor 493

7.7.7.7.D. with Refrain

Mendelssohn 41

7.7.7.7.4. with Refrain

Chautauqua 23

7.7.7.7.7.

Hendon 159

7.7.7.7.7.7.

Dix 7, 47
Pilot 338
Toplady 359

7.7.7.8.

Man of Sorrows 65

8.3.3.6.D.

Ebeling (Bonn) 51

8.4.8.4.5.4.5.4.

Stories of Jesus 54

8.6.7.6.

Gift of Life 53

8.6.8.6.7.6.8.6.

St. Louis 40

8.6.8.8.6.

Reverena 8
Whittier (Rest) 399, 459

8.7.8.7.

Dominus Regit Me 29
Brocklesbury 60
Galilee 186
Rathbun 67
Wellesley 32

8.7.8.7.D. — HYMN

Austrian Hymn 412
Beecher 98
Bradbury 122
Converse 401
Ellesdie 194
Hymn to Joy 2
Nettleton 13
Tell Me the Story 57

8.7.8.7.4.7.4.7.

Zion 345

8.7.8.7.6.6.6.6.7.

Ein' Feste Burg 25

8.7.8.7.8.7.

Regent Square 48, 418
Sicilian Mariners' Hymn 14, 457

8.8.6.D.

Ariel 84

8.8.8.4

Oldbridge 496

8.8.8.6. with Refrain

Kings of Orient 50

8.8.8.8.6.

St. Margaret 379

8.8.8.8.8.8.

St. Catherine 196, 458

10.4.10.4.10.10.

Lux Benigna 344

10.10.

Pax Tecum 365

10.10.10.10.

Ellers 16
Eventide 481
Morecambe 99, 432
National Hymn 438

10.10.11.11.

Lyons 6

11.8.11.8.

Beloved (Meditation) 383

11.10.11.10.

Alverstoke 455
Consolation (Felix) 489
Consolation (Webbe) 346
Cushman 56
O Perfect Love 456
Peek 190

11.10.11.10 with Refrain

Tidings 443

11.11.11.11.

Gordon 375
Muller 49

11.12.12.10.

Nicaea 3

12.11.12.11.

Kremser 5

Irregular

Beacon Hill 191
Margaret 55
Stille Nacht 46
Sweet Story 59
Worship the Lord 4

Irregular, with Refrain

Adeste Fideles 37, 323
The First Noel 42

Songs Particularly Suitable for Choir Presentation

HYMN

A Mighty Fortress Is Our God 25
All Hail the Power of Jesus' Name! (*Second Tune*) 87
All My Heart This Night Rejoices 51
Almighty Father 380
America, the Beautiful 500
"Are Ye Able," Said the Master 191
As with Gladness Men of Old 47
Beneath the Cross of Jesus 61
Bless Thou the Gifts 505
Fairest Lord Jesus 79
Faith Is the Victory 244
Give Me Thy Heart 140
God Is Love 36
God of Our Fathers 438
"Great Is Thy Faithfulness" 317
Hallelujah, Praise Jehovah! 28
Hear Our Prayer, O Lord 506
I'll Go Where You Want Me to Go 170
Is Your All on the Altar? 141
Joyful, Joyful, We Adore Thee 2
Lead On, O King Eternal 227
Let the Words of My Mouth 503
Lord of Life and King of Glory 457

HYMN

Mine Eyes Have Seen the Glory 238
My Redeemer 264
O God, Our Help in Ages Past 34
O Master, Let Me Walk with Thee 210
O Praise the Lord! 33
O That Will Be Glory 466
O Worship the King 6
O Worship the Lord (Response) 504
O Worship the Lord 4
O Zion, Haste 443
Our Best 180
Saved, Saved! 268
Stand by the Cross 236
The Church's One Foundation 419
The Lord Bless Thee, and Keep Thee 507
Together We Go to Make Disciples 204
Truehearted, Wholehearted 231
We Give Thee but Thine Own 173
We Plow the Fields, and Scatter 494
We've a Story to Tell to the Nations 442
We Would See Jesus; Lo! His Star 56
When Morning Gilds the Skies 19

Songs Particularly Suitable for Use with Children

	HYMN
A Thankful Song	464
America, the Beautiful	500
Away in a Manger	49
Bless Thou the Gifts	505
Christ the Lord Is Risen Today	68
Come, Ye Thankful People, Come	493
Day Is Dying in the West	23
Fairest Lord Jesus	79
Faith of Our Fathers	196
Father, We Thank Thee	461
For All the Blessings of the Year	496
For Health and Strength	463
For the Beauty of the Earth	7
Holy, Holy, Holy	3
I Think When I Read That Sweet Story	59
I Was Glad	462
I Would Be True	190
In Christ There Is No East or West	439
Jesus Loves Even Me	309
Jesus Shall Reign Where'er the Sun	80
Jesus Was a Loving Teacher	60
Joyful, Joyful, We Adore Thee	2
Let the Words of My Mouth	503
My Country, 'Tis of Thee	498
None Is like God	35
Now the Day Is Over	21
O Jesus, I Have Promised	205
O Lord of Heaven and Earth and Sea	497
O Master Workman of the Race	58
Onward, Christian Soldiers	224
Praise God, from Whom All Blessings Flow	501
Praise Him, Praise Him	460
Savior, like a Shepherd Lead Us	122
Savior, Teach Me, Day by Day	384
Tell Me the Stories of Jesus	54
Thanks for Bread	465
The Earth Is Hushed in Silence	12
This Is My Father's World	30
We Give Thee but Thine Own	173
We've a Story to Tell to the Nations	442
We Would See Jesus; Lo! His Star	56
When Morning Gilds the Skies	19

Also see Christ's Advent and Nativity, Hymns 37-53

Topical Index

HYMN

ABIDING
Adoration ... 483
All in Jesus ... 263
Filled with Grace ... 299
In Heavenly Love ... 348
My Heart Is Fixed ... 213
O Zion, Blessed City ... 422
Take Time to Be Holy ... 400
Trust and Obey ... 332
Under His Wings ... 333

ACTIVITY AND ZEAL
Bring Them In ... 189
Every Hour for Jesus ... 203
Every Hour of the Passing Day ... 212
Faith of Our Fathers ... 196
Forward, Ever Forward 221
Here Am I, Send Me ... 199
I Cannot Be Idle ... 211
I Will Do My Part ... 220
I'll Try to Bring One ... 206
On to the Goal ... 219
Onward, All Ye People ... 228
Rescue the Perishing ... 444
Rise Up, O Men of God ... 187
Send the Light ... 445
Tell What He's Done ... 245
To the Work ... 202
Together We Go ... 204
We Will Work for Jesus 207
Wholehearted Service ... 197
Work, for the Night ... 182

ADORATION AND PRAISE
All Glory, Laud ... 90
All Hail the Power ... 86
All Hail the Power ... 87
Blessed Be the Name ... 89
Come, Thou Almighty ... 1
Crown Him with Many 74
Day Is Dying in the ... 23
Fairest Lord Jesus ... 79
For the Beauty of the ... 7
Gloria Patri ... 502
Hallelujah, Praise Jehovah! ... 28
He Leadeth Me ... 343
Holy, Holy, Holy ... 3
Holy, Holy, Holy Is the Lord ... 27
In Holy Reverence ... 8
Jesus Shall Reign ... 80
Jesus, the Very Thought 93
Joyful, Joyful, We ... 2
O Could I Speak ... 84
O Day of Peace ... 10
O for a Thousand ... 92
O God, Our Help in ... 34
O God, the Rock of Ages 24
O Praise the Lord! ... 33
O Worship the King ... 6
O Worship the Lord ... 4
Once Again We Come ... 9
Praise God, from Whom 501
Praise Him! Praise Him! 81
We Praise Thee, O God, Our Redeemer ... 5
When Morning Gilds ... 19

ADVANCING YEARS
Abide with Me ... 481
Are You Building on ... 253
Holy Spirit, Faithful ... 94

ADVENT
See Jesus Christ, Advent and Nativity

ALTAR SERVICE
All Taken Away ... 301
Almost Persuaded ... 134
Hallelujah! 'Tis Done! ... 307
O How I Love Jesus! ... 261
There Is a Fountain Filled ... 116
Also see Invitation and Acceptance

ANNIVERSARIES
God of Our Fathers ... 438
O God, Our Help in ... 34

ANTICIPATION
Adoration ... 483
Heaven Holds All to Me 486
Heavenly Welcome ... 488
Hope of the Righteous ... 473
I Have a Home ... 474
O That Will Be Glory ... 466
On to the Goal ... 219
Pearly Gates ... 482
Safe in the Arms of ... 479
Shall We Gather at the 471
Shall We Meet Beyond 477
The Sweet By and By ... 478
We Would See Jesus ... 489
We're Marching to Zion 289
When My King Shall Call 468
When We All Get to ... 467
When We Get Home ... 469
Also see Heaven

ASPIRATION
Abide with Me ... 481
Break Thou the Bread ... 110
Breathe on Me, Breath ... 178
Dear Lord and Father ... 399
Draw Me Close to Thee 398
Draw Thou My Soul ... 169
I Am Thine, O Lord ... 395
I Need Thee Every Hour 373
Let Me See Jesus Only 390
Lord, I Hear of Showers 368
More About Jesus ... 393
More like Christ ... 391
Near the Cross ... 371
Nearer, My God, to Thee 377
Nearer, Still Nearer ... 372
O for a Closer Walk ... 397
O for a Heart of Calm ... 366
O Master Workman ... 58
O Thou in Whose ... 383
Prayer of My Heart ... 389
Savior, More than Life ... 388
Sitting at the Feet ... 370

ASSURANCE
Blessed Assurance ... 321
Blessed Quietness ... 104
He Is with Me Still ... 325
I Am the Lord's ... 324
I Know ... 319
I Know My Name Is ... 329
I Will Be with Thee ... 340

ATONEMENT
At the Cross ... 304
Jesus Paid It All ... 145
Rock of Ages ... 359

There Is a Fountain Filled ... 116
Also see Blood of Christ; Jesus Christ—Suffering and Crucifixion

BAPTISM
Buried with Jesus ... 435
Here, Savior, We Would 436
I'll Live for Him ... 163
O Jesus, I Have ... 205
O Master, Let Me Walk ... 210
Take My Life and Let ... 159
Where He Leads Me ... 164

BIBLE, THE
Back to the Blessed ... 425
Break Thou the Bread ... 110
Hold Fast to the Word ... 106
How Firm a Foundation 323
I Love to Tell the ... 297
O Precious Bible! ... 111
Praise God for His ... 109
Take Time to Be Holy ... 400
Tell Me the Old, Old ... 108
The Word of God ... 112
Thy Word Is like a ... 107
We've a Story to Tell ... 442
Wonderful Words of Life ... 105

BLOOD OF CHRIST
Alas! and Did My ... 66
All in Jesus ... 263
Are You Washed in the 114
Hallelujah! 'Tis Done! ... 307
Hallelujah, What a ... 65
I'm Redeemed ... 276
My Redeemer ... 264
Near the Cross ... 371
Nothing but the Blood ... 118
O for a Thousand ... 92
Power in the Blood of ... 117
Savior, More than Life ... 388
The Blameless Church ... 415
The Half Has Never ... 272
There Is a Fountain Filled ... 116
There Is Power in the ... 113
There's a Fountain Opened ... 293
When I Survey ... 62
When I Survey ... 63
Also see Atonement

BROTHERHOOD
See World Brotherhood

CALLS TO WORSHIP
A Call to Prayer ... 22
Come, Thou Almighty ... 1
Come, Thou Fount ... 13
I Was Glad ... 462
Jesus Calls Us ... 186
Let the Words ... 503
O Worship the Lord ... 504
Rise Up, O Men of God 187
The Earth Is Hushed ... 12

CHILDREN'S SONGS
See special index

CHOIR SELECTIONS
See special index

TOPICAL INDEX

HYMN

CHRIST
See Jesus Christ

CHRISTIAN HOME
Happy the Home When 454
Lord of Life and King 457
O Happy Home 455
O Lord of Heaven 497
O Thou Whose Gracious 459

CHRISTIAN UNITY
Blest Be the Tie 440
In Christ There Is No 439
The Bond of Perfectness 414
'Twas Sung by the Poets 424
Also see Church

CHRISTMAS
See Jesus Christ, Advent and Nativity

CHURCH, THE
Christ Is Made the 418
Church of God, Thou 411
Church of the Living 410
Faith of Our Fathers 196
Glorious Things of Thee 412
I Love Thy Kingdom 416
O Church of God 413
O Where Are Kings 428
O Zion, Blessed City 422
Onward, Christian 224
The Blameless Church 415
The Bond of Perfectness 414
The Church Has One 420
The Church Triumphant 426
The Church's Jubilee 430
The Church's One 419
Thy Children Are Gathering Home 423
Zion Stands with Hills 417

CLEANSING
Are You Washed 114
Down at the Cross 314
Nothing but the Blood 118
The Cleansing Wave 156
There's a Fountain Opened 293
This Is Why I Love My 286
What a Dear Friend 267
Whiter than Snow 158

CLOSING HYMNS
Blest Be the Tie 440
God Be with You 17
Lead On, O King Eternal 227
Lord, Dismiss Us with 14
O Gentle Savior 374
Once More, Before We 15
Savior, Again to Thy 16
The Lord Bless Thee 507

COMFORT
See Consolation

COMMUNION
See Lord's Supper

COMPLETENESS IN CHRIST
Ever Lead Me 339
For Me All Is Well 355
I've Found It, Lord 290
My Soul Is Satisfied 313
River of Peace 312
Saved, Saved! 268
The King of Love 29

HYMN

CONFESSION
See Invitation and Acceptance

CONFIDENCE
See Trust and Confidence

CONFLICT
See Victory

CONQUEST
A Mighty Fortress 25
Am I a Soldier 222
Be an Overcomer 242
Lead On, O King Eternal 227
Lift Up Your Heads 239
Mine Eyes Have Seen 238
More than a Conqueror 235
Must Jesus Bear the 200
My Soul, Be on Thy 223
Onward, All Ye People 228
Onward, Christian 224
Press On 233
Press the Battle On 237
Stand by the Cross 236
Stand Up for Jesus 184
Soldiers of Christ 230
Songs of Victory 232
The Army of the Lord 226
The Shield of Faith 241
Truehearted, Wholehearted 231
Victory Through Grace 225

CONSECRATION
A Living Sacrifice 165
"Are Ye Able," Said 191
Breathe on Me, Breath 178
Consecration 162
Draw Thou My Soul 169
Fill Me with Thy Spirit 168
Give of Your Best to 181
Have Thine Own Way 161
I Gave My Life for Thee 179
I Surrender All 157
I Will Follow Thee 193
I'll Go Where You Want 170
I'll Live for Him 163
Is Your All on the 141
Let the Fire Fall on Me 214
Lord, Speak to Me 160
Lord, Take the First 147
O Master, Let Me Walk 210
Only for Thee 177
Take My Life, and Let 159
Transformed 174
We Give Thee but Thine 173
Where He Leads Me 164
Whiter than Snow 158
With Thy Spirit Fill Me 167

CONSOLATION
Come, Ye Disconsolate 346
Consolation 408
Keep Praying, Toiling 409
Take the Name of Jesus 402
What a Friend 401

CONVERSION
See Regeneration; Invitation and Acceptance

COUNTRY
See Patriotism, Christian

COURAGE
Be Still 378
He Will Care for Me 352

HYMN

In Heavenly Love 348
My Home Is on the Rock 363
Stand Up for Jesus 184
Victory Through Grace 225
Also see Conquest

CROSS
At the Cross 304
At the Cross of Jesus 386
Beneath the Cross of 61
Crown After Cross 485
Down at the Cross 314
In the Cross of Christ 67
Jesus, I My Cross Have 194
Lift Up Your Heads 239
Must Jesus Bear 200
My Redeemer 264
Near the Cross 371
Onward, Christian 224
Stand by the Cross 236
"Take Up Thy Cross," the Savior Said 188
The Old Rugged Cross 381
When I Survey 62
When I Survey 63
Who Will Suffer 185

CROWN
Be an Overcomer 242
Crown After Cross 485
I'm Going On 218
Must Jesus Bear the 200
The Old Rugged Cross 381

CRUCIFIXION
See Jesus Christ, Suffering and Crucifixion

DECISION
Beneath the Cross of 61
Faith of Our Fathers 196
I Would Be True 190
I'm Going On 218
I've Enlisted in His 195
Let the Fire Fall on Me 214
My Heart Is Fixed 213
O Jesus, I Have 205
Wholehearted Service 197
Also see Invitation and Acceptance

DEDICATION
Of a Church
Christ Is Made the Sure 418
Come, O Thou God of 11
I Love Thy Kingdom 416
Also see Church

Of a Home
See Christian Home

Of Children
See special index of Children's Songs

Of Christian Teachers and Workers
How Shall I Follow Him 166
Jesus Was a Loving 60
Lord, Speak to Me 160
Also see Service

Of Organ
Come, O Thou God of 1
Come, Thou Almighty 11
For the Beauty of the 7

Of Resources
See Stewardship

TOPICAL INDEX

HYMN

Of Self
See Consecration

DEVOTION
Draw Thou My Soul 169
Jesus, Lover of My 357
Jesus, Lover of My 358
Jesus, the Very Thought 93
Keep Me, My Lord 351
My Jesus, I Love Thee 375
Near to the Heart of 385
O Love That Wilt Not 379
Pass Me Not 150
Sitting at the Feet 370
Something for Jesus 376
The Old Rugged Cross 381
Waves of Devotion 282

DISCIPLESHIP
A Charge to Keep I Have 201
"Are Ye Able," Said 191
Are You Adorning 250
At the Cross of Jesus 386
By Thy Blessed Word 216
Follow On! 198
Give of Your Best 181
God's Way Is Best 350
Here Am I, Send Me 199
How Shall I Follow Him 166
Jesus Calls Us 186
Jesus, I My Cross 194
Lead On, O King Eternal 227
My Faith Looks Up 396
O Master, Let Me Walk 210
Open My Eyes, That I 382
Our Best 180
Rise Up, O Men of God 187
Sunshine in the Soul 258
"Take Up Thy Cross," the Savior Said 188
The Lord Our Shepherd 341
The Son of God Goes 441
The Voice of God 192
Together We Go 204
We Would See Jesus: Lo 56
Where Cross the 437
Who Will Suffer 185
Also see Consecration; Decision

DISMISSAL
See Closing Hymns

DIVINE HEALING
See Healing

EASTER
See Jesus Christ, Resurrection

ETERNAL LIFE
See Future Life

ETERNITY
See Heaven

EVENING HYMNS
A Call to Prayer 22
Abide with Me 481
Day Is Dying in the 23
Now the Day Is Over 21
Sun of My Soul 20

EVENING LIGHT
Brighter Days Are 427
The Church Has One 420
The Church's Jubilee 430
The Reformation Glory 421

HYMN

EXAMINATION
Are You Adorning 250
Are You Building 253
Fire in the Soul 252
Humble Thyself to Walk 247
Soldiers of Christ 230
We Must Be Holy 251
We Reap as We Sow 248

EXPERIENCE
Beulah Land 294
Fade, Fade Each Earthly Joy 306
Filled with Grace 299
His Yoke Is Easy 265
I Know in My Heart 302
In the Light of God 288
I've Found It, Lord 290
Jesus Is All the World 310
My Soul Is Satisfied 313
Since Jesus Came into 256
The Half Has Never Been Told 272
The Lord Raised Me 285
'Tis So Sweet to Trust 337
What a Dear Friend 267
When My Savior Talks 305
Also see Rejoicing

FAITH
All the Way My Savior 334
By Faith and Not by 328
Faith Is the Victory 244
Have Faith in God 315
I Am Thine, O Lord 395
I Know 319
If Thou Wilt Know 316
Let Not Your Heart Be 331
My Faith Looks Up 396
The Shield of Faith 241

FAITHFULNESS
See God, Faithfulness; Loyalty

FAMILY
See Christian Home

FELLOWSHIP
Blest Be the Tie 440
In Christ There Is No 439
Leaning on the Everlasting Arms 353
The Church's Jubilee 430

FIRE
Breathe upon Us 95
Fire in the Soul 252
Let the Fire Fall on Me 214
Revive Us Again 271

FOLLOWING CHRIST
See Discipleship

FORGIVENESS
Dear Lord and Father 399
The Great Physician 115
We'll Praise the Lord 303
Also see Invitation and Acceptance

FOUNDATION
Christ Is Made the 418
How Firm a Foundation 323
I've Found It, Lord 290
The Church Has One 420
The Church's One 419

HYMN

FREEDOM
All in Jesus 263
Brighter Days Are 427
I Know 319
In His Love Let Me Hide 361
Joy Unspeakable 277
The Lord Raised Me 285
Victory 240

FRIENDSHIP
Of Jesus
See Jesus Christ, Friend

World
See World Brotherhood

FUNERAL HYMNS
Abide with Me 481
Crown After Cross 485
Heavenly Welcome 488
I'm Going Home 475
Safe in the Arms of 479
The Sweet By and By 478
Also see Heaven

FUTURE LIFE
Beulah Land 294
Heavenly Welcome 488
When the Roll Is 470
Also see Heaven

GATHERING
See Return and Restoration

GENTLENESS
Are You Adorning 250
Keep Me, My Lord 351
We Reap as We Sow 248

GETHSEMANE
See Jesus Christ, Suffering and Crucifixion

GIVING
See Stewardship

GOD
Care of
Guide Me, O Thou Great 345
He Will Care for Me 352
How Gentle God's 31
In Heavenly Love 348
None Is like God 35
O God, Our Help in 34
O Worship the King 6
There's a Wideness 32
This Is My Father's 30

Communion with
Alone with God 364
Take Time to Be Holy 400
When My Savior Talks 305
Wonderful Peace 356

Creator
For the Beauty of the 7
Hallelujah, Praise Jehovah! 28
This Is My Father's 30
We Praise Thee, O God, Our Redeemer 5

Faithfulness of
A Mighty Fortress 25
Consolation 408

TOPICAL INDEX

HYMN

"Great Is Thy Faithfulness" 317
Have Faith in God 315
O God, Our Help in 34
The Faithfulness of God 320

Fatherhood of
Dear Lord and Father 399
Joyful, Joyful, We 2
The Child of a King 298
This Is My Father's 30

Goodness of
"Great Is Thy Faithfulness" 317
How Gentle God's 31
Joyful, Joyful, We 2
O Lord of Heaven 497
O Praise the Lord! 33
The King of Love 29
This Is My Father's 30

Justice of
O Worship the King 6
There's a Wideness 32

Love of
God Is Love 36
Love Divine 98
O Love That Wilt Not 379
O Sing of His Mighty 88
Praise Him, Praise Him 460
Savior, Teach Me 384
The King of Love 29
There's a Wideness 32

Majesty and Power of
A Mighty Fortress 25
Come, Thou Almighty 1
Hallelujah, Praise Jehovah! 28
Holy, Holy, Holy 3
Holy, Holy, Holy Is the Lord 27
None Is like God 35
O God, Our Help in 34
O God, the Rock of Ages 24
O Worship the King 6
What a Mighty God 26

Mercy of
Amazing Grace 270
Come, Thou Fount 13
Come, Ye Disconsolate 346
Great God, We Sing 490
O Worship the King 6
There's a Wideness 32

Will of
A Charge to Keep I Have 201
Alone with God 364
God's Way Is Best 350
My Heart Says Amen 217

GRACE
A Song of Joy 255
Amazing Grace 270
Filled with Grace 299
How Firm a Foundation 323
Praise God for His Word 109
Soon the Summer 129
Wonderful Power in 407

GRATITUDE
See Thankfulness

GRIEF
See Consolation

HYMN

GUIDANCE
All the Way My Savior 334
Because He Loves Me 347
Ever Lead Me 339
God's Way Is Best 350
Guide Me, O Thou Great 345
He Leadeth Me 343
Heavenly Sunlight 283
Holy Spirit, Faithful 94
I Will Be with Thee 340
If Thou Wilt Know 316
Jesus, Savior, Pilot Me 338
Keep Me, My Lord 351
Lead, Kindly Light 344
No Friend like Jesus 335
O for a Closer Walk 397
O Gentle Savior 374
Savior, More than Life 388
Under His Wings 333

HARVEST OF SOULS
Bring Them In 189
Bringing in the Sheaves 208
I Cannot Be Idle 211
I'll Try to Bring One 206
Together We Go 204

HEALING
He Is Just the Same 450
Healing in His Wings 451
Let Me See Jesus Only 390
O Lord, Thou Healest 452
The Great Physician 115
The Hem of His Garment 453
We Would See Jesus; Lo 56

HEAVEN
Adoration 483
Beautiful 480
Heaven Holds All to Me 486
Home of the Soul 476
I Have a Home 474
I'm Going Home 475
Pearly Gates 482
Sin Can Never Enter 119
The Home Over There 472
The Unclouded Day 487
When We All Get to 467
When We Get Home 469
Will You Go with Us 484

HOLINESS
See Sanctification

HOLY SPIRIT
Blessed Quietness 104
Breathe upon Us 95
He Wants His Way in 175
Holy Spirit, Faithful 94
Holy Spirit, Truth 96
Let the Fire Fall on Me 214
Love Divine 98
Open My Eyes 382
Spirit Holy 97
Spirit of God, Descend 99

HOME
See Christian Home

HOME, HEAVENLY
See Heaven

HOME, SPIRITUAL
Come Home, Poor Sinner 132
Hope of the Righteous 473
I Am Dwelling on the 102
I Have a Home 474

HYMN

I'm Going Home 475
Lord, I'm Coming Home 151
My Home Is on the Rock 363
The Home of the Soul 103
The Home Over There 472
Thy Children Are Gathering Home 423

HOPE
Hope of the Righteous 473
O God, Our Help in 34
O Master, Let Me Walk 210
O Thou in Whose 383
Take the Name of Jesus 402
The Solid Rock 281
We Have a Hope 330

HOUSE OF GOD
Once Again We Come 9
Savior, Again to Thy 16

HUMILITY
By Thy Blessed Word 216
Have Thine Own Way 161
Humble Thyself to Walk 247
I Would Be True 190
O Master, Let Me Walk 210

IMMORTALITY
See Future Life

INSTALLATION
See Dedication of Christian Teachers and Workers

INTERNATIONAL GOOD WILL
See World Brotherhood

INVITATION AND ACCEPTANCE
Almost Persuaded 134
Are You Washed 114
Be Ready When He Comes 127
Christ the Friend 336
Come Home, Poor Sinner 132
Come, Sinner, Come 139
Give Me Thy Heart 140
Have Thine Own Way 161
He Is Calling 135
I Am Coming, Lord 155
I Am Coming to the 153
I Am Praying for You 124
I Believe Jesus Saves 154
I Hear Thy Welcome 146
I Surrender All 157
I Will Follow Thee 193
I'll Go Where You Want 170
I'll Live for Him 163
Is Your All on the 141
Jesus, I Come 148
Jesus Is Calling 136
Jesus Paid It All 145
Just as I Am 152
Let Him In 133
Lord, I'm Coming Home 151
Lord, Take the First 147
Lost Forever 125
O Why Not Now? 130
O Why Not Tonight? 131
Only for Thee 177
Only Trust Him 144
Pass Me Not 150
Softly and Tenderly 143
Soon the Summer Will Be 129

TOPICAL INDEX

HYMN

Take Me as I Am 149
Take My Life, and Let 159
The Cleansing Wave 156
The Last Call 137
To Be Lost in the 128
Transformed 174
Where He Leads Me 164
Whiter than Snow 158
Why Do You Wait? 138
Why Carelessly Wait? 126
Will You Come? 142
Will You Go with Us 484
With Thy Spirit Fill 167

JERUSALEM (SPIRITUAL)
See Zion

JERUSALEM (HEAVEN)
See Heaven

JESUS CHRIST
Advent and Nativity
All My Heart This 51
Angels, from the Realms 48
As with Gladness 47
Away in a Manger 49
Hark, the Herald 41
I Heard the Bells 45
It Came upon the 39
Joy to the World 38
O Come, All Ye Faithful 37
O Gracious Jesus 53
O Little Town of 40
Rejoice, All Ye 76
Silent Night, Holy 46
The First Noel 42
There's a Song 43
There's a Song 44
Thou Didst Leave Thy 55
We Three Kings 50
We Would See Jesus;Lo 56
While Shepherds 52

Cross, The
See Cross

Everliving Christ
All Hail the Power 86
All Hail the Power 87
Blessed Be the Name 89
Crown Him with Many 74
Fairest Lord Jesus 79
Hallelujah, What a 65
He Lives 279
I Know That My Redeemer 73
Joy to the World 38
Rejoice and Be Glad 71
We May Not Climb 72
Worthy Is the Lamb 75

Friend
All the Way My Savior 334
Christ the Friend 336
Jesus Is All the World 310
Jesus, Lover of My 357
Jesus, Lover of My 358
No Friend like Jesus 335
O Jesus, I Have 205
Saved, Saved! 268
'Tis the Blessed Hour 403
What a Friend 401

Life and Ministry
Fairest Lord Jesus 79
I Think When I Read 59
Jesus Was a Loving 60
O Master Workman of 58

HYMN

Tell Me the Stories 54
Tell Me the Story 57
Thou Didst Leave Thy 55
We Would See Jesus;Lo 56
Where Cross the Crowded 437

His Love
Because He Loves Me 347
I Ought to Love My 83
In His Love Let Me Hide 361
Jesus Loves Even Me 309
My Redeemer 264
O Love That Wilt Not 379
O Sing of His Mighty 88
The Bond of Perfectness 414
The More I Learn About 394
When I Survey 62
When I Survey 63

Name
A Blessing in Prayer 406
All Hail the Power 86
All Hail the Power 87
Blessed Be the Name 89
He Keeps Me Singing 274
Jesus Shall Reign 80
Jesus, the Very Thought 93
O for a Thousand 92
O How I Love Jesus! 261
Take the Name of Jesus 402
The Great Physician 115
There Is No Name So 82
'Tis the Sweetest Name 85

Resurrection
Christ Arose 69
Christ the Lord Is 68
Crown Him with Many 74
He Arose 70
I Know That My Redeemer 73
Rejoice and Be Glad 71

Savior, Our
Crown Him with Many 74
Hallelujah, What a 65
I Ought to Love My 83
Jesus, Savior, Pilot 338
My Redeemer 264
Savior, Like a Shepherd 122
Sun of My Soul 20
Tell Me the Old, Old 108
Worthy Is the Lamb 75

Second Coming
See Second Coming

Shepherd, The
Bring Them In 189
Come, Thou Fount 13
O Thou in Whose 383
Praise Him! Praise Him! 81
Savior, Like a Shepherd 122
The King of Love My 29

Suffering and Crucifixion
Alas! and Did My 66
At Calvary 280
Beneath the Cross of 61
Hallelujah, What a 65
I Gave My Life 179
In the Cross of Christ 67
'Tis Midnight, and on 64
When I Survey 62
When I Survey 63

Teacher, Our
Jesus Was a Loving 60
Lord, Speak to Me 160
O Master, Let Me Walk 210
Savior, Teach Me 384

HYMN

Triumphal Entry
All Glory, Laud 90
Praise Him! Praise Him! 81
Tell Me the Stories 54
Thou Didst Leave Thy 55

JOY
A Song of Joy 255
Blessed Quietness 104
Fairest Lord Jesus 79
Jesus Loves Even Me 309
Jesus Saves 229
Joy to the World 38
Joy Unspeakable 277
Joyful, Joyful, We 2
Since Jesus Came into 256
There Is Joy in the Lord 295
There Is Joy in the Service 311
We're Marching to Zion 289
When Morning Gilds 19
Also see Rejoicing

JUDGMENT
Lost Forever 125
Sin Can Never Enter 119
To Be Lost in the Night 128
Also see Warning

JUSTIFICATION
See Cleansing; Forgiveness; Salvation

KEEPING
Christ the Friend We 336
Close to Thee 369
For Me All Is Well 355
Hide Thou Me 367
I Am the Lord's 324
I Know 319
Jesus, Lover of My Soul 357
Jesus, Lover of My Soul 358
Keep Me, My Lord 351
My Prayer 209
Peace, Perfect Peace 365
Standing on the Promises 273
The Hollow of His Mighty 342
The Lord Our Shepherd 341
The Safe Retreat 360
Under His Wings 333

KINGDOM
I Love Thy Kingdom, Lord 416
Jesus Shall Reign 80
Lead On, O King Eternal 227
O Zion, Haste 443
Rise Up, O Men of God 187
The Kingdom of Peace 100
We've a Story to Tell 442

LIGHT
At the Cross 304
By Faith and Not by 328
I'm Redeemed 276
In the Light of God 288
Lead, Kindly Light 344
Send the Light 445
Shine in Me 246
Stepping in the Light 259
Sunshine in the Soul 258

LORD'S DAY
O Day of Peace and 10
The Earth Is Hushed 12

TOPICAL INDEX

HYMN

LORD'S SUPPER
A Parting Hymn We Sing 433
Alas! and Did My Savior 66
Blest Be the Tie That 440
Blest Feast of Love 431
Break Thou the Bread 110
Here at Thy Table, Lord 434
I'll Live for Him 163
In the Cross of Christ 67
We Meet, as in That 432
When I Survey 62
When I Survey 63
Where He Leads Me 164

LOVE
Blest Be the Tie That 440
Fire in the Soul 252
For the Beauty of the 7
Holy Spirit, Truth 96
I Ought to Love My 83
Love Divine 98
Love Lifted Me 269
More Love to Thee 392
My Jesus, I Love Thee 375
O How I Love Jesus! 261
Savior, Teach Me 384
Spirit of God, Descend 99
The Bond of Perfectness 414
The Half Has Never Been 272
We May Not Climb the 72
Also see God, Love of; Jesus Christ, Love of

LOYALTY
I've Enlisted in His 195
My Heart Is Fixed on 213
Also see Decision

MAJESTY
See God, Majesty and Power

MARRIAGE
O Happy Home 455
O Perfect Love 456
O Thou Whose Gracious 459
Also see Christian Home

MERCY
See God, Mercy

MERCY SEAT
A Blessing in Prayer 406
As with Gladness 47
Come, Ye Disconsolate 346

MINISTRY OF CHRIST
See Jesus Christ, Life and Ministry

MISSIONS
Christ for the World 449
Faith of Our Fathers 196
From Greenland's Icy 448
Hear Them Calling 447
Here Am I, Send Me 199
In Christ There Is No 439
Jesus Saves 229
Jesus Shall Reign 80
O Zion, Haste 443
Rescue the Perishing 444
Send the Light 445
The Touch of His Tender 446
The Voice of God Is 192
We've a Story to Tell 442
Where Cross the Crowded 437

HYMN

MORNING HYMNS
A Hymn of Morning 18
Father, We Thank Thee 461
For the Beauty of the 7
Holy, Holy, Holy 3
When Morning Gilds 19

NAME
See Jesus Christ, Name

NATIONAL
See Patriotism, Christian

NATIVITY
See Jesus Christ, Advent and Nativity

NATURE
Day Is Dying in the 23
Fairest Lord Jesus 79
For the Beauty of the 7
Hallelujah, Praise Jehovah 28
Joyful, Joyful, We 2
This Is My Father's 30
We Plow the Fields 494
What a Mighty God 26

NEW BIRTH
See Regeneration

NEW YEAR
Another Year Is 491
For All the Blessings 496
Great God, We Sing 490
Guide Me, O Thou Great 345
O God, Our Help in 34
Standing at the Portal 492

OBEDIENCE
By Thy Blessed Word 216
God's Way Is Best 350
I Would Be True 190
Jesus Calls Us 186
Like a Rock in the 215
My Heart Says Amen 217
The Voice of God Is 192
Trust and Obey 332

OFFERINGS
See Stewardship

OPENING HYMNS
Come, O Thou God of 11
Come, Thou Almighty 1
Come, Thou Fount 13
Gloria Patri 502
Holy, Holy, Holy 3
In Holy Reverence 8
Joy to the World 38
O God, Our Help in 34
O Worship the Lord 4
Once Again We Come 9
Praise God, from Whom 501
The Earth Is Hushed 12

PALM SUNDAY
See Jesus Christ, Triumphal Entry

PARDON
See Forgiveness

PARTING
Blest Be the Tie 440
God Be with You 17
Savior, Again to Thy 16

HYMN

PATIENCE
Are You Adorning 250
More like Christ 391
O Master, Let Me Walk 210
Spirit of God, Descend 99

PATRIOTISM, CHRISTIAN
America, the Beautiful 500
God of Our Fathers 438
God Save the King 499
Lead On, O King Eternal 227
My Country, 'Tis of Thee 498
O God, Our Help in 34

PEACE
International
Christ for the World 449
In Christ There Is No 439
Lead On, O King Eternal 227
The Son of God Goes 441
We've a Story to Tell 442

Of God
All the Way My Savior 334
Dear Lord and Father 399
I Need Thee Every Hour 373
It Is Well with My Soul 322
Leaning on the Everlasting Arms 353
Peace, Perfect Peace 365
River of Peace 312
The Kingdom of Peace 100
What a Friend 401
Wonderful Peace 356

PENTECOST
See Holy Spirit

PERSEVERANCE
Be an Overcomer 242
Faith of Our Fathers 196
Hold Fast to the Word 106
I'm Going On 218
I've Enlisted in His 195
O Jesus, I Have 205
On to the Goal 219
Onward, Christian 224
Press On 233

PRAISE
See Adoration and Praise

PRAYER
A Blessing in Prayer 406
A Call to Prayer 22
Almighty Father 380
Alone with God 364
At the Cross of Jesus 386
Come Closer to Me 349
Come, Ye Disconsolate 346
Hasten and Tell Him 404
Hear Our Prayer, O Lord 506
I Am Praying for You 124
I Am Thine, O Lord 395
Keep Praying, Toiling 409
More Love to Thee 392
My Prayer 209
Prayer of My Heart 389
Sitting at the Feet 370
Sweet Hour of Prayer 405
Take Time to Be Holy 400
'Tis the Blessed Hour 403
What a Friend 401
When Jesus Answers My 234
When My Savior Talks 305
Wonderful Power in 407
Also see Devotion

TOPICAL INDEX

HYMN

PROCESSIONAL HYMNS
Come, Ye Thankful 493
Crown Him with Many 74
For the Beauty of the 7
God of Our Fathers 438
Holy, Holy, Holy 3
Holy, Holy, Holy Is the Lord 27
How Firm a Foundation 323
Joy to the World 38
Joyful, Joyful, We 2
Lead On, O King Eternal 227
O Come, All Ye Faithful 37
Onward, Christian 224
Stand Up for Jesus 184
The Church's One 419
When Morning Gilds 19

PROMISE
Hold Fast to the Word 106
O Jesus, I Have 205
Standing on the 273

PROTECTION
See God, Care of

PROVIDENCE
See God, Care of

PURITY
Are You Faithful? 249
Sin Can Never Enter 119
We Must Be Holy 251
Wholehearted Service 197
Also see Sanctification

REDEMPTION
Amazing Grace 270
At Calvary 280
Hallelujah, What a 65
I'm Redeemed 276
Nothing but the Blood 118
Power in the Blood of 117
Rock of Ages, Cleft 359
Savior, Like a 122
There Is Joy in the Service 311

REFUGE
Come, Ye Disconsolate 346
Hide Thou Me 367
How Firm a Foundation 323
Jesus, Lover of My Soul 357
Jesus, Lover of My Soul 358
Near to the Heart of 385
Nearer, My God, to Thee 377
Nearer, Still Nearer 372
Rock of Ages, Cleft 359
Sweetly Resting 362
The Safe Retreat 360
Under His Wings 333

REGENERATION
Are You Washed in the 114
Down at the Cross 314
Hallelujah! 'Tis Done! 307
He Is Able to Deliver 121
He Lifted Me Out 284
O Happy Day 300
The Lord Raised Me 285
There's a Fountain Opened 293
"Whosoever Will" 308
Ye Must Be Born Again 120
Also see Salvation

REIGNING
If Thou Wilt Know 316
More than a Conqueror 235
Reigning in This Life 254

HYMN

REJOICING
A Child of God 262
All in Jesus 263
Bringing in the Sheaves 208
He Hideth My Soul 354
He Is with Me Still 325
Heavenly Sunlight 283
I Will Praise Him 260
I Will Sing the 257
I'm Redeemed 276
Joy Unspeakable 277
Look and Live 123
O Happy Day 300
Revive Us Again 271
Standing on the 273
There Is Joy in the Lord 295
We'll Crown Him Lord 91
We'll Praise the Lord 303
Also see Joy; Experience; Testimony

REPENTANCE
See Invitation and Acceptance

RESIGNATION
Consolation 408
My Jesus, as Thou Wilt 387

REST
A Blessing in Prayer 406
For Me All Is Well 355
Near the Cross 371
Near to the Heart of 385
Nearer, Still Nearer 372
O Love That Wilt Not 379
Sweetly Resting 362

RESURRECTION OF CHRIST
See Jesus Christ, Resurrection

RETURN AND RESTORATION
Back to the Blessed Old 425
O Zion, Blessed City 422
The Church Has One 420
The Reformation Glory 421
Thy Children Are 423
'Twas Sung by the Poets 424

REWARD
A Song of Joy 255
Crown After Cross 485
Gleams of the Golden 78
Heavenly Welcome 488
O That Will Be Glory 466
Also see Heaven

RICHES (SPIRITUAL)
Christ Is Mine 292
The Child of a King 298
There Is Joy in the Service 311
Unsearchable Riches 296

RIGHTEOUSNESS
Are You Adorning 250
Shine in Me 246
The Kingdom of Peace 100
We Must Be Holy 251
Also see Sanctification

ROCK
Are You Building on the 253
Glorious Things of Thee 412

HYMN

He Hideth My Soul 354
Hide Thou Me 367
Like a Rock in the 215
My Home Is on the Rock 363
O God, the Rock of 24
O Precious Bible! 111
Rock of Ages, Cleft 359
Sweetly Resting 362
The Solid Rock 281

SABBATH
See Lord's Day

SALVATION
I Know in My Heart 302
Look and Live 123
Saved, Saved! 268
There Is Power in the 113
Victory 240
Waves of Devotion 282
Also see Regeneration; Experience

SANCTIFICATION
Beulah Land 294
Come Over into Canaan 101
I Am Dwelling on the 102
Love Divine 98
The Home of the Soul 103
The Kingdom of Peace 100
Yielded to Thee 171

SANCTIFICATION—ENTREATY FOR
Breathe upon Us 95
Come Over into Canaan 101
Fill Me Now 172
Give Me Thy Heart 140
He Wants His Way with 175
His Way with Thee 176
Let the Fire Fall on Me 214
O for a Heart of Calm 366
Spirit Holy 97
Yielded to Thee 171
Also see Consecration

SCRIPTURES, HOLY
See Bible

SECOND COMING
Gleams of the Golden 78
Rejoice, All Ye 76
We Know Not the Hour 77

SECURITY
See Keeping; Refuge

SELF-DENIAL
Jesus, I My Cross Have 194
More like Christ 391
"Take Up Thy Cross," the Savior Said 188
Who Will Suffer with 185
Also see Consecration

SERVICE
A Living Sacrifice 165
Am I a Soldier 222
"Are Ye Able," Said 191
Consecration 162
Draw Thou My Soul 169
Here Am I, Send Me 199
His Yoke Is Easy 265
I Gave My Life for Thee 179
I Love to Serve My 266
I Will Follow Thee 193
Jesus Calls Us 186
Jesus, I My Cross Have 194

TOPICAL INDEX

HYMN

Lord, Speak to Me ... 160
O Jesus, I Have ... 205
O Master, Let Me Walk ... 210
O Master Workman of ... 58
Our Best ... 180
Remember Thy Creator 183
Rise Up, O Men of God ... 187
Something for Jesus ... 376
The Son of God Goes ... 441
The Voice of God Is ... 192
When My King Shall ... 468
Where Cross the Crowded ... 437
Wholehearted Service ... 197
Work, for the Night Is ... 182

SHEPHERD
See Jesus Christ, Shepherd

SIN
All Taken Away ... 301
Love Lifted Me ... 269
Power in the Blood of 117
Sin Can Never Enter ... 119
There Is Power in the ... 113

SOLDIERS OF CHRIST
Am I a Soldier ... 222
Faith Is the Victory ... 244
I'm on the Winning ... 243
I've Enlisted in His ... 195
Lead On, O King Eternal 227
Lift Up Your Heads ... 239
O Jesus, I Have ... 205
Onward, Christian ... 224
Press the Battle On ... 237
Soldiers of Christ ... 230
Stand by the Cross ... 236
Stand Up for Jesus ... 184
The Army of the Lord ... 226
The Shield of Faith ... 241
Truehearted, Wholehearted ... 231
Victory Through Grace ... 225

SONG
A Song of Joy ... 255
God Is Love ... 36
He Keeps Me Singing ... 274
I Will Sing the ... 257
Joy to the World ... 38
Joyful, Joyful, We ... 2
O Could I Speak ... 84
The Great Physician ... 115
There's a Song in the ... 43
There's a Song in the ... 44
There's Music in My ... 287
When My Savior Talks ... 305

SORROW
See Consolation

SOWING AND REAPING
Bringing in the Sheaves 208
Every Hour of the ... 212
We Reap as We Sow ... 248

SPECIAL DAYS
Children's Day
Fairest Lord Jesus ... 79
Also see special index, p. 493

Christmas
See Jesus Christ, Advent and Nativity

HYMN

Easter
See Jesus Christ, Resurrection

Father's Day
Faith of Our Fathers ... 196
God of Our Fathers ... 438

Good Friday
See Suffering and Crucifixion

Independence Day
See Patriotism, Christian

Labor Day
O Master Workman of ... 58

Memorial Day
Faith of Our Fathers ... 196
God of Our Fathers ... 438
O God, Our Help in ... 34

Mother's Day
Faith of Our Mothers ... 458
Happy the Home When ... 454
Lord of Life and King ... 457

New Year
See New Year

Palm Sunday
See Jesus Christ, Triumphal Entry

Thanksgiving Day
Come, Ye Thankful ... 493
For All the Blessings ... 496
For the Beauty of the ... 7
O Lord of Heaven and ... 497
Our Glad Thanksgiving ... 495
We Plow the Fields ... 494
We Praise Thee, O God, Our Redeemer ... 5
Also see Thankfulness

STEADFASTNESS
Are You Faithful? ... 249
I Will Do My Part ... 220
I Would Be True ... 190
Like a Rock in the ... 215
My Heart Is Fixed ... 213
O Jesus, I Have ... 205
The Solid Rock ... 281

STEWARDSHIP
A Living Sacrifice ... 165
As with Gladness ... 47
Bless Thou the Gifts ... 505
Our Best ... 180
Take My Life and Let ... 159
We Give Thee but Thine 173
We Must Be Holy ... 251
Also see. Consecration

SUBMISSION
Let Me See Jesus Only 390
My Heart Says Amen 217
My Jesus, as Thou Wilt 387
O for a Closer Walk ... 397

SUPPLICATION
See Devotion

SURRENDER
See Invitation and Acceptance; Decision

HYMN

TEMPTATION
Be Still ... 378
Jesus, Savior, Pilot Me ... 338
Also see Trials

TESTIMONY
A Child of God ... 262
At the Cross ... 304
Blessed Assurance ... 321
Christ Is Mine ... 292
He Hideth My Soul ... 354
He Keeps Me Singing ... 274
He Lives ... 279
I Love to Serve My ... 266
I Love to Tell the ... 297
I Will Shout His Praise ... 275
It Is Truly Wonderful ... 278
Jesus Saves ... 229
Look and Live ... 123
Since Jesus Came into ... 256
Sunshine in the Soul ... 258
River of Peace ... 312
There's Music in My ... 287
This Is Why I Love My ... 286
To the Work ... 202
Also see Rejoicing

THANKFULNESS
A Thankful Song ... 464
For Health and Strength 463
For the Beauty of the ... 7
O Lord of Heaven and ... 497
Thanks for Bread ... 465

THANKSGIVING DAY
See Special Days

TIME AND ETERNITY
See Future Life

TRIALS
All the Way My Savior ... 334
He Leadeth Me ... 343
In the Cross of Christ ... 67
Jesus, Savior, Pilot ... 338
Keep Praying, Toiling ... 409
'Tis the Blessed Hour ... 403
What a Friend ... 401
When Jesus Answers My 234

TRINITY
Come, Thou Almighty ... 1
Gloria Patri ... 502
Holy, Holy, Holy ... 3
O Day of Peace and ... 10
O Worship the Lord ... 4

TRUST AND CONFIDENCE
All the Way My Savior ... 334
Because He Loves Me ... 347
He Is with Me Still ... 325
He Will Care for Me 352
Hope of the Righteous ... 473
How Firm a Foundation 323
I Am the Lord's ... 324
I Know Whom I Have ... 318
In His Love Let Me Hide 361
In Holy Reverence, Lord 8
It Is Well with My Soul 322
Jesus, Lover of My Soul 357
Jesus, Lover of My Soul 358
Lead, Kindly Light ... 344
Let Not Your Heart Be 331
No Friend like Jesus ... 335
That's Enough for Me ... 327
The Faithfulness of God 320
The Hollow of His 342
The More I Learn About 394

TOPICAL INDEX

HYMN

'Tis So Sweet to Trust 337
Trust and Obey 332
Under His Wings 333

TRUTH
Break Thou the Bread 110
Church of the Living 410
Holy Spirit, Truth 96
Mine Eyes Have Seen 238
Open My Eyes, That I 382
The Reformation Glory 421

UNITY
See Christian Unity

VESPER
See Evening Hymns

VICTORY
Faith Is the Victory 244
I Love to Serve My 266
I'm Going On 218
I'm on the Winning Side 243
Songs of Victory 232
The Army of the Lord 226
Victory 240
Victory Through Grace 225
When We All Get to 467
Also see Conquest

WALKING WITH GOD
Close to Thee 369
He Is with Me Still 325
He Lives 279
He Will Care for Me 352

HYMN

Humble Thyself to Walk 247
In Heavenly Love 348
In His Love Let Me Hide 361
O for a Closer Walk 397
O Master, Let Me Walk 210

WARFARE, CHRISTIAN
See Conquest; Victory

WARNING
Be Ready When He Comes 127
Lost Forever 125
Soon the Summer Will 129
To Be Lost in the Night 128
Why Carelessly Wait? 126

WATCHFULNESS
A Charge to Keep I Have 201
My Soul, Be on Thy 223
To the Work 202
We Know Not the Hour 77

WILL OF GOD
See God, Will of

WITNESS OF THE SPIRIT
I Know in My Heart 302
I Know My Name Is There 329
We Have a Hope 330

WITNESSING
I Love to Tell the 297
Jesus Saves 229
O Zion, Haste 443

HYMN

Shine in Me 246
Tell What He's Done 245
Together We Go 204

WORD OF GOD
See Bible

WORK
See Activity and Zeal

WORLD BROTHERHOOD
In Christ There Is No 439
Jesus Shall Reign 80
Rise Up, O Men of God 187
Where Cross the Crowded 437

YOUTH
"Are Ye Able," Said 191
Fairest Lord Jesus 79
Give of Your Best 181
I Would Be True 190
O Master Workman of 58
Remember Thy Creator 183

ZION
Beautiful, Peaceful 429
Glorious Things of Thee 412
I Love Thy Kingdom 416
If Thou Wilt Know 316
O Zion, Blessed City 422
O Zion, Haste 443
Thy Children Are 423
We're Marching to Zion 289
Zion Stands with Hills 417

Index of Titles and First Lines

Titles are in capital and small capital letters; first lines, where sufficiently different from titles, are in regular letters (not capitals).

HYMN

A Blessing in Prayer 406
A Call to Prayer 22
A Charge to Keep I Have 201
A Child of God 262
A glorious blessing bestowed upon me 282
A Hymn of Morning Praise 18
A Living Sacrifice 165
A Mighty Fortress Is Our God 25
A Parting Hymn We Sing 433
A Song of Joy 255
A Thankful Song 464
A wonderful Savior is Jesus 354
Abide with Me 481
Adoration 483
Afar on the mountain 135
Alas! and Did My Savior Bleed 66
Alas! and did my Savior bleed 304
All Glory, Laud, and Honor 90
All Hail the Power of Jesus' Name 86, 87
All in Jesus 263
All My Heart This Night Rejoices 51
All praise to Him who reigns above 89
All Taken Away 301
All the burdens once so heavy 305
All the Way My Savior Leads Me 334
All this world, its wealth and honor 313
All to Jesus I surrender 157
Almighty Father 380
Almost Persuaded 134
Alone with God 364
Along a dark and gloomy path 288
Along life's rugged, thorny way 409
Along the way of life 243
Am I a Soldier of the Cross? 222
Amazing Grace 270
America, the Beautiful 500
Angels, from the Realms of Glory 48
Another Year Is Dawning 491
"Are Ye Able?" Said the Master 191
Are You Adorning the Doctrine? 250
Are You Building on the Rock? 253
Are You Faithful? 249
Are You Washed in the Blood? 114
As to thy banquet hall 434

HYMN

As with Gladness Men of Old 47
"Ask and it shall be given" 404
At Calvary 280
At the Cross 304
At the Cross of Jesus Bowing 386
Away in a Manger 49

Back to the Blessed Old Bible 425
Be an Overcomer 242
Be Ready When He Comes 127
Be Still 378
Beautiful 480
Beautiful, Peaceful Zion 429
Because He Loves Me 347
Beneath the Cross of Jesus 61
Beulah Land 294
Beyond this world of toil 473
Bless Thou the Gifts 505
Blessed Assurance 321
Blessed Be the Name 89
Blessed Quietness 104
Blessed Savior, I would live 177
Blest Be the Tie That Binds 440
Blest Feast of Love Divine 431
Break Thou the Bread of Life 110
Breathe on Me, Breath of God 178
Breathe upon Us 95
Brighter Days Are Sweetly Dawning 427
Bring Them In 189
Bringing in the Sheaves 208
Buried with Jesus 435
By Faith and Not by Sight 328
By the word of God 112
By Thy Blessed Word Obeying 216

Can the Lord count you faithful? 249
Child of God's boundless mercy 408
Christ Arose 69
Christ for the World We Sing 449
Christ Is Made the Sure Foundation 418
Christ Is Mine 292
Christ our mighty leader 204
Christ the Friend We Need 336
Christ the Lord Is Risen Today 68
Church of God, Thou Spotless Virgin 411
Church of the Living God 410
Close to Thee 369
Come Closer to Me 349

HYMN
Come, every soul by sin oppressed ... 144
Come Home, Poor Sinner ... 132
Come, O Thou God of Grace ... 11
Come Over into Canaan ... 101
Come, Sinner, Come ... 139
Come, Thou Almighty King ... 1
Come, Thou Fount ... 13
Come, we that love the Lord ... 289
Come, Ye Disconsolate ... 346
Come, Ye Thankful People, Come ... 493
Conquering now and still ... 225
Consecration ... 162
Consolation ... 408
Crown After Cross ... 485
Crown Him with Many Crowns ... 74

Day Is Dying in the West ... 23
Dead to every worldly pleasure ... 390
Dear Lord and Father of Mankind ... 399
Dear Lord, take up the tangled strands ... 174
Did you hear what Jesus said ... 301
Do you triumph, O my brother ... 254
Down at the Cross ... 314
Down in the valley ... 198
Down into the flowing river ... 435
Draw Me Close to Thee ... 398
Draw Thou My Soul, O Christ ... 169

Earth holds no treasures ... 486
Encamped along the hills ... 244
Ever Lead Me ... 339
Every Hour for Jesus ... 203
Every Hour of the Passing Day ... 212

Fade, Fade, Each Earthly Joy ... 306
Fairest Lord Jesus ... 79
Faith Is the Victory ... 244
Faith of Our Fathers ... 196
Faith of Our Mothers ... 458
Far away in a land ... 446
Far away in the depth ... 356
Father, We Thank Thee ... 461
Feet that have carried the gospel ... 488
Fill Me Now ... 172
Fill Me with Thy Spirit ... 168
Filled with Grace and Glory ... 299
Fire in the Soul ... 252
Follow On! ... 198
Following Jesus from day ... 328
For All the Blessings of the Year ... 496
For Health and Strength ... 463
For Me All Is Well ... 355
For the Beauty of the Earth ... 7

HYMN
Forward, Ever Forward ... 221
Forward, forward, is the battle cry ... 237
From Greenland's Icy Mountains ... 448

Give Me Thy Heart ... 140
Give of Your Best to the Master ... 181
Gleams of the Golden Morning ... 78
Gloria Patri ... 502
Glorious Things of Thee Are Spoken ... 412
Glory be to the Father ... 502
God Be with You ... 17
God has sent the Holy Spirit ... 175
God Is Love ... 36
God of light that illumes ... 246
God of Our Fathers ... 438
God Save the King ... 499
God's Way Is Best ... 350
Grace is offered you ... 129
Great God, We Sing That Mighty Hand ... 490
"Great Is Thy Faithfulness" ... 317
Guide Me, O Thou Great Jehovah ... 345

Hallelujah, Praise Jehovah! ... 28
Hallelujah! 'Tis Done! ... 307
Hallelujah! What a Savior! ... 65
Hallelujah, what a thought ... 240
Happy the Home When God Is There ... 454
Hark! my soul, seraphic music ... 36
Hark, the Herald Angels Sing ... 41
Hark! the voice of Jesus ... 199
Hark! 'tis the Shepherd's voice ... 189
Hasten and Tell Him ... 404
Have Faith in God ... 315
Have Thine Own Way, Lord ... 161
Have we any hope within us ... 330
Have you been to Jesus ... 114
Have you ever heard of Jesus ... 450
Have you found rest and peace ... 245
He Arose ... 70
He Hideth My Soul ... 354
He Is Able to Deliver ... 121
He Is Calling ... 135
He Is Just the Same Today ... 450
"He is risen," said the angel ... 70
He Is with Me Still ... 325
He Keeps Me Singing ... 274
He Leadeth Me ... 343
He Lifted Me Out ... 284
He lifted my burden of sorrow ... 267
He Lives ... 279
He pardoned my transgressions ... 278

INDEX OF TITLES AND FIRST LINES

HYMN

He Wants His Way in Thee 175
He Will Care for Me 352
Healing in His Wings 451
Hear Our Prayer, O Lord 506
Hear Them Calling 447
Hear ye the Master's call 180
Heaven Holds All to Me 486
Heaven is a holy place 119
Heavenly Sunlight 283
Heavenly Welcome 488
Here Am I, Send Me 199
Here at Thy Table, Lord 434
Here, Savior, We Would Come 436
Hide Thou Me 367
His Way with Thee 176
His Yoke Is Easy 265
Hold Fast to the Word 106
Holy, Holy, Holy 3
Holy, Holy, Holy Is the Lord 27
Holy Spirit, Faithful Guide 94
Holy Spirit, Truth Divine 96
Home of the Soul 476
Hope of the Righteous 473
Hover o'er me, Holy Spirit 172
How Firm a Foundation 323
How Gentle God's Commands 31
How Shall I Follow Him I Serve? 166
How sweet this bond of perfectness 414
Humble Thyself to Walk with God 247

I Am Coming, Lord, to Thee 155
I am coming to Jesus for rest 154
I Am Coming to the Cross 153
I Am Dwelling on the Mountain 102
I am fighting in the army 195
I am going to a home 482
I Am Praying for You 124
I am so glad that our Father 309
I Am the Lord's 324
I Am Thine, O Lord 395
I Believe Jesus Saves 154
I came to Jordan's sullen stream 101
I can hear my Savior calling 164
I Cannot Be Idle 211
I do not pray that life be spent 209
I Gave My Life for Thee 179
I have a dear Savior 206
I Have a Home 474
I have a Savior 124
I have found his grace 277
I have found the joy of God 483
I have left all sin's dominion 342
I have yielded myself 217
I hear the Savior say 145
I Hear Thy Welcome Voice 146

HYMN

I Heard the Bells on Christmas Day 45
I Know 319
I know I love thee better 272
I Know in My Heart What It Means 302
I Know My Name Is There 329
I know not why God's wondrous grace 318
I Know That My Redeemer Lives 73
I Know Whom I Have Believed 318
I love the Christ 165
I Love Thy Kingdom, Lord 416
I Love to Serve My Jesus 266
I Love to Tell the Story 297
I mean to go right on 218
I Need Thee Every Hour 373
I Ought to Love My Savior 83
I serve a risen Savior 279
I Surrender All 157
I Think When I Read That Sweet Story 59
I walk today in the Christian way 352
I Was Glad 462
I was out on the broad way of sin 284
I was sinking deep in sin 269
I Will Be with Thee 340
I Will Do My Part 220
I Will Follow Thee 193
I Will Praise Him, Hallelujah! 260
I Will Shout His Praise in Glory 275
I will sing hallelujah 295
I will sing of my Redeemer 264
I Will Sing the Wondrous Story 257
I will sing you a song 476
I would be nearer my Savior 398
I Would Be True 190
I yield to Thee, Savior 147
If Thou Wilt Know the Fountain Deep 316
If thou wouldst have the dear Savior 247
If we shall scatter tares 248
I'll Follow with Rejoicing 326
I'll Go Where You Want Me to Go 170
I'll Live for Him 163
I'll sing of a river divine 312
I'll Try to Bring One 206
I'm Going Home 475
I'm Going On 218
I'm on the Winning Side 243
I'm Redeemed 276

INDEX OF TITLES AND FIRST LINES

HYMN

IN CHRIST THERE IS NO EAST OR WEST 439
In faith she touched the hem 453
IN HEAVENLY LOVE ABIDING 348
IN HIS LOVE LET ME HIDE 361
IN HOLY REVERENCE, LORD 8
In the arms of my dear Savior 299
In the awful sea of sin 285
IN THE CROSS OF CHRIST I GLORY 67
In the holy army we've enlisted 226
IN THE LIGHT OF GOD 288
In the rifted Rock I'm resting 362
In thy cleft, O Rock of Ages 367
Is the Spirit glowing 252
IS YOUR ALL ON THE ALTAR? 141
IT CAME UPON THE MIDNIGHT CLEAR 39
IT IS TRULY WONDERFUL 278
IT IS WELL WITH MY SOUL 322
It may be little 220
It may not be on the mountain height 170
I've a message from the Lord 123
I'VE ENLISTED IN HIS SERVICE 195
I've found a friend 268
I'VE FOUND IT, LORD, IN THEE 290
I've found my Lord 265
I've reached the land of corn and wine 294
I've turned from the world 197
I've wandered far away 151

JESUS CALLS US 186
Jesus has taken my load 251
JESUS, I COME 148
JESUS, I MY CROSS HAVE TAKEN 194
JESUS IS ALL THE WORLD TO ME 310
JESUS IS CALLING 136
Jesus is tenderly calling 136
Jesus, keep me near the cross 371
JESUS, LOVER OF MY SOUL 357, 358
JESUS LOVES EVEN ME 309
Jesus, my Lord, to thee I cry 149
JESUS PAID IT ALL 145
JESUS SAVES 229
JESUS, SAVIOR, PILOT ME 338
JESUS SHALL REIGN WHERE'ER THE SUN 80
JESUS, THE VERY THOUGHT OF THEE 93
JESUS WAS A LOVING TEACHER 60
JOY TO THE WORLD 38
JOY UNSPEAKABLE 277
JOYFUL, JOYFUL, WE ADORE THEE 2
Joyful we walk 221
Joys are flowing like a river 104
JUST AS I AM 152

HYMN

Keep me in touch with thee 351
KEEP ME, MY LORD 351
KEEP PRAYING, TOILING ON 409

LEAD, KINDLY LIGHT 344
LEAD ON, O KING ETERNAL 227
LEANING ON THE EVERLASTING ARMS 353
LET HIM IN 133
LET ME SEE JESUS ONLY 390
Let me walk in the path 361
LET NOT YOUR HEART BE TROUBLED 331
Let not your weary heart be troubled 331
LET THE FIRE FALL ON ME 214
LET THE WORDS OF MY MOUTH 503
Let us sing a sweet song 103
LIFT UP YOUR HEADS, YE GATES OF BRASS 239
Light after darkness 485
LIKE A ROCK IN THE BILLOWS 215
Long scattered thy children, O Zion 423
LOOK AND LIVE 123
LORD, DISMISS US WITH THY BLESSING 14
LORD, I HEAR OF SHOWERS OF BLESSING 368
Lord, I would be wholly thine 214
LORD, I'M COMING HOME 151
Lord Jesus, I long 158
LORD OF LIFE AND KING OF GLORY 457
Lord, possess me now 167
LORD, SPEAK TO ME THAT I MAY SPEAK 160
LORD, TAKE THE FIRST PLACE 147
LOST FOREVER 125
LOVE DIVINE, ALL LOVES EXCELLING 98
LOVE LIFTED ME 269
Low in the grave he lay 69

"Man of Sorrows," what a name 65
Men speak of a "church triumphant" 426
MINE EYES HAVE SEEN THE GLORY 238
MORE ABOUT JESUS 393
MORE LIKE CHRIST 391
MORE LOVE TO THEE 392
MORE THAN A CONQUEROR 235
Morning has come 465
MUST JESUS BEAR THE CROSS ALONE? 200
MY COUNTRY, 'TIS OF THEE 498
MY FAITH LOOKS UP TO THEE 396

INDEX OF TITLES AND FIRST LINES

HYMN

My Father is rich ... 298
My Heart Is Fixed on Jesus ... 213
My Heart Says Amen ... 217
My heavenly home is bright ... 475
My Home Is on the Rock ... 363
My hope is built on nothing less ... 281
My Jesus, As Thou Wilt ... 387
My Jesus, I Love Thee ... 375
My life, my love I give ... 163
My name is in the book ... 329
My Prayer ... 209
My Redeemer ... 264
My Soul, Be on Thy Guard ... 223
My soul in trouble roamed ... 290
My Soul Is Satisfied ... 313

Near the Cross ... 371
Near to the Heart of God ... 385
Nearer, My God, to Thee ... 377
Nearer, Still Nearer ... 372
No Friend like Jesus ... 335
No matter how hard goes the battle ... 407
No sigh nor a tear ... 355
None Is like God ... 35
Nothing but the Blood of Jesus ... 118
Now the Day Is Over ... 21

O be still, thou soul ... 378
O beautiful for spacious skies ... 500
O bliss of the purified ... 88
O Church of God ... 413
O Come, All Ye Faithful ... 37
O come to the Lord today ... 126
O come to the Savior ... 128
O Could I Speak the Matchless Worth ... 84
O Day of Peace and Gladness ... 10
O do not let the word depart ... 131
O drink of the river of pleasure ... 291
O for a closer walk (Prayer of My Heart) ... 389
O for a Closer Walk with God ... 397
O for a Heart of Calm Repose ... 366
O for a Thousand Tongues ... 92
O Gentle Savior ... 374
O God, inspire our morning hymn ... 18
O God, Our Help in Ages Past ... 34
O God, the Rock of Ages ... 24
O God, who gives our daily bread ... 464
O Gracious Jesus, Child Divine ... 53
O Happy Day ... 300
O Happy Home ... 455
O How I Love Jesus! ... 261

HYMN

O I praise the Lord who bought me ... 260
O Jesus, I Have Promised ... 205
O Little Town of Bethlehem ... 40
O look at the faithfulness ... 320
O Lord of Heaven and Earth and Sea ... 497
O Lord, Thou Healest Me! ... 452
O Love That Wilt Not Let Me Go ... 379
O Master, Let Me Walk with Thee ... 210
O Master Workman of the Race ... 58
O now I see the cleansing wave ... 156
O Perfect Love ... 456
O Praise the Lord! ... 33
O Precious Bible! ... 111
O Sing of His Mighty Love ... 88
O sinner, heed the Spirit's voice ... 137
O That Will Be Glory ... 466
O the unsearchable riches ... 296
O they tell me of a home ... 487
O think of the home ... 472
O Thou in Whose Presence ... 383
O Thou Whose Gracious Presence Blest ... 459
O Where Are Kings and Empires Now ... 428
O Worship the King ... 6
O Worship the Lord ... 4
O Worship the Lord (Response) ... 504
O worship the Lord in the beauty of holiness ... 4
O Why Not Now? ... 130
O Why Not Tonight? ... 131
O Zion, Blessed City ... 422
O Zion, Haste ... 443
Oft my heart has bled ... 336
On a hill far away ... 381
On his throne of glory ... 75
On the borders of eternity ... 447
On to the Goal ... 219
Once Again We Come ... 9
Once More, Before We Part ... 15
Only for Thee ... 177
Only Trust Him ... 144
Onward, All Ye People ... 228
Onward, Christian Soldiers ... 224
Open My Eyes, That I May See ... 382
Our Best ... 180
Our Father's wondrous works we see ... 26
Our Glad Thanksgiving ... 495
Out of my bondage ... 148
Out on this dark world ... 339

Pass Me Not ... 150
Peace, Perfect Peace ... 365
Pearly Gates ... 482

INDEX OF TITLES AND FIRST LINES

HYMN

Power in the Blood of Jesus 117
Praise God for His Word 109
Praise God, from Whom All Blessings Flow 501
Praise God, I live in Beulah land 363
Praise him, praise him, all ye little children 460
Praise him! praise him! Jesus our blessed Redeemer 81
Praise the Lord! my heart 262
Prayer of My Heart 389
Press On 233
Press the Battle On 237

Reigning in This Life 254
Rejoice, All Ye Believers 76
Rejoice and Be Glad 71
Remember Thy Creator Now 183
Rescue the Perishing 444
Revive Us Again 271
Rise Up, O Men of God 187
River of Peace 312
Rock of Ages, Cleft for Me 359

Safe in the Arms of Jesus 479
Salvation's free, glad joy 255
Saved! Saved! 268
Savior, Again to Thy Dear Name 16
Savior, Like a Shepherd Lead Us 122
Savior, More than Life to Me 388
Savior, thy dying love 376
Savior, Teach Me, Day by Day 384
Send the Light 445
Shall I tell you why I ceased from folly? 286
Shall We Gather at the River? 471
Shall We Meet Beyond the River? 477
Shine in Me 246
Silent Night, Holy Night 46
Sin Can Never Enter There 119
Since I have found my Savior 287
Since Jesus Came into My Heart 256
Since Jesus gave his life 162
Sing the wondrous love 467
Sing them over again to me 105
Sitting at the Feet of Jesus 370
Softly and Tenderly 143
Softly the evening vespers 22
Soldiers of Christ, Arise 230
Something for Jesus 376
Songs of Victory 232
Soon the Summer Will Be Ended 129

HYMN

Sowing in the morning 208
Spirit Holy 97
Spirit of God, Descend upon My Heart 99
Stand by the Cross 236
Stand Up for Jesus 184
Standing at the Portal 492
Standing on the Promises 273
Stepping in the Light 259
Sun of My Soul 20
Sunshine in the Soul 258
Sweet Hour of Prayer 405
Sweetly Resting 362

Take Me as I Am 149
Take My Life, and Let It Be 159
Take the Name of Jesus with You 402
Take the shield of faith 241
Take Time to Be Holy 400
"Take Up Thy Cross," the Savior Said 188
Tell Me the Old, Old Story 108
Tell Me the Stories of Jesus 54
Tell Me the Story of Jesus 57
Tell What He's Done for You 245
Thanks for Bread 465
That heavenly Teacher 120
That's Enough for Me 327
The Army of the Lord 226
The Blameless Church 415
The Bond of Perfectness 414
The Child of a King 298
The Church Has One Foundation 420
The church of God one body is 413
The Church Triumphant 426
The Church's Jubilee 430
The Church's One Foundation 419
The Cleansing Wave 156
The Earth Is Hushed in Silence 12
The Faithfulness of God 320
The First Noel 42
The future lies unseen 326
The golden morning is fast approaching 78
The Great Physician 115
The Half Has Never Been Told 272
The Hem of His Garment 453
The Hollow of His Mighty Hand 342
The Home of the Soul 103
The Home Over There 472
The King of Love My Shepherd Is 29
The Kingdom of Peace 100
The Last Call 137

INDEX OF TITLES AND FIRST LINES

HYMN

The light of eventide now shines ... 430
The Lord Bless Thee, and Keep Thee ... 507
The Lord Our Shepherd ... 341
The Lord Raised Me ... 285
The More I Learn About Jesus ... 394
The Old Rugged Cross ... 381
The Reformation Glory ... 421
The River of Pleasure ... 291
The Safe Retreat ... 360
The Shield of Faith ... 241
The Solid Rock ... 281
The Son of God Goes Forth for Peace ... 441
The Sweet By and By ... 478
The Touch of His Tender Hand ... 446
The Unclouded Day ... 487
The Voice of God Is Calling ... 192
The Word of God ... 112
There Is a Fountain Filled with Blood ... 116
There is a name I love ... 261
There is a place of quiet rest ... 385
There Is Joy in the Lord ... 295
There Is Joy in the Service ... 311
There Is No Name So Sweet on Earth ... 82
There is not a friend like Jesus ... 335
There is peace and joy ... 263
There Is Power in the Blood ... 113
There is rest, sweet rest ... 406
There's a call comes ringing ... 445
There's a Fountain Opened ... 293
There's a land that is fairer ... 478
There's a mighty reformation ... 421
There's a Song in the Air ... 43, 44
There's a theme that is sweet ... 100
There's a Wideness in God's Mercy ... 32
There's Music in My Soul ... 287
There's power in the blood ... 117
There's sunshine in my soul ... 258
There's within my heart ... 274
This Is My Father's World ... 30
This Is Why I Love My Savior ... 286
Tho' I walk in ways unknown ... 325
Tho' the night has been long ... 234
Thou Didst Leave Thy Throne ... 55
Thou, my everlasting portion ... 369
Thy Children Are Gathering Home ... 423
Thy Word Is like a Garden, Lord ... 107
'Tis Midnight; and on Olive's Brow ... 64
'Tis So Sweet to Trust in Jesus ... 337

HYMN

'Tis the Blessed Hour of Prayer ... 403
'Tis the promise of God ... 307
'Tis the Sweetest Name ... 85
To Be Lost in the Night ... 128
To God, who gives our daily bread ... 464
To the Work ... 202
To thee, O Lord Jehovah ... 495
Together We Go to Make Disciples ... 204
Transformed ... 174
Truehearted, Wholehearted ... 231
Trust and Obey ... 332
Trying to walk in the steps ... 259
Turning thy face from all the past ... 219
'Twas Sung by the Poets ... 424

Under His Wings ... 333
Unsearchable Riches ... 296

Victory ... 240
Victory Through Grace ... 225

Walking in sunlight ... 283
Waves of Devotion ... 282
We are bound for the mansions ... 469
We are going home ... 484
We Give Thee But Thine Own ... 173
We Have a Hope ... 330
We have heard the joyful sound ... 229
We Know Not the Hour ... 77
We May Not Climb the Heavenly Steeps ... 72
We Meet, as in That Upper Room ... 432
We Must Be Holy ... 251
We Plow the Fields, and Scatter ... 494
We praise thee, O God! for the Son ... 271
We Praise Thee, O God, Our Redeemer ... 5
We Reap as We Sow ... 248
We Three Kings of Orient Are ... 50
We Will Work for Jesus ... 207
We Would See Jesus ... 489
We Would See Jesus; Lo! His Star ... 56
We'll Crown Him Lord of All ... 91
We'll follow the Lord all the way ... 341
We'll Praise the Lord ... 303
We'll shout and sing our Redeemer's praise ... 91
We're Marching to Zion ... 289

INDEX OF TITLES AND FIRST LINES

HYMN

WE'VE A STORY TO TELL TO THE NATIONS 442
WHAT A DEAR FRIEND IS JESUS 267
What a fellowship, what a joy 353
WHAT A FRIEND 401
WHAT A MIGHTY GOD WE SERVE! 26
What a wonderful change 256
What can wash away my stain? 118
When all my labors and trials are o'er 466
When I get weary with toils 349
When I read how my Savior was nailed 302
WHEN I SURVEY THE WONDROUS CROSS 62, 63
WHEN JESUS ANSWERS MY PRAYER 234
WHEN MORNING GILDS THE SKIES 19
WHEN MY KING SHALL CALL FOR ME 468
WHEN MY SAVIOR TALKS WITH ME 305
When my sky is clear 327
When peace like a river 322
When storms of life are round me beating 364
WHEN THE ROLL IS CALLED UP YONDER 470
When the storm clouds rise 360
When the storm winds rage 347
When the trumpet of the Lord shall sound 470
WHEN WE ALL GET TO HEAVEN 467
WHEN WE GET HOME 469
When we walk with the Lord 332
WHERE CROSS THE CROWDED WAYS OF LIFE 437
WHERE HE LEADS ME 164
Where is thy prospect 125
Where shall we look for help 452

HYMN

Whether I live or die 324
While Jesus whispers to you 139
WHILE SHEPHERDS WATCHED THEIR FLOCKS 52
WHITER THAN SNOW 158
Who is knocking at your heart 133
WHO WILL SUFFER WITH THE SAVIOR? 185
WHOLEHEARTED SERVICE 197
"Whosoever heareth," shout 308
"WHOSOEVER WILL" 308
WHY CARELESSLY WAIT? 126
WHY DO YOU WAIT? 138
Why not now? O sinner, listen 130
WILL YOU COME? 142
WILL YOU GO WITH US TO HEAVEN? 484
With a happy song I will haste 468
WITH THY SPIRIT FILL ME 167
Without spot and blameless 415
WONDERFUL PEACE 356
WONDERFUL POWER IN PRAYER 407
WONDERFUL WORDS OF LIFE 105
WORK, FOR THE NIGHT IS COMING 182
WORTHY IS THE LAMB 75
Would you be free from your burden of sin? 113
Would you flee from sin 127
Would you live for Jesus 176

Ye followers of Jesus 106
YE MUST BE BORN AGAIN 120
Years I spent in vanity 280
YIELDED TO THEE 171
You ask what makes me happy 275
You have longed for sweet peace 141

ZION STANDS WITH HILLS SURROUNDED 417